Suzuki SJ Series & Vitara Owners Workshop Manual

Bob Henderson and A K Legg LAE MIMI

Models covered

Suzuki SJ410 & SJ413 models,
including Santana, Samurai and special/limited editions;
970 cc, 1298 cc & 1324 cc

Suzuki Vitara models,
including special/limited editions; 1590 cc

ABCDE
FGHIJ
KLMNO
P

Haynes Publishing
Sparkford Nr Yeovil
Somerset BA22 7JJ England

Haynes North America, Inc
861 Lawrence Drive
Newbury Park
California 91320 USA

Acknowledgements

We are grateful for the help and co-operation of Suzuki Motor Co., Ltd., and General Motors Corporation for assistance with technical information, certain illustrations and vehicle photos. The Champion Spark Plug Company supplied the illustrations of various spark plug conditions. Technical writers who contributed to this project include Ken Freund, Jon LaCourse and Robert Maddox.

© **Haynes Publishing 1994**

A book in the **Haynes Owners Workshop Manual Series**

Printed by J. H. Haynes & Co. Ltd, Sparkford, Nr Yeovil, Somerset BA22 7JJ, England

ISBN 1 85010 942 7

British Library Cataloguing in Publication Data
A catalogue record for this book is available from the British Library.

We take great pride in the accuracy of information given in this manual, but vehicle manufacturers make alterations and design changes during the production run of a particular vehicle of which they do not inform us. No liability can be accepted by the authors or publishers for loss, damage or injury caused by any errors in, or omissions from, the information given.

Restoring and Preserving our Motoring Heritage

Few people can have had the luck to realise their dreams to quite the same extent and in such a remarkable fashion as John Haynes, Founder and Chairman of the Haynes Publishing Group.

Since 1965 his unique approach to workshop manual publishing has proved so successful that millions of Haynes Manuals are now sold every year throughout the world, covering literally thousands of different makes and models of cars, vans and motorcycles.

A continuing passion for cars and motoring led to the founding in 1985 of a Charitable Trust dedicated to the restoration and preservation of our motoring heritage. To inaugurate the new Museum, John Haynes donated virtually his entire private collection of 52 cars.

Now with an unrivalled international collection of over 210 veteran, vintage and classic cars and motorcycles, the Haynes Motor Museum in Somerset is well on the way to becoming one of the most interesting Motor Museums in the world.

A 70 seat video cinema, a cafe and an extensive motoring bookshop, together with a specially constructed one kilometre motor circuit, make a visit to the Haynes Motor Museum a truly unforgettable experience.

Every vehicle in the museum is preserved in as near as possible mint condition and each car is run every six months on the motor circuit.

Enjoy the picnic area set amongst the rolling Somerset hills. Peer through the William Morris workshop windows at cars being restored, and browse through the extensive displays of fascinating motoring memorabilia.

From the 1903 Oldsmobile through such classics as an MG Midget to the mighty 'E' type Jaguar, Lamborghini, Ferrari Berlinetta Boxer, and Graham Hill's Lola Cosworth, there is something for everyone, young and old alike, at this Somerset Museum.

Haynes Motor Museum

Situated mid-way between London and Penzance, the Haynes Motor Museum is located just off the A303 at Sparkford, Somerset (home of the Haynes Manual) and is open to the public 7 days a week all year round, except Christmas Day and Boxing Day.

Telephone 01963 440804.

Contents

4

Suzuki SJ410 Metal Top

Suzuki Vitara Metal Top JLX

About this manual

Its aim

The aim of this manual is to help you get the best value from your vehicle. It can do so in several ways. It can help you decide what work must be done (even should you choose to get it done by a garage), provide information on routine maintenance and servicing, and give a logical course of action and diagnosis when random faults occur. However, it is hoped that you will use the manual by tackling the work yourself. On simpler jobs, it may even be quicker than booking the vehicle into a garage and going there twice, to leave and collect it. Perhaps most important, a lot of money can be saved, by avoiding the costs a garage must charge to cover its labour and overheads.

The manual has drawings and descriptions to show the function of the various components, so that their layout can be understood. Then the tasks are described and photographed in a clear step-by-step sequence.

Its arrangement

The manual is divided into Chapters, each covering a logical sub-division of the vehicle. The Chapters are each divided into numbered Sections, which are headed in bold type between horizontal lines. Where required for ease of reference, some Sections are divided into sub-Sections, and in some cases into sub-sub-Sections; all such sub-divisions are indicated by appropriately-sized sub-headings. Each Section contains individual paragraphs which (except in the case of purely-descriptive "General description" Sections) are consecutively numbered; this numbering sequence is applied throughout the Section, regardless of any subdivision.

The manual is freely illustrated, especially in those parts where there is a detailed sequence of operations to be carried out. The reference numbers used in illustration captions indicate the Section, followed by the number of the paragraph within that Section, to which the illustration refers; where more than one illustration applies to a particular paragraph, letters are added in alphabetical order to each illustration caption's reference number - for example, illustration "6.7C" is the third illustration referring to paragraph 7 of Section 6 of that Chapter.

Procedures, once described in the appropriate place in the text, are not normally repeated. When it is necessary to refer to another Chapter, the reference will be given as Chapter and Section number. Cross-references given without use of the word "Chapter" apply to other Sections in the same Chapter. For example, a cross-reference such as "see Section 8" means Section 8 in that Chapter.

There is an alphabetical index at the back of the manual, as well as a contents list at the front. Each Chapter is also preceded by its own individual contents list.

References to the "left" or "right" of the vehicle are in the sense of a person in the driver's seat facing forward, however as this manual was originated in the US, any reference to the driver's side in Chapters 1 to 12 refers to the left-hand side.

Unless otherwise stated, nuts and bolts are removed by turning anti-clockwise, and tightened by turning clockwise.

We take great pride in the accuracy of information given in this manual, but vehicle manufacturers make alterations and design changes during the production run of a particular vehicle of which they do not inform us. No liability can be accepted by the authors or publishers for loss, damage or injury caused by any errors in, or omissions from, the information given.

Project vehicle

The UK project vehicle used for the compilation of the UK Supplement was a 1988 model Santana SJ410.

Notes for UK readers

General

Because this manual was originally written in the US, its layout differs from our UK-originated manuals. The preliminary sections (ie up to Chapter 1) have therefore been re-written specifically for the UK market; however, it will be noticed that references to components remain in the US style, so that the reader can identify these with the components described in the main Chapters of the manual. The UK equivalent of US components and various other US words is given in the Section headed "Use of English". It should be remembered that the project vehicle used in the main Chapters of this manual was a left-hand drive model; therefore, the position of the steering wheel, steering column, clutch and brake pedals, etc. will be on the opposite side of the vehicle on UK models. References to "right" and "left" will need to be considered carefully to decide which applies to UK models - for instance, the headlight dipped beams should be adjusted to dip to the left of the headlight vertical line described in Chapter 12, instead of to the right on US models. In other instances, no reference is made to the location of a particular item, but that item may be located on the opposite side of the vehicle on UK models (eg the windscreen wiper motor is on the right-hand side of the bulkhead on UK models, not the left).

The following information should be considered before referring to the main Chapters of this manual.

Model differences

The US equivalent models of the Suzuki SJ Series are as shown in the following chart:

UK model	US equivalent model
SJ410, SJ413, Santana and Samurai	Samurai
Vitara	Sidekick and Tracker

References to the US models in the main part of the manual should be taken as referring to the equivalent UK model as shown in the chart. Year references (ie 1987) in the main part of the manual apply to US models; however, these should be approximately the same for UK models.

Specifications

Where capacities or volumes appear in the Specifications Sections of each Chapter, note that reference to quarts means US quarts, and the correct conversion factor should be used accordingly (see "Conversion factors"). Where specifications in the main Chapters of the manual appear in imperial form; the equivalent metric values can be calculated using the Conversion factors page.

General specifications for UK models are given in the UK Supplement.

Maintenance intervals

The *main* Maintenance interval for UK models is every 12 000 miles or 12 months, and there are several differences which make it difficult to relate the UK schedule to the US schedule given in Chapter 1. For this reason, the UK maintenance schedule is shown separately in the UK Supplement.

Air conditioning system

The latter Sections of Chapter 3 describe work on the air conditioning system. Although air conditioning equipment is becoming more common in the UK, you are strongly advised to have a specialist carry out repairs to any part of it. The refrigerant used in the air conditioning system is potentially hazardous to health, so the evacuating and recharging of the air conditioning system must be performed by a specialist in any case. It therefore makes sense to have any other repairs carried out by that specialist at the same time.

Emission control information

US emission control laws call for an information label to be attached in a prominent position in the engine compartment. At the present time there is no requirement for this in the UK. US laws also call for the renewal of emission control components (such as the oxygen sensor and EGR valve) at specific intervals. Although renewal of these items could very well be beneficial in terms of engine efficiency, there are no equivalent laws in the UK at the moment.

Fuel injection system and fault codes

Because of the different emission control laws in the US, the instrument panel on US models includes a malfunction warning light, to warn the driver of a fault in the engine management system. This system is not normally fitted to UK models, and therefore some of the information given in Chapter 6 will not apply.

Chassis electrical system

The wiring diagrams shown in Chapter 12 were originated in the US, but they may be used as a guide for UK models.

Notes, cautions and warnings

A **Note** provides information necessary to properly complete a procedure, or information which will make the procedure easier to understand.

A **Caution** provides a special procedure or special steps which must be taken while completing the procedure where the **Caution** is found. Not heeding a **Caution** can result in damage to the assembly being worked on.

A **Warning** provides a special procedure or special steps which must be taken while completing the procedure where the **Warning** is found. Not heeding a **Warning** can result in personal injury.

Introduction to the Suzuki SJ Series and Vitara

The vehicles covered by this manual are available in two-door soft top or hard top styles.

The front-mounted in-line four-cylinder engine used in these vehicles is equipped with a carburettor or fuel injection, depending on model. The engine drives the rear wheels, through either a four- or five-speed manual transmission or a three-speed automatic transmission, via a driveshaft running between a transfer case and solid rear axle. The transfer case and another driveshaft are used to drive the front wheels.

The suspension features a solid axle at the rear on all models, supported by leaf springs (SJ410 or SJ413) or coil springs (Vitara). The front axle on SJ Series models is also solid, with leaf spring suspension. The Vitara uses an independent front suspension arrangement, with the wheels supported by control arms and MacPherson struts.

The steering box is mounted to the right of the engine, and is connected to the steering arms through a series of rods which incorporate a damper. Power assistance is optional on Vitara models.

The brakes are discs at the front (early SJ Series models have front drums), and drums at the rear, with power assistance standard.

Jacking, towing and wheel changing

Jacking and wheel changing

The jack supplied with the vehicle should be used only for raising the vehicle when changing a tire or placing jackstands under the frame. **Warning**: *Never work under the vehicle or start the engine when this jack is being used as the only means of support.*

The vehicle should be on level ground with the wheels blocked, the parking brake applied and the transmission in Park (automatic) or Reverse (manual). If a tire is being changed, loosen the wheel nuts one-half turn, and leave them in place until the wheel is raised off the ground.

Place the jack under the vehicle in the indicated position **(see illustrations)**. Operate the jack with a slow, smooth motion until the wheel is raised off the ground.

Install the wheel and wheel nuts, tightening the nuts as securely as possible. Lower the vehicle, remove the jack and tighten the nuts (if loosened or removed) in a criss-cross sequence to the torque listed in the Chapter 1 Specifications.

Towing

The vehicle should not be towed with all four wheels on the ground, unless the driveshafts are removed first (Chapter 8); the transmission, transfer case and driveshafts could be damaged otherwise. In the event of the vehicle needing to be towed, insist that a trailer is used. Refer to the owner's handbook supplied with the vehicle for more detailed information.

When towing another vehicle, equipment specifically designed for towing should be used, and should be attached to the main structural members of the vehicle, not to the bumper or brackets.

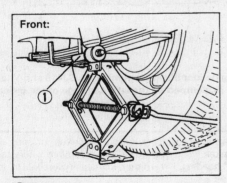

① Spring seat

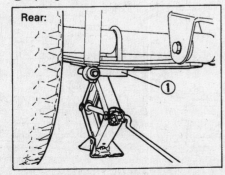

On SJ410 and SJ413 models, place the jack underneath the leaf spring seat at the corner of the vehicle to be lifted

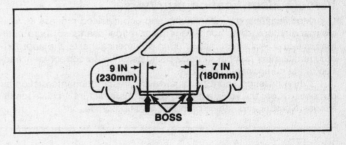

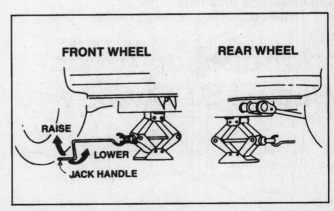

On Vitara models, position the jack under the sill the specified distance from the wheel arch

Buying spare parts and vehicle identification numbers

Buying spare parts

Spare parts are available from many sources; for example, Suzuki garages, other garages and accessory shops, and motor factors. Our advice regarding spare part sources is as follows.

Officially-appointed Suzuki garages - This is the best source for parts which are peculiar to your vehicle, and which are not generally available (eg complete cylinder heads, internal transmission components, badges, interior trim etc). It is also the only place at which you should buy parts if the vehicle is still under warranty. To be sure of obtaining the correct parts, it will be necessary to give the storeman the full Vehicle Identification Number, and if possible, to take the old parts along for positive identification. Many parts are available under a factory exchange scheme - any parts returned should always be clean. It obviously makes good sense to go straight to the specialists on your vehicle for this type of part, as they are best equipped to supply you.

Other garages and accessory shops - These are often very good places to buy materials and components needed for the maintenance of your vehicle (eg oil filters, spark plugs, bulbs, drivebelts, oils and greases, touch-up paint, filler paste, etc). They also sell general accessories, usually have convenient opening hours, charge lower prices, and can often be found not far from home.

Motor factors - Good factors will stock all the more important components which wear out comparatively quickly (eg exhaust systems, brake pads, seals and hydraulic parts, clutch components, bearing shells, pistons, valves etc). Motor factors will often provide new or reconditioned components on a part-exchange basis - this can save a considerable amount of money.

Vehicle identification numbers

Modifications are a continuing and unpublicised process in vehicle manufacture, quite apart from major model changes. Spare parts manuals and lists are compiled upon a numerical basis, the appropriate identification number or code being essential to correct identification of the component concerned.

When ordering spare parts, always give as much information as possible. Quote the vehicle model, year of manufacture, Vehicle Identification Number and engine numbers, as appropriate.

The *Vehicle Identification Number* is stamped on the chassis channel inside the right-hand side wheel arch. Turn the steering on full right-hand lock (SJ410 and SJ413) or full left-hand lock (Vitara) to gain access to the number.

The *engine number* is stamped on the right-hand side of the cylinder block on SJ410 models, or on the left-hand rear edge of the cylinder block on SJ413 and Vitara models **(see illustration)**.

The *transmission number* on manual transmissions is located on the top of the case **(see illustration)**. On automatic transmissions, the number is located on the top of the bellhousing **(see illustration)**.

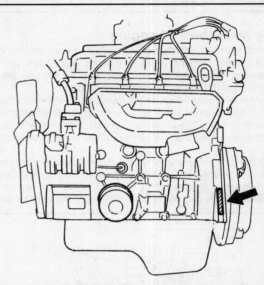

The engine identification number on SJ413 and Vitara models is stamped on the left rear edge of the cylinder block (arrowed)

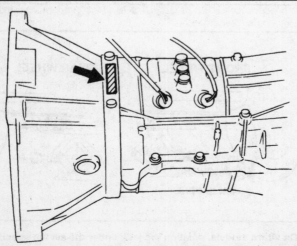

The identification number on manual transmissions is located on the top of the case (arrowed)

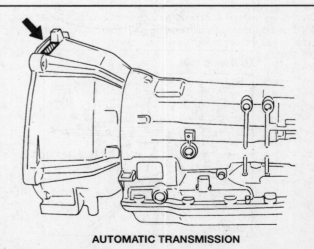

AUTOMATIC TRANSMISSION

The identification number on automatic transmissions is stamped on the top of the bellhousing (arrowed)

Safety first!

However enthusiastic you may be about getting on with the job in hand, do take the time to ensure that your safety is not put at risk. A moment's lack of attention can result in an accident, as can failure to observe certain elementary precautions. There will always be new ways of having accidents, and the following points do not pretend to be a comprehensive list of all dangers; they are intended rather to make you aware of the risks, and to encourage a safety-conscious approach to all work you carry out on your vehicle.

Essential DOs and DON'Ts

DON'T rely on a single jack when working underneath the vehicle. Always use reliable additional means of support, such as axle stands, securely placed under a structural part of the vehicle that you know will not give way.

DON'T attempt to loosen or tighten high-torque nuts (eg wheel hub nuts) while the vehicle is on a jack; it may be pulled off.

DON'T start the engine without first ascertaining that the transmission is in neutral (or "Park" where applicable) and the handbrake applied.

DON'T suddenly remove the filler cap from a hot cooling system - cover it with a cloth, and release the pressure gradually first, or you may get scalded by escaping coolant.

DON'T attempt to drain oil, automatic transmission fluid, or coolant until you are sure it has cooled sufficiently to avoid scalding you.

DON'T grasp any part of the engine, exhaust or catalytic converter without first ascertaining that it is sufficiently cool to avoid burning you.

DON'T allow brake fluid or antifreeze to contact vehicle paintwork.

DON'T siphon toxic liquids such as fuel, brake fluid or antifreeze by mouth, or allow them to remain on your skin.

DON'T inhale dust - it may be injurious to health (see *Asbestos* below).

DON'T allow any spilt oil or grease to remain on the floor - wipe it up straight away, before someone slips on it.

DON'T use ill-fitting spanners or other tools which may slip and cause injury.

DON'T attempt to lift a heavy component which may be beyond your capability - get assistance.

DON'T rush to finish a job, or take unverified short cuts.

DON'T allow children or animals in or around an unattended vehicle.

DON'T park vehicles with catalytic converters over combustible materials such as dry grass, oily rags, etc if the engine has recently been run. As catalytic converters reach extremely high temperatures, any such materials in close proximity may ignite.

DON'T run vehicles equipped with catalytic converters without the exhaust system heat shields fitted.

DO wear eye protection when using power tools such as an electric drill, sander, bench grinder etc, and when working under the vehicle.

DO use a barrier cream on your hands prior to undertaking dirty jobs - it will protect your skin from infection, as well as making the dirt easier to remove afterwards; but make sure your hands aren't left slippery. Note that long-term contact with used engine oil can be a health hazard.

DO keep loose clothing (cuffs, tie etc) and long hair well out of the way of moving mechanical parts.

DO remove rings, wristwatch etc, before working on the vehicle - especially the electrical system.

DO ensure that any lifting tackle or jacking equipment used has a safe working load rating adequate for the job, and is used precisely as recommended by the equipment manufacturer.

DO keep your work area tidy - it is only too easy to fall over articles left lying around.

DO get someone to check periodically that all is well when working alone on the vehicle.

DO carry out work in a logical sequence, and check that everything is correctly assembled and tightened afterwards.

DO remember that your vehicle's safety affects that of yourself and others. If in doubt on any point, get specialist advice.

IF, in spite of following these precautions, you are unfortunate enough to injure yourself, seek medical attention as soon as possible.

Asbestos

Certain friction, insulating, sealing, and other products - such as brake linings, brake bands, clutch linings, gaskets, etc - contain asbestos. *Extreme care must be taken to avoid inhalation of dust from such products, since it is hazardous to health.* If in doubt, assume that they *do* contain asbestos.

Fire

Remember at all times that petrol is highly flammable. Never smoke, or have any kind of naked flame around, when working on the vehicle. But the risk does not end there - a spark caused by an electrical short-circuit, by two metal surfaces contacting each other, by careless use of tools, or even by static electricity built up in your body under certain conditions, can ignite petrol vapour, which in a confined space is highly explosive.

Whenever possible, disconnect the battery earth terminal before working on any part of the fuel or electrical system, and never risk spilling fuel on to a hot engine or exhaust. Catalytic converters run at extremely high temperatures, and consequently can be an additional fire hazard. Observe the precautions outlined elsewhere in this section.

It is recommended that a fire extinguisher of a type suitable for fuel and electrical fires is kept handy in the garage or workplace at all times. Never try to extinguish a fuel or electrical fire with water.

Note: Any reference to a "torch" appearing in this manual should always be taken to mean a hand-held battery-operated electric light or flashlight. It does NOT mean a welding/gas torch or blowlamp.

Hydrofluoric acid

Hydrofluoric acid is extremely corrosive. It is formed when certain types of synthetic rubber, which may be found in O-rings, oil seals, brake hydraulic system seals, fuel hoses etc, are exposed to temperatures above 400°C. The obvious circumstance in which this could happen on a vehicle is in the case of a fire. The rubber does not burn but changes into a charred or sticky substance which contains the acid. *Once formed, the acid remains dangerous for years. If it gets onto the skin it may be necessary to amputate the limb concerned.*

When dealing with a vehicle which has suffered a fire, or with components salvaged from such a vehicle, always wear protective gloves and discard them carefully after use. Bear this in mind if obtaining components from a car breaker.

Fumes

Certain fumes are highly toxic, and can quickly cause unconsciousness and even death if inhaled to any extent, especially if inhalation takes place through a lighted cigarette or pipe. Petrol vapour comes into this category, as do the vapours from certain solvents such as trichloroethylene. Any draining or pouring of such volatile fluids should be done in a well-ventilated area.

When using cleaning fluids and solvents, read the instructions carefully. Never use materials from unmarked containers - they may give off poisonous vapours.

Never run the engine of a motor vehicle in an enclosed space such as a garage. Exhaust fumes contain carbon monoxide, which is extremely poisonous; if you need to run the engine, always do so in the open air, or at least have the rear of the vehicle outside the workplace. Although vehicles fitted with catalytic converters have greatly-reduced toxic exhaust emissions, the above precautions should still be observed.

If you are fortunate enough to have the use of an inspection pit, never drain or pour petrol, and never run the engine, while the vehicle is standing over it; the fumes, being heavier than air, will concentrate in the pit, with possibly lethal results.

The battery

Batteries which are sealed for life require special precautions, which are normally outlined on a label attached to the battery. Such precautions are primarily related to situations involving battery charging and jump starting from another vehicle.

With a conventional battery, never cause a spark, or allow a naked light, in close proximity to it. It will normally be giving off a certain amount of hydrogen gas, which is highly explosive.

Whenever possible, disconnect the battery earth terminal before working on the fuel or electrical systems.

If possible, loosen the battery filler plugs or battery cover when charging the battery from an external source. Do not charge at an excessive rate, or the battery may burst. Special care should be taken with the use of high-charge-rate boost chargers to prevent the battery from overheating.

Take care when topping-up and when carrying the battery. The acid electrolyte, even when diluted, is very corrosive, and should not be allowed to contact clothing, eyes or skin.

Always wear eye protection when cleaning the battery, to prevent the caustic deposits from entering your eyes.

The vehicle electrical system

Take care when making alterations or repairs to the vehicle wiring. Electrical faults are the commonest cause of vehicle fires. Make sure that any accessories are wired correctly, using an appropriately-rated fuse and wire of adequate current-carrying capacity. When possible, avoid the use of "piggy-back" or self-splicing connectors to power additional electrical equipment from existing feeds; make up a new feed with its own fuse instead.

When considering the current which a new circuit will have to handle, do not overlook the switch, especially when planning to use an existing switch to control additional components - for instance, if spotlights are to be fed via the main lighting switch. For preference, a relay should be used to switch heavy currents. If in doubt, consult an auto electrical specialist.

Any wire which passes through a body panel or bulkhead must be protected from chafing with a grommet or similar device. A wire which is allowed to chafe bare against the bodywork will cause a short-circuit and possibly a fire.

Mains electricity and electrical equipment

When using an electric power tool, inspection light, diagnostic equipment etc, which works from the mains, always ensure that the appliance is correctly connected to its plug, and that, where necessary, it is properly earthed. Do not use such appliances in damp conditions and, again, beware of creating a spark or applying excessive heat in the vicinity of fuel or fuel vapour. Also ensure that the appliances meet the relevant national safety standards.

Ignition HT voltage

A severe electric shock can result from touching certain parts of the ignition system, such as the HT leads, when the engine is running or being cranked, particularly if components are damp or the insulation is defective. Where an electronic ignition system is fitted, the HT voltage is much higher and could prove fatal, especially to wearers of cardiac pacemakers.

Jacking and vehicle support

The jack provided with the vehicle is designed primarily for emergency wheel changing, and its use for servicing and overhaul work on the vehicle is best avoided. Instead, a more substantial workshop jack (trolley jack or similar) should be used. Whichever type is employed, it is essential that additional safety support is provided by means of axle stands designed for this purpose. Never use makeshift means such as wooden blocks or piles of house bricks, as these can easily topple or, in the case of bricks, disintegrate under the weight of the vehicle. Further information on the correct positioning of the jack and axle stands is provided in the *"Jacking, towing and wheel changing"* section.

If removal of the wheels is not required, the use of drive-on ramps is recommended. Caution should be exercised to ensure that they are correctly aligned with the wheels, and that the vehicle is not driven too far along them, so that it promptly falls off the other ends, or tips the ramps.

General repair procedures

Whenever servicing, repair or overhaul work is carried out on the vehicle or its components, it is necessary to observe the following procedures and instructions. This will assist in carrying out the operation efficiently, and to a professional standard of workmanship.

Joint mating faces and gaskets

When separating components at their mating faces, never insert screwdrivers or similar implements into the joint between the faces in order to prise them apart. This can cause severe damage, which results in oil leaks, coolant leaks, etc upon reassembly. Separation is usually achieved by tapping along the joint with a soft-faced hammer in order to break the seal. However, note that this method may not be suitable where dowels are used for component location.

Where a gasket is used between the mating faces of two components, ensure that it is renewed on reassembly, and fit it dry, unless otherwise stated in the repair procedure. Make sure that the mating faces are clean and dry, with all traces of old gasket removed. When cleaning a joint face, use a tool which is not likely to score or damage the face, and remove any burrs or nicks with an oilstone or fine file.

Make sure that tapped holes are cleaned with a pipe cleaner, and keep them free of jointing compound, if this is being used, unless specifically instructed otherwise.

Ensure that all orifices, channels or pipes are clear, and blow through them, preferably using compressed air. *Wear eye protection when using compressed air!*

Oil seals

Oil seals can be removed by levering them out with a wide flat-bladed screwdriver or similar implement. Alternatively, a number of self-tapping screws may be screwed into the seal, and these used as a purchase for pliers or some similar device in order to pull the seal free.

Whenever an oil seal is removed from its working location, either individually or as part of an assembly, it should be renewed.

The very fine sealing lip of the seal is easily damaged, and will not seal if the surface it contacts is not completely clean and free from scratches, nicks or grooves. If the original sealing surface of the component cannot be restored, and the manufacturer has not made provision for slight relocation of the seal relative to the sealing surface, the component should be renewed.

Protect the lips of the seal from any surface which may damage them in the course of fitting. Use tape or a conical sleeve where possible. Lubricate the seal lips with oil before fitting and, on dual-lipped seals, fill the space between the lips with grease.

Unless otherwise stated, oil seals must be fitted with their sealing lips toward the lubricant to be sealed.

Use a tubular drift or block of wood of the appropriate size to install the seal and, if the seal housing is shouldered, drive the seal down to the shoulder. If the seal housing is unshouldered, the seal should be fitted with its face flush with the housing top face (unless otherwise instructed).

Screw threads and fastenings

Seized nuts, bolts and screws are quite a common occurrence where corrosion has set in, and the use of penetrating oil or releasing fluid will often overcome this problem if the offending item is soaked for a while before attempting to release it. The use of an impact driver may also provide a means of releasing such stubborn fastening devices, when used in conjunction with the appropriate screwdriver bit or socket. If none of these methods works, it may be necessary to resort to the careful application of heat, or the use of a hacksaw or nut splitter device.

Studs are usually removed by locking two nuts together on the threaded part, and then using a spanner on the lower nut to unscrew the stud. Studs or bolts which have broken off below the surface of the component in which they are mounted can sometimes be removed using a proprietary stud extractor (sometimes called "easy-outs"). Always ensure that a blind tapped hole is completely free from oil, grease, water or other fluid before installing the bolt or stud. Failure to do this could cause the housing to crack, due to the hydraulic action of the bolt or stud as it is screwed in.

When tightening a castellated nut to accept a split pin, tighten the nut to the specified torque, where applicable, and then tighten further to the next split pin hole. Never slacken the nut to align the split pin hole, unless stated in the repair procedure.

When checking or retightening a nut or bolt to a specified torque setting, slacken the nut or bolt by a quarter of a turn, and then retighten to the specified setting. However, this should not be attempted where angular tightening has been used.

For some screw fastenings, notably cylinder head bolts or nuts, torque wrench settings are no longer specified for the latter stages of tightening, "angular tightening" being called up instead. Typically, a fairly low torque wrench setting will be applied to the bolts/nuts in the correct sequence, followed by one or more stages of tightening through specified angles.

Locknuts, locktabs and washers

Any fastening which will rotate against a component or housing in the course of tightening should always have a washer between it and the relevant component or housing.

Spring or split washers should always be renewed when they are used to lock a critical component such as a big-end bearing retaining bolt or nut. Locktabs which are folded over to retain a nut or bolt should always be renewed.

Self-locking nuts can be re-used in non-critical areas, providing resistance can be felt when the locking portion passes over the bolt or stud thread. However, it should be noted that self-locking nuts tend to lose their effectiveness after long periods of use, and in such cases should be renewed as a matter of course.

Split pins must always be replaced with new ones of the correct size for the hole.

When thread-locking compound is found on the threads of a fastener which is to be re-used, it should be cleaned off with a wire brush and solvent, and fresh compound applied on reassembly.

Special tools

Some repair procedures in this manual entail the use of special tools such as a press, two- or three-legged pullers, spring compressors etc. Wherever possible, suitable readily-available alternatives to the manufacturer's special tools are described, and are shown in use. In some instances, where no alternative is possible, it has been necessary to resort to the use of a manufacturer's tool, and this has been done for reasons of safety, as well as the efficient completion of the repair operation. Unless you are highly skilled and have a thorough understanding of the procedures described, never attempt to bypass the use of any special tool when the procedure described specifies its use. Not only is there a very great risk of personal injury, but expensive damage could be caused to the components involved.

Environmental considerations

When disposing of used engine oil, brake fluid, antifreeze etc, give due consideration to any detrimental environmental effects. Do not, for instance, pour any of the above liquids down drains into the general sewage system, or onto the ground to soak away. Many local council refuse tips provide a facility for waste oil disposal, as do some garages. If none of these facilities are available, consult your local Environmental Health Department for further advice.

With the universal tightening-up of legislation regarding the emission of environmentally-harmful substances from motor vehicles, most current vehicles have tamperproof devices fitted to the main adjustment points of the fuel system. These devices are primarily designed to prevent unqualified persons from adjusting the fuel/air mixture with the chance of a consequent increase in toxic emissions. If such devices are encountered during servicing or overhaul, they should, wherever possible, be renewed or refitted in accordance with the vehicle manufacturer's requirements or current legislation. Owners taking their vehicles abroad should note that some countries have strict legislation relating to vehicles driven without these tamperproofing measures in place!

Tools and working facilities

Introduction

A selection of good tools is a fundamental requirement for anyone contemplating the maintenance and repair of a motor vehicle. For the owner who does not possess any, their purchase will prove a considerable expense, offsetting some of the savings made by doing-it-yourself. However, provided that the tools purchased meet the relevant national safety standards and are of good quality, they will last for many years and prove an extremely worthwhile investment.

To help the average owner to decide which tools are needed to carry out the various tasks detailed in this manual, we have compiled three lists of tools under the following headings: *Maintenance and minor repair*, *Repair and overhaul*, and *Special*. Newcomers to practical mechanics should start off with the *Maintenance and minor repair* tool kit, and confine themselves to the simpler jobs around the vehicle. Then, as confidence and experience grow, more difficult tasks can be undertaken, with extra tools being purchased as, and when, they are needed. In this way, a *Maintenance and minor repair* tool kit can be built up into a *Repair and overhaul* tool kit over a considerable period of time, without any major cash outlays. The experienced do-it-yourselfer will have a tool kit good enough for most repair and overhaul procedures, and will add tools from the *Special* category when it is felt that the expense is justified by the amount of use to which these tools will be put.

Maintenance and minor repair tool kit

The tools given in this list should be considered as a minimum requirement if routine maintenance, servicing and minor repair operations are to be undertaken. We recommend the purchase of combination spanners (ring one end, open-ended the other); although more expensive than open-ended ones, they do give the advantages of both types of spanner.

Combination spanners:
Metric - 8, 9, 10, 11, 12, 13, 14, 15, 17 & 19 mm
Adjustable spanner - 35 mm jaw (approx)
Transmission drain plug key (Allen type)

Spark plug spanner (with rubber insert)
Spark plug gap adjustment tool
Set of feeler gauges
Brake bleed nipple spanner
Screwdrivers:
Flat-bladed - approx 100 mm long x 6 mm dia
Cross-bladed - approx 100 mm long x 6 mm dia
Combination pliers
Hacksaw (junior)
Tyre pump
Tyre pressure gauge
Oil can
Oil filter removal tool
Fine emery cloth
Wire brush (small)
Funnel (medium size)

Repair and overhaul tool kit

These tools are virtually essential for anyone undertaking any major repairs to a motor vehicle, and are additional to those given in the *Maintenance and minor repair* list. Included in this list is a comprehensive set of sockets. Although these are expensive, they will be found invaluable as they are so versatile - particularly if various drives are included in the set. We recommend the 1/2 in square-drive type, as this can be used with most proprietary torque wrenches. If you cannot afford a socket set, even bought piecemeal, then inexpensive tubular box spanners are a useful alternative.

The tools in this list will occasionally need to be supplemented by tools from the *Special* list.

Sockets (or box spanners) to cover range in previous list
Reversible ratchet drive (for use with sockets) **(see illustration)**
Extension piece, 250 mm (for use with sockets)
Universal joint (for use with sockets)
Torque wrench (for use with sockets)
Self-locking grips
Ball pein hammer

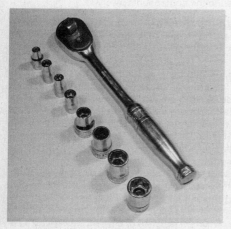

Sockets and reversible ratchet drive

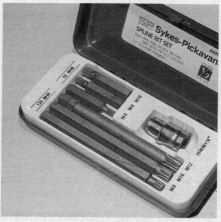

Spline bit set

Spline key set

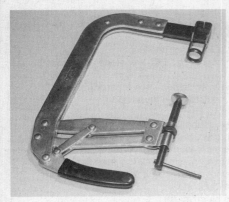

Valve spring compressor

Piston ring compressor

Piston ring removal/installation tool

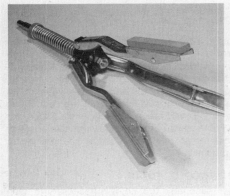

Cylinder bore hone

Three-legged hub and bearing puller

Micrometer set

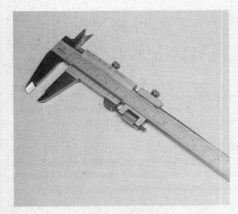

Vernier calipers

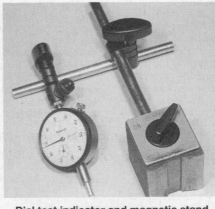

Dial test indicator and magnetic stand

Compression testing gauge

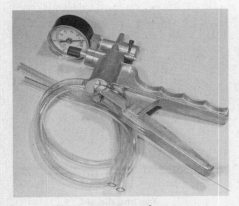

Vacuum pump and gauge

Clutch plate alignment set

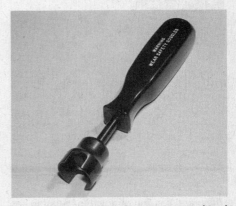

Brake shoe steady spring cup removal tool

Soft-faced mallet (plastic/aluminium or rubber)
Screwdrivers:
Flat-bladed - long & sturdy, short (chubby), and narrow
    (electrician's) types
Cross-bladed - Long & sturdy, and short (chubby) types
Pliers:
     Long-nosed
     Side cutters (electrician's)
     Circlip (internal and external)
Cold chisel - 25 mm
Scriber
Scraper
Centre-punch
Pin punch
Hacksaw
Brake hose clamp
Brake/clutch bleeding kit
Selection of twist drills
Steel rule/straight-edge
Allen keys (inc. splined/Torx type) **(see illustrations)**
Selection of files
Wire brush
Axle stands
Jack (strong trolley or hydraulic type)
Light with extension lead

Special tools

The tools in this list are those which are not used regularly, are expensive to buy, or which need to be used in accordance with their manufacturers' instructions. Unless relatively difficult mechanical jobs are undertaken frequently, it will not be economic to buy many of these tools. Where this is the case, you could consider clubbing together with friends (or joining a motorists' club) to make a joint purchase, or borrowing the tools against a deposit from a local garage or tool hire specialist. It is worth noting that many of the larger d-i-y superstores now carry a large range of special tools for hire at modest rates.

The following list contains only those tools and instruments freely available to the public, and not those special tools produced by the vehicle manufacturer specifically for its dealer network. You will find occasional references to these manufacturer's special tools in the text of this manual. Generally, an alternative method of doing the job without the vehicle manufacturer's special tool is given. However, sometimes there is no alternative to using them. Where this is the case and the relevant tool cannot be bought or borrowed, you will have to entrust the work to a franchised garage.

Valve spring compressor **(see illustration)**
Valve grinding tool
Piston ring compressor **(see illustration)**
Piston ring removal/installation tool **(see illustration)**

Cylinder bore hone **(see illustration)**
Balljoint separator
Coil spring compressors (where applicable)
Two-/three-legged hub and bearing puller **(see illustration)**
Impact screwdriver
Micrometer and/or vernier calipers **(see illustrations)**
Dial gauge/dial test indicator **(see illustration)**
Universal electrical multi-meter
Cylinder compression gauge **(see illustration)**
Hand-operated vacuum pump and gauge **(see illustration)**
Clutch plate alignment set **(see illustration)**
Brake shoe steady spring cup removal tool **(see illustration)**
Bush and bearing removal/installation set **(see illustration)**
Stud extractors **(see illustration)**
Tap and die set **(see illustration)**
Lifting tackle
Trolley jack

Buying tools

For practically all tools, a tool factor is the best source, since he will have a very comprehensive range compared with the average garage or accessory shop. Having said that, accessory shops often offer excellent quality tools at discount prices, so it pays to shop around.

Remember, you don't have to buy the most expensive items on the shelf, but it is always advisable to steer clear of the very cheap tools. There are plenty of good tools around at reasonable prices, but always aim to purchase items which meet the relevant national safety standards. If in doubt, ask the proprietor or manager of the shop for advice before making a purchase.

Care and maintenance of tools

Having purchased a reasonable tool kit, it is necessary to keep the tools in a clean and serviceable condition. After use, always wipe off any dirt, grease and metal particles using a clean, dry cloth, before putting the tools away. Never leave them lying around after they have been used. A simple tool rack on the garage or workshop wall, for items such as screwdrivers and pliers, is a good idea. Store all normal spanners and sockets in a metal box. Any measuring instruments, gauges, meters, etc, must be carefully stored, somewhere they cannot be damaged or become rusty.

Take a little care when tools are used. Hammer heads inevitably become marked, and screwdrivers lose the keen edge on their blades from time to time. A little timely attention with emery cloth or a file will soon restore items like this to a good serviceable finish.

Working facilities

Not to be forgotten when discussing tools is the workshop itself. If anything more than routine maintenance is to be carried out, some form of suitable working area becomes essential.

Bush and bearing removal/installation set

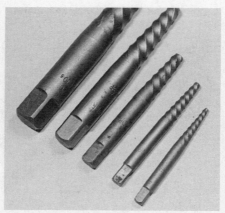

Stud extractor set

Tap and die set

Spanner jaw gap and bolt size comparison table

Jaw gap – in (mm)	Spanner size	Bolt size
0.197 (5.00)	5 mm	M 2.5
0.216 (5.50)	5.5 mm	M 3
0.218 (5.53)	$\frac{7}{32}$ in AF	
0.236 (6.00)	6 mm	M 3.5
0.250 (6.35)	$\frac{1}{4}$ in AF	
0.275 (7.00)	7 mm	M 4
0.281 (7.14)	$\frac{9}{32}$ in AF	
0.312 (7.92)	$\frac{5}{16}$ in AF	
0.315 (8.00)	8 mm	M 5
0.343 (8.71)	$\frac{11}{32}$ in AF	
0.375 (9.52)	$\frac{3}{8}$ in AF	
0.394 (10.00)	10 mm	M 6
0.406 (10.32)	$\frac{13}{32}$ in AF	
0.433 (11.00)	11 mm	M 7
0.437 (11.09)	$\frac{7}{16}$ in AF	$\frac{1}{4}$ in SAE
0.468 (11.88)	$\frac{15}{32}$ in AF	
0.500 (12.70)	$\frac{1}{2}$ in AF	$\frac{5}{16}$ in SAE
0.512 (13.00)	13 mm	M8
0.562 (14.27)	$\frac{9}{16}$ in AF	$\frac{3}{8}$ in SAE
0.593 (15.06)	$\frac{19}{32}$ in AF	
0.625 (15.87)	$\frac{5}{8}$ in AF	$\frac{7}{16}$ in SAE
0.669 (17.00)	17 mm	M 10
0.687 (17.44)	$\frac{11}{16}$ in AF	
0.709 (19.00)	19 mm	M 12
0.750 (19.05)	$\frac{3}{4}$ in AF	$\frac{1}{2}$ in SAE
0.781 (19.83)	$\frac{25}{32}$ in AF	
0.812 (20.62)	$\frac{13}{16}$ in AF	
0.866 (22.00)	22 mm	M 14
0.875 (22.25)	$\frac{7}{8}$ in AF	$\frac{9}{16}$ in SAE
0.937 (23.79)	$\frac{15}{16}$ in AF	$\frac{5}{8}$ in SAE
0.945 (24.00)	24 mm	M 16
0.968 (24.58)	$\frac{31}{32}$ in AF	
1.000 (25.40)	1 in AF	$\frac{11}{16}$ in SAE
1.062 (26.97)	$1\frac{1}{16}$ in AF	$\frac{3}{4}$ in SAE
1.063 (27.00)	27 mm	M 18
1.125 (28.57)	$1\frac{1}{8}$ in AF	
1.182 (30.00)	30 mm	M 20
1.187 (30.14)	$1\frac{3}{16}$ in AF	
1.250 (31.75)	$1\frac{1}{4}$ in AF	$\frac{7}{8}$ in SAE
1.260 (32.00)	32 mm	M 22
1.312 (33.32)	$1\frac{5}{16}$ in AF	
1.375 (34.92)	$1\frac{3}{8}$ in AF	
1.418 (36.00)	36 mm	M 24
1.437 (36.49)	$1\frac{7}{16}$ in AF	1 in SAE
1.500 (38.10)	$1\frac{1}{2}$ in AF	
1.615 (41.00)	41 mm	M 27

It is appreciated that many an owner-mechanic is forced by circumstances to remove an engine or similar item without the benefit of a garage or workshop. Having done this, however, any repairs should always be done under the cover of a roof.

Wherever possible, any dismantling should be done on a clean, flat workbench or table at a suitable working height.

Any workbench needs a vice; one with a jaw opening of 100 mm (4 in) is suitable for most jobs. As mentioned previously, some clean dry storage space is also required for tools, as well as for any lubricants, cleaning fluids, touch-up paints and so on, which become necessary.

Another item which may be required, and which has a much more general usage, is an electric drill with a chuck capacity of at least 8 mm (5/16 in). This, together with a good range of twist drills, is virtually essential for fitting accessories.

Last, but not least, always keep a supply of old newspapers and clean, lint-free rags available, and try to keep any working area as clean as possible.

Booster battery (jump) starting

When jump starting a vehicle using a booster battery, observe the following precautions:

(a) Before connecting the booster battery, make sure that the ignition is switched off.
(b) Ensure that all electrical equipment (lights, heater, wipers etc) is switched off.
(c) Make sure that the booster battery is the same voltage as the discharged one in the vehicle.
(d) If the battery is being jump-started from the battery in another vehicle, the two vehicles MUST NOT TOUCH each other.
(e) Make sure that the transmission is in Neutral (manual transmission) or Park (automatic transmission).

Connect one jump lead between the positive (+) terminals of the two batteries. Connect the other jump lead first to the negative (-) terminal of the booster battery, and then to a good earthing point on the vehicle to be started, such as a bolt or bracket on the engine block, at least 45 cm (18 in) from the battery if possible (see illustration). Make sure that the jump leads will not come into contact with the fan, drive-belts or other moving parts of the engine.

Start the engine using the booster battery, then with the engine running at idle speed, switch on the heater blower motor (to maximum speed) or heated rear window, to reduce voltage peaks when the jump leads are disconnected. (Do not switch on the headlights instead - a high peak could blow the bulbs.) Disconnect the jump leads in the reverse order of connection.

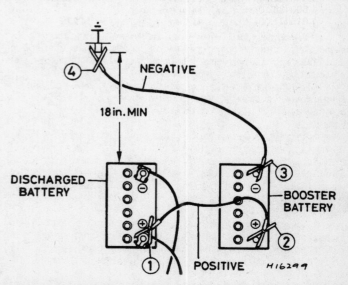

Jump start lead connections for negative-earth vehicles - connect leads in order shown

Automotive chemicals and lubricants

A number of automotive chemicals and lubricants are available for use during vehicle maintenance and repair. They include a wide variety of products ranging from cleaning solvents and degreasers to lubricants and protective sprays for rubber, plastic and vinyl.

Cleaners

Carburetor cleaner and choke cleaner is a strong solvent for gum, varnish and carbon. Most carburetor cleaners leave a dry-type lubricant film which will not harden or gum up. Because of this film it is not recommended for use on electrical components

Brake system cleaner is used to remove grease and brake fluid from the brake system, where clean surfaces are absolutely necessary. It leaves no residue and often eliminates brake squeal caused by contaminants.

Electrical cleaner removes oxidation, corrosion and carbon deposits from electrical contacts, restoring full current flow. It can also be used to clean spark plugs, carburetor jets, voltage regulators and other parts where an oil-free surface is desired.

Demoisturants remove water and moisture from electrical components such as alternators, voltage regulators, electrical connectors and fuse blocks. They are non-conductive, non-corrosive and non-flammable.

Degreasers are heavy-duty solvents used to remove grease from the outside of the engine and from chassis components. They can be sprayed or brushed on and, depending on the type, are rinsed off either with water or solvent.

Lubricants

Motor oil is the lubricant formulated for use in engines. It normally contains a wide variety of additives to prevent corrosion and reduce foaming and wear. Motor oil comes in various weights (viscosity ratings) from 5 to 80. The recommended weight of the oil depends on the season, temperature and the demands on the engine. Light oil is used in cold climates and under light load conditions. Heavy oil is used in hot climates and where high loads are encountered. Multi-viscosity oils are designed to have characteristics of both light and heavy oils and are available in a number of weights from 5W-20 to 20W-50.

Gear oil is designed to be used in differentials, manual transmissions and other areas where high-temperature lubrication is required.

Chassis and wheel bearing grease is a heavy grease used where increased loads and friction are encountered, such as for wheel bearings, balljoints, tie-rod ends and universal joints.

High-temperature wheel bearing grease is designed to withstand the extreme temperatures encountered by wheel bearings in disc brake equipped vehicles. It usually contains molybdenum disulphide (moly), which is a dry-type lubricant.

White grease is a heavy grease for metal-to-metal applications where water is a problem. White grease stays soft under both low and high temperatures, and will not wash off or dilute in the presence of water.

Assembly lube is a special extreme pressure lubricant, usually containing moly, used to lubricate high-load parts (such as main and rod bearings and cam lobes) for initial start-up of a new engine. The assembly lube lubricates the parts without being squeezed out or washed away until the engine oiling system begins to function.

Silicone lubricants are used to protect rubber, plastic, vinyl and nylon parts.

Graphite lubricants are used where oils cannot be used due to contamination problems, such as in locks. The dry graphite will lubricate metal parts while remaining uncontaminated by dirt, water, oil or acids. It is electrically conductive and will not foul electrical contacts in locks such as the ignition switch.

Moly penetrants loosen and lubricate frozen, rusted and corroded fasteners and prevent future rusting or freezing.

Heat-sink grease is a special electrically non-conductive grease that is used for mounting electronic ignition modules where it is essential that heat is transferred away from the module.

Sealants

RTV sealant is one of the most widely used gasket compounds. Made from silicone, RTV is air curing, it seals, bonds, waterproofs, fills surface irregularities, remains flexible, doesn't shrink, is relatively easy to remove, and is used as a supplementary sealer with almost all low and medium temperature gaskets.

Anaerobic sealant is much like RTV in that it can be used either to seal gaskets or to form gaskets by itself. It remains flexible, is solvent resistant and fills surface imperfections. The difference between an anaerobic sealant and an RTV-type sealant is in the curing. RTV cures when exposed to air, while an anaerobic sealant cures only in the absence of air. This means that an anaerobic sealant cures only after the assembly of parts, sealing them together.

Thread and pipe sealant is used for sealing hydraulic and pneumatic fittings and vacuum lines. It is usually made from a Teflon compound, and comes in a spray, a paint-on liquid and as a wrap-around tape.

Chemicals

Anti-seize compound prevents seizing, galling, cold welding, rust and corrosion in fasteners. High-temperature ant-seize, usually made with copper and graphite lubricants, is used for exhaust system and exhaust manifold bolts.

Anaerobic locking compounds are used to keep fasteners from vibrating or working loose and cure only after installation, in the absence of air. Medium strength locking compound is used for small nuts, bolts and screws that may be removed later. High-strength locking compound is for large nuts, bolts and studs which aren't removed on a regular basis.

Oil additives range from viscosity index improvers to chemical treatments that claim to reduce internal engine friction. It should be noted that most oil manufacturers caution against using additives with their oils.

Gas additives perform several functions, depending on their chemical makeup. They usually contain solvents that help dissolve gum and varnish that build up on carburetor, fuel injection and intake parts. They also serve to break down carbon deposits that form on the inside surfaces of the combustion chambers. Some additives contain upper cylinder lubricants for valves and piston rings, and others contain chemicals to remove condensation from the gas tank.

Miscellaneous

Brake fluid is specially formulated hydraulic fluid that can withstand the heat and pressure encountered in brake systems. Care must be taken so this fluid does not come in contact with painted surfaces or plastics. An opened container should always be resealed to prevent contamination by water or dirt.

Weatherstrip adhesive is used to bond weatherstripping around doors, windows and trunk lids. It is sometimes used to attach trim pieces.

Underseal is a petroleum-based, tar-like substance that is designed to protect metal surfaces on the underside of the vehicle from corrosion. It also acts as a sound-deadening agent by insulating the bottom of the vehicle.

Waxes and polishes are used to help protect painted and plated surfaces from the weather. Different types of paint may require the use of different types of wax and polish. Some polishes utilise a chemical or abrasive cleaner to help remove the top layer of oxidised (dull) paint on older vehicles. In recent years many non-wax polishes that contain a wide variety of chemicals such as polymers and silicones have been introduced. These non-wax polishes are usually easier to apply and last longer than conventional waxes and polishes.

Use of English

As the main part of this book has been written in the US, it uses the appropriate US component names, phrases, and spelling. Some of these differ from those used in the UK. Normally, these cause no difficulty, but to make sure, a glossary is printed below. When ordering spare parts, remember the parts list may use some of these words:

AMERICAN	ENGLISH	AMERICAN	ENGLISH
Aluminum	Aluminium	Muffler	Silencer
Antenna	Aerial	Odor	Odour
Auto parts stores	Motor factors	Oil pan	Sump
Axleshaft	Halfshaft	Open flame	Naked flame
Back-up	Reverse	Panel wagon/van	Van
Barrel	Choke/venturi	Parking brake	Handbrake
Block	Chock	Parking light	Sidelight
Box-end wrench	Ring spanner	Pinging	Pinking
Bushing	Bush	Piston pin or wrist pin	Gudgeon pin
Carburetor	Carburettor	Pitman arm	Drop arm
Center	Centre	Power brake booster	Servo unit
Coast	Freewheel	Primary shoe (of brake)	Leading shoe (of brake)
Color	Colour	Prussian blue	Engineer's blue
Convertible	Drop head coupe	Pry	Prise (force apart)
Cotter pin	Split pin	Prybar	Lever
Counterclockwise	Anti-clockwise	Prying	Levering
Countershaft (of gearbox)	Layshaft	Quarter window	Quarterlight
Dashboard	Facia	Recap	Retread
Denatured alcohol	Methylated spirit	Release cylinder	Slave cylinder
Dome lamp	Interior light	Repair shop	Garage
Driveaxle	Driveshaft	Replacement	Renewal
Driveshaft	Propeller shaft	Ring gear (of differential)	Crownwheel
Fender	Wing/mudguard	Rocker panel (beneath doors)	Sill panel (beneath doors)
Firewall	Bulkhead	Rod bearing	Big-end bearing
Flashlight	Torch	Rotor/disk	Disc (brake)
Float bowl	Float chamber	Secondary shoe (of brake)	Trailing shoe (of brake)
Floor jack	Trolley jack	Sedan	Saloon
Freeway, turnpike etc	Motorway	Setscrew	Grub screw
Freeze plug	Core plug	Shock absorber, shock	Damper
Frozen	Seized	Snap-ring	Circlip
Gas tank	Petrol tank	Soft top	Hood
Gasoline (gas)	Petrol	Spacer	Distance piece
Gearshift	Gearchange	Spare tire	Spare wheel
Ground (electrical)	Earth	Spark plug wires	HT leads
Header	Exhaust manifold	Spindle arm	Steering arm
Heat riser	Hot spot	Stabilizer or sway bar	Anti-roll bar
High	Top gear	Station wagon	Estate car
Hood (engine cover)	Bonnet	Stumbles	Hesitates
Installation	Refitting	Tang or lock	Tab washer
Intake	Inlet	Throw-out bearing	Thrust bearing
Jackstands	Axle stands	Tie-rod or connecting rod	
Jumper cable	Jump lead	(of steering)	Trackrod
Keeper	Collet	Tire	Tyre
Kerosene	Paraffin	Transmission	Gearbox
Knock pin	Roll pin	Troubleshooting	Fault finding/diagnosis
Lash	Clearance	Trunk	Boot (luggage compartment)
Lash	Free-play	Turn signal	Indicator
Latch	Catch	TV (throttle valve) cable	Kickdown cable
Latches	Locks	Valve cover	Rocker cover
License plate	Number plate	Valve lifter or tappet	Cam follower or tappet
Light	Lamp	Vapor	Vapour
Lock (for valve spring retainer)	Split cotter (for valve spring cap)	Vise	Vice
Lopes	Hunts	Wheel cover	Roadwheel trim
Lug nut/bolt	Wheel nut/bolt	Whole drive line	Transmission
Metal chips or debris	Swarf	Windshield	Windscreen
Misses	Misfires	Wrench	Spanner

Conversion factors

Length (distance)

Inches (in)	25.4	= Millimetres (mm)	X 0.0394	= Inches (in)
Feet (ft)	0.305	= Metres (m)	X 3.281	= Feet (ft)
Miles	1.609	= Kilometres (km)	X 0.621	= Miles

Volume (capacity)

Cubic inches (cu in; in³)	X 16.387	= Cubic centimetres (cc; cm³)	X 0.061	= Cubic inches (cu in; in³)
Imperial pints (Imp pt)	X 0.568	= Litres (l)	X 1.76	= Imperial pints (Imp pt)
Imperial quarts (Imp qt)	X 1.137	= Litres (l)	X 0.88	= Imperial quarts (Imp qt)
Imperial quarts (Imp qt)	X 1.201	= US quarts (US qt)	X 0.833	= Imperial quarts (Imp qt)
US quarts (US qt)	X 0.946	= Litres (l)	X 1.057	= US quarts (US qt)
Imperial gallons (Imp gal)	X 4.546	= Litres (l)	X 0.22	= Imperial gallons (Imp gal)
Imperial gallons (Imp gal)	X 1.201	= US gallons (US gal)	X 0.833	= Imperial gallons (Imp gal)
US gallons (US gal)	X 3.785	= Litres (l)	X 0.264	= US gallons (US gal)

Mass (weight)

Ounces (oz)	X 28.35	= Grams (g)	X 0.035	= Ounces (oz)
Pounds (lb)	X 0.454	= Kilograms (kg)	X 2.205	= Pounds (lb)

Force

Ounces-force (ozf; oz)	X 0.278	= Newtons (N)	X 3.6	= Ounces-force (ozf; oz)
Pounds-force (lbf; lb)	X 4.448	= Newtons (N)	X 0.225	= Pounds-force (lbf; lb)
Newtons (N)	X 0.1	= Kilograms-force (kgf; kg)	X 9.81	= Newtons (N)

Pressure

Pounds-force per square inch (psi; lbf/in²; lb/in²)	X 0.070	= Kilograms-force per square centimetre (kgf/cm²; kg/cm²)	X 14.223	= Pounds-force per square inch (psi; lbf/in²; lb/in²)
Pounds-force per square inch (psi; lbf/in²; lb/in²)	X 0.068	= Atmospheres (atm)	X 14.696	= Pounds-force per square inch (psi; lbf/in²; lb/in²)
Pounds-force per square inch (psi; lbf/in²; lb/in²)	X 0.069	= Bars	X 14.5	= Pounds-force per square inch (psi; lbf/in²; lb/in²)
Pounds-force per square inch (psi; lbf/in²; lb/in²)	X 6.895	= Kilopascals (kPa)	X 0.145	= Pounds-force per square inch (psi; lbf/in²; lb/in²)
Kilopascals (kPa)	X 0.01	= Kilograms-force per square centimetre (kgf/cm²; kg/cm²)	X 98.1	= Kilopascals (kPa)
Millibar (mbar)	X 100	= Pascals (Pa)	X 0.01	= Millibar (mbar)
Millibar (mbar)	X 0.0145	= Pounds-force per square inch (psi; lbf/in²; lb/in²)	X 68.947	= Millibar (mbar)
Millibar (mbar)	X 0.75	= Millimetres of mercury (mmHg)	X 1.333	= Millibar (mbar)
Millibar (mbar)	X 0.401	= Inches of water (inH₂O)	X 2.491	= Millibar (mbar)
Millimetres of mercury (mmHg)	X 0.535	= Inches of water (inH₂O)	X 1.868	= Millimetres of mercury (mmHg)
Inches of water (inH₂O)	X 0.036	= Pounds-force per square inch (psi; lbf/in²; lb/in²)	X 27.68	= Inches of water (inH₂O)

Torque (moment of force)

Pounds-force inches (lbf in; lb in)	X 1.152	= Kilograms-force centimetre (kgf cm; kg cm)	X 0.868	= Pounds-force inches (lbf in; lb in)
Pounds-force inches (lbf in; lb in)	X 0.113	= Newton metres (Nm)	X 8.85	= Pounds-force inches (lbf in; lb in)
Pounds-force inches (lbf in; lb in)	X 0.083	= Pounds-force feet (lbf ft; lb ft)	X 12	= Pounds-force inches (lbf in; lb in)
Pounds-force feet (lbf ft; lb ft)	X 0.138	= Kilograms-force metres (kgf m; kg m)	X 7.233	= Pounds-force feet (lbf ft; lb ft)
Pounds-force feet (lbf ft; lb ft)	X 1.356	= Newton metres (Nm)	X 0.738	= Pounds-force feet (lbf ft; lb ft)
Newton metres (Nm)	X 0.102	= Kilograms-force metres (kgf m; kg m)	X 9.804	= Newton metres (Nm)

Power

Horsepower (hp)	X 745.7	= Watts (W)	X 0.0013	= Horsepower (hp)

Velocity (speed)

Miles per hour (miles/hr; mph)	X 1.609	= Kilometres per hour (km/hr; kph)	X 0.621	= Miles per hour (miles/hr; mph)

Fuel consumption*

Miles per gallon, Imperial (mpg)	X 0.354	= Kilometres per litre (km/l)	X 2.825	= Miles per gallon, Imperial (mpg)
Miles per gallon, US (mpg)	X 0.425	= Kilometres per litre (km/l)	X 2.352	= Miles per gallon, US (mpg)

Temperature

Degrees Fahrenheit = (°C x 1.8) + 32   Degrees Celsius (Degrees Centigrade; °C) = (°F - 32) x 0.56

It is common practice to convert from miles per gallon (mpg) to litres/100 kilometres (l/100km), where mpg (Imperial) x l/100 km = 282 and mpg (US) x l/100 km = 235

Fault diagnosis

Contents

This Section provides an easy-reference guide to the more common problems which may occur during the operation of your vehicle. These problems and their possible causes are grouped under headings denoting various components or systems, such as Engine, Cooling system, etc. They also refer you to the Chapter and/or Section which deals with the problem.

Remember that successful fault diagnosis is not a mysterious black art practised only by professional mechanics. It is simply the result of the right knowledge combined with an intelligent, systematic approach to the problem. Always work by a process of elimination, starting with the simplest solution and working through to the most complex - and never overlook the obvious. Anyone can run the gas tank dry or leave the lights on overnight, so don't assume that you are exempt from such oversights.

Finally, always establish a clear idea of why a problem has occurred and take steps to ensure that it doesn't happen again. If the electrical system fails because of a poor connection, check all other connections in the system to make sure that they don't fail as well. If a particular fuse continues to blow, find out why - don't just renew one fuse after another. Remember, failure of a small component can often be indicative of potential failure or incorrect functioning of a more important component or system.

Engine and performance

1   Engine will not rotate when attempting to start

1   Battery terminal connections loose or corroded. Check the cable terminals at the battery; tighten cable clamp and/or clean off corrosion as necessary (see Chapter 1).
2   Battery discharged or faulty. If the cable ends are clean and tight on the battery posts, turn the key to the On position and switch on the headlights or windshield wipers. If they won't run, the battery is discharged.
3   Automatic transmission not engaged in park (P) or Neutral (N).
4   Broken, loose or disconnected wires in the starting circuit. Inspect all wires and connectors at the battery, starter solenoid and ignition switch (on steering column).
5   Starter motor pinion jammed in flywheel ring gear. If manual transmission, place transmission in gear and rock the vehicle to manually turn the engine. Remove starter (Chapter 5) and inspect pinion and flywheel (Chapter 2) at earliest convenience.
6   Starter solenoid faulty (Chapter 5).
7   Starter motor faulty (Chapter 5).
8   Ignition switch faulty (Chapter 12).
9   Engine seized. Try to turn the crankshaft with a large socket and breaker bar on the pulley bolt.

2   Engine rotates but will not start

1   Fuel tank empty.
2   Battery discharged (engine rotates slowly). Check the operation of electrical components as described in previous Section.
3   Battery terminal connections loose or corroded. See previous Section.
4   Fuel not reaching carburetor or fuel injector. Check for clogged fuel filter or lines and defective fuel pump. Also make sure the tank vent lines aren't clogged (UK Supplement and Chapter 4).
5   Choke not operating properly (UK Supplement and Chapter 1).
6   Faulty distributor components. Check the cap and rotor (UK Supplement and Chapter 1). Where applicable, check the contact breaker points.
7   Low cylinder compression. Check as described in Chapter 2.
8   Valve clearances not properly adjusted (UK Supplement or Chapter 1)
9   Water in fuel. Drain tank and fill with new fuel.
10   Defective ignition coil (UK Supplement and Chapter 5).

11   Dirty or clogged carburetor jets or fuel injector. Carburetor out of adjustment. Check the float level (UK Supplement or Chapter 4).
12   Wet or damaged ignition components (UK Supplement or Chapters 1 and 5).
13   Worn, faulty or incorrectly gapped spark plugs (Chapter 1).
14   Broken, loose or disconnected wires in the starting circuit (see previous Section).
15   Loose distributor (changing ignition timing). Turn the distributor body as necessary to start the engine, then adjust the ignition timing as soon as possible (UK Supplement or Chapter 1).
16   Broken, loose or disconnected wires at the ignition coil or faulty coil (UK Supplement or Chapter 5).
17   Timing belt failure or wear affecting valve timing (UK Supplement or Chapter 2).

3   Starter motor operates without turning engine

1   Starter motor bolts loose. Check and tighten if necessary (Chapter 5).
2   Starter pinion sticking. Remove the starter (Chapter 5) and inspect.
3   Starter pinion or flywheel/driveplate teeth worn or broken. Remove the inspection cover and inspect.

4   Engine hard to start when cold

1   Battery discharged or low. Check as described in Chapter 1.
2   Fuel not reaching the carburetor or fuel injectors. Check the fuel filter, lines and fuel pump (UK Supplement or Chapters 1 and 4).
3   Choke inoperative (UK Supplement or Chapters 1 and 4).
4   Defective spark plugs (Chapter 1).

5   Engine hard to start when hot

1   Air filter dirty (UK Supplement or Chapter 1).
2   Fuel not reaching carburetor or fuel injectors (see UK Supplement or Section 4). Check for a vapor lock situation, brought about by clogged fuel tank vent lines.
3   Bad engine ground connection.
4   Choke sticking (UK Supplement or Chapter 1).
5   Defective pick-up coil in distributor (Chapter 5). Where applicable, check contact breaker points (UK Supplement).
6   Float level too high (UK Supplement or Chapter 4).

6   Starter motor noisy or engages roughly

1   Pinion or flywheel/driveplate teeth worn or broken. Remove the inspection cover on the left side of the engine and inspect.
2   Starter motor mounting bolts loose or missing.

7   Engine starts but stops immediately

1   Loose or damaged wire harness connections at distributor, coil or alternator.
2   Intake manifold vacuum leaks. Make sure all mounting bolts/nuts are tight, and all vacuum hoses connected to the manifold are attached properly and in good condition.
3   Insufficient fuel flow (see UK Supplement or Chapter 4).

8   Engine "lopes" while idling, or idles erratically

1   Vacuum leaks. Check mounting bolts at the intake manifold for tightness. Make sure that all vacuum hoses are connected and in good

condition. Use a stethoscope or a length of fuel hose held against your ear to listen for vacuum leaks while the engine is running. A hissing sound will be heard. A soapy water solution will also detect leaks. Check the intake manifold gasket surfaces.

2   Leaking EGR valve or plugged PCV valve (see Chapters 1 and 6).
3   Air filter clogged (UK Supplement or Chapter 1).
4   Fuel pump not delivering sufficient fuel (UK Supplement or Chapter 4).
5   Leaking head gasket. Perform a cylinder compression check (Chapter 2).
6   Timing belt worn (UK Supplement or Chapter 2).
7   Camshaft lobes worn (UK Supplement or Chapter 2).
8   Valve clearance out of adjustment (UK Supplement or Chapter 1).
9   Valves burned or otherwise leaking (UK Supplement or Chapter 2).
10   Ignition timing out of adjustment (UK Supplement or Chapter 1).
11   Ignition system not operating properly (UK Supplement or Chapters 1 and 5). Where applicable, check the contact breaker points.
12   Thermostatic air cleaner not operating properly (Chapter 1).
13   Choke not operating properly (UK Supplement or Chapters 1 and 4).
14   Dirty or clogged injector(s). Carburetor dirty, clogged or out of adjustment. Check the float level (UK Supplement or Chapter 4).
15   Idle speed out of adjustment (UK Supplement or Chapter 1).

9   Engine misses at idle speed

1   Spark plugs faulty or not gapped properly (Chapter 1).
2   Faulty spark plug wires (Chapter 1).
3   Wet or damaged distributor components (UK Supplement or Chapter 1).
4   Short circuits in ignition, coil or spark plug wires.
5   Sticking or faulty emissions systems (see Chapter 6).
6   Clogged fuel filter and/or foreign matter in fuel. Remove the fuel filter (Chapter 1) and inspect.
7   Vacuum leaks at intake manifold or hose connections. Check as described in Section 8.
8   Incorrect idle speed (UK Supplement or Chapter 1) or idle mixture (UK Supplement or Chapter 4).
9   Incorrect ignition timing (UK Supplement or Chapter 1).
10   Low or uneven cylinder compression. Check as described in Chapter 2.
11   Choke not operating properly (UK Supplement or Chapter 1).
12   Clogged or dirty fuel injectors (Chapter 4).

10   Excessively-high idle speed

1   Sticking throttle linkage (UK Supplement or Chapter 4).
2   Choke opened excessively at idle (UK Supplement or Chapter 4).
3   Idle speed incorrectly adjusted (UK Supplement or Chapter 1).

11   Battery will not hold a charge

1   Alternator drivebelt defective or not adjusted properly (Chapter 1).
2   Battery cables loose or corroded (Chapter 1).
3   Alternator not charging properly (Chapter 5).
4   Loose, broken or faulty wires in the charging circuit (Chapter 5).
5   Short-circuit causing a continuous drain on the battery.
6   Battery defective internally.

12   Alternator light stays on

1   Fault in alternator or charging circuit (Chapter 5).
2   Alternator drivebelt defective or not properly adjusted (Chapter 1).

13   Alternator light fails to come on when key is turned on

1   Faulty bulb (Chapter 12).
2   Defective alternator (Chapter 5).
3   Fault in the printed circuit, wiring or bulbholder (Chapter 12).

14   Engine misses throughout driving speed range

1   Fuel filter clogged and/or impurities in the fuel system. Check fuel filter (Chapter 1) or clean system (Chapter 4).
2   Faulty or incorrectly gapped spark plugs (Chapter 1).
3   Incorrect ignition timing (UK Supplement or Chapter 1).
4   Cracked distributor cap, disconnected distributor wires or damaged distributor components. Where applicable, check the contact breaker points (UK Supplement or Chapter 1).
5   Defective spark plug wires (Chapter 1).
6   Emissions system components faulty (Chapter 6).
7   Low or uneven cylinder compression pressures. Check as described in Chapter 2.
8   Weak or faulty ignition coil (UK Supplement or Chapter 5).
9   Weak or faulty ignition system (UK Supplement or Chapter 5).
10   Vacuum leaks at intake manifold or vacuum hoses (see Section 8).
11   Dirty or clogged carburetor or fuel injector (UK Supplement or Chapter 4).
12   Leaky EGR valve (Chapter 6).
13   Carburetor out of adjustment (UK Supplement or Chapter 4).
14   Idle speed out of adjustment (UK Supplement or Chapter 1).

15   Hesitation or stumble during acceleration

1   Ignition timing incorrect (UK Supplement or Chapter 1).
2   Ignition system not operating properly (UK Supplement or Chapter 5). Where applicable, check the contact breaker points (UK Supplement).
3   Dirty or clogged carburetor or fuel injector (UK Supplement or Chapter 4).
4   Low fuel pressure. Check for proper operation of the fuel pump and for restrictions in the fuel filter and lines (UK Supplement or Chapter 4).
5   Carburetor out of adjustment (UK Supplement or Chapter 4).

16   Engine stalls

1   Idle speed incorrect (UK Supplement or Chapter 1).
2   Fuel filter clogged and/or water and impurities in the fuel system (Chapter 1).
3   Choke not operating properly (UK Supplement or Chapter 1).
4   Damaged or wet distributor cap and HT leads.
5   Emissions system components faulty (Chapter 6).
6   Faulty or incorrectly gapped spark plugs (Chapter 1). Also check the spark plug wires (Chapter 1).
7   Vacuum leak at the carburetor, intake manifold or vacuum hoses. Check as described in Section 8.
8   Valve clearances incorrect (UK Supplement or Chapter 1).

17   Engine lacks power

1   Incorrect ignition timing (UK Supplement or Chapter 1).
2   Excessive play in distributor shaft. At the same time, check for faulty distributor cap, wires, etc. (UK Supplement or Chapter 1).
3   Faulty or incorrectly gapped spark plugs (Chapter 1).
4   Air filter dirty (UK Supplement or Chapter 1).
5   Faulty ignition coil (UK Supplement or Chapter 5).

6   Brakes binding (UK Supplement or Chapters 1 and 9).
7   Automatic transmission fluid level incorrect, causing slippage (Chapter 1).
8   Clutch slipping (Chapter 8).
9   Fuel filter clogged and/or impurities in the fuel system (Chapters 1 and 4).
10 EGR system not functioning properly (Chapter 6).
11 Use of sub-standard fuel. Fill tank with proper octane fuel.
12 Low or uneven cylinder compression pressures. Check as described in Chapter 2.
13 Air leak at carburetor or intake manifold (check as described in Section 8).
14 Dirty or clogged carburetor jets or malfunctioning choke (UK Supplement or Chapters 1 and 4).

18   Engine backfires

1   EGR system not functioning properly (Chapter 6).
2   Ignition timing incorrect (UK Supplement or Chapter 1).
3   Thermostatic air cleaner system not operating properly (Chapter 6).
4   Vacuum leak (refer to Section 8).
5   Valve clearances incorrect (UK Supplement or Chapter 1).
6   Damaged valve springs or sticking valves (UK Supplement or Chapter 2).
7   Intake air leak (see Section 8).
8   Carburetor float level out of adjustment (UK Supplement or Chapter 4).

19   Engine surges while holding accelerator steady

1   Intake air leak (see Section 8).
2   Fuel pump not working properly (UK Supplement or Chapter 4).

20   Pinging or knocking engine sounds when engine is under load

1   Incorrect grade of fuel. Fill tank with fuel of the proper octane rating.
2   Ignition timing incorrect (UK Supplement or Chapter 1).
3   Carbon build-up in combustion chambers. Remove cylinder head(s) and clean combustion chambers (UK Supplement or Chapter 2).
4   Incorrect spark plugs (UK Supplement or Chapter 1).

21   Engine diesels (continues to run) after being turned off

1   Idle speed too high (UK Supplement or Chapter 1).
2   Ignition timing incorrect (UK Supplement or Chapter 1).
3   Incorrect spark plug heat range (UK Supplement or Chapter 1).
4   Intake air leak (see Section 8).
5   Carbon build-up in combustion chambers. Remove the cylinder head and clean the combustion chambers (UK Supplement or Chapter 2).
6   Valves sticking (Chapter 2).
7   Valve clearances incorrect (UK Supplement or Chapter 1).
8   EGR system not operating properly (Chapter 6).
9   Fuel shut-off system not operating properly (Chapter 6).
10 Check for causes of overheating (Section 27).

22   Low oil pressure

1   Oil level low.
2   Improper grade of oil.

3   Oil pump worn or damaged (UK Supplement or Chapter 2).
4   Engine overheating (refer to Section 27).
5   Clogged oil filter (Chapter 1).
6   Clogged oil pickup (UK Supplement or Chapter 2).
7   Oil pressure gauge not working properly (Chapter 2).

23   Excessive oil consumption

1   Loose oil drain plug.
2   Loose bolts or damaged oil pan gasket (UK Supplement or Chapter 2).
3   Loose bolts or damaged front cover or oil pump gasket (UK Supplement or Chapter 2).
4   Front or rear crankshaft oil seal leaking (UK Supplement or Chapter 2).
5   Loose bolts or damaged camshaft cover gasket (UK Supplement or Chapter 2).
6   Loose oil filter (Chapter 1).
7   Loose or damaged oil pressure switch (Chapter 2).
8   Pistons and cylinders excessively worn (UK Supplement or Chapter 2).
9   Piston rings not installed correctly on pistons (UK Supplement or Chapter 2).
10 Worn or damaged piston rings (UK Supplement or Chapter 2).
11 Intake and/or exhaust valve oil seals worn or damaged (UK Supplement or Chapter 2).
12 Worn valve stems.
13 Worn or damaged valves/guides (UK Supplement or Chapter 2).

24   Excessive fuel consumption

1   Dirty or clogged air filter element (UK Supplement or Chapter 1).
2   Incorrect ignition timing (UK Supplement or Chapter 1).
3   Incorrect idle speed (UK Supplement or Chapter 1).
4   Low tire pressure or incorrect tire size (Chapter 11).
5   Fuel leakage. Check all connections, lines and components in the fuel system (Chapter 4).
6   Choke not operating properly (UK Supplement or Chapter 1).
7   Dirty or clogged carburetor jets or fuel injectors (UK Supplement or Chapter 4).

25   Fuel odor

1   Fuel leakage. Check all connections, lines and components in the fuel system (Chapter 4).
2   Fuel tank overfilled. Fill only to automatic shut-off.
3   Charcoal canister filter in Evaporative Emissions Control system clogged (Chapter 1).
4   Vapor leaks from Evaporative Emissions Control system lines (Chapter 6).

26   Miscellaneous engine noises

1   A strong dull noise that becomes more rapid as the engine accelerates indicates worn or damaged crankshaft bearings or an unevenly worn crankshaft. To pinpoint the trouble spot, remove the spark plug wire from one plug at a time and crank the engine over. If the noise stops, the cylinder with the removed plug wire indicates the problem area. Replace the bearing and/or service or replace the crankshaft (UK Supplement or Chapter 2).
2   A similar (yet slightly higher pitched) noise to the crankshaft knocking described in the previous paragraph, that becomes more rapid as the engine accelerates, indicates worn or damaged connecting rod bearings (UK Supplement or Chapter 2). The procedure for locating the problem cylinder is the same as described in Paragraph 1.

3   An overlapping metallic noise that increases in intensity as the engine speed increases, yet diminishes as the engine warms up indicates abnormal piston and cylinder wear (UK Supplement or Chapter 2). To locate the problem cylinder, use the procedure described in Paragraph 1.

4   A rapid clicking noise that becomes faster as the engine accelerates indicates a worn piston pin or piston pin hole. This sound will happen each time the piston hits the highest and lowest points in the stroke (UK Supplement or Chapter 2). The procedure for locating the problem piston is described in Paragraph 1.

5   A metallic clicking noise coming from the water pump indicates worn or damaged water pump bearings or pump. Replace the water pump with a new one (UK Supplement or Chapter 3).

6   A rapid tapping sound or clicking sound that becomes faster as the engine speed increases indicates "valve tapping" or improperly adjusted valve clearances. This can be identified by holding one end of a section of hose to your ear and placing the other end at different spots along the rocker arm cover. The point where the sound is loudest indicates the problem valve. Adjust the valve clearance (UK Supplement or Chapter 1). If the problem persists, you likely have a collapsed valve lifter or other damaged valve train component. Changing the engine oil and adding a high-viscosity oil treatment will sometimes cure a stuck lifter problem. If the problem still persists, the lifters and rocker arms must be removed for inspection (see UK Supplement or Chapter 2).

7   A steady metallic rattling or rapping sound coming from the area of the timing chain cover indicates a worn, damaged or out-of-adjustment timing chain. Service or replace the chain and related components (UK Supplement or Chapter 2).

Cooling system

27   Overheating

1   Insufficient coolant in system (Chapter 1).
2   Drivebelt defective or not adjusted properly (Chapter 1).
3   Radiator core blocked or radiator grille dirty or restricted (Chapter 3).
4   Thermostat faulty (UK Supplement or Chapter 3).
5   Fan not functioning properly (UK Supplement or Chapter 3).
6   Radiator cap not maintaining proper pressure. Have cap pressure-tested by gas station or repair shop.
7   Ignition timing incorrect (UK Supplement or Chapter 1).
8   Defective water pump (UK Supplement or Chapter 3).
9   Improper grade of engine oil.
10   Inaccurate temperature gauge (Chapter 12).

28   Overcooling

1   Thermostat faulty (UK Supplement or Chapter 3).
2   Inaccurate temperature gauge (Chapter 12).

29   External coolant leakage

1   Deteriorated or damaged hoses. Loose clamps at hose connections (Chapter 1).
2   Water pump seals defective. If this is the case, water will drip from the weep hole in the water pump body (UK Supplement or Chapter 3).
3   Leakage from radiator core or header tank. This will require the radiator to be professionally repaired (see Chapter 3 for removal procedures).
4   Engine drain plugs or water jacket freeze plugs leaking (see Chapters 1 and 2).

5   Leak from coolant temperature switch (Chapter 3).
6   Leak from damaged gaskets or small cracks (Chapter 2).
7   Damaged head gasket. This can be verified by checking the condition of the engine oil as noted in Section 30.

30   Internal coolant leakage

Note: *Internal coolant leaks can usually be detected by examining the oil. Check the dipstick and inside the rocker arm cover for water deposits and an oil consistency like that of a milkshake.*

1   Leaking cylinder head gasket. Have the system pressure tested or remove the cylinder head (UK Supplement or Chapter 2) and inspect.
2   Cracked cylinder bore or cylinder head. Dismantle engine and inspect (UK Supplement or Chapter 2).
3   Loose cylinder head bolts (tighten as described in UK Supplement or Chapter 2).

31   Abnormal coolant loss

1   Overfilling system (UK Supplement or Chapter 1).
2   Coolant boiling away due to overheating (see causes in Section 27).
3   Internal or external leakage (see Sections 29 and 30).
4   Faulty radiator cap. Have the cap pressure tested.
5   Cooling system being pressurised by engine compression. This could be due to a cracked head or block or leaking head gasket.

32   Poor coolant circulation

1   Inoperative water pump. A quick test is to pinch the top radiator hose closed with your hand while the engine is idling, then release it. You should feel a surge of coolant if the pump is working properly (UK Supplement or Chapter 3).
2   Restriction in cooling system. Drain, flush and refill the system (UK Supplement or Chapter 1). If necessary, remove the radiator (Chapter 3) and have it reverse flushed or professionally cleaned.
3   Loose water pump drivebelt (Chapter 1).
4   Thermostat sticking (UK Supplement or Chapter 3).
5   Insufficient coolant (UK Supplement or Chapter 1).

33   Corrosion

1   Excessive impurities in the water. Soft, clean water is recommended. Distilled or rainwater is satisfactory.
2   Insufficient antifreeze solution (refer to UK Supplement or Chapter 1 for the proper ratio of water to antifreeze).
3   Infrequent flushing and draining of system. Regular flushing of the cooling system should be carried out at the specified intervals as described in (UK Supplement or Chapter 1).

Clutch

Note: *All clutch-related service information is located in Chapter 8, unless otherwise noted.*

34   Fails to release (pedal pressed to the floor - shift lever does not move freely in and out of Reverse)

1   Freeplay incorrectly adjusted (see Chapter 1).
2   Clutch contaminated with oil. Remove clutch plate and inspect.
3   Clutch plate warped, distorted or otherwise damaged.

4   Diaphragm spring fatigued. Remove clutch cover/pressure plate assembly and inspect.
5   Broken, binding or damaged release cable or linkage (models with a cable-operated release system).
6   Leakage of fluid from clutch hydraulic system. Inspect master cylinder, operating cylinder and connecting lines.
7   Air in clutch hydraulic system. Bleed the system.
8   Insufficient pedal height. Check and adjust as necessary.
9   Piston seal in operating cylinder deformed or damaged.
10 Lack of grease on pilot bushing/bearing.

35   Clutch slips (engine speed increases with no increase in vehicle speed)

1   Worn or oil-soaked clutch plate.
2   Clutch plate not broken in. It may take 30 or 40 normal starts for a new clutch to seat.
3   Diaphragm spring weak or damaged. Remove clutch cover/pressure plate assembly and inspect.
4   Flywheel warped (Chapter 2).
5   Clutch cable sticking.

36   Grabbing (chattering) as clutch is engaged

1   Oil on clutch plate. Remove and inspect. Repair any leaks.
2   Worn or loose engine or transmission mounts. They may move slightly when clutch is released. Inspect mounts and bolts.
3   Worn splines on transmission input shaft. Remove clutch components and inspect.
4   Warped pressure plate or flywheel. Remove clutch components and inspect.
5   Diaphragm spring fatigued. Remove clutch cover/pressure plate assembly and inspect.
6   Clutch linings hardened or warped.
7   Clutch lining rivets loose.

37   Squeal or rumble with clutch engaged (pedal released)

1   Improper pedal adjustment. Adjust pedal freeplay (Chapter 1).
2   Release bearing binding on transmission shaft. Remove clutch components and check bearing. Remove any burrs or nicks, clean and re-lubricate before reinstallation.
3   Clutch rivets loose.
4   Clutch plate cracked.
5   Fatigued clutch plate torsion springs. Replace clutch plate.

38   Squeal or rumble with clutch disengaged (pedal depressed)

1   Worn or damaged release bearing.
2   Worn or broken pressure plate diaphragm fingers.
3   Pilot bearing worn or damaged.

39   Clutch pedal stays on floor when disengaged

Binding linkage or release bearing. Inspect linkage or remove clutch components as necessary.

Manual transmission

Note: *All manual transmission service information is located in UK Supplement or Chapter 7, unless otherwise noted.*

40   Noisy in Neutral with engine running

1   Input shaft bearing worn.
2   Damaged main drive gear bearing.
3   Insufficient transmission oil (Chapter 1).
4   Transmission oil in poor condition. Drain and fill with proper grade oil. Check old oil for water and debris (Chapter 1).
5   Noise can be caused by variations in engine torque. Change the idle speed and see if noise disappears.

41   Noisy in all gears

1   Any of the above causes, and/or:
2   Worn or damaged output gear bearings or shaft.

42   Noisy in one particular gear

1   Worn, damaged or chipped gear teeth.
2   Worn or damaged synchroniser.

43   Slips out of gear

1   Transmission loose on clutch housing.
2   Stiff shift lever seal.
3   Shift linkage binding.
4   Broken or loose input gear bearing retainer.
5   Dirt between clutch lever and engine housing.
6   Worn linkage.
7   Damaged or worn check balls, fork rod ball grooves or check springs.
8   Worn mainshaft or countershaft bearings.
9   Loose engine mounts (Chapter 2).
10 Excessive gear end play.
11 Worn synchronisers.

44   Oil leaks

1   Excessive amount of lubricant in transmission (see Chapter 1 for correct checking procedures). Drain lubricant as required.
2   Rear oil seal or speedometer oil seal damaged.
3   To pinpoint a leak, first remove all built-up dirt and grime from the transmission. Degreasing agents and/or steam cleaning will achieve this. With the underside clean, drive the vehicle at low speeds so the airflow will not blow the leak far from its source. Raise the vehicle and determine where the leak is located.

45   Difficulty engaging gears

1   Clutch not releasing completely.
2   Loose or damaged shift linkage. Make a thorough inspection, replacing parts as necessary.
3   Insufficient transmission oil (Chapter 1).
4   Transmission oil in poor condition. Drain and fill with proper grade oil. Check oil for water and debris (Chapter 1).
5   Worn or damaged striking rod.
6   Sticking or jamming gears.

46   Noise occurs while shifting gears

1   Check for proper operation of the clutch (Chapter 8).
2   Faulty synchroniser assemblies. Check for wear or damage to baulk rings or any parts of the synchromesh assemblies.

Automatic transmission

Note: *Due to the complexity of the automatic transmission, it's difficult for the home mechanic to properly diagnose and service. For problems other than the following, the vehicle should be taken to a reputable mechanic.*

47   Fluid leakage

1   Automatic transmission fluid is a deep red color, and fluid leaks should not be confused with engine oil which can easily be blown by air flow to the transmission.
2   To pinpoint a leak, first remove all built-up dirt and grime from the transmission. Degreasing agents and/or steam cleaning will achieve this. With the underside clean, drive the vehicle at low speeds so the airflow will not blow the leak far from its source. Raise the vehicle and determine where the leak is located. Common areas of leakage are:
(a) **Fluid pan:** tighten mounting bolts and/or replace pan gasket as necessary (Chapter 1). Some models have a drain plug; make sure it's tight.
(b) **Rear extension:** tighten bolts and/or replace oil seal as necessary.
(c) **Filler pipe:** replace the rubber oil seal where pipe enters transmission case.
(d) **Transmission oil lines:** tighten fittings where lines enter transmission case and/or replace lines.
(e) **Vent pipe:** transmission overfilled and/or water in fluid (see checking procedures, Chapter 1).
(f) **Speedometer connector:** replace the O-ring where speedometer cable enters transmission case.

48   General shift mechanism problems

Chapter 7 deals with checking and adjusting the shift linkage on automatic transmissions. Common problems which may be caused by out-of-adjustment linkage are:
(a) Engine starting in gears other than P (park) or N (Neutral).
(b) Indicator pointing to a gear other than the one actually engaged.
(c) Vehicle moves with transmission in P (Park) position.

49   Transmission will not downshift with the accelerator pedal pressed to the floor

Chapter 7 deals with adjusting the TV (kickdown) linkage to enable the transmission to downshift properly.

50   Engine will start in gears other than Park or Neutral

Chapter 7 deals with adjusting the Neutral start switch installed on automatic transmissions.

51   Transmission slips, shifts rough, is noisy, or has no drive in forward or Reverse gears

1   There are many probable causes for the above problems, but the home mechanic should concern himself only with one possibility; fluid level.
2   Before taking the vehicle to a shop, check the fluid level and condition as described in Chapter 1. Add fluid, if necessary, or change the fluid and filter if needed. If problems persist, have a professional diagnose the transmission.

Driveshaft

52   Leaks at front of driveshaft

Defective transmission rear seal. See Chapter 7 for replacement procedure. As this is done, check the splined yoke for burrs or roughness that could damage the new seal. Remove burrs with a fine file or whetstone.

53   Knock or clunk when transmission is under initial load (just after transmission is put into gear)

1   Loose or disconnected rear suspension components. Check all mounting bolts and bushings (Chapters 7 and 10).
2   Loose driveshaft bolts. Inspect all bolts and nuts, and tighten them securely.
3   Worn or damaged universal joint bearings. Inspect the universal joints (Chapter 8).
4   Worn sleeve yoke and mainshaft spline.

54   Metallic grating sound consistent with vehicle speed

Pronounced wear in the universal joint bearings. Replace U-joints or driveshafts, as necessary.

55   Vibration

Note: *Before blaming the driveshaft, make sure the tires are perfectly balanced, and perform the following test.*
1   Install a tachometer inside the vehicle to monitor engine speed as the vehicle is driven. Drive the vehicle and note the engine speed at which the vibration (roughness) is most pronounced. Now shift the transmission to a different gear and bring the engine speed to the same point.
2   If the vibration occurs at the same engine speed (rpm) regardless of which gear the transmission is in, the driveshaft is NOT at fault since the driveshaft speed varies.
3   If the vibration decreases or is eliminated when the transmission is in a different gear at the same engine speed, refer to the following probable causes.
4   Bent or dented driveshaft. Inspect and replace as necessary.
5   Undercoating or built-up dirt, etc. on the driveshaft. Clean the shaft thoroughly.
6   Worn universal joint bearings. Replace the U-joints or driveshaft as necessary.
7   Driveshaft and/or companion flange out of balance. Check for missing weights on the shaft. Remove driveshaft and reinstall 180-degrees from original position, then recheck. Have the driveshaft balanced if problem persists.
8   Loose driveshaft mounting bolts/nuts.
9   Defective center bearing, if so equipped.
10   Worn transmission rear bushing (Chapter 7).

56   Scraping noise

Make sure the dust cover on the sleeve yoke isn't rubbing on the transmission extension housing.

57   Whining or whistling noise

Defective center bearing, if so equipped.

Rear axle and differential

58 Noise - same when in drive as when vehicle is coasting

1   Road noise. No corrective action available.
2   Tire noise. Inspect tires and check tire pressures (UK Supplement or Chapter 1).
3   Front wheel bearings loose, worn or damaged (Chapter 1).
4   Insufficient differential oil (Chapter 1).
5   Defective differential.

59 Knocking sound when starting or shifting gears

Defective or incorrectly adjusted differential.

60 Noise when turning

Defective differential.

61 Vibration

See probable causes under Driveshaft. Proceed under the guidelines listed for the driveshaft. If the problem persists, check the rear wheel bearings by raising the rear of the vehicle and spinning the wheels by hand. Listen for evidence of rough (noisy) bearings. Remove and inspect (Chapter 8).

62 Oil leaks

1   Pinion oil seal damaged (Chapter 8).
2   Axleshaft oil seals damaged (Chapter 8).
3   Differential cover leaking. Tighten mounting bolts or replace the gasket as required.
4   Loose filler or drain plug on differential (Chapter 1).
5   Clogged or damaged breather on differential.

Transfer case

63 Gear jumping out of mesh

1   Interference between the control lever and the console.
2   Play or fatigue in the transfer case mounts.
3   Internal wear or incorrect adjustments.

64 Difficult shifting

1   Lack of oil.
2   Internal wear, damage or incorrect adjustment.

65 Noise

1   Lack of oil in transfer case.
2   Noise in 4H and 4L, but not in 2H indicates cause is in the front differential or front axle.
3   Noise in 2H, 4H and 4L indicates cause is in rear differential or rear axle.
4   Noise in 2H and 4H but not in 4L, or in 4L only, indicates internal wear or damage in transfer case.

Brakes

Note: Before assuming a brake problem exists, make sure the tires are in good condition and inflated properly, the front end alignment is correct and the vehicle is not loaded with weight in an unequal manner. All service procedures for the brakes are included in Chapter 9, unless otherwise noted.

66 Vehicle pulls to one side during braking

1   Defective, damaged or oil contaminated brake pad on one side. Inspect as described in Chapter 1. Refer to Chapter 10 if replacement is required.
2   Excessive wear of brake pad material or disc on one side. Inspect and repair as necessary.
3   Loose or disconnected front suspension components. Inspect and tighten all bolts securely (Chapters 1 and 9).
4   Defective caliper assembly. Remove caliper and inspect for stuck piston or damage.
5   Scored or out of round rotor.
6   Loose caliper mounting bolts.
7   Incorrect wheel bearing adjustment.

67 Noise (high-pitched squeal)

1   Brake pads worn out. This noise comes from the wear sensor rubbing against the disc. Replace pads with new ones immediately!
2   Glazed or contaminated pads.
3   Dirty or scored disc.
4   Bent support plate.

68 Excessive brake pedal travel

1   Partial brake system failure. Inspect entire system (Chapter 1) and correct as required.
2   Insufficient fluid in master cylinder. Check (Chapter 1) and add fluid bleed system if necessary.
3   Air in system. Bleed system.
4   Excessive lateral disc play.
5   Brakes out of adjustment. Check the operation of the automatic adjusters.

69 Brake pedal feels spongy when depressed

1   Air in brake lines. Bleed the brake system.
2   Deteriorated rubber brake hoses. Inspect all system hoses and lines. Replace parts as necessary.
3   Master cylinder mounting nuts loose. Inspect master cylinder bolts (nuts) and tighten them securely.
4   Master cylinder faulty.
5   Incorrect shoe or pad clearance.
6   Clogged reservoir cap vent hole.
7   Deformed rubber brake lines.
8   Soft or swollen caliper seals.
9   Poor quality brake fluid. Bleed entire system and fill with new approved fluid.

70 Excessive effort required to stop vehicle

1   Power brake booster not operating properly.
2   Excessively worn linings or pads. Check and replace if necessary.
3   One or more caliper pistons seized or sticking. Inspect and rebuild as required.

4   Brake pads or linings contaminated with oil or grease. Inspect and replace as required.
5   New pads or linings installed and not yet seated. It'll take a while for the new material to seat against the disc or drum.
6   Worn or damaged master cylinder or caliper assemblies. Check particularly for frozen pistons.
7   Also see causes listed under Section 69.

71   Pedal travels to the floor with little resistance

1   Little or no fluid in the master cylinder reservoir caused by leaking caliper piston(s) or loose, damaged or disconnected brake lines. Inspect entire system and repair as necessary.
2   Defective master cylinder.

72   Brake pedal pulsates during brake application

1   Wheel bearings damaged, worn or out of adjustment (Chapter 1).
2   Caliper not sliding properly due to improper installation or obstructions. Remove and inspect.
3   Disc not within specifications. Remove the disc and check for excessive lateral runout and parallelism. Have the discs resurfaced or replace them with new ones. Also make sure that all discs are the same thickness.
4   Out-of-round front or rear brake drums (as applicable). Remove the drums and have them turned or replace them with new ones.

73   Brakes drag (indicated by sluggish engine performance or wheels being very hot after driving)

1   Output rod adjustment incorrect at the brake pedal.
2   Obstructed master cylinder compensator. Disassemble master cylinder and clean.
3   Master cylinder piston seized in bore. Overhaul master cylinder.
4   Caliper assembly in need of overhaul.
5   Brake pads or shoes worn out.
6   Piston cups in master cylinder or caliper assembly deformed. Overhaul master cylinder.
7   Parking brake assembly will not release.
8   Clogged brake lines.
9   Wheel bearings out of adjustment (Chapter 1).
10   Brake pedal height improperly adjusted.
11   Wheel cylinder needs overhaul.
12   Improper shoe-to-drum clearance. Adjust as necessary.

74   Rear brakes lock up under light brake application

1   Tire pressures too high.
2   Tires excessively worn (Chapter 1).
3   Defective or misadjusted Load Sensing Proportioning Valve.

75   Rear brakes lock up under heavy brake application

1   Tire pressures too high.
2   Tires excessively worn (Chapter 1).
3   Front brake pads contaminated with oil, mud or water. Clean or replace the pads.
4   Front brake pads excessively worn.
5   Defective master cylinder or caliper assembly.

Suspension and steering

Note: All service procedures for the suspension and steering systems are included in Chapter 10, unless otherwise noted.

76   Vehicle pulls to one side

1   Tire pressures uneven (Chapter 1).
2   Defective tire (Chapter 1).
3   Excessive wear in suspension or steering components (Chapter 1).
4   Wheel alignment incorrect.
5   Front brakes dragging. Inspect as described in Section 73.
6   Wheel bearings improperly adjusted (Chapter 1).
7   Wheel lug nuts loose.

77   Shimmy, shake or vibration

1   Tire or wheel out of balance or out of round. Have them balanced on the vehicle.
2   Loose, worn or out of adjustment wheel bearings (Chapter 8).
3   Shock absorbers and/or suspension components worn or damaged. Check for worn bushings.
4   Wheel lug nuts loose.
5   Incorrect tire pressures.
6   Excessively worn or damaged tire.
7   Loosely mounted steering gear housing.
8   Steering gear improperly adjusted.
9   Loose, worn or damaged steering components.
10   Damaged idler arm.
11   Worn balljoint.

78   Excessive pitching and/or rolling around corners or during braking

1   Defective shock absorbers. Replace as a set.
2   Broken or weak leaf springs and/or suspension components.
3   Worn or damaged stabilizer bar or bushings.

79   Wandering or general instability

1   Improper tire pressures.
2   Worn or damaged upper and lower link or tension rod bushings.
3   Incorrect front end alignment.
4   Worn or damaged steering linkage or suspension components.
5   Improperly adjusted steering gear.
6   Out-of-balance wheels.
7   Loose wheel lug nuts.
8   Worn rear shock absorbers.
9   Fatigued or damaged springs.

80   Excessively-stiff steering

1   Lack of lubricant in power steering fluid reservoir, where appropriate (Chapter 1).
2   Incorrect tire pressures (Chapter 1).
3   Lack of lubrication at balljoints (Chapter 1).
4   Front end out of alignment.
5   Steering gear out of adjustment or lacking lubrication.
6   Improperly-adjusted wheel bearings.
7   Worn or damaged steering gear.
8   Interference of steering column with turn signal switch.
9   Low tire pressures.
10   Worn or damaged balljoints.

81 Excessive play in steering

1 Loose wheel bearings (Chapter 1).
2 Excessive wear in suspension bushings (Chapter 1).
3 Steering gear improperly adjusted.
4 Incorrect wheel alignment.
5 Steering gear mounting bolts loose.
6 Worn steering linkage.

82 Lack of power assistance

1 Steering pump drivebelt faulty or not adjusted properly (Chapter 1).
2 Fluid level low (Chapter 1).
3 Hoses or pipes restricting the flow. Inspect and replace parts as necessary.
4 Air in power steering system. Bleed system.
5 Defective power steering pump.

83 Steering wheel fails to return to straight-ahead position

1 Incorrect front end alignment.
2 Tire pressures low.
3 Steering gears improperly engaged.
4 Steering column out of alignment.
5 Worn or damaged balljoint.
6 Worn or damaged steering linkage.
7 Improperly lubricated idler arm.
8 Insufficient oil in steering gear.
9 Lack of fluid in power steering pump.

84 Steering effort not the same in both directions (power system)

1 Leaks in steering gear.
2 Clogged fluid passage in steering gear

85 Noisy power steering pump

1 Insufficient oil in pump.
2 Clogged hoses or oil filter in pump.
3 Loose pulley.

4 Improperly adjusted drivebelt (Chapter 1).
5 Defective pump.

86 Miscellaneous noises

1 Improper tire pressures.
2 Insufficiently-lubricated balljoint or steering linkage.
3 Loose or worn steering gear, steering linkage or suspension components.
4 Defective shock absorber.
5 Defective wheel bearing.
6 Worn or damaged suspension bushings.
7 Damaged spring.
8 Loose wheel lug nuts.
9 Worn or damaged rear axleshaft spline.
10 Worn or damaged rear shock absorber mounting bushing.
11 Incorrect rear axle end play.
12 See also causes of noises at the rear axle and driveshaft.

87 Excessive tire wear (not specific to one area)

1 Incorrect tire pressures.
2 Tires out of balance. Have them balanced on the vehicle.
3 Wheels damaged. Inspect and replace as necessary.
4 Suspension or steering components worn (Chapter 1).

88 Excessive tire wear on outside edge

1 Incorrect tire pressure.
2 Excessive speed in turns.
3 Front end alignment incorrect (excessive toe-in).

89 Excessive tire wear on inside edge

1 Incorrect tire pressure.
2 Front end alignment incorrect (toe-out).
3 Loose or damaged steering components (Chapter 1).

90 Tire tread worn in one place

1 Tires out of balance. Have them balanced on the vehicle.
2 Damaged or buckled wheel. Inspect and replace if necessary.
3 Defective tire.

Chapter 1 Tune-up and routine maintenance

Contents

Recommended lubricants and fluids

Engine oil	API grade SF/CC SF/CD multigrade and fuel efficient oil
Viscosity	See accompanying chart
Automatic transmission fluid	Dexron II automatic transmission fluid
Manual transmission lubricant	API GL-5 SAE 75W-90 or 80W-90 gear lubricant
Transfer case lubricant	API GL-5 SAE 75W-90 or 80W-90 gear lubricant
Rear axle differential lubricant	API GL-5 SAE 75W-90 or 80W-90 gear lubricant
Front axle differential lubricant	API GL-5 SAE 75W-90 or 80W-90 gear lubricant
Brake fluid	DOT 3 brake fluid
Power steering system fluid	Dexron II automatic transmission fluid

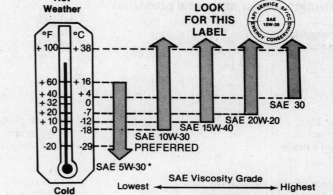

Recommended SAE viscosity grade engine oils

For best fuel economy and cold starting, select the lowest SAE viscosity grade oil for the expected temperature range.

* PREFERRED IN 4 CYL ENGINES UP TO 38°C (100°F)

ENGINE OIL VISCOSITY CHART

Capacities

Engine oil	4.7 qts
Cooling system	Approximately 5.3 qts
Fuel tank	10.6 gal
Differential lubricant	
Samurai	
Front	2.1 qts
Rear	1.6 qts
Sidekick/Tracker	
Front	1.1 qts
Rear	2.3 qts
Automatic transmission fluid	3.0 qts
Manual transmission lubricant	
Samurai	2.7 pts
Sidekick/Tracker	3.2 pts
Transfer case lubricant	
Samurai	1.7 pts
Sidekick/Tracker	3.6 pts

Ignition system

Spark plug	
Type	
1990 and earlier	NGK BPR-5ES
1991 and later	NGK BKR-6E
Gap	0.028 to 0.031 inch (0.7 to 0.8 mm)
Ignition timing	
Samurai	10-degrees BTDC at 800 RPM
Sidekick/Tracker	8-degrees BTDC at 800 RPM
Engine firing order	1-3-4-2

Valve clearances
8-valve engine
  Intake
    Cold .... 0.005 to 0.007 inch (0.13 to 0.17 mm)
    Hot .... 0.009 to 0.011 inch (0.23 to 0.27 mm)
  Exhaust
    Cold .... 0.006 to 0.008 inch (0.16 to 0.20 mm)
    Hot .... 0.010 to 0.012 inch (0.26 to 0.30 mm)
16-valve engine (intake and exhaust)
  Cold .... 0.003 to 0.004 inch (0.08 to 0.12 mm)
  Hot .... 0.005 to 0.006 inch (0.12 to 0.16 mm)

Thermostat rating
Starts to open .... 179-degrees F (82-degrees C)
Fully open .... 212-degrees F (100-degrees C)

Drivebelt deflection (under moderate pressure)
Alternator 1/4-inch
Air conditioning compressor 1/4-inch
Power steering pump 1/2-inch

Clutch
Clutch pedal
  Freeplay .... 0.6 to 1.0 in (15 to 25 mm)
  Height
    Samurai .... Level with brake pedal
    Sidekick/Tracker .... 0.2 in (5.0 mm) above brake pedal
Clutch release arm freeplay .... 0.02 to 0.06 in (0.5 to 1.5 mm)

Brakes
Disc brake pad lining thickness (minimum) .... 0.04 in (1 mm)
Drum brake shoe lining thickness (minimum) .... 0.04 in (1 mm)
Brake pedal freeplay .... 0.04 to 0.32 in (1 to 8 mm)
Brake pedal height .... 5.12 in (130 mm)
Parking brake adjustment .... 5 to 8 clicks

Steering wheel freeplay limit .... 0.40 to 1.2 in (10 to 30 mm)

Torque specifications   Ft-lbs (unless otherwise specified)
Automatic transmission Pan bolts 9
Manual transmission drain and check/fill plugs 20
Engine mounting center member bolt 43
Wheel lug nuts 55
Spark plugs 21
Steering knuckle seal retainer bolts .... 96 in-lbs
Carburetor/throttle body mounting nuts .... 13.5 to 20
Oxygen sensor 40
Differential drain plug
  Front 32
  Rear 36

1   Introduction

This Chapter is designed to help the home mechanic maintain the Suzuki Samurai/Sidekick and Geo Tracker with the goals of maximum performance, economy, safety and reliability in mind.

Included is a master maintenance schedule (page 36), followed by procedures dealing specifically with each item on the schedule. Visual checks, adjustments, component replacement and other helpful items are included. Refer to the accompanying illustrations of the engine compartment and the underside of the vehicle for the locations of various components.

Servicing your vehicle in accordance with the mileage/time maintenance schedule and the step-by-step procedures will result in a planned maintenance program that should produce a long and reliable service life. Keep in mind that it is a comprehensive plan, so maintaining some items but not others at the specified intervals will not produce the same results.

As you service your vehicle, you will discover that many of the procedures can – and should – be grouped together because of the nature of the particular procedure you're performing or because of the close proximity of two otherwise unrelated components to one another.

For example, if the vehicle is raised for chassis lubrication, you should inspect the exhaust, suspension, steering and fuel systems while you're under the vehicle. When you're rotating the tires, it makes good sense to check the brakes since the wheels are already removed. Finally, let's suppose you have to borrow or rent a torque wrench. Even if you only need it to tighten the spark plugs, you might as well check the torque of as many critical fasteners as time allows.

The first step in this maintenance program is to prepare yourself before the actual work begins. Read through all the procedures you're planning to do, then gather up all the parts and tools needed. If it looks like you might run into problems during a particular job, seek advice from a mechanic or an experienced do-it-yourselfer.

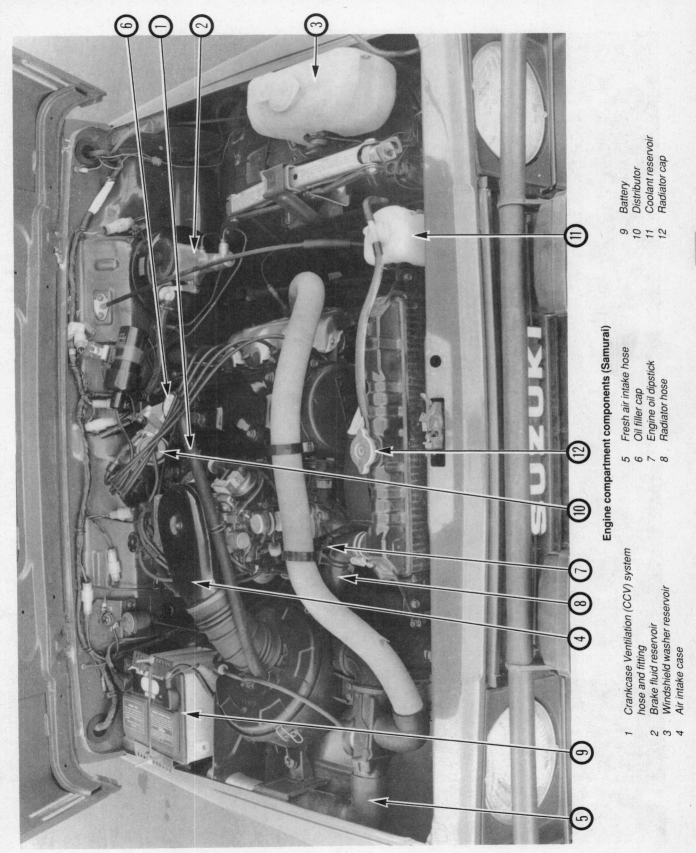

Engine compartment components (Samurai)

1   Crankcase Ventilation (CCV) system hose and fitting
2   Brake fluid reservoir
3   Windshield washer reservoir
4   Air intake case
5   Fresh air intake hose
6   Oil filler cap
7   Engine oil dipstick
8   Radiator hose
9   Battery
10 Distributor
11 Coolant reservoir
12 Radiator cap

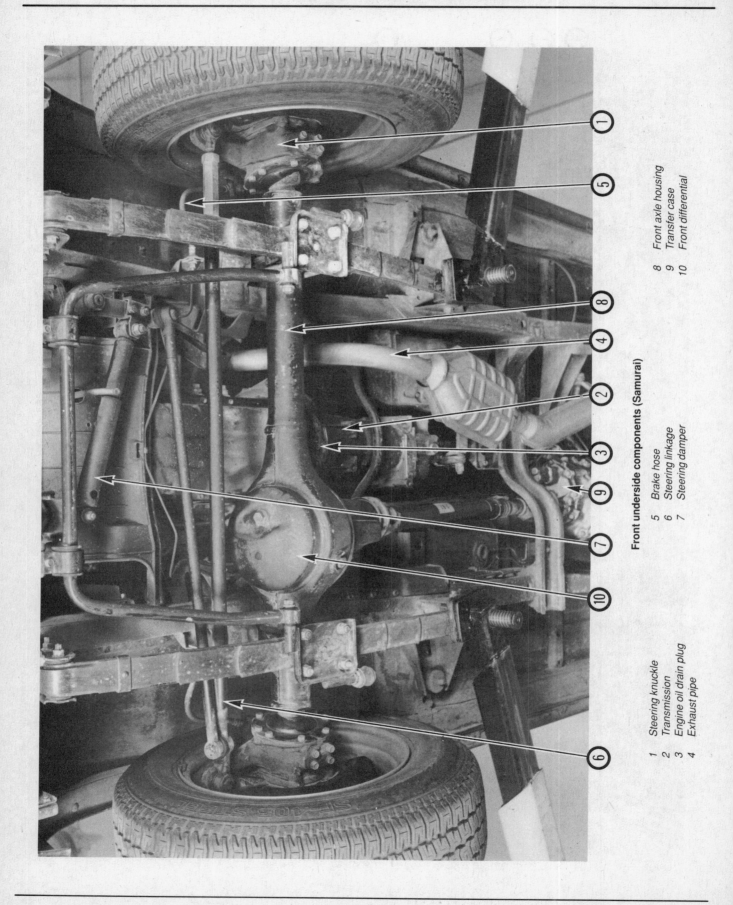

Front underside components (Samurai)

1 Steering knuckle	5 Brake hose	8 Front axle housing
2 Transmission	6 Steering linkage	9 Transfer case
3 Engine oil drain plug	7 Steering damper	10 Front differential
4 Exhaust pipe		

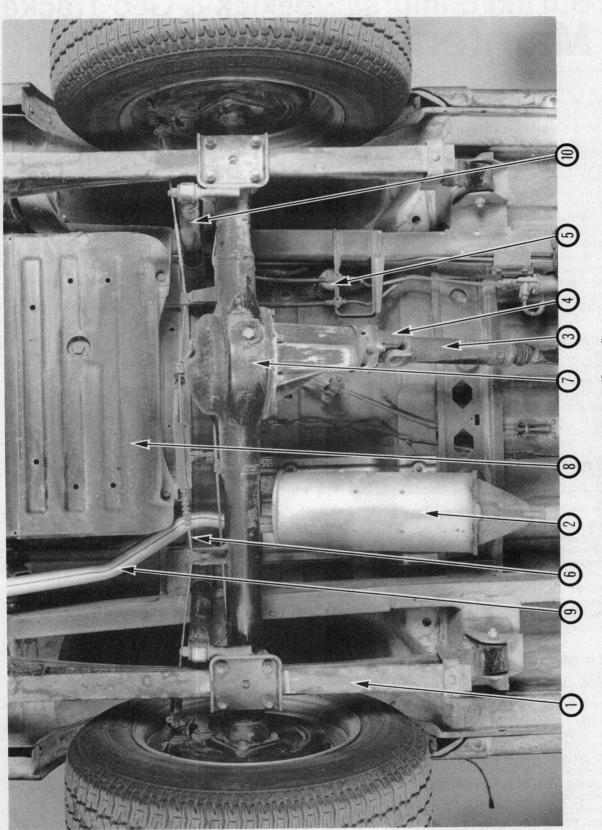

Rear underside components (Samurai)

1	Rear leaf spring	5	Fuel filter	8	Fuel tank
2	Muffler	6	Parking brake cable	9	Exhaust pipe
3	Driveshaft	7	Rear differential	10	Shock absorber
4	Universal joint				

Suzuki Samurai/Sidekick & Geo Tracker Maintenance schedule

The following maintenance intervals are based on the assumption that the vehicle owner will be doing the maintenance or service work, as opposed to having a dealer service department do the work. Although the time/mileage intervals are loosely based on factory recommendations, most have been shortened to ensure, for example, that such items as lubricants and fluids are checked/changed at intervals that promote maximum engine/driveline service life. Also, subject to the preference of the individual owner interested in keeping his or her vehicle in peak condition at all times, and with the vehicle's ultimate resale in mind, many of the maintenance procedures may be performed more often than recommended in the following schedule. We encourage such owner initiative.

When the vehicle is new it should be serviced initially by a factory authorized dealer service department to protect the factory warranty. In many cases the initial maintenance check is done at no cost to the owner (check with your dealer service department for more information).

Every 250 miles or weekly, whichever comes first

Check the engine oil level (Section 4)
Check the engine coolant level (Section 4)
Check the windshield washer fluid level (Section 4)
Check the brake and clutch fluid levels (Section 4)
Check the tires and tire pressures (Section 5)

Every 3000 miles or 3 months, whichever comes first

All items listed above plus . . .
Check the automatic transmission fluid level (Section 6)
Check the power steering fluid level (Section 7)
Check and service the battery (Section 8)
Check the cooling system (Section 9)
Inspect and replace if necessary all underhood hoses (Section 10)
Inspect and replace if necessary the windshield wiper blades (Section 11)
Change the engine oil and oil filter (Section 12)

Every 7500 miles or 6 months, whichever comes first

All items listed above plus . . .
Check and adjust if necessary the engine drivebelts (Section 13)
Rotate the tires (Section 14)
Check the clutch pedal for proper height and freeplay (Section 15)
Check and adjust if necessary the brake pedal height (Section 17)
Inspect the brake system (Section 18)
Check the manual transmission lubricant (Section 19)*
Check the transfer case lubricant (Section 20)*
Check the differential lubricant (Section 21)*

Every 15,000 miles or 12 months, whichever comes first

All items listed above plus . . .
Inspect the suspension and steering components (Section 22)**
Check the driveaxle boots (Sidekick/Tracker only) (Section 23)**
Check the driveshafts and lubricate the driveaxles (Section 24)
Inspect the fuel system (Section 25)
Check the carburetor choke (Section 26)
Check and adjust if necessary the engine valve clearances (Section 16)
Check and adjust if necessary the engine idle speed (Section 33)
Check and repack the front wheel bearings (see Chapter 8)

Every 22,500 miles or 18 months, whichever comes first

Replace the steering knuckle oil seals (Samurai only) (Section 27)

Every 30,000 miles or 24 months, whichever comes first

Replace the spark plugs (Section 28)**
Check and replace if necessary the spark plug wires (Section 29)
Inspect and replace if necessary the distributor cap and rotor (Section 30)**
Replace the air filter (Section 31)**
Check the operation of the thermostatic air cleaner (Samurai only) (Section 32)
Service the cooling system (drain, flush and refill) (Section 34)
Inspect the exhaust system (Section 35)
Change the automatic transmission fluid and filter (Sidekick/Tracker only) (Section 36)
Change the manual transmission lubricant (Section 37)
Change the transfer case lubricant (Section 38)
Change the differential lubricant (Section 39)
Replace the fuel filter (Section 40)

Every 50,000 miles or 40 months, whichever comes first

Check the EGR system (Section 41)
Replace the PCV valve (Section 42)

Every 60,000 miles or 48 months, whichever comes first

Replace the fuel tank cap gasket (Section 43)
Replace the brake fluid (Section 44)***
Replace the charcoal canister and inspect the evaporative emissions control system (Section 45)
Check the ignition timing (Section 46)

Check the distributor advance operation (Chapter 5)
Have the fuel/air mixture checked by a dealer
   service department
Check the carburetor mounting nut torque (Section 47)
Replace the oxygen sensor (1986 Samurai models
   only) (Section 48)

Every 80,000 miles or 80 months, whichever comes first

Replace the oxygen sensor (1987 and later models
   only) (Section 48)

Every 100,000 miles or 100 months, whichever comes first

Check the timing belt (Chapter 2)
Have the ECM and associated sensors checked by a dealer
   service department (1988 and later models)

Check the operation of the fuel injection system (Sidekick &
   Tracker) (Chapter 4)
Have the operation of the catalytic converter checked
   by a dealer
* *Transmission, transfer case, and differential oil changes per-*
formed initially at the 7500 mile/6 month service and at 30,000
mile intervals thereafter (also see "severe" conditions below).
** *This item is affected by "severe" operating conditions as de-*
scribed below. If your vehicle is operated under "severe" condi-
tions, perform all maintenance indicated with a (*) at 7500 mile/6
month intervals.
Consider the conditions "sever" if most driving is done . . .
   In dusty areas
   Idling for extended periods and/or low speed operation
   When outside temperatures remain below freezing and most
     trips are less than four miles
*** *If operated under one or more of the following conditions,*
change brake fluid every 15,000 miles:
   Continuous hard driving
   Operation in extremely humid climate
   After extensive use of brakes in hilly or mountainous terrain

1

3 Tune-up general information

The term tune-up is used in this manual to represent a combination of individual operations rather than one specific procedure.

If, from the time the vehicle is new, the routine maintenance schedule is followed closely and frequent checks are made of fluid levels and high wear items, as suggested throughout this manual, the engine will be kept in relatively good running condition and the need for additional work will be minimized.

More likely than not, however, there will be times when the engine is running poorly due to lack of regular maintenance. This is even more likely if a used vehicle, which has not received regular and frequent mainte-nance checks, is purchased. In such cases, an engine tune-up will be needed outside of the regular routine maintenance intervals.

The first step in any tune-up or diagnostic procedure to help correct a poor running engine is a cylinder compression check. A compression check (see Chapter 2 Part B) will help determine the condition of internal engine components and should be used as a guide for tune-up and repair procedures. If, for instance, a compression check indicates serious inter-nal engine wear, a conventional tune-up will not improve the performance of the engine and would be a waste of time and money. Because of its im-portance, the compression check should be done by someone with the right equipment and the knowledge to use it properly.

The following procedures are those most often needed to bring a gen-erally poor running engine back into a proper state of tune.

Minor tune-up

Check all engine related fluids (Section 4)
Clean, inspect and test the battery (Section 8)
Check and adjust the drivebelts (Section 13)
Replace the spark plugs (Section 28)
Inspect the distributor cap and rotor (Section 30)
Inspect the spark plug and coil wires (Section 29)
Check and adjust the ignition timing (Section 46)
Check the PCV valve (Section 42)
Check the air and PCV filters (Section 31)
Check the cooling system (Section 9)
Check all underhood hoses (Section 10)

Major tune-up

All items listed under Minor tune-up plus . . .
Check the EGR system (Section 41)
Check the ignition system (Chapter 5)
Check the charging system (Chapter 5)

Check the fuel system (Section 25)
Replace the air and PCV filters (Section 31)
Replace the distributor cap and rotor (Section 30)
Replace the spark plug wires (Section 29)

4 Fluid level checks

Refer to illustrations 4.2, 4.4, 4.6, 4.8, 4.14 and 4.19
Note: *The following are fluid level checks to be done on a 250 mile or weekly basis. Additional fluid level checks can be found in specific mainte-nance procedures which follow. Regardless of intervals, be alert to fluid leaks under the vehicle which would indicate a fault to be corrected imme-diately.*
1   Fluids are an essential part of the lubrication, cooling, brake, clutch and windshield washer systems. Because the fluids gradually become de-pleted and/or contaminated during normal operation of the vehicle, they must be periodically replenished. See Recommended lubricants and fluids at the beginning of this Chapter before adding fluid to any of the fol-lowing components. **Note:** *The vehicle must be on level ground when fluid levels are checked.*

Engine oil

2   The engine oil level is checked with a dipstick that extends through a tube and into the oil pan at the bottom of the engine **(see illustration)**.

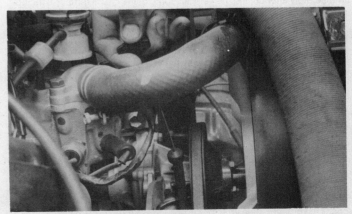

4.2 The dipstick is located on the passenger side of the engine near the water pump

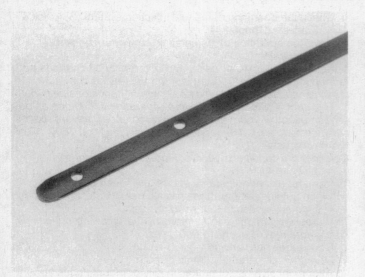

4.4   The engine oil level must be maintained between the marks at all times – it takes one full quart of oil to raise the level from the Add mark (lower hole) to the Full mark (upper hole)

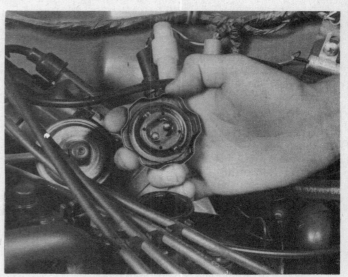

4.6   The twist-off oil filler cap is located on the camshaft cover – always make sure the area around this opening is clean before unscrewing the cap to prevent dirt from contaminating the engine

4.8   Remember to add coolant to the reservoir only when the engine is off and cold in order to obtain an accurate level

3   The oil level should be checked before the vehicle has been driven, or about 15 minutes after the engine has been shut off. If the oil is checked immediately after driving the vehicle, some of the oil will remain in the upper engine components, resulting in an inaccurate reading on the dipstick.

4   Pull the dipstick from the tube and wipe all the oil from the end with a clean rag or paper towel. Insert the clean dipstick all the way back into the tube, then pull it out again. Note the oil at the end of the dipstick. Add oil as necessary to keep the level between the ADD mark and the FULL mark on the dipstick **(see illustration)**.

5   Do not overfill the engine by adding too much oil since this may result in oil fouled spark plugs, oil leaks or oil seal failures.

6   Oil is added to the engine after removing the cap **(see illustration)**. An oil can spout or funnel may help to reduce spills.

7   Checking the oil level is an important preventive maintenance step. A consistently low oil level indicates oil leakage through damaged seals, defective gaskets or past worn rings or valve guides. If the oil looks milky in color or has water droplets in it, the cylinder head gasket may be blown or the head or block may be cracked. The engine should be checked immediately. The condition of the oil should also be checked. Whenever you check the oil level, slide your thumb and index finger up the dipstick before wiping off the oil. If you see small dirt or metal particles clinging to the dipstick, the oil should be changed (see Section 12).

Engine coolant

Warning: *Do not allow antifreeze to come in contact with your skin or painted surfaces of the vehicle. Flush contaminated areas immediately with plenty of water. Don't store new coolant or leave old coolant lying around where it's accessible to children or pets – they're attracted by its sweet taste. Ingestion of even a small amount of coolant can be fatal! Wipe up garage floor and drip pan coolant spills immediately. Keep antifreeze containers covered and repair leaks in the cooling system immediately.*

8   All vehicles covered by this manual are equipped with a pressurized coolant recovery system. A white plastic coolant reservoir located in the engine compartment is connected by a hose to the radiator filler neck **(see illustration)**. If the engine overheats, coolant escapes through a valve in the radiator cap and travels through the hose into the reservoir. As the engine cools, the coolant is automatically drawn back into the cooling system to maintain the correct level.

9   The coolant level in the reservoir should be checked regularly. **Warning:** *Do not remove the radiator cap to check the coolant level when the engine is warm.* The level in the reservoir varies with the temperature of the engine. When the engine is cold, the coolant level should be at or slightly above the FULL COLD mark on the reservoir. Once the engine has warmed up, the level should be at or near the FULL HOT mark. If it isn't, allow the engine to cool, then remove the cap from the reservoir and add a 50/50 mixture of ethylene glycolbased antifreeze and water.

10   Drive the vehicle and recheck the coolant level. If only a small amount of coolant is required to bring the system up to the proper level, water can be used. However, repeated additions of water will dilute the antifreeze and water solution. In order to maintain the proper ratio of antifreeze and water, always top up the coolant level with the correct mixture. An empty plastic milk jug or bleach bottle makes an excellent container for mixing coolant. Do not use rust inhibitors or additives.

11   If the coolant level drops consistently, there may be a leak in the system. Inspect the radiator, hoses, filler cap, drain plugs and water pump (see Section 9). If no leaks are noted, have the radiator cap pressure tested by a service station.

12   If you have to remove the radiator cap, wait until the engine has cooled, then wrap a thick cloth around the cap and turn it to the first stop. If coolant or steam escapes, let the engine cool down longer, then remove the cap.

13   Check the condition of the coolant as well. It should be relatively clear. If it's brown or rust colored, the system should be drained, flushed and refilled. Even if the coolant appears to be normal, the corrosion inhibitors wear out, so it must be replaced at the specified intervals.

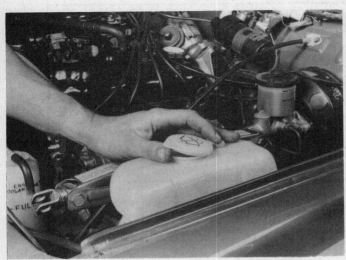

4.14   The windshield washer reservoir is located on the left fender panel – special windshield washer solvent and/or water can be added after opening the cap

4.19   The brake fluid level is easily checked by looking through the clear brake fluid reservoir.

Windshield washer fluid

14   Fluid for the windshield washer system is located in a plastic reservoir in the engine compartment **(see illustration)**.

15   In milder climates, plain water can be used in the reservoir, but it should be kept no more than 2/3 full to allow for expansion if the water freezes. In colder climates, use windshield washer system antifreeze, available at any auto parts store, to lower the freezing point of the fluid. Mix the antifreeze with water in accordance with the manufacturer's directions on the container. **Caution:** *Don't use cooling system antifreeze – it will damage the vehicle's paint.*

16   To help prevent icing in cold weather, warm the windshield with the defroster before using the washer.

Battery electrolyte

17   All vehicles with which this manual is concerned are equipped with a battery which is permanently sealed (except for vent holes) and has no filler caps. Water doesn't have to be added to these batteries at any time. If a maintenance-type battery is installed, the caps on the top of the battery should be removed periodically to check for a low water level. This check is most critical during the warm summer months.

Brake fluid

18   The brake master cylinder is mounted on the front of the power booster unit in the engine compartment.

19   The fluid inside is readily visible. The level should be above the MIN marks on the reservoirs **(see illustration)**. If a low level is indicated, be sure to wipe the top of the reservoir cover with a clean rag to prevent contamination of the brake system before removing the cover.

20   When adding fluid, pour it carefully into the reservoir to avoid spilling it onto surrounding painted surfaces. Be sure the specified fluid is used, since mixing different types of brake fluid can cause damage to the system. See *Recommended lubricants and fluids* at the front of this Chapter or your owner's manual. **Warning:** *Brake fluid can harm your eyes and damage painted surfaces, so use extreme caution when handling or pouring it. Do not use brake fluid that has been standing open or is more than one year old. Brake fluid absorbs moisture from the air. Excess moisture can cause a dangerous loss of braking effectiveness.*

21   At this time the fluid and master cylinder can be inspected for contamination. The system should be drained and refilled if deposits, dirt particles or water droplets are seen in the fluid.

22   After filling the reservoir to the proper level, make sure the cover is on tight to prevent fluid leakage.

23   The brake fluid level in the master cylinder will drop slightly as the pads and the brake shoes at each wheel wear down during normal operation. If the master cylinder requires repeated additions to keep it at the proper level, it's an indication of leakage in the brake system, which should be corrected immediately. Check all brake lines and connections (see Section 18 for more information).

24   If, upon checking the master cylinder fluid level, you discover one or both reservoirs empty or nearly empty, the brake system should be bled (see Chapter 9).

5   Tire and tire pressure checks

Refer to illustrations 5.2, 5.3, 5.4a, 5.4b and 5.8

1   Periodic inspection of the tires may spare you the inconvenience of being stranded with a flat tire. It can also provide you with vital information regarding possible problems in the steering and suspension systems before major damage occurs.

2   The original tires on this vehicle are equipped with 1/2-inch side bands that will appear when tread depth reaches 1/16-inch, but they don't appear until the tires are worn out. Tread wear can be monitored with a simple, inexpensive device known as a tread depth indicator **(see illustration)**.

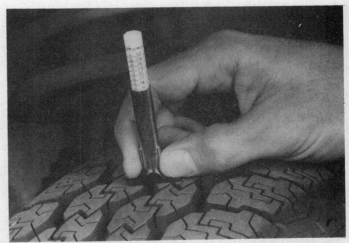

5.2   A tire tread depth indicator should be used to monitor tire wear – they are available at auto parts stores and service stations and cost very little

Condition	Probable cause	Corrective action	Condition	Probable cause	Corrective action
Shoulder wear	• Underinflation (both sides wear) • Incorrect wheel camber (one side wear) • Hard cornering • Lack of rotation	• Measure and adjust pressure. • Repair or replace axle and suspension parts. • Reduce speed. • Rotate tires.	Feathered edge Toe wear	• Incorrect toe	• Adjust toe-in.
Center wear	• Overinflation • Lack of rotation	• Measure and adjust pressure. • Rotate tires.	Uneven wear	• Incorrect camber or caster • Malfunctioning suspension • Unbalanced wheel • Out-of-round brake drum • Lack of rotation	• Repair or replace axle and suspension parts. • Repair or replace suspension parts. • Balance or replace. • Turn or replace. • Rotate tires.

5.3   This chart will help you determine the condition of the tires, the probable cause(s) of abnormal wear and the corrective action necessary

3   Note any abnormal tread wear **(see illustration)**. Tread pattern irregularities such as cupping, flat spots and more wear on one side than the other are indications of front end alignment and/or balance problems. If any of these conditions are noted, take the vehicle to a tire shop or service station to correct the problem.

4   Look closely for cuts, punctures and embedded nails or tacks. Sometimes a tire will hold air pressure for a short time or leak down very slowly after a nail has embedded itself in the tread. If a slow leak persists, check the valve stem core to make sure it's tight **(see illustration)**. Examine the tread for an object that may have embedded itself in the tire or for a "plug" that may have begun to leak (radial tire punctures are repaired with a plug that's installed in a puncture). If a puncture is suspected, it can be easily verified by spraying a solution of soapy water onto the puncture area **(see illustration)**. The soapy solution will bubble if there's a leak. Unless the puncture is unusually large, a tire shop or service station can usually repair the tire.

5   Carefully inspect the inner sidewall of each tire for evidence of brake fluid leakage. If you see any, inspect the brakes immediately.

6   Correct air pressure adds miles to the lifespan of the tires, improves mileage and enhances overall ride quality. Tire pressure cannot be accurately estimated by looking at a tire, especially if it's a radial. A tire pressure gauge is essential. Keep an accurate gauge in the vehicle. The pressure gauges attached to the nozzles of air hoses at gas stations are often inaccurate.

7   Always check tire pressure when the tires are cold. Cold, in this case, means the vehicle has not been driven over a mile in the three hours preceding a tire pressure check. A pressure rise of four to eight pounds is not uncommon once the tires are warm.

8   Unscrew the valve cap protruding from the wheel or hubcap and push the gauge firmly onto the valve stem **(see illustration)**. Note the reading

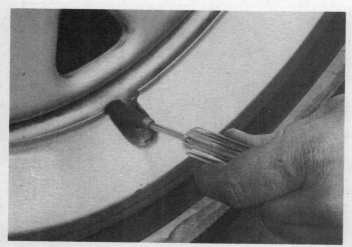

5.4a   If a tire loses air on a steady basis, check the valve core first to make sure it's snug (special inexpensive wrenches are commonly available at auto parts stores)

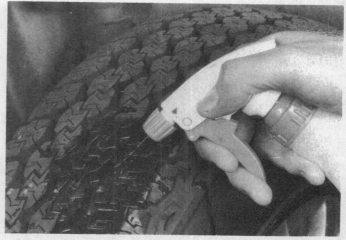

5.4b   If the valve core is tight, jack up the low tire and spray a soapy water solution onto the tread as the tire is turned slowly – leaks will cause small bubbles to appear

5.8   To extend the life of the tires, check the air pressure at least once a week with an accurate gauge (don't forget the spare!)

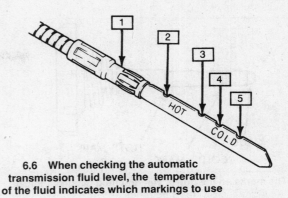

6.6   When checking the automatic transmission fluid level, the temperature of the fluid indicates which markings to use

1	Dipstick	4	Full cold notch
2	Full hot notch	5	Low cold notch
3	Low hot notch		

on the gauge and compare the figure to the recommended tire pressure shown on the placard on the driver's side door pillar. Be sure to reinstall the valve cap to keep dirt and moisture out of the valve stem mechanism. Check all four tires and, if necessary, add enough air to bring them up to the recommended pressure.

9   Don't forget to keep the spare tire inflated to the specified pressure (refer to your owner's manual or the tire sidewall).

6   Automatic transmission fluid level check

Refer to illustration 6.6

1   The automatic transmission fluid level should be carefully maintained. Low fluid level can lead to slipping or loss of drive, while overfilling can cause foaming and loss of fluid.

2   The automatic transmission fluid level is normally checked with the engine at normal operating temperature. This temperature is reached after approximately 15 miles of highway driving. With the parking brake set, start the engine, then move the shift lever through all the gear ranges, ending in Park. The fluid level must be checked with the vehicle level and the engine running at idle. **Note:** *Incorrect fluid level readings will result if the vehicle has just been driven at high speeds for an extended period, in hot*

weather in city traffic, or if it has been pulling a trailer. If any of these conditions apply, wait until the fluid has cooled (about 30 minutes).

3   With the transmission at normal operating temperature, remove the dipstick from the filler tube.

4   Wipe the fluid from the dipstick with a clean rag and push it back into the filler tube until the cap seats.

5   Pull the dipstick out again and note the fluid level.

6   The level should at or near the upper HOT mark **(see illustration)**. If additional fluid is required, add it directly into the tube using a funnel. It takes about one pint to raise the level from the LOW HOT notch to the FULL HOT notch with a hot transmission, so add the fluid a little at a time and keep checking the level until it's correct.

7   The condition of the fluid should also be checked along with the level. If the fluid at the end of the dipstick is a dark reddish-brown color, or if it smells burned, it should be changed. If you are in doubt about the condition of the fluid, purchase some new fluid and compare the two for color and smell.

7   Power steering fluid level check

Refer to illustrations 7.2 and 7.6

1   Unlike manual steering, the power steering system relies on fluid which may, over a period of time, require replenishing.

2   The fluid reservoir for the power steering pump is located on the inner fender on the driver's side **(see illustration)**.

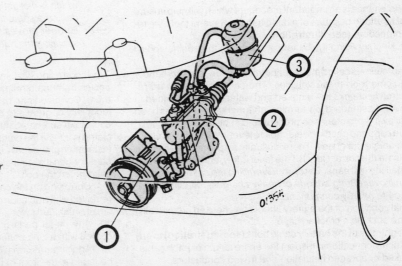

7.2   Locations of the power steering system components

1   Power steering pump
2   Power steering gear
3   Power steering fluid reservoir

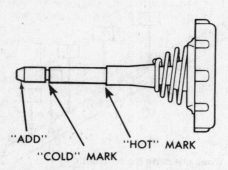

7.6   The marks on the power steering fluid dipstick indicate the safe range

3   For the check, the front wheels should be pointed straight ahead and the engine should be off.

4   Use a clean rag to wipe off the reservoir cap and the area around the cap. This will help prevent any foreign matter from entering the reservoir during the check.

5   Twist off the cap and check the temperature of the fluid at the end of the dipstick with your finger.

6   Wipe off the fluid with a clean rag, reinsert the dipstick, then withdraw it and read the fluid level. The level should be at the HOT mark if the fluid was hot to the touch **(see illustration)**. It should be at the COLD mark if the fluid was cool to the touch. Never allow the fluid level to drop below the ADD mark.

7   If additional fluid is required, pour the specified type directly into the reservoir, using a funnel to prevent spills.

8   If the reservoir requires frequent fluid additions, all power steering hoses, hose connections and the power steering pump should be carefully checked for leaks.

---

8   Battery check and maintenance

Refer to illustrations 8.1 and 8.6

Warning: *Certain precautions must be followed when checking and servicing the battery. Hydrogen gas, which is highly flammable, is always present in the battery cells, so keep lighted tobacco and all other open flames and sparks away from the battery. The electrolyte inside the battery is actually dilute sulfuric acid, which will cause injury if splashed on your skin or in your eyes. It will also ruin clothes and painted surfaces. When removing the battery cables, always detach the negative cable first and hook it up last!*

1   Battery maintenance is an important procedure which will help ensure that you are not stranded because of a dead battery. Several tools are required for this procedure **(see illustration)**.

2   When checking/servicing the battery, always turn the engine and all accessories off.

3   A sealed (sometimes called maintenance-free), side-terminal battery is standard equipment on these vehicles. The cell caps cannot be removed, no electrolyte checks are required and water cannot be added to the cells. However, if a standard top-terminal aftermarket battery has been installed, the following maintenance procedure can be used.

4   Remove the caps and check the electrolyte level in each of the battery cells. It must be above the plates. There's usually a split-ring indicator in each cell to indicate the correct level. If the level is low, add distilled water only, then reinstall the cell caps. **Caution:** *Overfilling the cells may cause electrolyte to spill over during periods of heavy charging, causing corrosion and damage to nearby components.*

5   The external condition of the battery should be checked periodically. Look for damage such as a cracked case.

6   Check the tightness of the battery cable bolts **(see illustration)** to ensure good electrical connections. Inspect the entire length of each cable, looking for cracked or abraded insulation and frayed conductors.

8.1   Tools and materials required for battery maintenance

1   *Face shield/safety goggles – When removing corrosion with a brush, the acidic particles can easily fly up into your eyes*

2   *Baking soda – A solution of baking soda and water can be used to neutralize corrosion*

3   *Petroleum jelly – A layer of this on the battery posts will help prevent corrosion*

4   *Battery post/cable cleaner – This wire brush cleaning tool will remove all traces of corrosion from the battery posts and cable clamps*

5   *Treated felt washers – Placing one of these on each post, directly under the cable clamps, will help prevent corrosion*

6   *Puller – Sometimes the cable clamps are very difficult to pull off the posts, even after the nut/bolt has been completely loosened. This tool pulls the clamp straight up and off the post without damage.*

7   *Battery post/cable cleaner – Here is another cleaning tool which is a slightly different version of number 4 above, but it does the same thing*

8   *Rubber gloves – Another safety item to consider when servicing the battery; remember that's acid inside the battery!*

7   If corrosion (visible as white, fluffy deposits) is evident, remove the cables from the terminals, clean them with a battery brush and reinstall them. Corrosion can be kept to a minimum by applying a layer of petroleum jelly or grease to the bolt threads.

8   Make sure the battery carrier is in good condition and the holddown clamp is tight. If the battery is removed (see Chapter 5 for the removal and installation procedure), make sure that no parts remain in the bottom of the carrier when it's reinstalled. When reinstalling the hold-down clamp, don't overtighten the bolt.

9   Corrosion on the carrier, battery case and surrounding areas can be removed with a solution of water and baking soda. Apply the mixture with a small brush, let it work, then rinse it off with plenty of clean water.

10   Any metal parts of the vehicle damaged by corrosion should be coated with a zinc-based primer, then painted.

11   Additional information on the battery, charging and jump starting can be found in the front of this manual and in Chapter 5.

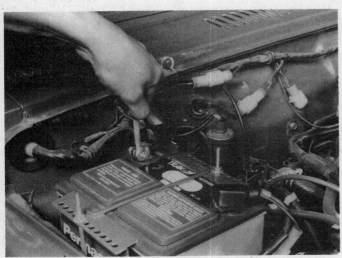

8.6   Remove the terminal and cable from the battery post with a box end wrench – sometimes a special tool is required for this procedure if corrosion has caused deterioration of the terminal nuts (always remove the negative cable first and hook it up last)

9   Cooling system check

Refer to illustration 9.4

1   Many major engine failures can be attributed to a faulty cooling system. If the vehicle is equipped with an automatic transmission, the cooling system also cools the transmission fluid and thus plays an important role in prolonging transmission life.

ALWAYS CHECK hose for chafed or burned areas that may cause an untimely and costly failure.

SOFT hose indicates inside deterioration. This deterioration can contaminate the cooling system and cause particles to clog the radiator.

HARDENED hose can fail at any time. Tightening hose clamps will not seal the connection or stop leaks.

SWOLLEN hose or oil soaked ends indicate danger and possible failure from oil or grease contamination. Squeeze the hose to locate cracks and breaks that cause leaks.

9.4   Hoses, like drivebelts, have a habit of failing at the worst possible time – to prevent the inconvenience of a blown radiator or heater hose, inspect them carefully as shown here

2   The cooling system should be checked with the engine cold. Do this before the vehicle is driven for the day or after it has been shut off for at least three hours.

3   Remove the radiator cap by turning it to the left until it reaches a stop. If you hear a hissing sound (indicating there is still pressure in the system), wait until this stops. Now press down on the cap with the palm of your hand and continue turning to the left until the cap can be removed. Thoroughly clean the cap, inside and out, with clean water. Also clean the filler neck on the radiator. All traces of corrosion should be removed. The coolant inside the radiator should be relatively transparent. If it is rust colored, the system should be drained and refilled (see Section 37). If the coolant level is not up to the top, add additional antifreeze/coolant mixture (see Section 4).

4   Carefully check the large upper and lower radiator hoses along with the smaller diameter heater hoses which run from the engine to the firewall. On some models the heater return hose runs directly to the radiator. Inspect each hose along its entire length, replacing any hose which is cracked, swollen or shows signs of deterioration. Cracks may become more apparent if the hose is squeezed (**see illustration**). Regardless of condition, it's a good idea to replace hoses with new ones every two years.

5   Make sure that all hose connections are tight. A leak in the cooling system will usually show up as white or rust colored deposits on the areas adjoining the leak. If wire-type clamps are used at the ends of the hoses, it may be a good idea to replace them with more secure screw-type clamps.

6   Use compressed air or a soft brush to remove bugs, leaves, etc. from the front of the radiator or air conditioning condenser. Be careful not to damage the delicate cooling fins or cut yourself on them.

7   Every other inspection, or at the first indication of cooling system problems, have the cap and system pressure tested. If you don't have a pressure tester, most gas stations and repair shops will do this for a minimal charge.

10   Underhood hose check and replacement

Refer to illustration 10.1

General

1   **Caution:** *Replacement of air conditioning hoses must be left to a dealer service department or air conditioning shop that has the equipment to depressurize the system safely. Never remove air conditioning components or hoses* (**see illustration**) *until the system has been depressurized.*

2   High temperatures in the engine compartment can cause the deterioration of the rubber and plastic hoses used for engine, accessory and emission systems operation. Periodic inspection should be made for cracks, loose clamps, material hardening and leaks. Information specific to the cooling system hoses can be found in Section 9.

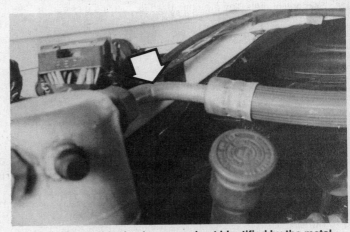

10.1   Air conditioning hoses are best identified by the metal tubes used at all bends (arrows) – DO NOT disconnect or accidently damage the air conditioning hoses as the system is under high pressure

3　Some, but not all, hoses are secured to the fittings with clamps. Where clamps are used, check to be sure they haven't lost their tension, allowing the hose to leak. If clamps aren't used, make sure the hose has not expanded and/or hardened where it slips over the fitting, allowing it to leak.

Vacuum hoses

4　It's quite common for vacuum hoses, especially those in the emissions system, to be color coded or identified by colored stripes molded into them. Various systems require hoses with different wall thicknesses, collapse resistance and temperature resistance. When replacing hoses, be sure the new ones are made of the same material.

5　Often the only effective way to check a hose is to remove it completely from the vehicle. If more than one hose is removed, be sure to label the hoses and fittings to ensure correct installation.

6　When checking vacuum hoses, be sure to include any plastic T-fittings in the check. Inspect the fittings for cracks and the hose where it fits over the fitting for distortion, which could cause leakage.

7　A small piece of vacuum hose (1/4-inch inside diameter) can be used as a stethoscope to detect vacuum leaks. Hold one end of the hose to your ear and probe around vacuum hoses and fittings, listening for the "hissing" sound characteristic of a vacuum leak. **Warning:** *When probing with the vacuum hose stethoscope, be very careful not to come into contact with moving engine components such as the drivebelt, cooling fan, etc.*

Fuel hose

Warning: *There are certain precautions which must be taken when inspecting or servicing fuel system components. Work in a well ventilated area and do not allow open flames (cigarettes, appliance pilot lights, etc.) or bare light bulbs near the work area. Mop up any spills immediately and do not store fuel soaked rags where they could ignite. On vehicles equipped with fuel injection, the fuel system is under pressure, so if any fuel lines are to be disconnected, the pressure in the system must be relieved first (see Chapter 4 for more information).*

8　Check all rubber fuel lines for deterioration and chafing. Check especially for cracks in areas where the hose bends and just before fittings, such as where a hose attaches to the fuel filter.

9　High quality fuel line, usually identified by the word Fluroelastomer printed on the hose, should be used for fuel line replacement. Never, under any circumstances, use unreinforced vacuum line, clear plastic tubing or water hose for fuel lines.

10　Spring-type clamps are commonly used on fuel lines. These clamps often lose their tension over a period of time, and can be "sprung" during removal. Replace all spring-type clamps with screw clamps whenever a hose is replaced.

Metal lines

11　Sections of metal line are often used for fuel line between the fuel pump and carburetor or fuel injection unit. Check carefully to be sure the line has not been bent or crimped and that cracks have not started in the line.

12　If a section of metal fuel line must be replaced, only seamless steel tubing should be used, since copper and aluminum tubing don't have the strength necessary to withstand normal engine vibration.

13　Check the metal brake lines where they enter the master cylinder and brake proportioning unit (if used) for cracks in the lines or loose fittings. Any sign of brake fluid leakage calls for an immediate thorough inspection of the brake system.

11　Wiper blade inspection and replacement

Refer to illustration 11.6

1　The windshield wiper and blade assembly should be inspected periodically for damage, loose components and cracked or worn blade elements.

2　Road film can build up on the wiper blades and affect their efficiency, so they should be washed regularly with a mild detergent solution.

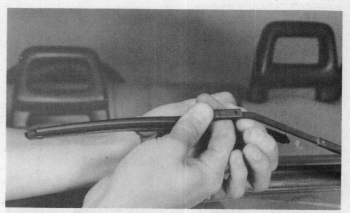

11.6　Remove the blade assembly by angling it slightly away from the retaining stud

3　The action of the wiping mechanism can loosen the bolts, nuts and fasteners, so they should be checked and tightened, as necessary, at the same time the wiper blades are checked.

4　If the wiper blade elements (sometimes called inserts) are cracked, worn or warped, they should be replaced with new ones.

5　Pull the wiper blade/arm assembly away from the glass.

6　Depress the blade-to-arm connector and slide the blade assembly off the wiper arm and over the retaining stud. Angle the blade slightly **(see illustration)**.

7　Pinch the tabs at the end, then slide the element out of the blade assembly.

8　Compare the new element with the old for length, design, etc.

9　Slide the new element into place. It will automatically lock at the correct location.

10　Reinstall the blade assembly on the arm, wet the windshield and check for proper operation.

12　Engine oil and filter change

Refer to illustrations 12.3, 12.9, 12.14 and 12.18

1　Frequent oil changes are the most important preventive maintenance procedures that can be done by the home mechanic. As engine oil ages, it becomes diluted and contaminated, which leads to premature engine wear.

2　Although some sources recommend oil filter changes every other oil change, we feel that the minimal cost of an oil filter and the relative ease with which it is installed dictate that a new filter be installed every time the oil is changed.

3　Gather together all necessary tools and materials before beginning this procedure **(see illustration)**.

4　You should have plenty of clean rags and newspapers handy to mop up any spills. Access to the underside of the vehicle is greatly improved if the vehicle can be lifted on a hoist, driven onto ramps or supported by jackstands. **Warning:** *Do not work under a vehicle which is supported only by a bumper, hydraulic or scissors-type jack.*

5　If this is your first oil change, get under the vehicle and familiarize yourself with the locations of the oil drain plug and the oil filter. The engine and exhaust components will be warm during the actual work, so note how they are situated to avoid touching them when working under the vehicle.

6　Warm the engine to normal operating temperature. If the new oil or any tools are needed, use this warm-up time to gather everything necessary for the job. The correct type of oil for your application can be found in *Recommended lubricants and fluids* at the beginning of this Chapter.

7　With the engine oil warm (warm engine oil will drain better and more built-up sludge will be removed with it), raise and support the vehicle. Make sure it's safely supported!

8　Move all necessary tools, rags and newspapers under the vehicle. Set the drain pan under the drain plug. Keep in mind that the oil will initially flow from the pan with some force; position the pan accordingly.

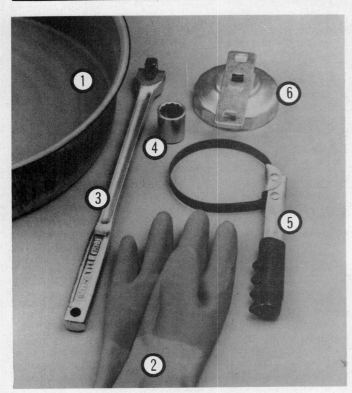

12.3   These tools are required when changing the engine oil and filter

1   *Drain pan – It should be fairly shallow in depth, but wide to prevent spills*
2   *Rubber gloves – When removing the drain plug and filter, you will get oil on your hands (the gloves will prevent burns)*
3   *Breaker bar – Sometimes the oil drain plug is tight and a long breaker bar is needed to loosen it*
4   *Socket – To be used with the breaker bar or a ratchet (must be the correct size to fit the drain plug – 6-point preferred)*
5   *Filter wrench – This is a metal band-type wrench, which requires clearance around the filter to be effective*
6   *Filter wrench – This type fits on the bottom of the filter and can be turned with a ratchet or breaker bar (different size wrenches are available for different types of filters)*

12.9   The oil drain plug is located at the bottom of the pan and should be removed with a socket or box-end wrench, as the corners on the bolt can be easily rounded off

12.14   Use a strap type oil filter wrench to loosen the filter – if access makes removal difficult, other types of filter wrenches are available

12.18   Lubricate the oil filter gasket with clean engine oil before installing the filter on the engine

9   Being careful not to touch any of the hot exhaust components, use a wrench to remove the drain plug near the bottom of the oil pan **(see illustration)**. Depending on how hot the oil is, you may want to wear gloves while unscrewing the plug the final few turns.
10   Allow the old oil to drain into the pan. It may be necessary to move the pan as the oil flow slows to a trickle.
11   After all the oil has drained, wipe off the drain plug with a clean rag. Small metal particles may cling to the plug and would immediately contaminate the new oil.
12   Clean the area around the drain plug opening and reinstall the plug. Tighten the plug securely with the wrench. If a torque wrench is available, use it to tighten the plug.
13   Move the drain pan into position under the oil filter.
14   Use the filter wrench to loosen the oil filter **(see illustration)**. Chain or metal band filter wrenches may distort the filter canister, but it doesn't matter since the filter will be discarded anyway.
15   Completely unscrew the old filter. Be careful; it's full of oil. Empty the oil inside the filter into the drain pan.
16   Compare the old filter with the new one to make sure they're the same type.
17   Use a clean rag to remove all oil, dirt and sludge from the area where the oil filter mounts to the engine. Check the old filter to make sure the rubber gasket isn't stuck to the engine. If the gasket is stuck to the engine (use a flashlight if necessary), remove it.
18   Apply a light coat of clean oil to the rubber gasket on the new oil filter **(see illustration)**.

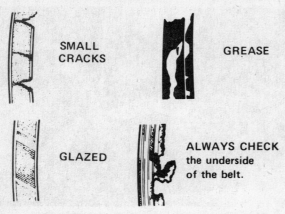

13.3   Here are some of the more common problems associated with drivebelts (check the belts very carefully to prevent an untimely breakdown)

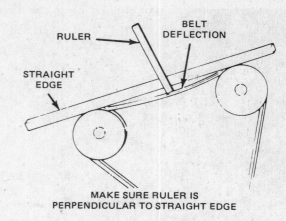

13.4   Measuring drivebelt deflection with a straightedge and ruler

19   Attach the new filter to the engine, following the tightening directions printed on the filter canister or packing box. Most filter manufacturers recommend against using a filter wrench due to the possibility of overtightening and damage to the seal.

20   Remove all tools, rags, etc. from under the vehicle, being careful not to spill the oil in the drain pan, then lower the vehicle.

21   Move to the engine compartment and locate the oil filler cap.

22   If an oil can spout is used, push the spout into the top of the oil can and pour the fresh oil through the filler opening. A funnel may also be used.

23   Pour four quarts of fresh oil into the engine. Wait a few minutes to allow the oil to drain into the pan, then check the level on the oil dipstick (see Section 4 if necessary). If the oil level is above the ADD mark, start the engine and allow the new oil to circulate.

24   Run the engine for only about a minute and then shut it off. Immediately look under the vehicle and check for leaks at the oil pan drain plug and around the oil filter. If either is leaking, tighten with a bit more force.

25   With the new oil circulated and the filter now completely full, recheck the level on the dipstick and add more oil as necessary.

26   During the first few trips after an oil change, make it a point to check frequently for leaks and proper oil level.

27   The old oil drained from the engine cannot be reused in its present state and should be disposed of. Oil reclamation centers, auto repair shops and gas stations will normally accept the oil, which can be refined and used again. After the oil has cooled it can be drained into a suitable container (capped plastic jugs, topped bottles, milk cartons, etc.) for transport to one of these disposal sites.

13   Drivebelt check, adjustment and replacement

Refer to illustrations 13.3, 13.4, 13.5a and 13.5b

1   The drivebelts, or V-belts as they are often called, are located at the front of the engine and play an important role in the overall operation of the engine and accessories. Due to their function and material makeup, the belts are prone to failure after a period of time and should be inspected and adjusted periodically to prevent major engine damage.

2   The number of belts used on a particular vehicle depends on the accessories installed. Drivebelts are used to turn the alternator, power steering pump, water pump and air conditioning compressor. Depending on the pulley arrangement, more than one of the components may be driven by a single belt.

3   With the engine off, locate the drivebelts at the front of the engine. Using your fingers (and a flashlight, if necessary), move along the belts checking for cracks and separation of the belt plies. Also check for fraying and glazing, which gives the belt a shiny appearance **(see illustration)**. Both sides of each belt should be inspected, which means you'll have to

twist each belt to check the underside. Check the pulleys for nicks, cracks, distortion and corrosion.

4   The tension of each belt is checked by pushing on it at a distance halfway between the pulleys. Push firmly with your thumb and see how much the belt moves (deflects) **(see illustration)**. A rule of thumb is that if the distance from pulley center-to-pulley center is between 7 and 11 inches, the belt should deflect 1/4-inch. If the belt travels between pulleys spaced 12-to-16 inches apart, the belt should deflect 1/2-inch.

5   If adjustment is needed, either to make the belt tighter or looser, it's done by moving the belt-driven accessory on the bracket **(see illustrations)**.

6   Each component usually has an adjusting bolt and a pivot bolt. Both bolts must be loosened slightly to enable you to move the component. Some components have an adjusting bolt that can be turned to change the belt tension after the mounting bolt is loosened. Others are equipped with an idler pulley that must be moved to change the belt tension.

7   After the two bolts have been loosened, move the component away from the engine to tighten the belt or toward the engine to loosen the belt. Hold the accessory in position and check the belt tension. If it's correct, tighten the two bolts until just snug, then recheck the tension. If the tension is correct, tighten the bolts.

8   You may have to use some sort of pry bar to move the accessory while the belt is adjusted. If this must be done to gain the proper leverage, be very careful not to damage the component being moved or the part being pried against.

9   To replace a belt, follow the above procedures for drivebelt adjustment but slip the belt off the pulleys and remove it. Since belts tend to wear out more or less at the same time, it's a good idea to replace all of them at the same time. Mark each belt and the corresponding pulley grooves so the replacement belts can be installed properly.

10   Take the old belts with you when purchasing new ones in order to make a direct comparison for length, width and design.

11   Adjust the belts as described earlier in this Section.

14   Tire rotation

Refer to illustration 14.2

1   The tires should be rotated at the specified intervals and whenever uneven wear is noticed.

2   Refer to the accompanying illustration for the preferred tire rotation pattern.

3   Refer to the information in Jacking and towing at the front of this manual for the proper procedures to follow when raising the vehicle and changing a tire. If the brakes are to be checked, don't apply the parking brake as stated. Make sure the tires are blocked to prevent the vehicle from rolling as it's raised.

13.5a   Loosen the bracket bolt (arrow) to allow the alternator to slide within the pulley adjustment bracket

13.5b   Loosen the two lower mounting bolts (viewed from under the vehicle) to allow the alternator to pivot

14.2   Tire rotation diagram

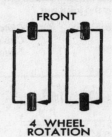
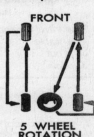

4 WHEEL ROTATION   5 WHEEL ROTATION   4 WHEEL ROTATION   5 WHEEL ROTATION

4   Preferably, the entire vehicle should be raised at the same time. This can be done on a hoist or by jacking up each corner and then lowering the vehicle onto jackstands placed under the frame rails. Always use four jackstands and make sure the vehicle is safely supported.

5   After rotation, check and adjust the tire pressures as necessary and be sure to check the lug nut tightness.

6   For additional information on the wheels and tires, refer to Chapter 10.

15   Clutch pedal height and free play check and adjustment

Refer to illustrations 15.2, 15.3 and 15.4

1   On vehicles equipped with a manual transmission, the clutch pedal height and free play must be correctly adjusted.

2   The height of the clutch pedal is the distance the pedal sits off the floor (see illustration). The distance should be as specified. If the pedal height is not within the specified range, loosen the locknut on the pedal stopper or switch located to the rear of the clutch pedal and turn the stopper or switch in or out until the pedal height is correct. Retighten the locknut.

3   The free play is the pedal slack, or the distance the pedal can be depressed before it begins to have any effect on the clutch (see illustration). The distance should be as specified. If it isn't, loosen the locknuts on the clutch cable bracket (located on the transmission housing) and adjust until freeplay is correct. Then tighten the nuts.

4   Adjust the clutch release arm free play by turning the joint nut at the end of the clutch cable (see illustration).

16   Valve clearance check and adjustment (every 15,000 miles or 12 months)

Refer to illustrations 16.5a, 16.5b, 16.6a, 16.6b, 16.7 and 16.10
Note: *On 16-valve engines, a special tool (see Step 7) is required for this procedure.*

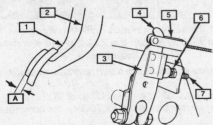

15.2   Clutch pedal height is adjusted by loosening the lock nut behind the pedal bracket and turning the adjusting bolt

A Height difference 0.2 in (5 mm)	*4 Clutch pedal shaft arm*
1 Clutch pedal	*5 Clutch cable assembly*
2 Brake pedal	*6 Lock nut*
3 Pedal bracket	*7 Adjusting bolt*

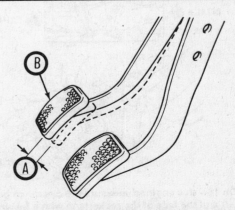

15.3   To determine clutch freeplay, depress the clutch pedal and stop the moment the clutch resistance is felt

A   Free travel   *1   Clutch pedal*

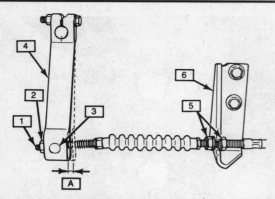

15.4   Loosen the inner and outer nuts on the clutch cable bracket and set the pedal freeplay to the amount listed in this Chapter's Specifications – also set the clutch release arm freeplay by turning the joint nut

A	Free travel of release arm	4	Clutch release arm
1	Inner cable	5	Cable outer nut
2	Joint nut	6	Clutch cable bracket
3	Joint pin		

INTAKE

0661H

EXHAUST

16.5b   Valve numbering on 16-valve engines – with the number one piston at TDC on the compression stroke, adjust valves 1, 2, 5 and 7; with the number four piston at TDC on the compression stroke, adjust valves 3, 4, 6 and 8

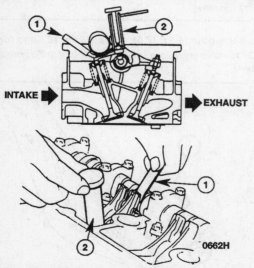

INTAKE   EXHAUST

0662H

16.6b   On 16-valve engines, measure the clearance between the camshaft and the face of the rocker arm with a feeler gauge (1) (the upper illustration shows adjusting the clearance on an intake valve, while the lower illustration shows adjusting the clearance on an exhaust valve) – a special tool (2) is necessary for adjustment, because there's not much room to work

16.5a   On 8-Valve engines, with the number one piston at TDC on the compression stroke, adjust the valves indicated by the arrows

16.6a   On 8-Valve engines, insert the feeler gauge between the valve stem and the adjusting screw

16.7   To adjust the valve clearance on 8–valve engines, use a box end wrench to slightly loosen the lock nut and a screwdriver to change the adjustment

1   Start the engine and allow it to reach normal operating temperature, then shut it off.

2   Remove the camshaft cover (see Chapter 2).

3   Position the number one piston at TDC on the compression stroke (see Chapter 2).

4   Make sure the rocker arms for the number one cylinder valves are loose and number four are tight. If they aren't, the number one piston is not at TDC on the compression stroke.

5   On 8-valve engines, check and adjust only the valves shown (**see illustration**). On 16-valve engines, check and adjust the valves numbered 1, 2, 5 and 7 in the accompanying illustration (**see illustration**). The valve clearances can be found in the Specifications at the beginning of this Chapter.

16.10   On 8-valve engines, turn the crankshaft one complete revolution (360-degrees), then adjust the remaining valves (arrows)

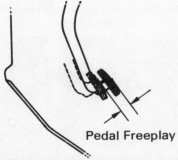

Pedal Freeplay

17.2   To check brake pedal freeplay, measure the distance between the naatural resting place of the pedal and the point at which you first encounter resistance

6   On 8-valve engines, the clearance is measured by inserting the specified size feeler gauge between the end of the valve stem and the adjusting screw **(see illustration)**. On 16-valve engines, measure between the camshaft and the face of the rocker arm where it rides on the camshaft **(see illustration)**. On either engine type, you should feel a slight amount of drag when the feeler gauge is moved back-and-forth.

7   If the gap is too large or too small, loosen the locknut and turn the adjusting screw to obtain the correct gap **(see illustration)**. On 16-valve engines, you will need a special tool (Suzuki 09917-18210 or equivalent) to loosen and tighten the locknuts and screws because they are difficult to reach.

8   Once the gap has been set, hold the screw in position with a screwdriver (8-valve) or special tool (16-valve) and retighten the locknut. Recheck the valve clearance – sometimes it will change slightly when the locknut is tightened. If so, readjust it until it's correct.

9   Repeat the procedure for the remaining valves **(see illustrations 16.5a and 16.5b)**, then turn the crankshaft one complete revolution (360-degrees) and realign the notch in the pulley with the zero on the engine.

10   Adjust the remaining valves. On 8-valve engines, adjust the valves shown **(see illustration)**. On 16-valve engines, adjust valves 3, 4, 6 and 8 in illustration 16.5b.

11   Reinstall the camshaft cover.

17   Brake pedal check and adjustment

Refer to illustration 17.2

1   Brake pedal height is the distance the pedal sits away from the floor. The distance should be as listed in this Chapter's Specifications). If the pedal height is not within the specified range, loosen the locknut on the brake light switch located in the bracket to the rear of the brake pedal and turn the switch in or out until the pedal height is correct. Retighten the locknut.

2   The free play is the pedal slack, or the distance the pedal can be depressed before it begins to have any effect on the brakes **(see illustration)**. It should be as specified. If it isn't, loosen the locknut on the brake booster input rod, to which the brake pedal is attached. Turn the input rod until the free play is correct, then retighten the locknut.

18   Brake check

Refer to illustrations 18.6, 18.11, 18.13a, 18.13b and 18.15
Note: *For detailed photographs of the brake system, refer to Chapter 9.*
Warning: *Dust created by the brake system may contain asbestos, which is harmful to your health. Never blow it out with compressed air and don't inhale any of it. An approved filtering mask should be worn when working on the brakes. Do not, under any circumstances, use petroleum-based solvents to clean brake parts. Use brake cleaner or denatured alcohol only!*

1   In addition to the specified intervals, the brakes should be inspected every time the wheels are removed or whenever a defect is suspected.

2   To check the brakes, the vehicle must be raised and supported securely on jackstands.

Disc brakes

3   Disc brakes are used on the front wheels. Extensive disc damage can occur if the pads are allowed to wear beyond the limit listed in this Chapter's Specifications.

4   Raise the vehicle and support it securely on jackstands, then remove all four wheels (see *Jacking and Towing* at the front of the manual if necessary).

5   The disc brake calipers, which contain the pads, are visible with the wheels removed. There's an outer pad and an inner pad in each caliper. All four pads should be inspected.

18.6   The disc brake pads are visible through the opening in the caliper (arrow) – be sure to measure only the lining material and not the metal backing to which the lining is attached

18.11   Use a slide hammer to remove stubborn brake drums

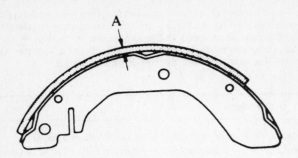

18.13a   The rear brake shoe lining thickness (A) is measured from the outer surface of the lining to the metal shoe

18.15   Carefully peel back the rubber boots on both sides of the wheel cylinder – if there's any brake fluid behind the boots, the wheel cylinders must be rebuilt or replaced

6   Each caliper has openings, which will allow you to inspect the pads **(see illustration)**. If the pad material has worn down near the minimum thickness listed in this Chapter's Specifications, the pads should be replaced.

7   If you're unsure about the exact thickness of the remaining lining material, remove the pads for further inspection or replacement (see Chapter 9).

8   Before installing the wheels, check for leakage and/or damage (cracks, splitting, etc.) around the brake hose connections. Replace the hose or fittings as necessary, referring to Chapter 9.

9   Check the condition of the disc. Look for score marks, deep scratches and burned spots. If these conditions exist, the hub/disc assembly should be removed for servicing.

Drum brakes

10   On rear brakes, remove the drum by pulling it off the axle and brake assembly. If it's stuck, make sure the parking brake is released, then squirt penetrating oil into the joint between the hub and drum. Allow the oil to soak in and try to pull the drum off again (see Chapter 9).

11   As a last resort, use a slide hammer on the wheel bolts to force the drum off **(see illustration)**.

12   With the drum removed, be careful not to touch any brake dust (see the Warning at the beginning of this Section).

13   Note the thickness of the lining material on both the leading and trailing brake shoes. If the material has worn down near the minimum thickness listed in this Chapter's Specifications, the shoes should be replaced **(see illustration)**. The shoes should also be replaced if they're cracked, glazed (shiny surface) or contaminated with brake fluid or oil.

14   Make sure that all the brake assembly springs are connected and in good condition.

15   Check the brake components for signs of fluid leakage. Carefully pry back the rubber cups on the wheel cylinders located at the top of the brake shoes with your finger **(see illustration)**. Any leakage is an indication that the wheel cylinders should be overhauled immediately (see Chapter 9). Also check brake hoses and connections for leakage.

18.13b   Check the thickness of the lining at several points on the shoes (arrows)

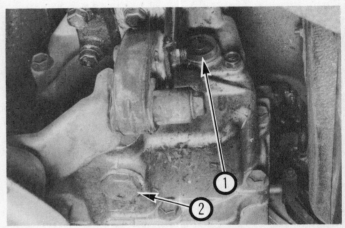

19.1a   The manual transmission check/fill plugs are accessible from under the vehicle (Samurai)

1   Oil level check plug   2   Oil drain plug

16   Wipe the inside of the drum with a clean rag and brake cleaner or denatured alcohol. Again, be careful not to breath the asbestos dust.

17   Check the inside of the drum for cracks, score marks, deep scratches and hard spots, which will appear as small discolorations. If imperfections cannot be removed with fine emery cloth, the drum must be taken to a machine shop equipped to turn the drums.

18   If after the inspection process all parts are in good working condition, reinstall the brake drum.

19   Install the wheels and lower the vehicle.

Parking brake

20   The parking brake operates from a hand lever and locks the rear brake system. The easiest, and perhaps most obvious method of periodically checking the operation of the parking brake assembly is to park the vehicle on a steep hill with the parking brake set and the transmission in Neutral. If the parking brake cannot prevent the vehicle from rolling within 6 to 10 clicks, it's in need of adjustment (see Chapter 9).

19   Manual transmission lubricant level check

Refer to illustrations 19.1a and 19.1b

1   Manual transmissions don't have a dipstick. The oil level is checked by removing a plug from the side of the transmission case **(see illustrations)**. Locate the plug and use a rag to clean the plug and the area around it. If the vehicle is raised to gain access to the plug, be sure to support it safely on jackstands – DO NOT crawl under the vehicle when it's supported only by a jack!

CARBON DEPOSITS

Symptoms: Dry sooty deposits indicate a rich mixture or weak ignition. Causes misfiring, hard starting and hesitation.

Recommendation: Check for a clogged air cleaner, high float level, sticky choke and worn ignition points. Use a spark plug with a longer core nose for greater anti-fouling protection.

OIL DEPOSITS

Symptoms: Oily coating caused by poor oil control. Oil is leaking past worn valve guides or piston rings into the combustion chamber. Causes hard starting, misfiring and hesition.

Recommendation: Correct the mechanical condition with necessary repairs and install new plugs.

TOO HOT

Symptoms: Blistered, white insulator, eroded electrode and absence of deposits. Results in shortened plug life.

Recommendation: Check for the correct plug heat range, over-advanced ignition timing, lean fuel mixture, intake manifold vacuum leaks and sticking valves. Check the coolant level and make sure the radiator is not clogged.

PREIGNITION

Symptoms: Melted electrodes. Insulators are white, but may be dirty due to misfiring or flying debris in the combustion chamber. Can lead to engine damage.

Recommendation: Check for the correct plug heat range, over-advanced ignition timing, lean fuel mixture, clogged cooling system and lack of lubrication.

HIGH SPEED GLAZING

Symptoms: Insulator has yellowish, glazed appearance. Indicates that combustion chamber temperatures have risen suddenly during hard acceleration. Normal deposits melt to form a conductive coating. Causes misfiring at high speeds.

Recommendation: Install new plugs. Consider using a colder plug if driving habits warrant.

GAP BRIDGING

Symptoms: Combustion deposits lodge between the electrodes. Heavy deposits accumulate and bridge the electrode gap. The plug ceases to fire, resulting in a dead cylinder.

Recommendation: Locate the faulty plug and remove the deposits from between the electrodes.

NORMAL

Symptoms: Brown to grayish-tan color and slight electrode wear. Correct heat range for engine and operating conditions.

Recommendation: When new spark plugs are installed, replace with plugs of the same heat range.

ASH DEPOSITS

Symptoms: Light brown deposits encrusted on the side or center electrodes or both. Derived from oil and/or fuel additives. Excessive amounts may mask the spark, causing misfiring and hesitation during acceleration.

Recommendation: If excessive deposits accumulate over a short time or low mileage, install new valve guide seals to prevent seepage of oil into the combustion chambers. Also try changing gasoline brands.

WORN

Symptoms: Rounded electrodes with a small amount of deposits on the firing end. Normal color. Causes hard starting in damp or cold weather and poor fuel economy.

Recommendation: Replace with new plugs of the same heat range.

DETONATION

Symptoms: Insulators may be cracked or chipped. Improper gap setting techniques can also result in a fractured insulator tip. Can lead to piston damage.

Recommendation: Make sure the fuel anti-knock values meet engine requirements. Use care when setting the gaps on new plugs. Avoid lugging the engine.

SPLASHED DEPOSITS

Symptoms: After long periods of misfiring, deposits can loosen when normal combustion temperature is restored by an overdue tune-up. At high speeds, deposits flake off the piston and are thrown against the hot insulator, causing misfiring.

Recommendation: Replace the plugs with new ones or clean and reinstall the originals.

MECHANICAL DAMAGE

Symptoms: May be caused by a foreign object in the combustion chamber or the piston striking an incorrect reach (too long) plug. Causes a dead cylinder and could result in piston damage.

Recommendation: Remove the foreign object from the engine and/or install the correct reach plug.

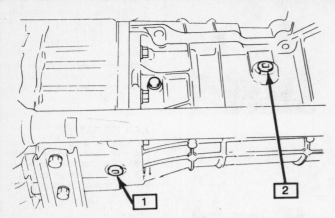

19.1b   The filler and drain plugs on the manual transmission of the Tracker/Sidekick

1   Drain plug   *2   Filler plug*

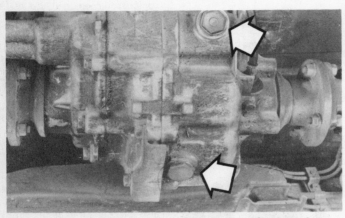

20.1a   On Samurai models, locate the two transfer case plugs – the upper one is used for checking and refilling and the lower one is used for draining

2   With the engine and transmission cold, remove the plug. If lubricant immediately starts leaking out, thread the plug back into the transmission – the level is correct. If it doesn't, completely remove the plug and reach inside the hole with your little finger. The level should be even with the bottom of the plug hole.
3   If the transmission needs more lubricant, use a syringe or small pump to add it through the plug hole.
4   Thread the plug back into the transmission and tighten it securely. Drive the vehicle, then check for leaks around the plug.

20   Transfer case lubricant level check

Refer to illustrations 20.1a and 20.1b
1   The transfer case oil level is checked by removing a plug from the side of the case (see illustrations). Remove the rock guard, then locate the plug and use a rag to clean the plug and the area around it. If the vehicle is raised to gain access to the plug, be sure to support it safely on jackstands – DO NOT crawl under the vehicle when it's supported only by a jack!
2   With the engine and transfer case cold, remove the plug. If lubricant immediately starts leaking out, thread the plug back into the case – the level is correct. If it doesn't, completely remove the plug and reach inside the hole with your little finger. The level should be even with the bottom of the plug hole.
3   If more oil is needed, use a syringe or small pump to add it through the opening.

4   Thread the plug back into the case and tighten it securely. Drive the vehicle, then check for leaks around the plug. Install the rock guard.

21   Differential oil level check

Refer to illustrations 21.2a, 21.2b and 21.3
1   The differential has a check/fill plug which must be removed to check the oil level. If the vehicle is raised to gain access to the plug, be sure to support it safely on jackstands – DO NOT crawl under the vehicle when it's supported only by a jack.
2   Remove the oil check/fill plug from the differential (see illustrations).
3   The oil level should be at the bottom of the plug opening (see illustration). If not, use a syringe to add the recommended lubricant until it just starts to run out of the opening.
4   Install the plug and tighten it securely.

22   Suspension and steering check

1   Whenever the front of the vehicle is raised for any reason, it's a good idea to visually check the suspension and steering components for wear.
2   Indications of steering or suspension problems include excessive play in the steering wheel before the front wheels react, excessive swaying around corners or body movement over rough roads and binding at some point as the steering wheel is turned.

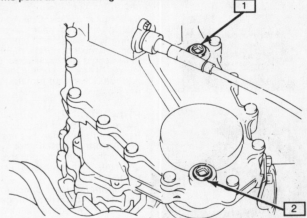

20.1b   The check/fill and drain plugs are located on the rear section of the transfer case on the Sidekick/Tracker

1   Filler plug   *2   Drain plug*

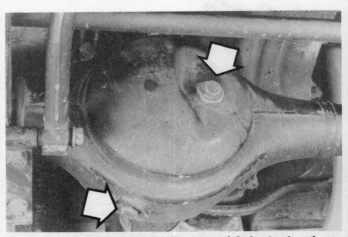

21.2a   Front differential check/fill plug and drain plug locations

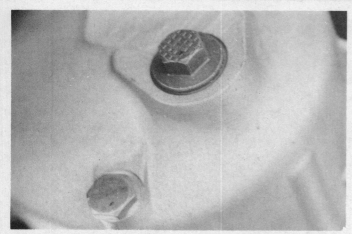

21.2b   Fill/check (upper) and drain (lower) bolt locations on the front differential of the Tracker/Sidekick

3   Before the vehicle is raised for inspection, test the shock absorbers by pushing down aggressively at each corner. If the vehicle doesn't come back to a level position within one or two bounces, the shocks are worn and should be replaced. As this is done listen for squeaks and other noises from the suspension components. Information on shock absorber and suspension components can be found in Chapter 10.
4   Raise the front end of the vehicle and support it on jackstands. Make sure it's safely supported!
5   Crawl under the vehicle and check for loose bolts, broken or disconnected parts and deteriorated rubber bushings on all suspension and steering components. Look for grease or fluid leaking from around the steering gear assembly and shock absorbers. If equipped, check the power steering hoses and connections for leaks.
6   The balljoint seals should be checked at this time (Tracker and Sidekick). This includes not only the upper and lower suspension balljoints, but those connecting the steering linkage parts as well. After cleaning around the balljoints, inspect the seals for cracks and damage.
7   Grip the top and bottom of each wheel and try to move it in and out. It won't take a lot of effort to be able to feel any play in the wheel bearings. If the play is noticeable it would be a good idea to adjust it right away or it could confuse further inspections.
8   Grip each side of the wheel and try rocking it laterally. Steady pressure will, of course, turn the steering, but back and forth pressure will reveal a loose steering joint. If some play is felt it would be easier to get assistance from someone so while one person rocks the wheel from side to side, the other can look at the joints, bushings and connections in the steering linkage. On models equipped with a steering gearbox there are

eight places where the play may occur. The two outer balljoints on the tie-rods are the most likely, followed by the two inner joints on the same rods, where they join to the center rod. Any play in them means replacement of the tie-rod end. Next are two swivel bushings, one at each end of the center gear rod. Finally, check the steering gear arm balljoint and the one on the idler arm which supports the center rod on the side opposite the steering box. This unit is bolted to the side of the frame member and any play calls for replacement of the bushings.
9   To check the steering box, first make sure the bolts holding the steering box to the frame are tight. Then get another person to help examine the mechanism. One should look at, or hold onto, the arm at the bottom of the steering box while the other turns the steering wheel a little from side to side. The amount of lost motion between the steering wheel and the gear arm indicates the degree of wear in the steering box mechanism. This check should be carried out with the wheels first in the straight ahead position and then at nearly full lock on each side. If the play only occurs noticeably in the straight ahead position then the wear is most likely in the worm and/or nut. If it occurs at all positions, then the wear is probably in the sector shaft bearing. Oil leaks from the unit are another indication of such wear. In either case the steering box will need removal for closer examination and repair.
10   Moving to the vehicle interior, check the play in the steering wheel by turning it slowly in both directions until the wheels can just be felt turning. The steering wheel free play should be less than 1 3/8-inch (35 mm). Excessive play is another indication of wear in the steering gear or linkage.
11   Following the inspection of the front, a similar inspection should be made of the rear suspension components, again checking for loose bolts, damaged or disconnected parts and deteriorated rubber bushings.

23   Driveaxle boot check

Refer to illustration 23.2
1   The driveaxle boots are very important because they prevent dirt, water and foreign material from entering and damaging the constant velocity (CV) joints. Oil and grease can cause the boot material to deteriorate prematurely, so it's a good idea to wash the boots with soap and water.
2   Inspect the boots for tears and cracks as well as loose clamps (see illustration). If there is any evidence of cracks and leaking lubricant, they must be replaced as described in Chapter 8.

24   Driveshaft check and lubrication

Refer to illustration 24.9
1   Raise the rear of the vehicle and support it securely on jackstands. Block the front wheels. The transmission should be in Neutral.

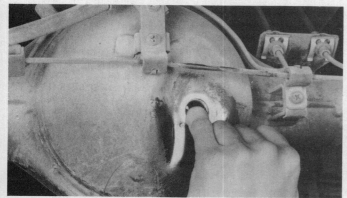

21.3   Use your finger as a dipstick to make sure the lubricant level is even with the bottom of the hole

23.2   Flex the driveaxle boots by hand to check for cracks and/or leaking grease

24.9   The driveshafts are lubricated at the fitting and also at the boot (arrows)

26.3   With the air intake case removed, the choke plate is visible at the top of the carburetor

2   Crawl under the vehicle and visually inspect the driveshaft. Look for dents and cracks in the tube. If any are found, the driveshaft must be replaced (see Chapter 8).

3   Check for oil leakage at the front and rear of the driveshaft. Leakage where the driveshaft enters the transmission indicates a defective rear transmission seal. Leakage where the driveshaft enters the differential indicates a defective pinion seal. For these repair operations refer to Chapters 7 and 8 respectively.

4   While still under the vehicle, have an assistant turn the rear wheel so the driveshaft will rotate. As it does, check for binding, noise and excessive play in the U-joints.

5   The universal joints can also be checked with the driveshaft motionless, by gripping both sides of the joint and attempting to twist it. Any movement at all in the joint is a sign of considerable wear. Lifting up on the shaft will also indicate movement in the universal joints.

6   Check the driveshaft mounting bolts at both ends to make sure they're tight.

7   The above driveshaft checks should be repeated on all driveshafts. In addition check for grease leakage around the sleeve yoke, indicating failure of the yoke seal.

8   Check for leakage where the driveshafts connect to the transfer case.

9   The driveshafts must be lubricated periodically as indicated in the maintenance schedule. Use the grease gun to insert grease into the fitting **(see illustration)**. Also pull back the boot at the rear of the axle and inject grease.

25   Fuel system check

Warning: *There are certain precautions to take when inspecting or servicing the fuel system components. Work in a well ventilated area and don't allow open flames (cigarettes, appliance pilot lights, etc.) in the work area. Mop up spills immediately and don't store fuel soaked rags where they could ignite. On fuel injection equipped models the fuel system is under pressure. No components should be disconnected until the pressure has been relieved (see Chapter 4).*

1   On most models the main fuel tank is located under the left side of the vehicle.

2   The fuel system is most easily checked with the vehicle raised on a hoist so the components underneath the vehicle are readily visible and accessible.

3   If the smell of gasoline is noticed while driving or after the vehicle has been in the sun, the system should be thoroughly inspected immediately.

4   Remove the gas tank cap and check for damage, corrosion and an unbroken sealing imprint on the gasket. Replace the cap with a new one if necessary.

5   With the vehicle raised, check the gas tank and filler neck for punctures, cracks and other damage. The connection between the filler neck and the tank is especially critical. Sometimes a rubber filler neck will leak due to loose clamps or deteriorated rubber, problems a home mechanic can usually rectify. **Warning:** *Do not, under any circumstances, try to repair a fuel tank yourself (except rubber components). A welding torch or any open flame can easily cause the fuel vapors to explode if the proper precautions are not taken!*

6   Carefully check all rubber hoses and metal lines leading away from the fuel tank. Look for loose connections, deteriorated hoses, crimped lines and other damage. Follow the lines to the front of the vehicle, carefully inspecting them all the way. Repair or replace damaged sections as necessary.

7   If a fuel odor is still evident after the inspection, refer to Chapter 4.

26   Carburetor choke check

Refer to illustration 26.3

1   The choke operates only when the engine is cold, so this check should be performed before the engine has been started for the day.

2   Open the hood and remove the air intake case from the carburetor. It's held in place by a nut at the center. If any vacuum hoses must be disconnected, tag them to ensure reinstallation in their original positions.

3   Look at the center of the carburetor. You'll notice a flat plate at the carburetor opening **(see illustration)**.

4   Have an assistant press the throttle pedal to the floor. The plate should close completely. Start the engine while you watch the plate at the carburetor. Don't position your face near the carburetor, as the engine could backfire, causing serious burns! When the engine starts, the choke plate should open slightly.

5   Allow the engine to continue running at an idle speed. As the engine warms up to operating temperature, the plate should slowly open, allowing more air to enter through the top of the carburetor.

6   After a few minutes, the choke plate should be completely open to the vertical position. Blip the throttle to make sure the fast idle cam disengages.

7   You'll notice that engine speed corresponds to the plate opening. With the plate closed, the engine should run at a fast idle speed. As the plate opens and the throttle is moved to disengage the fast idle cam, the engine speed will decrease.

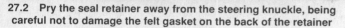

27.2   Pry the seal retainer away from the steering knuckle, being careful not to damage the felt gasket on the back of the retainer

27.3   Pull the old seal out with a pair of needle-nose pliers

8   With the engine off and the throttle held half-way open, open and close the choke several times. Check the linkage to see if it's hooked up correctly and make sure it doesn't bind.
9   If the choke or linkage binds, sticks or works sluggishly, clean it with choke cleaner (an aerosol spray available at auto parts stores). If the condition persists after cleaning, replace the troublesome parts.
10   Visually inspect all vacuum hoses to be sure they're securely connected and look for cracks and deterioration. Replace as necessary.
11   Refer to Chapter 4 for more information on the choke.

27   Steering knuckle oil seal replacement (Samurai only)

Refer to illustrations 27.2, 27.3, 27.4, 27.5 and 27.6
1   Raise the front of the vehicle and support it securely on jackstands.
2   Remove the bolts that secure the seal retainer to the steering knuckle. Using a screwdriver or pry bar, pry the retainer away from the knuckle and slide it over the axle housing **(see illustration)**.
3   Grasp the old seal with a pair of pliers and pull it out **(see illustration)**. Cut the seal with a knife or pair of scissors and remove it from the vehicle.
4   Cut the new seal in one place, lubricate its inner circumference with grease and position it in the steering knuckle, with the cut portion at the top

(see illustration).
5   Apply a bead of RTV sealant to the retainer mating surface on the steering knuckle **(see illustration)**.
6   Install the seal retainers up to the steering knuckle **(see illustration)**. Align the holes and install the bolts. Install one half loosely before tightening both of them to the torque listed in this Chapter's Specifications.

28   Spark plug replacement

Refer to illustrations 28.2, 28.5a, 28.5b, 28.6 and 28.10
1   Replace the spark plugs with new ones at the intervals recommended in the *Routine maintenance schedule*.
2   In most cases, the tools necessary for spark plug replacement include a spark plug socket which fits onto a ratchet (spark plug sockets are padded inside to prevent damage to the porcelain insulators on the new plugs), various extensions and a gap gauge to check and adjust the gaps on the new plugs **(see illustration)**. A special plug wire removal tool is available for separating the wire boots from the spark plugs, but it isn't absolutely necessary. A torque wrench should be used to tighten the new plugs.

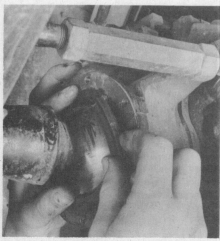

27.4   Cut the new seal, apply grease to the inside surface, and install it with the cut portion on top

27.5   Apply a bead of RTV sealant to the steering knuckle, inside of the bolt holes

27.6   Apply some sealant to the ends of the seal retainers when installing them

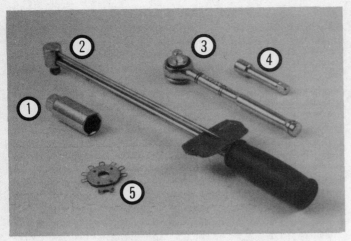

28.2   Tools required for changing spark plugs

1   **Spark plug socket** – This will have special padding inside to protect the spark plug's porcelain insulator
2   **Torque wrench** – Although not mandatory, using this tool is the best way to ensure the plugs are tightened properly
3   **Ratchet** – Standard hand tool to fit the spark plug socket
4   **Extension** – Depending on model and accessories, you may need special extensions and universal joints to reach one or more of the plugs
5   **Spark plug gap gauge** – This gauge for checking the gap comes in a variety of styles. Make sure the gap for your engine is included.

28.5a   Spark plug manufacturers recommend using a wire-type gauge when checking the gap – if the wire does not slide between the electrodes with a slight drag, adjustment is required

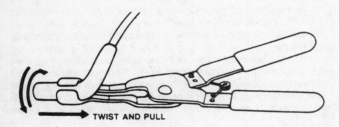

TWIST AND PULL

28.6   When removing the spark plug wires, pull only on the boot and use a twisting/pulling motion

3   The best approach when replacing the spark plugs is to purchase the new ones in advance, adjust them to the proper gap and replace them one at a time. When buying the new spark plugs, be sure to obtain the correct plug type for your particular engine. This information can be found on the Emission Control Information label located under the hood and in the factory owner's manual. If differences exist between the plug specified on the emissions label and in the owner's manual, assume the emissions label is correct.

4   Allow the engine to cool completely before attempting to remove any of the plugs. While you're waiting for the engine to cool, check the new plugs for defects and adjust the gaps.

5   The gap is checked by inserting the proper thickness gauge between the electrodes at the tip of the plug **(see illustration)**. The gap between the electrodes should be the same as the one specified on the Emissions Control Information label. The wire should just slide between the electrodes with a slight amount of drag. If the gap is incorrect, use the adjuster on the gauge body to bend the curved side electrode slightly until the proper gap is obtained **(see illustration)**. If the side electrode is not exactly over the center electrode, bend it with the adjuster until it is. Check for

28.5b   To change the gap, bend the side electrode only, as indicated by the arrows, and be very careful not to crack or chip the porcelain insulator surrounding the center electrode

cracks in the porcelain insulator (if any are found, the plug shouldn't be used).

6   With the engine cool, remove the spark plug wire from one spark plug. Pull only on the boot at the end of the wire – don't pull on the wire. A plug wire removal tool should be used if available **(see illustration)**.

7   If compressed air is available, use it to blow any dirt or foreign material away from the spark plug hole. A common bicycle pump will also work. The idea here is to eliminate the possibility of debris falling into the cylinder as the spark plug is removed.

8   Place the spark plug socket over the plug and remove it from the engine by turning it in a counterclockwise direction.

9   Compare the spark plug to those shown in the photos on page 57 to get an indication of the general running condition of the engine.

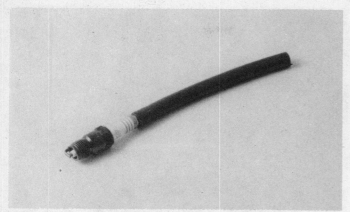

28.10   A length of 3/16-inch ID rubber hose will save time and prevent damaged threads when installing the spark plugs

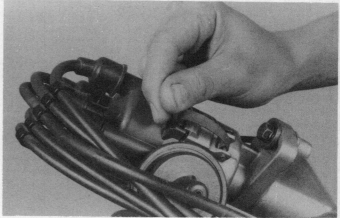

30.2   Release the two spring clips then remove the distributor cap – the distributor cap will only fit on the distributor body one way, so make sure the new cap is in the same position as the old one when transferring the wires

1

10   Thread one of the new plugs into the hole until you can no longer turn it with your fingers, then tighten it with a torque wrench (if available) or the ratchet. It might be a good idea to slip a short length of rubber hose over the end of the plug to use as a tool to thread it into place **(see illustration)**. The hose will grip the plug well enough to turn it, but will start to slip if the plug begins to cross-thread in the hole – this will prevent damaged threads and the accompanying repair costs.
11   Before pushing the spark plug wire onto the end of the plug, inspect it following the procedures outlined in Section 29.
12   Attach the plug wire to the new spark plug, again using a twisting motion on the boot until it's seated on the spark plug.
13   Repeat the procedure for the remaining spark plugs, replacing them one at a time to prevent mixing up the spark plug wires.

29   Spark plug wire check and replacement

1   The spark plug wires should be checked at the recommended intervals and whenever new spark plugs are installed in the engine.
2   The wires should be inspected one at a time to prevent mixing up the order, which is essential for proper engine operation.
3   Disconnect the plug wire from one spark plug. To do this, grab the rubber boot, twist slightly and pull the wire free. Do not pull on the wire itself,

only on the rubber boot **(see illustration 28.6)**.
4   Check inside the boot for corrosion, which will look like a white crusty powder. Push the wire and boot back onto the end of the spark plug. It should be a tight fit on the plug. If it isn't, remove the wire and use a pair of pliers to carefully crimp the metal connector inside the boot until it fits securely on the end of the spark plug.
5   Using a clean rag, wipe the entire length of the wire to remove any built-up dirt and grease. Once the wire is clean, check for holes, burned areas, cracks and other damage. Don't bend the wire excessively or the conductor inside might break.
6   Disconnect the wire from the distributor cap. Again, pull only on the rubber boot. Check for corrosion and a tight fit in the same manner as the spark plug end. Reattach the wire to the distributor cap.
7   Check the remaining spark plug wires one at a time, making sure they are securely fastened at the distributor and the spark plug when the check is complete.
8   If new spark plug wires are required, purchase a new set for your specific engine model. Wire sets are available pre-cut, with the rubber boots already installed. Remove and replace the wires one at a time to avoid mix-ups in the firing order. The wire routing is extremely important, so be sure to note exactly how each wire is situated before removing it.

30   Distributor cap and rotor check and replacement

Refer to illustrations 30.2, 30.4 and 30.7

Note: *It's common practice to install a new distributor cap and rotor whenever new spark plug wires are installed.*

1   Although the breakerless distributor used on these vehicles requires much less maintenance than a conventional distributor, periodic inspections should be performed at the intervals specified in the routine maintenance schedule and whenever any work is performed on the distributor.
2   Disconnect the ignition coil wire from the coil, then unsnap the spring clips or loosen the screws that hold the cap to the distributor body **(see illustration)**. Detach the distributor cap and wires.
3   Place the cap, with the spark plug and coil wires still attached, out of the way. Use a length of wire or rope to secure it, if necessary.
4   The rotor is now visible on the end of the distributor shaft. Check it carefully for cracks and carbon tracks. Make sure the center terminal spring tension is adequate and look for corrosion and wear on the rotor tip **(see illustration)**. If in doubt about its condition, replace it with a new one.
5   If replacement is required, detach the rotor from the shaft and install a new one.

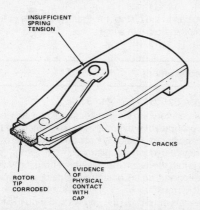

INSUFFICIENT SPRING TENSION

CRACKS

ROTOR TIP CORRODED

EVIDENCE OF PHYSICAL CONTACT WITH CAP

30.4   The ignition rotor should be checked for wear and corrosion as indicated here (if in doubt about its condition, buy a new one)

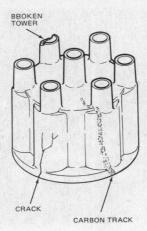

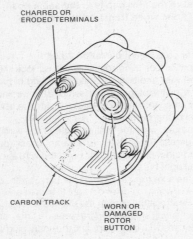

30.7   Shown here are some of the common defects to look for when inspecting the distributor cap (if in doubt about its condition, install a new one)

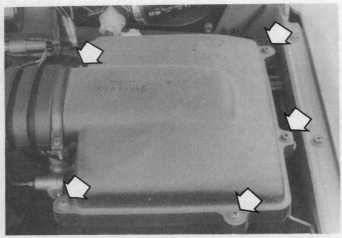

31.3c   On Sidekick/Tracker models, the air filter housing is located in the engine compartment on the driver's side inner fender wall – remove the screws (arrows) and lift the cover up

31.3a   Disengage the clips on the air cleaner housing, remove the nut securing the air intake case to the carburetor, . . .

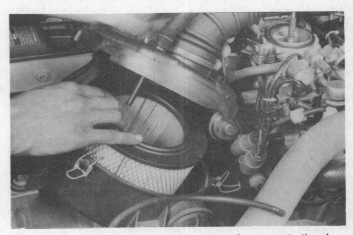

31.3b   . . . then lift the assembly up to gain access to the air filter (Samurai)

6   While the distributor cap is off, check the air gap as described in Chapter 5.

7   Check the distributor cap for carbon tracks, cracks and other damage. Closely examine the terminals on the inside of the cap for excessive corrosion and damage (see illustration). Slight deposits are normal. Again, if in doubt about the condition of the cap, replace it with a new one.

8   When replacing the cap, simply transfer the spark plug and coil wires, one at a time, from the old cap to the new cap. Be very careful not to mix up the wires!

9   Reattach the cap to the distributor, then tighten the screws or reposition the spring clips to hold it in place.

31   Air filter replacement

Refer to illustrations 31.3a, 31.3b and 31.3c

1   At the specified intervals, the air filter should be replaced with a new one. A thorough program of preventative maintenance would also call for the filter to be inspected periodically between changes, especially if the vehicle is often driven in dusty conditions.

2   The air filter is located inside the air cleaner housing which is mounted on the inner fender panel on the passenger side (Samurai) or on the driver's side (Sidekick/Tracker).

3   Release the clips or remove the screws securing the top plate to the air cleaner body. On Samurai models, remove the air intake case-to-carburetor nut. Disconnect any electrical connections or vacuum lines and carefully mark them for reinstallation purposes (see illustrations). Lift the air filter out of the housing. If it's covered with dirt, it should be replaced.

33.8 Set the idle to the speed listed on the Vehicle Emission Control Information label under the hood – turning the adjustment screw clockwise will cause the idle speed to increase, turning it counterclockwise will cause it to decrease

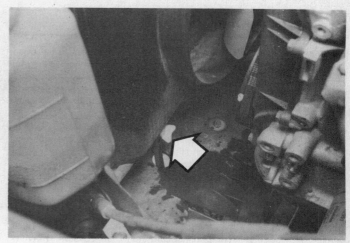

34.4 Open the drain fitting (arrow) but be careful not to completely remove it

1

4 Wipe the inside of the air cleaner housing with a clean rag.
5 Place the old filter (if in good condition) or the new filter in the air cleaner housing.
6 Reinstall the top plate and any hoses which were disconnected. Secure the clips or tighten the screws.

32 Thermostatically Controlled Air Cleaner (TCAC) check

The Thermostatically Controlled Air Cleaner and related components are covered in detail in Chapter 6.

33 Idle speed check and adjustment

Refer to illustration 33.8
1 Engine idle speed is the speed at which the engine operates when no throttle pedal pressure is applied. The idle speed is critical to the performance of the engine itself, as well as many engine sub-systems.
2 A hand-held tachometer must be used when adjusting idle speed to get an accurate reading. The exact hook-up for these meters varies with the manufacturer, so follow the particular directions included.
3 Set the parking brake and block the wheels. Be sure the transmission is in Neutral (manual transmission) or Park (automatic transmission).
4 Turn off the air conditioner (if equipped), the headlights and any other accessories during this procedure.
5 Start the engine and allow it to reach normal operating temperature.
6 Open the hood and run the engine at about 2000 rpm for approximately three minutes, then allow it to idle again for about one minute.
7 Check the engine idle speed with the tachometer and compare it to the VECI label on the hood.
8 If the idle speed is not correct, turn the idle speed adjusting screw (clockwise for faster, counterclockwise for slower) until the idle speed is correct **(see illustration)**.

34 Cooling system servicing (draining, flushing and refilling)

See illustration 34.4
Warning: *Do not allow antifreeze to come in contact with your skin or painted surfaces of the vehicle. Rinse off spills immediately with plenty of water. NEVER leave antifreeze lying around in an open container or in a puddle in the driveway or on the garage floor. Children and pets are attrac-*

ted by it's sweet smell. Antifreeze is fatal if ingested. Consult local authorities regarding proper disposal procedures for antifreeze before draining the cooling system. In many areas, reclamation centers have been established to collect used oil and coolant mixtures.

1 Periodically, the cooling system should be drained, flushed and re-filled to replenish the antifreeze mixture and prevent formation of rust and corrosion, which can impair the performance of the cooling system and cause engine damage. When the cooling system is serviced, all hoses and the radiator cap should be checked and replaced if necessary.
2 Apply the parking brake and block the wheels. If the vehicle has just been driven, wait several hours to allow the engine to cool down before beginning this procedure.
3 Once the engine is completely cool, remove the radiator cap.
4 Move a large container under the radiator drain to catch the coolant. Open the drain fitting **(see illustration)** (a pair of pliers may be required to turn it). Be careful not to remove the fitting completely.
5 After the coolant stops flowing out of the radiator, move the container under the engine block drain plug (if so equipped). Remove the plug and allow the coolant in the block to drain.
6 While the coolant is draining, check the condition of the radiator hoses, heater hoses and clamps (refer to Section 9 if necessary).
7 Replace any damaged clamps or hoses.
8 Once the system is completely drained, flush the radiator with fresh water from a garden hose until it runs clear at the drain. The flushing action of the water will remove sediments from the radiator but will not remove rust and scale from the engine and cooling tube surfaces.
9 These deposits can be removed with a chemical cleaner. Follow the procedure outlined in the manufacturer's instructions. If the radiator is severely corroded, damaged or leaking, it should be removed (see Chapter 3) and taken to a radiator repair shop.
10 Remove the overflow hose from the coolant recovery reservoir. Drain the reservoir and flush it with clean water, then reconnect the hose.
11 Close and tighten the radiator drain. Install and tighten the block drain plug.
12 Place the heater temperature control in the maximum heat position.
13 Slowly add new coolant (a 50/50 mixture of water and antifreeze) to the radiator until it's full. Add coolant to the reservoir up to the lower mark.
14 Leave the radiator cap off and run the engine in a well-ventilated area until the thermostat opens (coolant will begin flowing through the radiator and the upper radiator hose will become hot).
15 Turn the engine off and let it cool. Add more coolant mixture to bring the level back up to the lip on the radiator filler neck.
16 Squeeze the upper radiator hose to expel air, then add more coolant mixture if necessary. Replace the radiator cap.
17 Start the engine, allow it to reach normal operating temperature and check for leaks.

35   Exhaust system check

1   With the engine cold (at least three hours after the vehicle has been driven), check the complete exhaust system from the manifold to the end of the tailpipe. Be careful around the catalytic converter, which may be hot even after three hours. The inspection should be done with the vehicle on a hoist to permit unrestricted access. If a hoist isn't available, raise the vehicle and support it securely on jackstands.

2   Check the exhaust pipes and connections for signs of leakage and/or corrosion indicating a potential failure. Make sure that all brackets and hangers are in good condition and tight.

3   Inspect the underside of the body for holes, corrosion, open seams, etc. which may allow exhaust gases to enter the passenger compartment. Seal all body openings with silicone or body putty.

4   Rattles and other noises can often be traced to the exhaust system, especially the hangers, mounts and heat shields. Try to move the pipes, mufflers and catalytic converter. If the components can come in contact with the body or suspension parts, secure the exhaust system with new brackets and hangers.

36   Automatic transmission fluid and filter change

Refer to illustration 36.8

1   At the specified time intervals, the transmission fluid should be drained and replaced. Since the fluid will remain hot long after driving, perform this procedure only after the engine has cooled down completely.

2   Before beginning work, purchase the specified transmission fluid (see *Recommended lubricants and fluids* at the front of this Chapter) and a new filter.

3   Other tools necessary for this job include jackstands to support the vehicle in a raised position, a drain pan capable of holding at least eight pints, newspapers and clean rags.

4   Raise the vehicle and support it securely on jackstands.

5   To provide adequate clearance, unbolt the universal joint flange of the lower driveshaft and pull it aside to the right.

6   With a drain pan in place, remove the pan front and side mounting bolts.

7   Loosen the rear bolts approximately four turns.

8   Carefully pry the transmission pan loose with a screwdriver, allowing the fluid to drain **(see illustration)**.

9   Remove the remaining bolts, pan and gasket. Carefully clean the gasket surface of the transmission to remove all traces of the old gasket and sealant.

10   Drain the fluid from the transmission pan, clean it with solvent and dry it with compressed air.

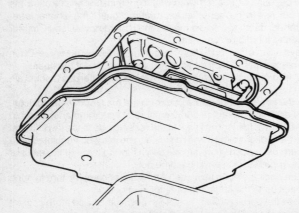

36.8 Carefully pry the transmission pan loose with a screwdriver, allowing the fluid to drain

11   Remove the filter from the mount inside the transmission.

12   Install a new filter and O-ring.

13   Make sure the gasket surface on the transmission pan is clean, then install a new gasket. Put the pan in place against the transmission and, working around the pan, tighten each bolt a little at a time until the torque figure listed in this Chapter's Specifications is reached.

14   Install the universal joint flange.

15   Lower the vehicle and add the specified amount of automatic transmission fluid through the filler tube (see Section 6).

16   With the transmission in Park and the parking brake set, run the engine at a fast idle, but don't race it.

17   Move the gear selector through each range and back to Park. Check the fluid level.

18   Check under the vehicle for leaks during the first few trips.

19   Finalize your automatic transmission fluid level check by driving the vehicle to reach normal operating temperature and then filling to the FULL HOT mark on the dipstick (see Section 6).

37   Manual transmission lubricant change

1   Drive the vehicle for a few miles to thoroughly warm up the transmission oil.

2   Raise the vehicle and support it securely on jackstands.

3   Move a drain pan, rags, newspapers and a wrench under the vehicle. With the drain pan and newspapers in position under the transmission, use the wrench to loosen the drain plug located in the bottom of the transmission case **(see illustrations 19.1a and 19.1b)**.

4   Once loosened, carefully unscrew it with your fingers until you can remove it from the transmission. Allow all of the oil to drain into the pan. If the plug is too hot to touch, use the wrench to remove it.

5   If the transmission is equipped with a magnetic drain plug, see if there are bits of metal clinging to it. If there are, it's a sign of excessive internal wear, indicating that the transmission should be carefully inspected in the near future. If the transmission isn't equipped with a magnetic drain plug, allow the oil in the pan to cool, then feel with your hands along the bottom of the drain pan for debris.

6   Clean the drain plug, then reinstall it in the transmission and tighten it to the torque listed in this Chapter's Specifications.

7   Remove the transmission oil check/fill plug (see Section 19). Using a hand pump or syringe, fill the transmission with the correct amount and grade of oil (see the Specifications), until the level is just at the bottom of the plug hole.

8   Reinstall the check/fill plug and tighten it securely.

38   Transfer case lubricant change

1   Drive the vehicle for at least 15 minutes in 4WD to warm up the oil in the case.

2   Raise the vehicle and support it securely on jackstands. Remove the rock guard.

3   Move a drain pan, rags, newspapers and a wrench under the vehicle.

4   Remove the check/fill plug **(see illustrations 20.1a and 20.1b)**.

5   Remove the drain plug from the lower part of the case and allow the old oil to drain completely.

6   Carefully clean and install the drain plug after the case is completely drained. Tighten the plug securely.

7   Fill the case with the specified lubricant until it's level with the lower edge of the filler hole.

8   Install the check/fill plug and tighten it securely.

9   Lower the vehicle.

10   Check carefully for leaks around the drain plug after the first few miles of driving.

39   Differential lubricant change

Note: *The following procedure can be used for both differentials.*

1   Drive the vehicle for several miles to warm up the differential oil, then raise the vehicle and support it securely on jackstands.

2   Move a drain pan, rags, newspapers and a wrench under the vehicle.

3   With the drain pan under the differential, use the wrench to loosen the drain plug. It's the lower of the two plugs **(see illustrations 21.2a and 21.2b)**.

4   Once loosened, carefully unscrew the plug with your fingers until you can remove it from the case.

5   Allow all of the oil to drain into the pan, then replace the drain plug and tighten it to the torque listed in this Chapter's Specifications.

6   Feel with your hands along the bottom of the drain pan for any metal bits that may have come out with the oil. If there are any, it's a sign of excessive wear, indicating that the internal components should be carefully inspected in the near future.

7   Remove the differential check/fill plug located above the drain plug. Using a hand pump, syringe or funnel, fill the differential with the correct amount and grade of oil (see this Chapter's Specifications) until the level is just at the bottom of the plug hole.

8   Reinstall the plug and tighten it securely.

9   Lower the vehicle. Check for leaks at the drain plug after the first few miles of driving.

40   Fuel filter replacement

Refer to illustrations 40.2 and 40.7

Warning: *Gasoline is extremely flammable, so extra safety precautions must be observed when working on the fuel system. DO NOT smoke or allow open flames or bare light bulbs near the vehicle. Also, don't perform fuel system maintenance procedures in a garage where a natural gas type appliance, such as a water heater or clothes dryer, is present.*

1   This job should be done with the engine cold (after sitting at least three hours). Place a metal container, rags or newspapers under the filter to catch spilled fuel. **Warning:** *Before attempting to remove the fuel filter, disconnect the negative cable from the battery and position it out of the way so it can't accidentally contact the battery post.*

Carburetor equipped models

2   The fuel filter is located under the vehicle near the rear differential **(see illustration)**.

3   To replace the filter, loosen the clamps and slide them down the hoses, past the fittings on the filter.

4   Carefully twist and pull on the hoses to separate them from the filter. If the hoses are in bad shape, now would be a good time to replace them with new ones.

5   Pull the filter out of the clip and install the new one, then hook up the hoses and tighten the clamps securely. Start the engine and check carefully for leaks at the filter hose connections.

Fuel injected models

6   Depressurize the fuel system (see Chapter 4).

7   The fuel filter can be found in the fuel feed line attached to the chassis frame above the upper right hand side of the rear differential **(see illustration)**. To replace the filter, loosen the flange fittings (use two wrenches). Replace the old seals.

8   Note how the filter is installed (which end is facing up) so the new filter doesn't get installed backwards. If the hoses are in bad shape, now would be a good time to replace them with new ones.

9   Remove the filter.

10   Install the new filter in the clamp and tighten the bolts. Make sure the filter is properly oriented – fuel filters usually have an arrow on the canister that indicates the direction of fuel flow.

11   Connect the hoses to the new filter and tighten the fittings securely.

12   Start the engine and check carefully for leaks at the filter hose connections.

41   Exhaust Gas Recirculation (EGR) system check

Refer to illustration 41.2

1   The EGR valve is usually located on the intake manifold, adjacent to the carburetor or TBI unit. Most of the time when a problem develops in this emissions system, it's due to a stuck or corroded EGR valve.

2   With the engine cold to prevent burns, push on the EGR valve diaphragm. Using moderate pressure, you should be able to press the diaphragm in-and-out within the housing **(see illustration)**.

3   If the diaphragm doesn't move or moves only with much effort, replace the EGR valve with a new one. If in doubt about the condition of the valve, compare the free movement of your EGR valve with a new valve.

4   Refer to Chapter 6 for more information on the EGR system.

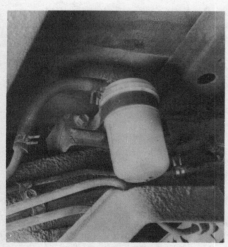

40.2   The fuel filter is located under the vehicle on the frame, near the rear axle (Samurai)

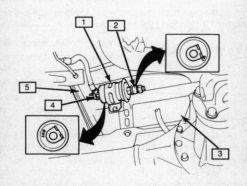

40.7   Sidekick/Tracker fuel filter location

1   *Fuel filter assembly*
2   *Fuel filter inlet*
3   *Fuel tank*
4   *Fuel filter outlet*
5   *Chassis frame (passenger side)*

41.2   To check the EGR valve, reach under it and push on the diaphragm (arrow) with a finger – it should move smoothly within the housing

42.1   Locate the positive crankcase ventilation valve (PCV valve) on the intake manifold (arrow)

45.2   The charcoal canister functions as a holding tank for fuel vapors – inspect it periodically as indicated in the maintenance schedule (Samurai shown)

42   Positive Crankcase Ventilation (PCV) valve check and replacement

Refer to illustration 42.1

1   The PCV valve threads into the intake manifold and is connected by a rubber hose to the camshaft cover **(see illustration)**.
2   When purchasing a replacement PCV valve, make sure it's the correct one for your vehicle.
3   Loosen the clamp securing the hose to the PCV valve and disconnect the hose from the valve.
4   Unscrew the valve from the intake manifold.
5   Compare the old valve with the new one to make sure they're the same.
6   Screw the new valve into the manifold and connect the hose to it.
7   More information on the PCV system can be found in Chapter 6.

43   Fuel tank cap gasket replacement

1   Obtain a new gasket.
2   Remove the tank cap and carefully pry the old gasket out of the recess. Be very careful not to damage the sealing surface inside the cap.
3   Work the new gasket into the cap recess.
4   Install the cap, then remove it and make sure the gasket seals all the way around.

44   Brake fluid replacement

1   Because brake fluid absorbs moisture which could ultimately cause corrosion of the brake components, and air which could make the braking system less effective, the fluid should be replaced at the specified intervals. This job can be accomplished for a nominal fee by a properly equipped brake shop using a pressure bleeder. The task can also be done by the home mechanic with the help of an assistant. To bleed the air and old fluid and replace it with fresh fluid from sealed containers, refer to the brake bleeding procedure in Chapter 9.
2   If there is any possibility that incorrect fluid has been used in the system, drain all the fluid and flush the system with brake cleaner. Replace all piston seals and cups, as they will be affected and could possibly fail under pressure.

45   Evaporative emissions control system check and canister replacement

Refer to illustration 45.2

1   The function of the evaporative emissions control system is to draw fuel vapors from the gas tank and fuel system, store them in a charcoal canister and route them to the intake manifold during normal engine operation.
2   The most common symptom of a fault in the evaporative emissions system is a strong fuel odor in the engine compartment. If a fuel odor is detected, inspect the charcoal canister and all hoses for damage and deterioration **(see illustration)**.
3   At the specified intervals, the charcoal canister must be replaced with a new one. Label the hoses and fittings, disconnect the hoses, unbolt the bracket from the firewall and lift the canister from the engine compartment. Installation is the reverse of removal.
4   The evaporative emissions control system is explained in more detail in Chapter 6.

46   Ignition timing check and adjustment

Refer to illustrations 46.1 and 46.3
Note: *If the information in this Section differs from the Vehicle Emission Control Information label in the engine compartment of the vehicle, the label should be considered correct.*

1   Some special tools are required for this procedure **(see illustration)**. The engine must be at normal operating temperature and the air conditioner must be Off.
2   Apply the parking brake and block the wheels to prevent movement of the vehicle. The transmission must be in Park (automatic) or Neutral (manual).
3   Locate the timing marks at the front of the engine (they should be visible from above after the hood is opened) **(see illustration)**. The crankshaft pulley has a notch in it and a plate with raised numbers is attached to the timing cover. Clean the plate with solvent so the numbers are visible.
4   Use chalk or white paint to mark the notch in the pulley.
5   Highlight the point on the timing plate that corresponds to the ignition timing specification on the Vehicle Emission Control Information label.
6   Hook up the timing light by following the manufacturer's instructions (an inductive pick-up timing light is preferred). Generally, the power leads

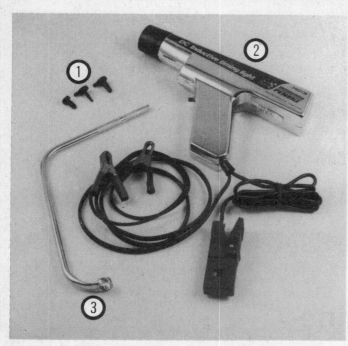

46.1 Tools needed to check and adjust the ignition timing

1 *Vacuum plugs* – *Vacuum hoses will, in most cases, have to be disconnected and plugged. Molded plugs in various shapes and sizes are available for this.*
2 *Inductive pick-up timing light* – *Flashes a bright concentrated beam of light when the number one spark plug fires. Connect the leads according to the instructions supplied with the light.*
3 *Distributor wrench* – *On some models, the hold-down bolt for the distributor is difficult to reach and turn with conventional wrenches or sockets. A special wrench like this must be used.*

are attached to the battery terminals and the pick-up lead is attached to the number one spark plug wire. The number one spark plug is the one closest to the drivebelt end of the engine. **Caution:** *If an inductive pick-up timing light isn't available, don't puncture the spark plug wire to attach the timing light pick-up lead. Instead, use an adapter between the spark plug and plug wire. If the insulation on the plug wire is damaged, the secondary voltage will jump to ground at the damaged point and the engine will misfire.*
7 Make sure the timing light wires are routed away from the drivebelts and fan, then start the engine.
8 Allow the idle speed to stabilize, then point the flashing timing light at the timing marks – be very careful of moving engine components!
9 The mark on the pulley will appear stationary. If it's aligned with the specified point on the timing plate, the ignition timing is correct.
10 If the marks aren't aligned, adjustment is required. Loosen the distributor mounting nut and turn the distributor very slowly until the marks are aligned.
11 Tighten the nut and recheck the timing.
12 Turn off the engine and remove the timing light (and adapter, if used).

47 Carburetor/throttle body mounting nut torque check

1 The carburetor or TBI unit is attached to the top of the intake manifold by several bolts or nuts. The fasteners can sometimes work loose from vibration and temperature changes during normal engine operation and cause a vacuum leak.
2 If you suspect that a vacuum leak exists at the bottom of the carburetor or throttle body, obtain a two-foot length of fuel line hose. Start the en-

46.3 The ignition timing marks are located at the front of the engine

gine and place one end of the hose next to your ear as you probe around the base with the other end. You'll hear a hissing sound if a leak exists (be careful of hot or moving engine components).
3 Remove the air cleaner assembly, tagging each hose that's disconnected with a piece of numbered tape to make reassembly easier.
4 Locate the mounting nuts or bolts at the base of the carburetor or throttle body. Decide what special tools or adapters will be necessary, if any, to tighten the fasteners.
5 Tighten the nuts or bolts to the torque listed in this Chapter's specifications. Don't overtighten them, as the threads could strip.

48 Oxygen sensor replacement

Refer to illustration 48.2

1 The oxygen (exhaust gas) sensor, used on all 1986 and later models, should be replaced at the intervals specified in the *Maintenance schedule* at the beginning of this Chapter.
2 The sensor is threaded into the exhaust manifold and can be identified by the wires attached to it **(see illustration)**. Replacement consists of disconnecting the wire harness and unthreading the sensor from the manifold. Before installing it in the manifold, coat the threads with an anti-seize compound. Tighten the sensor to the torque listed in this Chapter's Specifications, then reconnect the wire harness. A special oxygen sensor socket, which can be purchased at most auto parts stores, should be used.

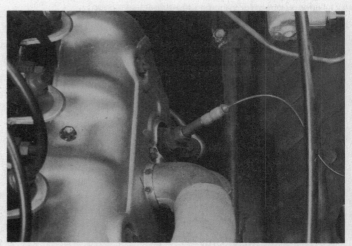

48.2 To remove the oxygen sensor, disconnect the wire and unscrew the sensor from the exhaust manifold

Chapter 2 Part A   Engine

Contents

Specifications

General

Firing order	1-3-4-2
Cylinder numbers (drivebelt end-to-transmission end)	1-2-3-4

Cylinder head

Warpage limit	0.002 in (0.5 mm)

Oil pump

Outer gear-to-oil pump housing clearance lim	0.0122 in (0.310 mm)
Gear end play limit	0.0059 in (0.15 mm)
Pressure relief spring free length	1.77 in (45 mm)

Rocker arms and shafts

Rocker shaft diameter	0.628 to 0.629 in (15.973 to 15.988 mm)
Rocker arm inside diameter	0.629 to 0.630 in (16.000 to 16.018 mm)
Shaft-to-arm clearance	
Standard	
8-valve engine	0.0005 to 0.0017 in (0.012 to 0.045 mm)
16-valve engine	0.0001 to 0.0014 in (0.012 to 0.045 mm)
Service limit	0.0035 in (0.09 mm)

Torque specifications

	Ft-lbs
Camshaft cover bolts	3 to 3.5
Intake/exhaust manifold nuts/bolts	13.5 to 20

Torque specifications (continued)

	Ft-lbs
Camshaft sprocket bolt	41 to 46
Cylinder head bolts	
8-valve engine	46 to 50
16-valve engine	
Step 1	25
Step 2	40
Step 3	48 to 50
Crankshaft pulley bolts	7.5 to 9
Crankshaft pulley center bolt	52
8-valve engine	52
16-valve engine	76 to 83
Oil pump gear plate bolts	7.0 to 8.5
Oil pump-to-block bolts	7.0 to 8.5
Oil pan bolts/nuts	7.0 to 8.5
Flywheel/driveplate bolts	58
Timing belt cover	7.0 to 8.5
Rear main oil seal housing bolts	8
Rocker arm shaft retaining screws	7 to 8.5
Timing belt tensioner bolt	17.5 to 21.5
Timing belt tensioner nut	7 to 8.5

2A

1 General information

This Part of Chapter 2 is devoted to in-vehicle repair procedures for the engine. All information concerning engine removal and installation and engine block and cylinder head overhaul can be found in Part B of this Chapter.

Models through 1991 are equiped with an 8-valve engine (two valves per cylinder). Some 1992 and later models are equiped with a 16-valve engine (four valves per cylinder). Other than the valve components, the two engines are very similar.

The following repair procedures are based on the assumption that the engine is installed in the vehicle. If the engine has been removed from the vehicle and mounted on a stand, many of the steps outlined in this Part of Chapter 2 will not apply.

The Specifications included in this Part of Chapter 2 apply only to the procedures contained in this Part. Part B of Chapter 2 contains the Specifications necessary for cylinder head and engine block rebuilding.

2 Repair operations possible with the engine in the vehicle

Many major repair operations can be accomplished without removing the engine from the vehicle.

Clean the engine compartment and the exterior of the engine with some type of degreaser before any work is done. It will make the job easier and help keep dirt out of the internal areas of the engine.

Depending on the components involved, it may be helpful to remove the hood to improve access to the engine as repairs are performed (see Chapter 11, if necessary). Cover the fenders to prevent damage to the paint. Special pads are available, but an old bedspread or blanket will also work.

If vacuum, exhaust, oil or coolant leaks develop, indicating a need for gasket or seal replacement, the repairs can generally be made with the engine in the vehicle. The intake and exhaust manifold gaskets, oil pan gasket, crankshaft oil seals and cylinder head gasket are all accessible with the engine in place.

Exterior engine components, such as the intake and exhaust manifolds, the oil pan (and the oil pump), the water pump, the starter motor, the alternator, the distributor and the fuel system components can be removed for repair with the engine in place.

Since the cylinder head can be removed without pulling the engine, valve component servicing can also be accomplished with the engine in the vehicle. Replacement of the camshaft, timing belt and sprockets is also possible with the engine in the vehicle.

In extreme cases caused by a lack of necessary equipment, repair or replacement of piston rings, pistons, connecting rods and rod bearings is possible with the engine in the vehicle. However, this practice is not recommended because of the cleaning and preparation work that must be done to the components involved.

3 Top Dead Center (TDC) for number one piston – locating

Refer to illustrations 3.6, 3.8 and 3.9

Note: *The following procedure is based on the assumption that the spark plug wires and distributor are correctly installed. If you are trying to locate TDC to install the distributor correctly, piston position must be determined by feeling for compression at the number one spark plug hole, then aligning the ignition timing marks as described in step 8.*

1   Top Dead Center (TDC) is the highest point in the cylinder that each piston reaches as it travels up-and-down when the crankshaft turns. Each piston reaches TDC on the compression stroke and again on the exhaust stroke, but TDC generally refers to piston position on the compression stroke.

2   Positioning the piston(s) at TDC is an essential part of many procedures such as rocker arm removal, camshaft and timing belt/sprocket removal and distributor removal.

3   Before beginning this procedure, be sure to place the transmission in Neutral and apply the parking brake or block the rear wheels. Also, disable the ignition system by detaching the coil wire from the center terminal of the distributor cap and grounding it on the block with a jumper wire. Remove the spark plugs (see Chapter 1).

4   In order to bring any piston to TDC, the crankshaft must be turned using one of the methods outlined below. When looking at the front of the engine, normal crankshaft rotation is clockwise.

   a) The preferred method is to turn the crankshaft with a socket and ratchet attached to the bolt threaded into the front of the crankshaft.

   b) A remote starter switch, which may save some time, can also be used. Follow the instructions included with the switch. Once the piston is close to TDC, use a socket and ratchet as described in the previous paragraph.

   c) If an assistant is available to turn the ignition switch to the Start position in short bursts, you can get the piston close to TDC without a remote starter switch. Make sure your assistant is out of the vehicle, away from the ignition switch, then use a socket and ratchet as described in Paragraph a) to complete the procedure.

5   Note the position of the terminal for the number one spark plug wire on the distributor cap. If the wire isn't marked, follow the plug wire from the number one cylinder spark plug to the cap.

3.6 Make a mark on the distributor housing below the number one terminal on the cap

3.8 Turn the crankshaft until the notch in the pulley is aligned with the O on the timing belt cover (arrows)

3.9 When the number one piston is at Top Dead Center on the compression stroke, the rotor should point toward the mark you made on the distributor

4.5a Camshaft cover bolt locations (8-valve engine)

6   Use a felt-tip pen or chalk to make a mark on the distributor body directly under the terminal (**see illustration**).

7   Detach the cap from the distributor and set it aside (see Chapter 1 if necessary).

8   Turn the crankshaft clockwise (see Paragraph 3 above) until the notch in the crankshaft pulley is aligned with the 0 on the timing plate (located at the front of the engine) (**see illustration**).

9   Look at the distributor rotor – it should be pointing directly at the mark you made on the distributor body (**see illustration**). If it is, go to Step 12.

10   If the rotor is 180-degrees off, the number one piston is at TDC on the exhaust stroke. Go to Step 11.

11   To get the piston to TDC on the compression stroke, turn the crankshaft one complete turn (360-degrees) clockwise. The rotor should now be pointing at the mark on the distributor. When the rotor is pointing at the number one spark plug wire terminal in the distributor cap and the ignition timing marks are aligned, the number one piston is at TDC on the compression stroke.

12   After the number one piston has been positioned at TDC on the compression stroke, TDC for any of the remaining pistons can be located by turning the crankshaft and following the firing order. Mark the remaining spark plug wire terminal locations on the distributor body just like you did for the number one terminal, then number the marks to correspond with the cylinder numbers. As you turn the crankshaft, the rotor will also turn. When it's pointing directly at one of the marks on the distributor, the piston for that particular cylinder is at TDC on the compression stroke.

4   Camshaft cover – removal and installation

Refer to illustrations 4.5a and 4.5b

1   Disconnect the negative cable from the battery.

2   On throttle body fuel-injected models, remove the air intake case from the throttle body (see Chapter 4). On multi-port fuel-injected models, remove the air intake pipe.

3   On multi-port fuel-injected models, remove the PCV hose from the camshaft cover. Also on multi-port fuel-injected models, disconnect the accelerator and (if equipped) cruise control cables from the throttle body.

4   Detach the spark plug wires from the plugs, unclip the wire loom from the top of the cover, then set the wires aside, leaving them attached to the loom. Disconnect the breather hose from the camshaft cover.

5   Remove the camshaft cover bolts and lift the cover off (**see illustrations**). If the cover sticks to the cylinder head, tap on it with a soft-face hammer or place a block of wood against the cover and tap on the wood with a hammer.

6   Thoroughly clean the camshaft cover and remove all traces of old gasket material. On 16-valve engines, be sure to remove the spark plug opening O-rings.

7   Install a new gasket and, if equipped, O-rings on the cover, using RTV to hold them in place. Place new grommets, if equipped, in the bolt holes in the cover, install the cover, then install the bolts.

8   Working from the center out, tighten the bolts to the torque listed in this Chapter's Specifications.

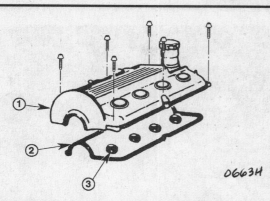

4.5b Camshaft cover mounting details (16-valve engines)

1 Camshaft cover	3 O-rings
2 Gasket	

5.4 Label the connections before detaching them

5.9 The intake manifold has eight mounting bolts/nuts — four upper (arrows) and four lower (hidden by the manifold in this photo)

9 The remaining steps are the reverse of removal. When finished, run the engine and check for oil leaks.

5 Intake manifold – removal and installation

Refer to illustrations 5.4, 5.9 and 5.10
Note: *The intake manifold can be removed with the throttle body and plenum assembly still attached. If, however, you plan to remove the plenum and throttle body anyway (for example, if you're replacing the manifold), it may be easier to remove the throttle body and intake plenum before you begin removing the manifold (see Chapter 4 for the throttle body and plenum removal procedures).*

1 Disconnect the negative cable from the battery and relieve the fuel injection system pressure (see Chapter 4).
2 Drain the cooling system (see Chapter 1). If the coolant is in good condition it can be reused.
3 Remove the air cleaner (carbureted models), air intake case (throttle body fuel-injected models) or disconnect the air intake pipe (multi-port fuel-injected models) (see Chapter 4).
4 Clearly label, then disconnect all hoses, wires, brackets and emission lines which run to the carburetor/throttle body and intake manifold **(see illustration)**.
5 Disconnect the fuel lines and cap the fittings to prevent leakage (see Chapter 4). On carbureted models, disconnect the line at the carburetor. On throttle body fuel-injected models, disconnect the lines at the throttle body assembly. On multi-port fuel-injected models, it may be necessary to raise the vehicle and support it securely on jackstands, since the line connections are usually at the lower rear of the engine compartment. Also, on multi-port fuel-injected models, use a back-up wrench when disconnecting the fuel feed line.

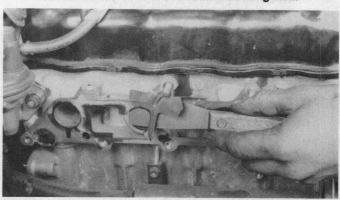

5.10 Remove all traces of old gasket material – scrape gently to avoid gouging the aluminum

6 Disconnect the throttle cable from the carburetor/throttle body (see Chapter 4).
7 Detach the cable which runs from the carburetor/throttle body to the transmission (automatic transmission only) and the cruise control cable, on vehicles so equipped.
8 On multi-port fuel-injected models, unbolt and remove the three brackets that attach the intake manifold/intake plenum assembly to the engine.
9 Using a socket, ratchet and long extension, unscrew the bolts and nuts and remove the intake manifold from the engine **(see illustration)**. If it sticks, tap the manifold with a soft-face hammer. **Caution:** *Do not pry between gasket sealing surfaces or tap on the carburetor/throttle body. If there are any clamps under the bolts or nuts, note their locations before you remove them so they can be returned to their original locations.*
10 Thoroughly clean the manifold and cylinder head mating surfaces, removing all traces of gasket material **(see illustration)**. Be very careful not to scratch or gouge the delicate aluminum gasket surfaces on the manifold and cylinder head. Gasket removal solvents are available from auto parts stores and may prove helpful.
11 Install the manifold, using a new gasket and tighten the bolts and nuts in several stages, working from the center out, until you reach the torque listed this Chapter's Specifications.
12 Reinstall the remaining parts in the reverse order of removal.
13 Add coolant, run the engine and check for leaks and proper operation.

6 Exhaust manifold – removal and installation

Refer to illustrations 6.6, 6.7 and 6.11
Warning: *Allow the engine to cool completely before following this procedure.*
1 Disconnect the negative cable from the battery.
2 Set the parking brake and block the rear wheels. Raise the front of the vehicle and support it securely on jackstands.

2A

6.6   Apply penetrating oil and remove the nuts/bolts (arrows),
then remove the heat shields from the manifold

6.7   Remove the exhaust manifold nuts/bolts (arrows) – three of
the lower ones are hidden from view in this photo

6.11   Slip the gasket over the studs with the spark plug wells
facing outward

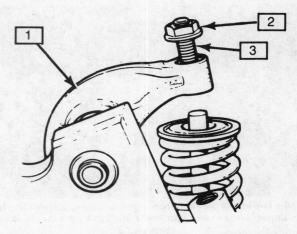

7.4   On 8-valve engines, loosen the locknut and back off the
valve adjustment screw

1 Rocker arm	3 Adjustment screw
2 Locknut	

3   Working from under the vehicle, remove the nuts that secure the exhaust system to the bottom of the exhaust manifold. Apply penetrating oil
to the threads to make removal easier.
4   On fuel injected models, remove the air cleaner assembly (see Chapter 4).
5   Unplug the oxygen sensor wire (see Chapter 1).
6   Remove the fasteners that secure the heat shields to the exhaust
manifold and to each other (see illustration). Remove the heat shields.
7   Apply penetrating oil to the threads, then remove the exhaust manifold mounting nuts/bolts (see illustration).
8   Slip the manifold off the studs and remove it from the engine compartment.
9   Clean and inspect all threaded fasteners and repair as necessary.
10   Remove all traces of gasket material from the mating surfaces and
inspect them for wear and cracks.
11   Install a new gasket (see illustration), install the manifold and tighten
the nuts in several stages, working from the center out, to the torque listed
in this Chapter's Specifications.
12   Reinstall the remaining parts in the reverse order of removal.
13   Run the engine and check for exhaust leaks.

7   Timing belt and sprockets – removal, inspection and installation

Removal

Refer to illustrations 7.4, 7.8a, 7.8b, 7.8c, 7.9, 7.10, 7.11, 7.14, 7.15a, and
7.15b

Warning: The air conditioning system is under high pressure. Do not loos-
en any fittings or remove any components until after the system has been
discharged by an air conditioning technician. Always wear eye protection
when disconnecting refrigerant fittings.

Caution 1: Do not try to turn the crankshaft with the camshaft sprocket bolt
and do not rotate the crankshaft counterclockwise.

Caution 2: Do not bend, twist or turn the timing belt inside out. Do not allow
it to come in contact with oil, coolant or fuel. Do not utilize timing belt tension to keep the camshaft or crankshaft from turning when installing the
pulley bolt(s). Do not turn the crankshaft or camshaft more than a few degrees (necessary for tooth alignment) while the timing belt is removed.

1   On air conditioned models, if necessary for clearance, have the refrigerant discharged by an air conditioning technician (see Warning above),
then detach the hose from the suction pipe on the compressor (the suction
pipe is the larger diameter pipe).
2   Position the number one piston at Top Dead Center (see Section 3).
3   Disconnect the negative cable from the battery.
4   On 8-valve engines, remove the camshaft cover (see Section 4).
Loosen the locknuts and back off the valve adjustment screws until they're
not in contact with the valves (see illustration).
5   Set the parking brake and block the rear wheels. Raise the front of the
vehicle and support it securely on jackstands.
6   Loosen the four water pump pulley nuts, then remove the drivebelts
(see Chapter 1).

7.8a Samurai crankshaft pulley mounting details

1   Crankshaft pulley bolts   3   Center bolt
2   Indexing notch

7.8c   Wrap duct tape or a rag around the pulley and grip it with a
chain wrench

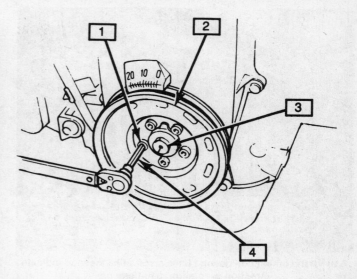

7.8b   Sidekick/Tracker crankshaft pulley mounting details

1   Crankshaft pulley bolt   4   5 mm hex drive (used to
2   Crankshaft pulley   remove the pulley bolts)
3   Center bolt

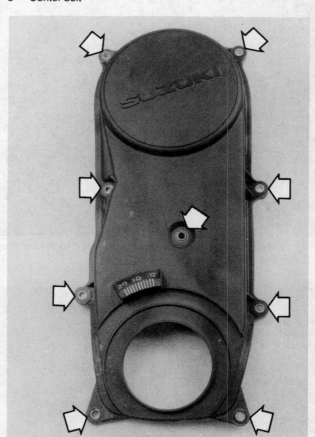

7.9   Timing belt cover bolt locations (arrows) – cover removed
for clarity

7   Remove the fan, fan shroud and water pump pulley (see Chapter 3).
8   Remove the crankshaft pulley bolts (see illustrations). Note: If
you're only replacing the timing belt, it's not necessary to remove the
crankshaft center bolt; however, if you will be removing the crankshaft
sprocket to replace the oil pump or oil seal, you must remove the center
bolt. Do this before you remove the pulley bolts. The center bolt is very
tight, so, to break it loose, remove the splash pan from beneath the front of

the engine, wrap a rag or duct tape around the pulley and attach a chain
wrench to hold the pulley in place (see illustration). Use a breaker bar
and socket to loosen the bolt.
9   Remove the bolts that secure the timing belt cover and lift the cover off
(see illustration).

2A

7.10   If the timing belt doesn't have arrows like these to indicate direction of rotation, paint one on

7.11   Loosen the adjusting nut and pulley bolt and move the tensioner pulley as far as possible towards the water pump

A	Adjusting nut	C	Tensioner pulley
B	Pulley bolt		

10   If you plan to reuse the timing belt, and it doesn't already have arrows painted on it, paint one on to indicate the direction of rotation (clockwise) **(see illustration)**.

11   Loosen the adjusting nut and pulley bolt. Move the tensioner pulley towards the water pump as far as possible **(see illustration)**.

12   Temporarily secure the tensioner pulley by tightening the adjusting nut.

13   Slip the timing belt off the sprockets and set it aside.

14   If you intend to replace the oil pump or crankshaft front oil seal, slide off the crankshaft sprocket and the belt guide located behind the crankshaft sprocket **(see illustration)**. When removing the guide, note the way it's installed (the chamfered side faces out).

15   If you intend to replace the camshaft oil seal, unscrew the camshaft sprocket securing bolt and slide the sprocket off – a large screwdriver inserted through a hole in the sprocket will keep it from turning while you remove the bolt **(see illustration)**. Unbolt the cover **(see illustration)** to get at the seal.

Inspection

Refer to illustrations 7.16 and 7.17

16   Rotate the tensioner pulley by hand and move it from side-to-side to detect roughness and excess play **(see illustration)**. Visually inspect the sprockets for any signs of damage and wear. Replace parts as necessary.

7.14   The belt guide has a notch which allows it to fit over the crankshaft key (arrows)

7.15a   Hold the camshaft sprocket from turning with a large screwdriver

7.15b   To get to the camshaft seal, remove the two mounting bolts and detach the cover (arrows)

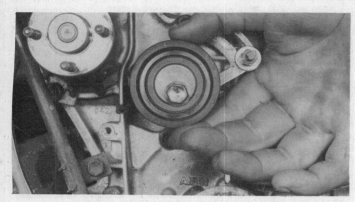

7.16   Check the tensioner pulley for roughness and excess play

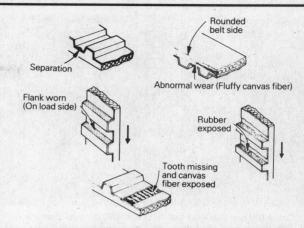

7.17   Carefully inspect the timing belt for the conditions shown here

2A

7.18a   The camshaft sprocket is indexed by a dowel (arrow)

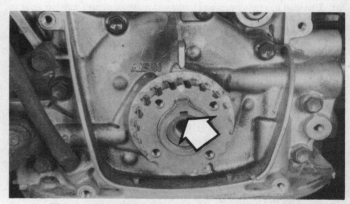

7.18b   The crankshaft sprocket has a slot (keyway) which must align with the key in the crankshaft

7.19a   The mark on the lower timing belt sprocket must align with the mark on the engine front cover (arrows)

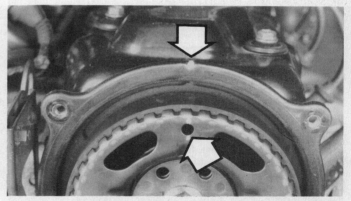

7.19b   The timing mark on the camshaft sprocket must align with the V mark on the camshaft seal cover (arrows)

17 Inspect the timing belt for cracks, separation, wear, missing teeth and oil contamination (see illustration). Replace the belt if it's worn or damaged. **Note:** *Unless the engine has very low mileage, it's common practice to replace the timing belt with a new one every time it's removed. Don't reinstall the original belt unless it's in like-new condition. Never reinstall a belt in questionable condition.*

Installation
Refer to illustrations 7.18a, 7.18b, 7.19a and 7.19b
Note: *Earlier models use timing belts with squared-off teeth, while later models have rounded teeth on the belt. Be sure to use the correct belt type, since it must match the pulleys.*

18 Reinstall the camshaft seal cover and timing belt sprockets, if they were removed. Note that the camshaft sprocket is indexed by a dowel (see illustration). Slip the belt guide onto the crankshaft before installing the crankshaft sprocket—the chamfered side of the guide faces away from the belt. The crankshaft sprocket has a keyway which matches the key on the crankshaft (see illustration).
19 Align the valve timing marks located on the camshaft and crankshaft sprockets (see illustrations). **Note:** *On 16-valve engines, there's an "E" adjacent to the timing mark.*
20 Slip the timing belt onto the crankshaft sprocket. While maintaining tension on the side of the belt opposite to the tensioner, slip the belt onto the camshaft sprocket.

8.2   Carefully pry the seal out with a small screwdriver – wrap the tip with tape to prevent damaging the seal bore and crankshaft sealing surface

8.4   Install the new seal by gently tapping it into place with a socket and a small hammer

21   Release the tensioner adjusting nut to allow spring tension against the belt. Rotate the crankshaft clockwise two complete revolutions (720-degrees). Retighten the nut.

22   Temporarily install the crankshaft pulley, taking care to align the notch in the pulley with the raised area on the sprocket. Install the crankshaft pulley bolts and the center bolt, if removed. Tighten the center bolt to the torque listed in this Chapter's Specifications. When tightening the bolts, hold the crankshaft in place using the method discussed in Step 8. Remove the pulley, leaving the center bolt in place.

23   Using the bolt in the center of the crankshaft sprocket, turn the crankshaft clockwise through two complete revolutions (720-degrees). Recheck the alignment of the valve timing marks. If the marks do not align properly, loosen the tensioner, slip the belt off the camshaft sprocket, align the marks, reinstall the belt, and check the alignment again.

24   Tighten the tensioner bolt and nut to the torque listed in this Chapter's Specifications. Start with the nut, then tighten the bolt.

25   Reinstall the remaining parts in the reverse order of removal.

26   On eight-valve engines, set the valve clearancees with the engine cold (see Chapter 1).

27   Start the engine, allow it to reach normal operating temperature, set the ignition timing and, on eight-valve engines, check the valve clearance (see Chapter 1). Road test the vehicle.

---

8   Crankshaft front oil seal – replacement

Refer to illustrations 8.2 and 8.4

1   Remove the timing belt, crankshaft sprocket and inner belt guide (see Section 7).

2   Wrap the tip of a small screwdriver with tape. Working from below, use the screwdriver to pry the seal out of its bore (see illustration). Take care to prevent damaging the crankshaft and the seal bore.

3   Thoroughly clean and inspect the seal bore and sealing surface on the crankshaft. Minor imperfections can be removed with emery cloth. If there is a groove worn in the crankshaft sealing surface (from contact with the seal), installing a new seal will probably not stop the leak. Try installing a repair sleeve which fits over the crankshaft sealing surface. These are normally available at larger auto parts stores.

4   Lubricate the new seal with engine oil and drive the seal into place with a hammer and socket (see illustration).

5   Reinstall the timing belt and related components as described in Section 7.

6   Run the engine, checking for oil leaks.

---

9   Camshaft oil seal – replacement

Refer to illustrations 9.3 and 9.5

1   Remove the timing belt, camshaft sprocket and camshaft seal cover (see Section 7).

9.2   Carefully pry the camshaft oil seal out with a small screwdriver – wrap the tip with tape to prevent damaging the seal bore and camshaft sealing surface

2   Note how far the seal is seated in the bore, then carefully pry it out with a small screwdriver (see illustration). Wrap the tip of the screwdriver with tape so you don't scratch the bore or damage the camshaft in the process (if the camshaft is damaged, the new seal will end up leaking).

3   Clean the bore and coat the outer edge of the new seal with engine oil or multi-purpose grease. Apply moly-base grease to the seal lip.

4   Using a socket with an outside diameter slightly smaller than the outside diameter of the seal, carefully drive the new seal into place with a hammer (see illustration). Make sure it's installed squarely and driven in to the same depth as the original. If a socket isn't available, a short section of pipe will also work.

5   Reinstall the seal cover, camshaft sprocket and timing belt (see Section 7).

6   Run the engine and check for oil leaks at the camshaft seal.

---

10   Rocker arms and shafts – removal, inspection and installation

---

Note: *This procedure also includes camshaft removal and installation on 16-valve engines.*

Removal

1   Disconnect the negative cable from the battery.

2   Remove the radiator (see Chapter 3).

3   Set the number one piston at top dead center and remove the camshaft cover (see Sections 3 and 4).

4   Loosen the locknuts and back off the valve adjustment screws until they're not in contact with the valves (see illustration 7.4).

5   Remove the timing belt and camshaft sprocket (see Section 7).

9.4 Gently tap the new oil seal into place with a socket and a small hammer

10.6 Remove the ten retaining screws (arrows)

10.8 Push the rear of the rocker arm shaft until it protrudes enough at the front to grip it

10.9 Slowly pull the shaft out the front of the cylinder head

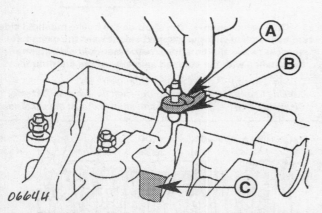

10.16 Detaching an intake valve rocker arm (16-valve engines)

A Intake rocker arm C Rocker arm shaft
B Clip

Eight-valve engines

Refer to illustrations 10.6, 10.8 and 10.9

6 Remove the ten rocker arm shaft retaining screws (see illustration).

7 Number the rocker arms with a scribe. Start with number one at the front and criss-cross until all are marked. When you are done, the rocker arms on the intake manifold side should be numbered 1, 3, 5, 7 and the ones on the exhaust manifold side should be marked 2, 4, 6, 8.

8 Push the rear of one rocker arm shaft until it protrudes enough at the front to grip (see illustration).

9 Slowly pull each rocker arm shaft out the front of the engine (see illustration). Lift the rocker arms and springs out of the head as they are released from the shaft.

Sixteen-valve engines

Refer to illustrations 10.16 and 10.19

10 Remove the radiator grille (see Chapter 11) and remove the hood latch and front upper member (the long, narrow panel the hood latch is attached to).

11 Remove the distributor (see Chapter 5) and housing (see Cylinder head – disassembly in Chapter 2B). **Note:** *Position a drain pan under the housing before removing it, since a small amount of oil usually flows out when the housing is removed.*

12 Remove the camshaft cover, timing belt and camshaft sprocket (see Sections 4 and 7).

13 Reverse the order shown in illustration 10.24 to loosen the camshaft bearing cap bolts, until they are all loose, then remove them and lift the camshaft bearing caps and camshaft off the cylinder head. **Note:** *The camshaft bearing caps must be installed in their original locations, with the same ends facing forward. The caps should be numbered and an arrow on each cap should point toward the front of the engine. If the caps are not marked, mark them before disassembly.*

14 Remove the timing belt inner cover and, using a hex-drive tool, unscrew the rocker arm shaft plug from the front of the cylinder head.

15 Mark the intake and exhaust rocker arms so they can be returned to their original locations on reassembly.

16 Taking care not to bend the clips, remove the intake rocker arms. Keep the rocker arms in order so they can be reinstalled in their original positions (see illustration).

17 Remove the rocker arm shaft bolts, which are at the top of the cylinder head, just above the rocker arm shaft.

18 Push the rocker arm shaft out of the cylinder head, toward the distributor opening, and detach the O-ring on the end of the shaft. Install a new O-ring when reinstalling the shaft.

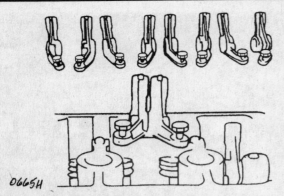

0665H

10.19 The proper relationship of the exhaust rocker arms (16-valve engines)

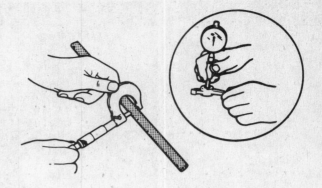

10.21a   Measure the inside diameter of the rocker arms and the outside diameter of the rocker arm shafts (8-valve engine shown, 16-valve engine similar)

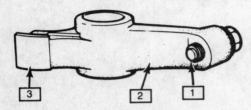

10.21b   Inspect the tips of the valve adjusting screws and the cam-riding faces (8-valve engine shown, 16-valve engine similar)

1	Valve adjusting screw	3	Cam—riding face
2	Rocker arm		

19   Slowly pull the rocker arm shaft out the front of the engine. Lift the exhaust valve rocker arms and wave washers out of the head as they are released from the shaft. Keep the rocker arms and washers in order **(see illustration)**.

Inspection

Refer to illustrations 10.21a and 10.21b

Note: Camshaft inspection procedures and specifications are in Part B of this Chapter.

20   Thoroughly clean the parts in solvent and wipe them off with a lint-free cloth. On 16-valve engines, be sure to clean the camshaft bearing cap mating surfaces and camshaft saddles in the cylinder head.
21   Measure the inside diameter of each rocker arm and the outside diameter of the shaft where the rocker arm rides **(see illustration)**. Compare the measurements to this Chapter's Specifications. Subtract the rocker arm shaft diameter from the rocker arm inside diameter to calculate the shaft-to-arm clearance. Visually inspect the rocker arms for wear **(see illustration)** and the springs (if equipped) for wear and damage. Replace any components that are not within specifications, damaged or excessively worn.

Installation

Refer to illustrations 10.23 and 10.24

22   Thoroughly lubricate the shafts, rocker arms and camshaft journals and lobes (16-valve engines) with engine assembly lube.
23   Slowly push a rocker arm shaft into the cylinder head while guiding it into the rocker arms and springs or washers. Note the rocker arm markings and be sure to install them in the same positions they were in originally. On eight-valve engines, note that the shafts are different and must be installed with the stepped sides facing the correct direction **(see illustration)**. On 16-valve engines, make sure the shaft is rotated so the flattened area on the front end of the shaft is facing down and is parallel with the head gasket surface.
24   On 16-valve engines, install the intake rocker arms, then the camshaft and bearing caps. Apply a thin layer of anaerobic sealant to the rear

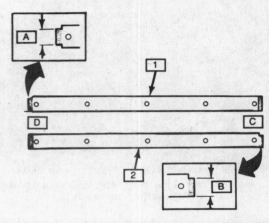

10.23   On 8-valve engines, The shaft on the intake manifold side must be installed with the stepped side toward the camshaft sprocket – the shaft on the exhaust manifold side must be installed with the stepped side toward the distributor

A	0.55 in (14 mm)	D	Camshaft sprocket side
B	0.59 in (15 mm)	1	Rocker arm shaft (intake manifold side)
C	Distributor side	2	Rocker arm shaft (exhaust manifold side)

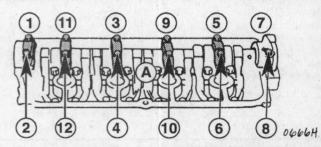

0666H

10.24 Camshaft bearing cap bolt TIGHTENING sequence (16-valve engines)

bearing cap before installation. Tighten the camshaft bearing cap bolts, in the sequence shown **(see illustration)** to the torque listed in the Part B Specifications.
25   When all the rocker arm components are positioned correctly, install the retaining screws and tighten them to the torque listed in this Chapter's Specifications. You may have to rotate the shafts to get the bolt holes to line up.
26   Adjust the valves as described in Chapter 1.
27   Install the remaining components in the reverse order of removal.

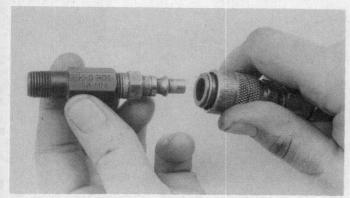

11.4 This is what the air hose adapter that threads into the spark plug hole looks like – they're commonly available from auto parts stores

11.9 Compress the spring enough to release the keepers (arrows)

11.17 Apply a small dab of grease to each keeper before installation to hold them in place on the valve stem until the spring is released

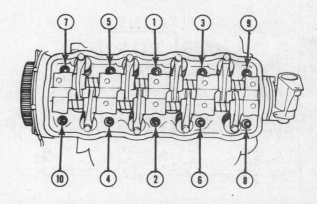

12.10a Cylinder head bolt TIGHTENING sequence (8-valve engine) – to *loosen* the bolts, reverse this sequence

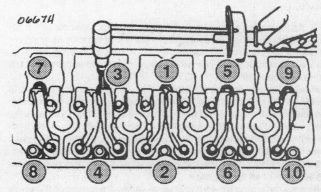

12.10b Cylinder head bolt TIGHTENING sequence (16-valve engines) – to loosen the bolts, reverse this sequence

2A

11 Valve spring, retainer and seals – replacement

Refer to illustrations 11.4, 11.9 and 11.17

Note: *Broken valve springs and defective valve stem seals can be replaced without removing the cylinder head. Two special tools and a compressed air source are normally required to perform this operation, so read through this Section carefully and rent or buy the tools before beginning the job. If compressed air isn't available, a length of nylon rope can be used to keep the valves from falling into the cylinder during this procedure.*

1 Refer to Section 10 and remove the rocker arms and shafts from the cylinder head.
2 Remove the spark plug from the cylinder which has the defective component. If all of the valve stem seals are being replaced, all of the spark plugs should be removed.
3 Turn the crankshaft until the piston in the affected cylinder is at top dead center on the compression stroke (refer to Section 3 for instructions). If you're replacing all of the valve stem seals, begin with cylinder number one and work on the valves for one cylinder at a time. Move from cylinder-to-cylinder following the firing order sequence (see this Chapter's Specifications).
4 Thread an adapter into the spark plug hole **(see illustration)** and connect an air hose from a compressed air source to it. Most auto parts stores can supply the air hose adapter. **Note:** *Many cylinder compression gauges utilize a screw-in fitting that may work with your air hose quick-disconnect fitting.*

5 Apply compressed air to the cylinder. **Warning:** *The piston may be forced down by compressed air, causing the crankshaft to turn suddenly. If the wrench used when positioning the number one piston at TDC is still attached to the bolt in the crankshaft nose, it could cause damage or injury when the crankshaft moves. Keep your hands clear of the drivebelts and rotating engine components.*
6 The valves should be held in place by the air pressure. If the valve faces or seats are in poor condition, leaks may prevent air pressure from retaining the valves – refer to the alternative procedure below.
7 If you don't have access to compressed air, an alternative method can be used. Position the piston at a point just before TDC on the compression stroke.

12.11   Use casting protrusions to pry against – don't pry between the gasket surfaces

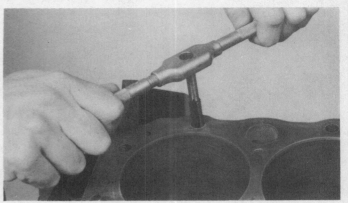

12.12   A tap should be used to remove sealant and corrosion from the head bolt threads prior to installation

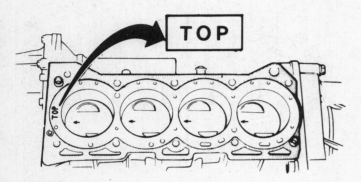

12.13   The head gasket must be installed with the word Top facing up

8   Feed a long piece of nylon rope through the spark plug hole until it fills the combustion chamber. Be sure to leave the end of the rope hanging out of the engine so it can be removed easily. Use a large ratchet and socket to rotate the crankshaft in the normal direction of rotation (clockwise) until slight resistance is felt.

9   Stuff shop rags into the cylinder head holes above and below the valves to prevent parts and tools from falling into the engine, then use a valve spring compressor to compress the spring (see illustration). Remove the keepers with a small needle-nose pliers or a magnet. **Note:** *A couple of different types of tools are available for compressing the valve springs with the head in place. One type, shown here, grips the lower spring coils and presses on the retainer as the handle is turned, while the other type utilizes the rocker arm shaft for leverage.*

10   Remove the spring retainer and valve spring, then remove the guide seal. **Note:** *If air pressure fails to hold the valve in the closed position during this operation, the valve face and/or seat is probably damaged. If so, the cylinder head will have to be removed for additional repair operations.*

11   Wrap a rubber band or tape around the top of the valve stem so the valve won't fall into the combustion chamber, then release the air pressure. **Note:** *If a rope was used instead of air pressure, turn the crankshaft slightly in the direction opposite normal rotation.*

12   Inspect the valve stem for damage. Rotate the valve in the guide and check the end for eccentric movement, which would indicate that the valve is bent.

13   Move the valve up-and-down in the guide and make sure it doesn't bind. If the valve stem binds, either the valve is bent or the guide is damaged. In either case, the head will have to be removed for repair.

14   Reapply air pressure to the cylinder to retain the valve in the closed position, then remove the tape or rubber band from the valve stem. If a

rope was used instead of air pressure, rotate the crankshaft clockwise until slight resistance is felt.

15   Lubricate the valve stem with engine oil and install a new guide seal.

16   Install the spring in position over the valve.

17   Install the valve spring retainer. Compress the valve spring and carefully position the keepers in the groove. Apply a small dab of grease to the inside of each keeper to hold it in place if necessary (see illustration).

18   Remove the pressure from the spring tool and make sure the keepers are seated.

19   Disconnect the air hose and remove the adapter from the spark plug hole. If a rope was used in place of air pressure, pull it out of the cylinder.

20   Refer to Section 10 and install the rocker arm(s) and shaft(s).

21   Install the spark plugs(s) and hook up the wire(s).

22   Refer to Section 4 and install the camshaft cover.

23   Start and run the engine, then check for oil leaks and unusual sounds coming from the rocker arm cover area.

12   Cylinder head – removal and installation

Refer to illustrations 12.10a, 12.10b 12.11, 12.12 and 12.13
Caution: *Allow the engine to cool completely before following this procedure.*

1   Position the number one piston at Top Dead Center (see Section 3).

2   Disconnect the negative cable from the battery.

3   Drain the cooling system and remove the spark plugs (see Chapter 1).

4   Remove the intake manifold (see Section 5).

5   Remove the exhaust manifold (see Section 6).

6   Remove the distributor (see Chapter 5), including the cap and wires.

7   On carbureted models, remove the fuel pump (see Chapter 4).

8   Remove the timing belt (see Section 7).

9   Remove the camshaft cover (see Section 4). On 16-valve engines, also remove the camshaft and intake rocker arms (see Section 10).

10   Using a 14 mm socket, loosen the cylinder head bolts, 1/4-turn at a time, in the reverse of the sequence shown (see illustrations) until they can be removed by hand.

11   Carefully lift the cylinder head straight up and place the head on wooden blocks to prevent damage to the sealing surfaces. If the head sticks to the engine block, dislodge it by prying against a protrusion on the head casting (see illustration). **Note:** *Cylinder head disassembly and inspection procedures are covered in Chapter 2, Part B. It's a good idea to inspect the camshaft and have the head checked for warpage, even if you're just replacing the gasket.*

12   Remove all traces of old gasket material from the block and head. Do not allow anything to fall into the engine. Clean and inspect all threaded fasteners and be sure the threaded holes in the block are clean and dry.

13   Place a new gasket (see illustration) and the cylinder head in position.

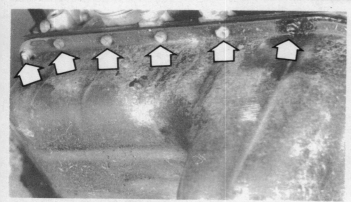

13.6a   The bolts (arrows) are spaced evenly around the perimeter of the oil pan

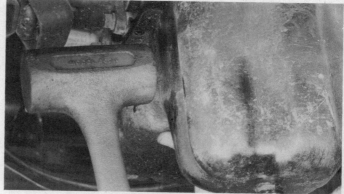

13.6b   Use a soft–face hammer to dislodge the oil pan

2A

13.7a   On Samurai models, lower the oil pan and unbolt the oil pickup tube at the front (arrow) . . .

13.7b   . . . and at the rear (arrow); let the tube fall into the oil pan and remove the pan and tube as a unit

14   The cylinder head bolts should be tightened in several stages following the proper sequence **(see illustration 12.10)** to the torque listed in this Chapter's Specifications.

15   Reinstall the timing belt (see Section 7).

16   Reinstall the remaining parts in the reverse order of removal.

17   Be sure to refill the cooling system and check all fluid levels. Rotate the crankshaft clockwise slowly by hand through two complete revolutions. Recheck the camshaft timing marks (see Section 7).

18   Start the engine and set the ignition timing (see Chapter 1). Run the engine until normal operating temperature is reached. Check for leaks and proper operation. Shut off the engine, remove the camshaft cover and re-torque the cylinder head bolts, unless the gasket manufacturer states otherwise. Recheck the valve adjustment.

13   Oil pan – removal and installation

Refer to illustrations 13.6a, 13.6b, 13.7a and 13.7b

1   Raise the front of the vehicle and support it securely on jackstands placed under the frame.

2   Drain the engine oil (see Chapter 1).

3   Remove the splash shield from under the engine.

4   On Tracker and Sidekick models, remove the front differential carrier assembly as described in Chapter 8.

5   Remove the bellhousing lower plate.

6   Remove the bolts and detach the oil pan **(see illustration)**. Don't pry between the block and pan or damage to the sealing surfaces may result

and oil leaks could develop. Use a soft-face hammer to dislodge the pan if it's stuck **(see illustration)**.

7   On Samurai models, the oil pickup tube must be unbolted and dropped into the oil pan before the oil pan can be removed **(see illustrations)**.

8   Use a scraper to remove all traces of old gasket material and sealant from the block and oil pan. Clean the gasket sealing surfaces with lacquer thinner or acetone and make sure the bolt holes in the block are clean.

9   Check the oil pan flange for distortion, particularly around the bolt holes. If necessary, place the pan on a block of wood and use a hammer to flatten and restore the gasket surface.

10   Before installing the oil pan, apply a thin coat of RTV sealant to the flange. Attach the new gasket to the pan (make sure the bolt holes are aligned).

11   Position the oil pan against the engine block and install the mounting bolts. Tighten them to the torque listed in this Chapter's Specifications in a criss-cross pattern.

12   Wait at least 30 minutes before filling the engine with oil, then start the engine and check the pan for leaks.

14   Oil pump – removal, inspection and installation

Removal

Refer to illustrations 14.3, 14.4a, 14.4b, 14.5 and 14.7

1   Remove the timing belt, tensioner, crankshaft sprocket and belt guide (see Section 7).

14.3   Oil pump mounting details

1   *Alternator bracket nut*   2   *Dipstick tube mounting bolt*

14.4b   Gently separate the front cover from the engine with a prybar (arrow)

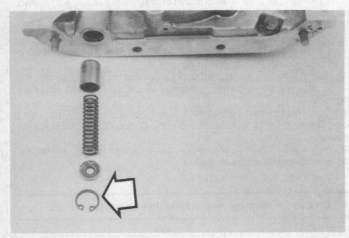

14.7   After you remove the snap-ring (arrow) with a pair of snap-ring pliers, the retainer, spring and plunger can be removed – if the plunger sticks in the bore, tap the front cover on a block of wood to dislodge it

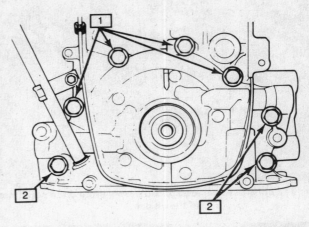

14.4a   Remove the front cover-to-block bolts – note that they come in different lengths

1   *Short bolts*   2   *Long bolts*

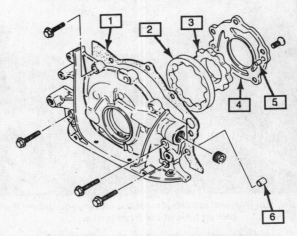

14.5   Oil pump components – exploded view

1 *Oil pump gasket*	4 *Gear plate*
2 *Oil pump outer gear*	5 *Oil pump gear plate pin*
3 *Oil pump inner gear*	6 *Oil pump pin*

2   Remove the oil pan and oil pickup tube (see Section 13).

3   Remove the alternator (see Chapter 5) and bracket **(see illustration)**. Unbolt the dipstick tube and pull the tube out of the engine front case.

4   Remove the front cover-to-block bolts and carefully separate the front cover from the engine **(see illustrations)**.

5   Detach the cover from the rear of the case and remove the inner and outer oil pump gears **(see illustration)**.

6   Remove the crankshaft oil seal from the front case (see Section 8).

7   Remove the pressure relief valve retainer, spring and plunger **(see illustration)**.

Inspection

Refer to illustrations 14.9a, 14.9b, and 14.9c

8   Clean all parts thoroughly and remove all traces of old gasket material from the sealing surfaces. Visually inspect all parts for wear, cracks and other damage. Replace parts as necessary.

9   Install the oil pump outer and inner gears and measure the clearances **(see illustrations)**. Compare the clearances to this Chapter's Specifications. Measure the free height of the relief valve spring and compare the measurement to this Chapter's Specifications. Replace parts as necessary. Pack the pump cavity with petroleum jelly and install the cover. Tighten the bolts to the torque listed in this Chapter's Specifications.

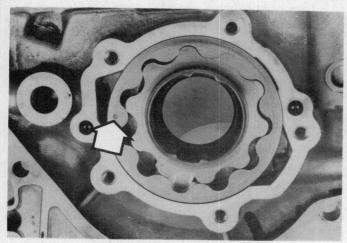

14.9a   Install the outer gear with the dot (arrow) visible – the inner gear will only fit one way: with the raised center collar facing out

14.9b   Measure the outer gear–to–oil pump housing clearance with a feeler gauge

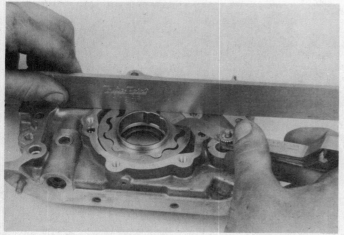

14.9c   Measure the gear end play with a precision straightedge and feeler gauge

14.12a   The oil pump has two tangs (arrows) . . .

14.12b   . . . which must be aligned with the flats on the crankshaft (arrows)

Installation

Refer to illustrations 14.12a and 14.12b

10   Replace the front crankshaft oil seal with a new seal (see Section 8).

11   Install the pressure relief valve components.

12   Using a new gasket, position the front cover on the engine **(see illustrations)**. Install the bolts in their proper locations. Tighten the bolts to the torque listed in this Chapter's Specifications.

13   Reinstall the remaining parts in the reverse order of removal.

14   Add oil, start the engine and check for oil pressure and leaks.

15 Flywheel/driveplate – removal and installation

Refer to illustrations 15.8a and 15.8b

1   Raise the vehicle and support it securely on jackstands, then refer to Chapter 7 and remove the transmission. If it's leaking, now would be a very good time to replace the front pump seal/O-ring (automatic transmission only).

2   Remove the pressure plate and clutch disc (see Chapter 8) (manual transmission equipped models). Now is a good time to check/replace the clutch components and pilot bearing.

2A

15.8a   An alignment dowel (arrow) ensures the flywheel can only
be installed one way . . .

15.8b   . . . it must be aligned with the dowel hole in the
flywheel (arrow)

16.2a   Gently pry out the old seal with a thin screwdriver – wrap
the tip with tape to prevent damaging the seal bore and
crankshaft sealing surface

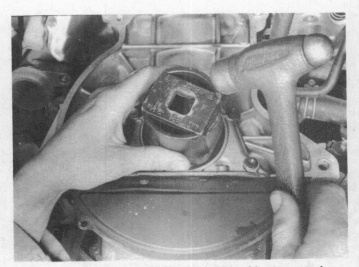

16.2b   Gently tap the new seal into place with a large socket

3   On driveplate-equipped models, mark the relationship between the driveplate and crankshaft to ensure correct alignment during reinstallation.
4   Remove the bolts that secure the flywheel/driveplate to the crankshaft. If the crankshaft turns on flywheel-equipped models, immobilize it by reinstalling two of the pressure plate bolts halfway and holding a prybar between them. On driveplate-equipped models, wedge a screwdriver through the starter opening and into the ring gear teeth to immobilize the crankshaft.
5   Remove the flywheel/driveplate from the crankshaft. Since the flywheel is fairly heavy, be sure to support it while removing the last bolt.
6   Clean the flywheel to remove grease and oil. Inspect the surface for cracks, rivet grooves, burned areas and score marks. Light scoring can be removed with emery cloth. Check for cracked and broken ring gear teeth. Lay the flywheel on a flat surface and use a straightedge to check for warpage.
7   Clean and inspect the mating surfaces of the flywheel/driveplate and the crankshaft. If the crankshaft rear seal is leaking, replace it before reinstalling the flywheel/driveplate (see Section 16).
8   Position the flywheel/driveplate against the crankshaft. On flywheel-equipped models, be sure to align the hole in the flywheel with the alignment dowel in the crankshaft (see illustrations). On driveplate-equipped

models, align the marks you made during removal. Before installing the bolts, apply thread locking compound to the threads.
9   Tighten the bolts to the torque listed in this Chapter's Specifications. Hold the crankshaft from turning as described previously.
10   The remainder of installation is the reverse of the removal procedure.

16   Rear crankshaft oil seal – replacement

Refer to illustrations 16.2a, 16.2b, 16.5 and 16.6
1   The transmission must be removed from the vehicle for this procedure (see Chapter 7).
2   The seal can be replaced without dropping the oil pan or removing the seal retainer. However, this method is not recommended because the lip of the seal is quite stiff and it's possible to cock the seal in the retainer bore or damage it during installation. If you want to take the chance, pry out the old seal (see illustration). Apply moly-base grease to the crankshaft seal journal and the lip of the new seal and carefully tap the new seal into place (see illustration). The lip is stiff so carefully work it onto the seal journal of the crankshaft with a smooth object like the end of an extension as you tap the seal into place. Don't rush it or you may damage the seal.

16.5   After removing the retainer from the engine, support it on wood blocks and drive out the old seal with a punch and hammer

16.6   Drive the new seal into the retainer with a block of wood or a section of pipe, if you have one large enough — make sure that you don't cock the seal in the retainer bore

2A

3   The following method is recommended but requires removal of the oil pan (see Section 13) and the seal retainer.

4   After the oil pan has been removed, remove the bolts, detach the seal retainer and peel off all the old gasket material.

5   Position the seal and retainer assembly on a couple of wood blocks on a workbench and drive the old seal out from the back side with a punch and hammer (see illustration).

6   Drive the new seal into the retainer with a block of wood (see illustration) or a section of pipe slightly smaller in diameter than the outside diameter of the seal.

7   Lubricate the crankshaft seal journal and the lip of the new seal with moly-base grease. Position a new gasket on the engine block.

8   Slowly and carefully push the seal onto the crankshaft. The seal lip is stiff, so work it onto the crankshaft with a smooth object such as the end of an extension as you push the retainer against the block.

9   Install and tighten the retainer bolts to the torque listed in this Chapter's Specifications.

10   The remaining steps are the reverse of removal.

11   Run the engine and check for oil leaks.

17   Engine mounts – check and replacement

Refer to illustration 17.8

1   Engine mounts seldom require attention, but broken or deteriorated mounts should be replaced immediately or the added strain placed on the driveline components may cause damage or wear.

Check

2   During the check, the engine must be raised slightly to remove the weight from the mounts.

3   Raise the vehicle and support it securely on jackstands, then position a jack under the engine bellhousing. Place a large block of wood between the jack head and the bellhousing, then carefully raise the engine just enough to take the weight off the mounts. **Warning:** *DO NOT place any part of your body under the engine when it's supported only by a jack!*

4   Check the mounts to see if the rubber is cracked, hardened or separated from the metal plates. Sometimes the rubber will split right down the center.

5   Check for relative movement between the mount plates and the engine or frame (use a large screwdriver or pry bar to attempt to move the mounts). If movement is noted, lower the engine and tighten the mount fasteners.

6   Rubber preservative should be applied to the mounts to slow deterioration.

Replacement

7   Disconnect the negative battery cable from the battery, then raise the vehicle and support it securely on jackstands (if not already done).

8   Remove the nut and detach the mount from the frame bracket (see illustration).

9   Raise the engine slightly with a jack or hoist (make sure the fan doesn't hit the radiator or shroud). Remove the mount-to-engine bracket nut and detach the mount.

10   Installation is the reverse of removal. Use thread locking compound on the mount bolts and be sure to tighten them securely.

17.8   The engine mounts are secured to the frame and engine brackets with nuts (arrows)

Chapter 2 Part B
General engine overhaul procedures

Contents

Specifications

General

Cylinder compression pressure (at 400 rpm)	
Standard	199 psi
Minimum	170 psi
Maximum allowable variation between cylinders	14.2 psi
Oil pressure (engine warm)	42 to 60 psi at 3000 rpm

Cylinder head

Warpage Service limit	0.002 in (0.05 mm)

Camshaft

8-valve engine

Camshaft endplay (service limit)	0.0295 in (0.75 mm)
Cam lobe height (intake and exhaust)	
Standard	1.4763 in (37.5 mm)
Wear limit	1.4724 in (37.4 mm)
Camshaft bearing oil clearance	
Standard	0.002 to 0.0035 in (0.05 to 0.09 mm)
Service limit	0.006 in (0.15 mm)
Camshaft journal diameter (front to rear)	
1	1.7372 to 1.7381 in (44.125 to 44.150 mm)
2	1451 to 1.7460 in (44.325 to 44.350 mm)
3	1.7530 to 1.7539 in (44.525 to 44.550 mm)
4	1.7609 to 1.7618 in (44.725 to 44.750 mm)
5	1.7687 to 1.7697 in (44.925 to 44.950 mm)
Camshaft journal bore (inside) diameter	
1	1.7402 to 1.7407 in (44.200 to 44.216 mm)
2	1.7480 to 1.7486 in (44.400 to 44.416 mm)
3	1.7560 to 1.7565 in (44.600 to 44.616 mm)
4	1.7638 to 1.7644 in (44.800 to 44.816 mm)
5	1.7716 to 1.7723 in (45.000 to 45.016 mm)

16-valve engine

Camshaft runout service limit	0.0039 in (0.10 mm)
Camshaft lobe height	
Intake	
Standard	1.4130 to 1.4192 in (35.888 to 36.048 mm)
Service limit	1.4090 in (35.788 mm)
Exhaust	
Standard	1.4300 to 1.4362 in (36.322 to 36.482 mm)
Service limit	1.4261 in (36.222 mm)
Camshaft bearing oil clearance	
Standard	0.0016 to 0.0032 in (0.040 to 0.082 mm)
Service limit	0.0047 in (0.12 mm)
Camshaft journal diameter	1.1000 to 1.1008 in (27.939 to 27.960 mm)
Camshaft journal bore (inside) diameter	1.1024 to 1.1031 in (28.000 to 28.021 mm)

Valves and related components

Valve margin width
  Intake
    Standard .... 0.039 in (1.0 mm)
    Service limit .... 0.0236 in (0.6 mm)
  Exhaust
    Standard .... 0.039 in (1.0 mm)
    Service limit .... 0.0275 in (0.7 mm)
Valve stem diameter
  Intake .... 0.2742 to 0.2748 in (6.965 to 6.980 mm)
  Exhaust .... 0.2737 to 0.2742 in (6.950 to 6.965mm)
Valve stem-to-guide clearance
  Intake
    Standard .... 0.0008 to 0.0019 in (0.02 to 0.05 mm)
    Service limit .... 0.0027 in (0.07 mm)
  Exhaust
    Standard .... 0.0014 to 0.0025 in (0.035 to 0.65 mm)
    Service limit .... 0.0035 in (0.09 mm)
Valve spring
  Out-of-square limit .... 0.079 in (2.0 mm)
  Installed height .... 1.63 in (41.5 mm)
  Free length
    Standard .... 1.9409 in (49.3 mm)
    Service limit .... 1.8937 in (48.1 mm)
  Pressure
    Standard .... 54.7 to 64.3 lbs at 1.63 in (24.8 to 29.2 Kg at 41.5 mm)
    Service limit .... 50.2 lbs at 1.63 in (22.8 Kg at 41.5 mm)

16-valve engine

Valve margin width
  Intake
    Standard .... 0.03 to 0.047 in (0.8 to 1.2 mm)
    Service limit .... 0.0236 in (0.6 mm)
  Exhaust
    Standard .... 0.03 to 0.047 in (0.8 to 1.2 mm)
    Service limit .... 0.0275 in (0.7 mm)
Valve stem diameter
  Intake .... 0.2152 to 0.2157 in (5.465 to 5.480 mm)
  Exhaust .... 0.2142 to 0.2148 in (5.440 to 5.455 mm)
Valve guide inner diameter (intake and exhaust) .... 0.2166 to 0.2170 in (5.500 to 5.512 mm)
Valve stem-to-guide clearance
  Intake
    Standard .... 0.0008 to 0.0019 in (0.02 to 0.05 mm)
    Service limit .... 0.0027 in (0.07 mm)
  Exhaust
    Standard .... 0.0018 to 0.0028 in (0.045 to 0.72 mm)
    Service limit .... 0.0035 in (0.09 mm)
Valve spring
  Out-of-square limit .... 0.079 in (2.0 mm)
  Installed height .... 1.24 in (31.5 mm)
  Free length
    Standard .... 1.4500 in (36.67 mm)
    Service limit .... 1.4043 in (35.67 mm)
  Pressure
    Standard .... 23.6 to 27.5 lbs at 1.24 in (10.7 to 12.5 kg at 31.5 mm)
    Service limit .... 20.5 lbs at 1.24 in (9.3 kg at 31.5 mm)

Crankshaft and connecting rods

Crankshaft endplay
  Standard .... 0.002 to 0.007 in (0.05 to 0.18 mm)
  Service limit .... 0.0149 in (0.38 mm)
Crankshaft runout limit (at middle) .... 0.0023 in (0.06 mm)
Connecting rod journal
  Diameter .... 1.6529 to 1.6535 in (41.982 to 42.00 mm)
  Out-of-round/taper limits .... 0.0004 in (0.01 mm)
  Bearing oil clearance
    Standard .... 0.0012 to 0.0019 in (0.03 to 0.05mm)
    Service limit .... 0.0031 in (0.08 mm)

Connecting rod end play (side clearance)
   Standard .... 0.0039 to 0.0078 in (0.10 to 0.20 mm)
   Service limit .... 0.0137 in (0.35mm)
Main bearing journal
   Diameters (numbers stamped on crankshaft webs at no. 3 bearing)
    Sidekick and Tracker models
     No. 1 .... 2.0470 to 2.0472 in (51.994 to 52.000 mm)
     No. 2 .... 2.0468 to 2.0470 in (51.988 to 51.994 mm)
     No. 3 .... 2.0465 to 2.0468 in (51.982 to 51.988 mm)
    Samurai models
     No. 1 .... 1.7714 to 1.7716 in (44.994 to 45.000 mm)
     No. 2 .... 1.7712 to 1.7714 in (44.988 to 44.994 mm)
     No. 3 .... 1.7710 to 1.7712 in (44.982 to 44.988 mm)
   Out-of-round/taper limits .... 0.0004 in (0.01 mm)
   Bearing oil clearance
    Standard .... 0.0008 to 0.0016 in (0.02 to 0.04 mm)
    Service limit .... 0.0023 in (0.06 mm)
   Main bearing thicknesses (standard size bearing color codes)
    Green .... 0.0786 to 0.0787 in (1.996 to 2.000 mm)
    Black .... 0.0787 to 0.0788 in (1.999 to 2.003 mm)
    Colorless .... 0.0788 to 0.0789 in (2.002 to 2.006 mm)
    Yellow .... 0.0789 to 0.0790 in (2.005 to 2.009 mm)
    Blue .... 0.0790 to 0.0791 in (2.008 to 2.012 mm)
   Main bearing bore sizes (markings stamped on oil pan mating surface)
    Sidekick and tracker models
     Marking "A" .... 2.2047 to 2.2050 in (56.000 to 56.006 mm)
     Marking "B" .... 2.2050 to 2.2052 in (56.006 to 56.012 mm)
     Marking "C" .... 2.2052 to 2.2054 in (56.012 to 56.018 mm)
    Samurai models
     Marking "A" .... 1.9292 to 1.9294 in (49.000 to 49.006 mm)
     Marking "B" .... 1.9294 to 1.9296 in (49.006 to 49.012 mm)
     Marking "C" .... 1.9296 to 1.9298 in (49.012 to 49.018 mm)

Cylinder bore

Diameter
   1300 cc engine
    Marking "1" .... 2.9138 to 2.9142 in (74.01 to 74.02 mm)
    Marking "2" .... 2.9134 to 2.9138 in (74.01 to 74.02 mm)
   1600 cc engine
    Marking "1" .... 2.9531 to 2.9535 in (75.01 to 75.02 mm)
    Marking "2" .... 2.9528 to 2.9531 in (75.00 to 75.01 mm)
Out-of-round/taper limits .... 0.0039 in (0.10 mm)

Pistons and rings

Piston diameter*
   1300 cc engine
    Marking "1" .... 2.9126 to 2.9130 in (73.98 to 73.99 mm)
    Marking "2" .... 2.9122 to 2.9126 in (73.97 to 73.98 mm)
   1600 cc engine
    Marking "1" .... 2.9520 to 2.9524 in (74.98 to 74.99 mm)
    Marking "2" .... 2.9516 to 2.9520 in (74.97 to 74.98 mm)
Piston-to-bore clearance .... 0.0008 to 0.0015 in (0.02 to 0.04 mm)
Piston ring end gap
   Compression rings .... 0.008 to 0.014 in (0.20 to 0.35 mm)
   Oil ring .... 0.0079 to 0.0275 in (0.020 to 0.070 mm)
Piston ring side clearance
   No. 1 (top) compression ring
    Standard .... 0.0012 to 0.0027 in (0.03 to 0.07 mm)
    Service limit .... 0.005 in (0.12 mm)
   No. 2 compression ring
    Standard .... 0.0008 to 0.0023 in (0.02 to 0.06 mm)
    Service limit .... 0.004 in (0.10 mm)
* Measured 0.63-inch (16 mm) up from bottom of skirt

Torque specifications**

                                               Ft-lbs

Distributor gear case bolts .... 5.8 to 7.2
Main bearing cap bolts .... 36.5 to 41
Connecting rod cap nuts .... 24 to 26.5
Rear oil seal housing bolts .... 7 to 8.5
** Note: Refer to Part A for additional torque specifications.

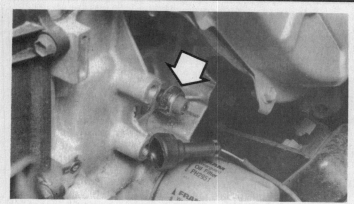

2.4   The oil pressure sending unit is located between the oil filter and exhaust manifold (arrow)

3.6   A compression gauge with a threaded fitting for the spark plug hole is preferred over the type that requires hand pressure to maintain the seal – be sure to open the throttle and choke valves as far as possible during the compression check!

1   General information

Included in this portion of Chapter 2 are the general overhaul procedures for the cylinder head(s) and internal engine components.

The information ranges from advice concerning preparation for an overhaul and the purchase of replacement parts to detailed, step-by-step procedures covering removal and installation of internal engine components and the inspection of parts.

The following Sections have been written based on the assumption that the engine has been removed from the vehicle. For information concerning in-vehicle engine repair, as well as removal and installation of the external components necessary for the overhaul, see Part A of this Chapter and Section 7 of this Part.

The Specifications included in this Part are only those necessary for the inspection and overhaul procedures which follow.

Refer to Part A for additional Specifications.

2   Engine overhaul – general information

Refer to illustrations 2.4

It's not always easy to determine when, or if, an engine should be completely overhauled, as a number of factors must be considered.

High mileage is not necessarily an indication that an overhaul is needed, while low mileage doesn't preclude the need for an overhaul. Frequency of servicing is probably the most important consideration. An engine that's had regular and frequent oil and filter changes, as well as other required maintenance, will most likely give many thousands of miles of reliable service. Conversely, a neglected engine may require an overhaul very early in its life.

Excessive oil consumption is an indication that piston rings, valve seals and/or valve guides are in need of attention. Make sure that oil leaks aren't responsible before deciding that the rings and/or guides are bad. Perform a cylinder compression check to determine the extent of the work required (see Section 3).

Check the oil pressure with a gauge installed in place of the oil pressure sending unit **(see illustration)** and compare it to this Chapter's Specifications. If it's extremely low, the bearings and/or oil pump are probably worn out.

Loss of power, rough running, knocking or metallic engine noises, excessive valve train noise and high fuel consumption rates may also point to the need for an overhaul, especially if they're all present at the same time. If a complete tune-up doesn't remedy the situation, major mechanical work is the only solution.

An engine overhaul involves restoring the internal parts to the specifications of a new engine. During an overhaul, the piston rings are replaced and the cylinder walls are reconditioned (rebored and/or honed). If a rebore is done by an automotive machine shop, new oversize pistons will also be installed. The main bearings, connecting rod bearings and camshaft bearings are generally replaced with new ones and, if necess-

ary, the crankshaft may be reground to restore the journals. Generally, the valves are serviced as well, since they're usually in less-than-perfect condition at this point.

While the engine is being overhauled, other components, such as the distributor, starter and alternator, can be rebuilt as well. The end result should be a like new engine that will give many trouble free miles. **Note:** *Critical cooling system components such as the hoses, drivebelts, thermostat and water pump MUST be replaced with new parts when an engine is overhauled. The radiator should be checked carefully to ensure that it isn't clogged or leaking (see Chapter 3). Also, we don't recommend overhauling the oil pump – always install a new one when an engine is rebuilt.*

Before beginning the engine overhaul, read through the entire procedure to familiarize yourself with the scope and requirements of the job. Overhauling an engine isn't difficult if you follow all of the instructions carefully, have the necessary tools and equipment and pay close attention to all specifications; however, it can be time consuming. Plan on the vehicle being tied up for a minimum of two weeks, especially if parts must be taken to an automotive machine shop for repair or reconditioning. Check on availability of parts and make sure that any necessary special tools and equipment are obtained in advance. Most work can be done with typical hand tools, although a number of precision measuring tools are required for inspecting parts to determine if they must be replaced. Often an automotive machine shop will handle the inspection of parts and offer advice concerning reconditioning and replacement. **Note:** *Always wait until the engine has been completely disassembled and all components, especially the engine block, have been inspected before deciding what service and repair operations must be performed by an automotive machine shop. Since the block's condition will be the major factor to consider when determining whether to overhaul the original engine or buy a rebuilt one, never purchase parts or have machine work done on other components until the block has been thoroughly inspected.* As a general rule, time is the primary cost of an overhaul, so it doesn't pay to install worn or substandard parts.

As a final note, to ensure maximum life and minimum trouble from a rebuilt engine, everything must be assembled with care in a spotlessly clean environment.

3   Cylinder compression check

Refer to illustration 3.6

1   A compression check will tell you what mechanical condition the upper end (pistons, rings, valves, head gaskets) of your engine is in. Specifically, it can tell you if the compression is down due to leakage caused by worn piston rings, defective valves and seats or a blown head gasket. **Note:** *The engine must be at normal operating temperature and the battery must be fully charged for this check. Also, if the engine is equipped with a carburetor, the choke valve must be all the way open to get an accurate compression reading (if the engine's warm, the choke should be open).*

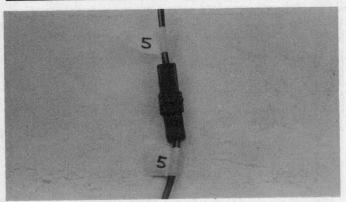

5.5   Label both ends of each wire before disconnecting them

2   Begin by cleaning the area around the spark plugs before you remove them (compressed air should be used, if available, otherwise a small brush or even a bicycle tire pump will work). The idea is to prevent dirt from getting into the cylinders as the compression check is being done.
3   Remove all of the spark plugs from the engine (see Chapter 1).
4   Block the throttle wide open.
5   Detach the coil wire from the center of the distributor cap and ground it on the engine block. Use a jumper wire with alligator clips on each end to ensure a good ground. On EFI equipped vehicles, the fuel pump circuit should also be disabled (see Chapter 4).
6   Install the compression gauge in the number one spark plug hole **(see illustration)**.
7   Crank the engine over at least seven compression strokes and watch the gauge. The compression should build up quickly in a healthy engine. Low compression on the first stroke, followed by gradually increasing pressure on successive strokes, indicates worn piston rings. A low compression reading on the first stroke, which doesn't build up during successive strokes, indicates leaking valves or a blown head gasket (a cracked head could also be the cause). Deposits on the valve seats can also cause low compression. Record the highest gauge reading obtained.
8   Repeat the procedure for the remaining cylinders and compare the results to this Chapter's Specifications.
9   Add some engine oil (about three squirts from a plunger-type oil can) to each cylinder, through the spark plug hole, and repeat the test.
10   If the compression increases after the oil is added, the piston rings are definitely worn. If the compression doesn't increase significantly, the leakage is occurring at the valves or head gasket. Leakage past the valves may be caused by burned valve seats and/or faces or warped, cracked or bent valves.
11   If two adjacent cylinders have equally low compression, there's a strong possibility that the head gasket between them is blown. The appearance of coolant in the combustion chambers or the crankcase would verify this condition.
12   If one cylinder is 20 percent lower than the others, and the engine has a slightly rough idle, a worn exhaust lobe on the camshaft could be the cause.
13   If the compression is unusually high, the combustion chambers are probably coated with carbon deposits. If that's the case, the cylinder head(s) should be removed and decarbonized.
14   If compression is way down or varies greatly between cylinders, it would be a good idea to have a leak-down test performed by an automotive repair shop. This test will pinpoint exactly where the leakage is occurring and how severe it is.

4   Engine removal – methods and precautions

If you've decided that an engine must be removed for overhaul or major repair work, several preliminary steps should be taken.

Locating a suitable place to work is extremely important. Adequate work space, along with storage space for the vehicle, will be needed. If a shop or garage isn't available, at the very least a flat, level, clean work surface made of concrete or asphalt is required.

Cleaning the engine compartment and engine before beginning the removal procedure will help keep tools clean and organized.

An engine hoist or A-frame will also be necessary. Make sure the equipment is rated in excess of the combined weight of the engine and accessories. Safety is of primary importance, considering the potential hazards involved in lifting the engine out of the vehicle.

If the engine is being removed by a novice, a helper should be available. Advice and aid from someone more experienced would also be helpful. There are many instances when one person cannot simultaneously perform all of the operations required when lifting the engine out of the vehicle.

Plan the operation ahead of time. Arrange for or obtain all of the tools and equipment you'll need prior to beginning the job. Some of the equipment necessary to perform engine removal and installation safely and with relative ease are (in addition to an engine hoist) a heavy duty floor jack, complete sets of wrenches and sockets as described in the front of this manual, wooden blocks and plenty of rags and cleaning solvent for mopping up spilled oil, coolant and gasoline. If the hoist must be rented, make sure that you arrange for it in advance and perform all of the operations possible without it beforehand. This will save you money and time.

Plan for the vehicle to be out of use for quite a while. A machine shop will be required to perform some of the work which the do-it-yourselfer can't accomplish without special equipment. These shops often have a busy schedule, so it would be a good idea to consult them before removing the engine in order to accurately estimate the amount of time required to rebuild or repair components that may need work.

Always be extremely careful when removing and installing the engine. Serious injury can result from careless actions. Plan ahead, take your time and a job of this nature, although major, can be accomplished successfully.

5   Engine – removal and installation

Refer to illustrations 5.5, 5.24a and 5.24b
Warning: *The air conditioning system is under high pressure! If it is necessary to disconnect air conditioning hoses for engine removal, first have a dealer service department or service station discharge the system. Carefully inspect the routing of air conditioning system refrigerant lines before beginning engine removal to see if line disconnection, and therefore professional discharging, is necessary.*

Removal

1   Refer to Chapter 4 and relieve the fuel system pressure (EFI equipped vehicles only), then disconnect the negative cable from the battery.
2   Cover the fenders and cowl and remove the hood (see Chapter 11). Special pads are available to protect the fenders, but an old bedspread or blanket will also work.
3   Remove the air cleaner assembly.
4   Drain the cooling system (see Chapter 1).
5   Label the vacuum lines, emissions system hoses, wiring connectors, ground straps and fuel lines, to ensure correct reinstallation, then detach them. Pieces of masking tape with numbers or letters written on them work well **(see illustration)**. If there's any possibility of confusion, make a sketch of the engine compartment and clearly label the lines, hoses and wires.
6   Label and detach all coolant hoses from the engine.
7   Remove the cooling fan, shroud and radiator (see Chapter 3).
8   Remove the drivebelts (see Chapter 1).
9   **Warning:** *Gasoline is extremely flammable, so extra precautions must be taken when working on any part of the fuel system. DO NOT smoke or allow open flames or bare light bulbs near the vehicle. Also, don't work in a garage if a natural gas appliance with a pilot light is present.* Disconnect the fuel lines running from the engine to the chassis (see Chapter 4). Plug or cap all open fittings/lines.
10   Disconnect the throttle linkage (and TV linkage/speed control cable, if equipped) from the engine (see Chapter 4).
11   On power steering equipped vehicles, unbolt the power steering pump (see Chapter 10). Leave the lines/hoses attached and make sure

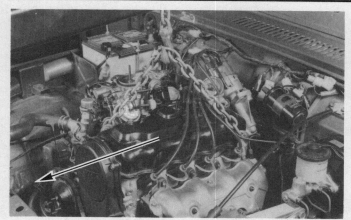

5.24a   Pull the engine forward as far as possible to clear the transmission . . .

5.24b   . . . then slowly raise the engine until it clears the body

the pump is kept in an upright position in the engine compartment (use wire or rope to restrain it out of the way).

12   On A/C equipped vehicles, unbolt the compressor (see Chapter 3) and set it aside. Do not disconnect the hoses unless it is necessary.

13   Drain the engine oil (see Chapter 1) and remove the filter.

14   Remove the starter motor (see Chapter 5).

15   Remove the alternator (see Chapter 5).

16   Unbolt the exhaust system from the engine (see Chapter 4).

17   If you're working on a vehicle with an automatic transmission, refer to Chapter 7 and remove the torque converter-to-driveplate fasteners.

18   Support the transmission with a jack. Position a block of wood between them to prevent damage to the transmission. Special transmission jacks with safety chains are available – use one if possible.

19   Attach an engine sling or a length of chain to the lifting brackets on the engine.

20   Roll the hoist into position and connect the sling to it. Take up the slack in the sling or chain, but don't lift the engine.

Warning: *DO NOT place any part of your body under the engine when it's supported only by a hoist or other lifting device.*

21   Remove the transmission-to-engine block bolts.

22   Remove the engine mount-to-frame bolts.

23   Recheck to be sure nothing is still connecting the engine to the transmission or vehicle. Disconnect anything still remaining.

24   Raise the engine slightly. Carefully work it forward to separate it from the transmission **(see illustration)**. If you're working on a vehicle with an automatic transmission, be sure the torque converter stays in the transmission (clamp a pair of vise-grips to the housing to keep the converter from sliding out). If you're working on a vehicle with a manual transmission, the input shaft must be completely disengaged from the clutch. Slowly raise the engine out of the engine compartment **(see illustration)**. Check carefully to make sure nothing is hanging up.

25   Remove the flywheel/driveplate and mount the engine on an engine stand.

Installation

26   Check the engine and transmission mounts. If they're worn or damaged, replace them.

27   If you're working on a manual transmission equipped vehicle, install the clutch and pressure plate (see Chapter 8). Now is a good time to install a new clutch.

28   Carefully lower the engine into the engine compartment – make sure the engine mounts line up.

29   If you're working on an automatic transmission equipped vehicle, guide the torque converter into the crankshaft following the procedure outlined in Chapter 7.

30   If you're working on a manual transmission equipped vehicle, apply a dab of high-temperature grease to the input shaft and guide it into the crankshaft pilot bearing until the bellhousing is flush with the engine block.

31   Install the transmission-to-engine bolts and tighten them securely.

Caution: *DO NOT use the bolts to force the transmission and engine together!*

32   Reinstall the remaining components in the reverse order of removal.

33   Add coolant, oil, power steering and transmission fluid as needed.

34   Run the engine and check for leaks and proper operation of all accessories, then install the hood and test drive the vehicle.

35   Have the A/C system recharged and leak tested, if it was discharged.

2B

6   Engine rebuilding alternatives

The do-it-yourselfer is faced with a number of options when performing an engine overhaul. The decision to replace the engine block, piston/connecting rod assemblies and crankshaft depends on a number of factors, with the number one consideration being the condition of the block. Other considerations are cost, access to machine shop facilities, parts availability, time required to complete the project and the extent of prior mechanical experience on the part of the do-it-yourselfer.

Some of the rebuilding alternatives include:

Individual parts – If the inspection procedures reveal that the engine block and most engine components are in reusable condition, purchasing individual parts may be the most economical alternative. The block, crankshaft and piston/connecting rod assemblies should all be inspected carefully. Even if the block shows little wear, the cylinder bores should be surface honed.

Short block – A short block consists of an engine block with a crankshaft and piston/connecting rod assemblies already installed. All new bearings are incorporated and all clearances will be correct. The existing camshaft, valve train components, cylinder head(s) and external parts can be bolted to the short block with little or no machine shop work necessary.

Long block – A long block consists of a short block plus an oil pump, oil pan, cylinder head(s), rocker arm cover(s), camshaft and valve train components, timing sprockets and chain or gears and timing cover. All components are installed with new bearings, seals and gaskets incorporated throughout. The installation of manifolds and external parts is all that's necessary.

Give careful thought to which alternative is best for you and discuss the situation with local automotive machine shops, auto parts dealers and experienced rebuilders before ordering or purchasing replacement parts.

7   Engine overhaul – disassembly sequence

Refer to illustration 7.5

1   It's much easier to disassemble and work on the engine if it's mounted on a portable engine stand. A stand can often be rented quite cheaply from an equipment rental yard. Before the engine is mounted on a stand, the flywheel/driveplate and rear oil seal housing should be removed from the engine.

2   If a stand isn't available, it's possible to disassemble the engine with it blocked up on the floor. Be extra careful not to tip or drop the engine when working without a stand.

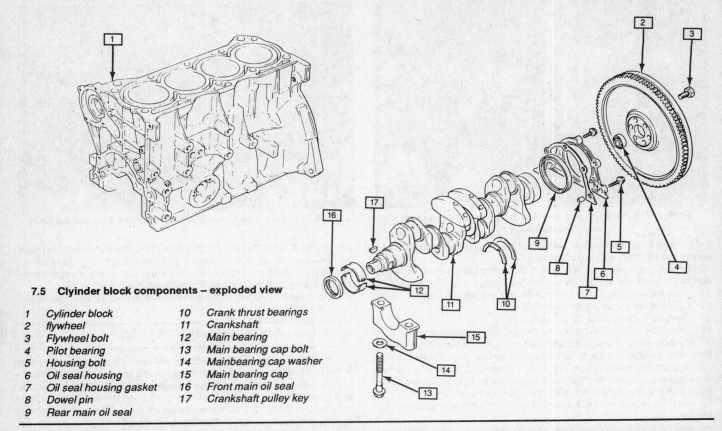

7.5 Clyinder block components – exploded view

1 Cylinder block	10 Crank thrust bearings
2 flywheel	11 Crankshaft
3 Flywheel bolt	12 Main bearing
4 Pilot bearing	13 Main bearing cap bolt
5 Housing bolt	14 Mainbearing cap washer
6 Oil seal housing	15 Main bearing cap
7 Oil seal housing gasket	16 Front main oil seal
8 Dowel pin	17 Crankshaft pulley key
9 Rear main oil seal	

3   If you're going to obtain a rebuilt engine, all external components must come off first, to be transferred to the replacement engine, just as they will if you're doing a complete engine overhaul yourself. These include:

    Alternator and brackets
    Emissions control components
    Distributor, spark plug wires and spark plugs
    Thermostat and housing cover
    Water pump
    EFI components or carburetor
    Intake/exhaust manifolds
    Oil filter
    Engine mounts
    Clutch and flywheel/driveplate
    Engine rear plate

Note: *When removing the external components from the engine, pay close attention to details that may be helpful or important during installation. Note the installed position of gaskets, seals, spacers, pins, brackets, washers, bolts and other small items.*

4   If you're obtaining a short block, which consists of the engine block, crankshaft, pistons and connecting rods all assembled, then the cylinder head, oil pan and oil pump will have to be removed as well. See *Engine rebuilding alternatives* for additional information regarding the different possibilities to be considered.

5   If you're planning a complete overhaul, the engine must be disassembled and the internal components removed in the following order:

    Camshaft cover
    Intake and exhaust manifolds
    Timing belt and sprockets
    Rocker arms and shafts
    Cylinder head
    Oil pan
    Oil pump
    Piston/connecting rod assemblies
    Crankshaft and main bearings

6   Before beginning the disassembly and overhaul procedures, make sure the following items are available. Also, refer to *Engine overhaul – reassembly sequence* for a list of tools and materials needed for engine reassembly.

    Common hand tools
    Small cardboard boxes or plastic bags for storing parts
    Gasket scraper
    Ridge reamer
    Micrometers
    Telescoping gauges
    Dial indicator set
    Valve spring compressor
    Cylinder surfacing hone
    Piston ring groove cleaning tool
    Electric drill motor
    Tap and die set
    Wire brushes
    Oil gallery brushes
    Cleaning solvent

8   Cylinder head – disassembly

Refer to illustrations 8.2a, 8.2b, 8.3, 8.4, 8.5, 8.6a and 8.6b
Note: *New and rebuilt cylinder heads are commonly available for most engines at dealerships and auto parts stores. Due to the fact that some specialized tools are necessary for the disassembly and inspection procedures, and replacement parts may not be readily available, it may be more practical and economical for the home mechanic to purchase replacement head rather than taking the time to disassemble, inspect and recondition the original.*

1   Cylinder head disassembly involves removal of the camshaft, intake and exhaust valves and related components. If they're still in place, remove the rocker arms and shafts from the cylinder head (see Chapter 2A, Section 10). Label the parts or store them separately so they can be reinstalled in their original locations.

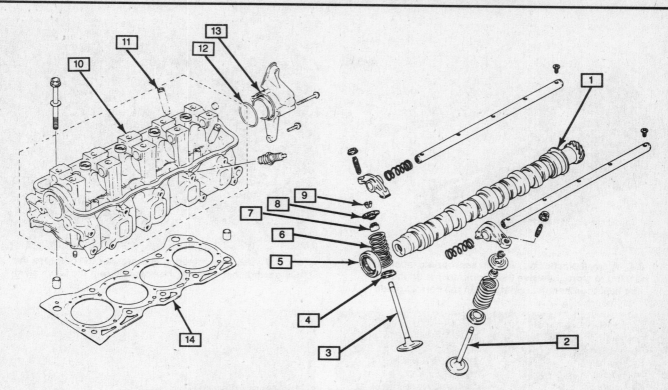

8.2a   Cylinder head components — exploded view (8-valve engines)

1	Camshaft	6	Valve spring	11	Valve guide
2	Exhaust valve	7	Valve stem seal	12	Distributor case O-ring
3	Intake valve	8	Valve spring retainer	13	Distributor case
4	Valve spring seat	9	Valve keepers	14	Cylinder head gasket
5	Camshaft oil seat	10	Cylinder head		

2B

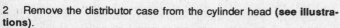

8.2b   Remove the three bolts (arrows) and pull the distributor case off

8.3   Carefully slip the camshaft out the rear (distributor end) of the cylinder head — guide the camshaft with your other hand and be careful not to damage the bearing surfaces in the head (8-valve engines)

2   Remove the distributor case from the cylinder head (**see illustrations**).

3   On 8-valve engines, gently guide the camshaft out of the cylinder head (**see illustration**). **Note:** Refer to the Rocker arms and shafts — removal and installation procedure in part A for camshaft removal and installation on 16-valve engines.

4   Before the valves are removed, arrange to label and store them, along with their related components, so they can be kept separate and re-

installed in the same valve guides they are removed from (**see illustration**).

5   Compress the springs on the first valve with a spring compressor and remove the keepers (**see illustration**). Carefully release the valve spring compressor and remove the retainer, the spring and the spring seat (if used).

6   Pull the valve out of the head, then remove the oil seal from the guide (**see illustration**). If the valve binds in the guide (won't pull through), push

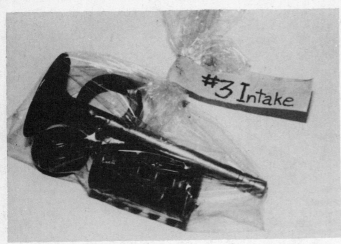

8.4   A small plastic bag, with an appropriate label, can be used to store the valve train components so they can be kept together and reinstalled in the correct guide

8.5   Use a valve spring compressor to compress the spring, then remove the keepers from the valve stem

8.6a   The valve seals may be pulled off with pliers

8.6b   If the valve won't pull through the guide, deburr the edge of the stem end and the area around the top of the keeper groove with a file

it back into the head and deburr the area around the keeper groove with a fine file or whetstone (**see illustration**).

7   Repeat the procedure for the remaining valves. Remember to keep all the parts for each valve together so they can be reinstalled in the same locations.

8   Once the valves and related components have been removed and stored in an organized manner, the head should be thoroughly cleaned and inspected. If a complete engine overhaul is being done, finish the engine disassembly procedures before beginning the cylinder head cleaning and inspection process.

9   Cylinder head and camshaft – cleaning and inspection

Refer to illustrations 9.12, 9.14, 9.15, 9.16, 9.17, 9.18, 9.24, 9.25 and 9.26

1   Thorough cleaning of the cylinder head and related valve train components, followed by a detailed inspection, will enable you to decide how much valve service work must be done during the engine overhaul. **Note:** *If the engine was severely overheated, the cylinder head is probably warped (see Step 12).*

Cleaning

2   Scrape all traces of old gasket material and sealing compound off the head gasket, intake manifold and exhaust manifold sealing surfaces. Be very careful not to gouge the cylinder head. Special gasket removal solvents that soften gaskets and make removal much easier are available at auto parts stores.

3   Remove all built up scale from the coolant passages.

4   Run a stiff wire brush through the various holes to remove deposits that may have formed in them.

5   Run an appropriate size tap into each of the threaded holes to remove corrosion and thread sealant that may be present. If compressed air is available, use it to clear the holes of debris produced by this operation. **Warning:** *Wear eye protection when using compressed air!*

6   Clean the rocker arm shaft oil holes with a wire and compressed air. (if available). **Warning:** *Wear eye protection.*

7   Clean the cylinder head and with solvent and dry it thoroughly. Compressed air will speed the drying process and ensure that all holes and recessed areas are clean. **Note:** *Decarbonizing chemicals are available and may prove very useful when cleaning cylinder heads and valve train components. They are very caustic and should be used with caution. Be sure to follow the instructions on the container.*

8   Clean the rocker arms, rocker shafts and camshaft with solvent and dry them thoroughly (don't mix them up during the cleaning process).

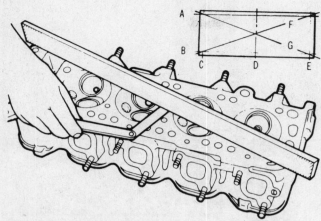

9.12   Check the cylinder head gasket surface for warpage by trying to slip a feeler gauge under the straightedge (see the Specifications for the maximum warpage allowed and use a feeler gauge of that thickness)

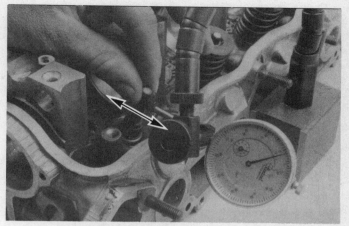

9.14   A dial indicator can be used to determine the valve stem-to-guide clearance (move the valve stem as indicated by the arrows)

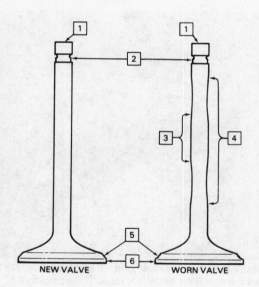

9.15   Check for valve wear at the points shown here

1	Valve tip	4	Stem (most worn area)
2	Keeper groove	5	Valve face
3	Stem (least worn area)	6	Margin

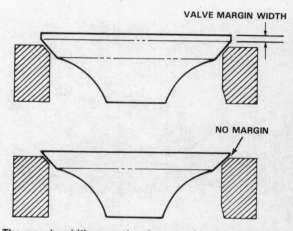

9.16   The margin width on each valve must be as specified (if no margin exists, the valve cannot be reused)

Compressed air will speed the drying process and can be used to clean out the oil passages.

9   Clean all the valve springs, spring seats, keepers and retainers with solvent and dry them thoroughly. Do the components from one valve at a time to avoid mixing up the parts.

10   Scrape off any heavy deposits that may have formed on the valves, then use a motorized wire brush to remove deposits from the valve heads and stems. Again, make sure the valves don't get mixed up.

Inspection

Note: *Be sure to perform all of the following inspection procedures before concluding that machine shop work is required. Make a list of the items that need attention.*

Cylinder head

11   Inspect the head very carefully for cracks, evidence of coolant leakage and other damage. If cracks are found, check with an automotive ma-

chine shop concerning repair. If repair isn't possible, a new cylinder head should be obtained.

12   Using a straightedge and feeler gauge, check the head gasket mating surface for warpage (see illustration). If the warpage exceeds the limit listed in this Chapter's Specifications, it can be resurfaced at an automotive machine shop.

13   Examine the valve seats in each of the combustion chambers. If they're pitted, cracked or burned, the head will require valve service that's beyond the scope of the home mechanic.

14   Check the valve stem-to-guide clearance by measuring the lateral movement of the valve stem with a dial indicator attached securely to the head (see illustration). The valve must be in the guide and approximately 1/16-inch off the seat. The total valve stem movement indicated by the gauge needle must be divided by two to obtain the actual clearance. After this is done, if there's still some doubt regarding the condition of the valve guides they should be checked by an automotive machine shop (the cost should be minimal).

Valves

15   Carefully inspect each valve face for uneven wear, deformation, cracks, pits and burned areas (see illustration). Check the valve stem for scuffing and galling and the neck for cracks. Rotate the valve and check for any obvious indication that it's bent. Look for pits and excessive wear on the end of the stem. The presence of any of these conditions indicates the need for valve service by an automotive machine shop.

16   Measure the margin width on each valve (see illustration). Any valve

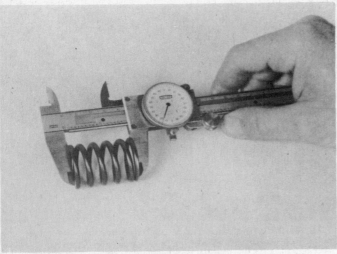

9.17   Measure the free length of each valve spring with a dial or vernier caliper

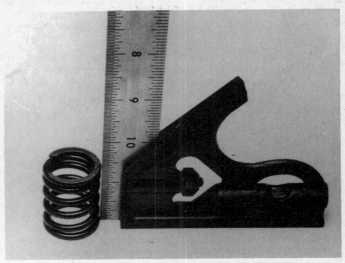

9.18   Check each valve spring for squareness

9.24   Check the cam lobes for pitting, wear and score marks – if scoring is excessive, as is the case here, replace the camshaft

9.25   Measure the height of each lobe – if any lobe height is less than the specified minimum, replace the camshaft

9.26   Measure the diameter of each journal – if any journal measures less than the specified minimum, replace the camshaft

with a margin narrower than specified will have to be replaced with a new one.

Valve components

17   Check each valve spring for wear (on the ends) and pits. Measure the free length and compare it to the Specifications in this Chapter (**see illustration**). Any springs that are shorter than specified have sagged and should not be reused. The tension of all springs should be checked with a special fixture before deciding that they're suitable for use in a rebuilt engine (take the springs to an automotive machine shop for this check).

18   Stand each spring on a flat surface and check it for squareness (**see illustration**). If any of the springs are distorted or sagged, replace all of them with new parts.

19   Check the spring retainers and keepers for obvious wear and cracks. Any questionable parts should be replaced with new ones, as extensive damage will occur if they fail during engine operation.

Rocker arm components

20   Check the rocker arm faces (the areas that contact the camshaft and valve stems) for pits, wear, galling, score marks and rough spots. Check the rocker arm pivot contact areas and shafts as well. Look for cracks in each rocker arm.

21   Check the rocker arm adjusting screws for damaged threads and nuts.

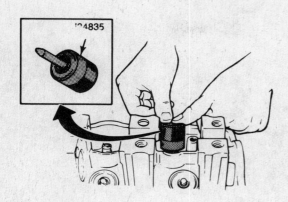

11.3a   Special tool J34835 is recommended for valve seal installation, . . .

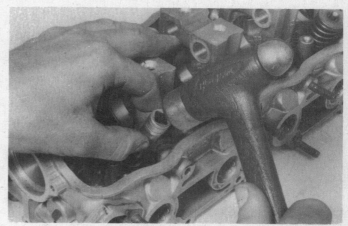

11.3b . . . but a deep socket and a hammer can be used if the tool isn't available – don't hammer on the seals once they're installed

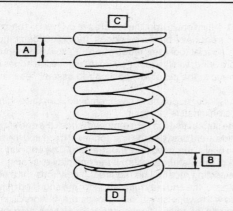

11.5   Ensure that the valve springs are installed with the small-pitch coils nearest to the cylinder head

A	Large-pitch coils	C	Valve spring retainer side
B	Small-pitch coils	D	Cylinder head side

22   Any damaged or excessively worn parts must be replaced with new ones.

23   If the inspection process indicates that the valve components are in generally poor condition and worn beyond the limits specified, which is usually the case in an engine that's being overhauled, reassemble the valves in the cylinder head and refer to Section 10 for valve servicing recommendations.

Camshaft

24   Visually examine the camshaft journals and rocker arms. Check for score marks, pitting and evidence of overheating (blue, discolored areas) **(see illustration)**. If wear is excessive or damage is evident, the component will have to be replaced.

25   Using a micrometer or an accurate caliper, measure the cam lobe height and compare it to this Chapter's Specifications. If the lobe height is less than the minimum allowable, the camshaft is worn and must be replaced **(see illustration)**.

26   Using a micrometer or accurate caliper, measure the diameter of each journal and compare it to this Chapter's Specifications **(see illustration)**. If the journals are worn or damaged, replace the camshaft.

27   Using an inside micrometer or a telescoping gauge, measure each housing bore. Subtract the journal diameter measurements from the housing bore measurements to determine the bearing oil clearance. Compare it to this Chapter's Specifications. If the clearance is greater than the maximum, replace the camshaft and, if necessary, the cylinder head.

10   Valves – servicing

1   Because of the complex nature of the job and the special tools and equipment needed, servicing of the valves, the valve seats and the valve guides, commonly known as a valve job, should be done by a professional.

2   The home mechanic can remove and disassemble the head, do the initial cleaning and inspection, then reassemble and deliver it to a dealer service department or an automotive machine shop for the actual service work. Doing the inspection will enable you to see what condition the head and valvetrain components are in and will ensure that you know what work and new parts are required when dealing with an automotive machine shop.

3   The dealer service department, or automotive machine shop, will remove the valves and springs, recondition or replace the valves and valve seats, recondition the valve guides, check and replace the valve springs, spring retainers and keepers (as necessary), replace the valve seals with new ones, reassemble the valve components and make sure the installed spring height is correct. The cylinder head gasket surface will also be resurfaced if it's warped.

4   After the valve job has been performed by a professional, the head will be in like new condition. When the head is returned, be sure to clean it again before installation on the engine to remove any metal particles and abrasive grit that may still be present from the valve service or head resurfacing operations. Use compressed air, if available, to blow out all the oil holes and passages.

11   Cylinder head – reassembly

Refer to illustrations 11.3a, 11.3b, 11.5, 11.6 and 11.8

1   Regardless of whether or not the head was sent to an automotive repair shop for valve servicing, make sure it's clean before beginning reassembly.

2   If the head was sent out for valve servicing, the valves and related components will already be in place. Begin the reassembly procedure with Step 8.

3   Install new seals on each of the valve guides. Using a hammer and a deep socket or seal installation tool, gently tap each seal into place until it's completely seated on the guide **(see illustrations)**. Don't twist or cock the seals during installation or they won't seal properly on the valve stems.

4   Beginning at one end of the head, lubricate and install the first valve. Apply moly-base grease or clean engine oil to the valve stem.

5   Drop the spring seat or shim(s) (if used) over the valve guide and set the valve spring and retainer in place **(see illustration)**.

6   Compress the springs with a valve spring compressor and carefully install the keepers in the groove, then slowly release the compressor and

11.6   Keepers don't always stay in place, so apply a small dab of grease to each one as shown here before installation – it'll hold them in place on the valve stem as the spring is released

11.8   Be sure to check the valve spring installed height (the distance from the top of the seat/shims to the top of the spring)

make sure the keepers seat properly. Apply a small dab of grease to each keeper to hold it in place if necessary **(see illustration)**.

7   Repeat the procedure for the remaining valves. Be sure to return the components to their original locations – don't mix them up!

8   Check the installed valve spring height with a ruler graduated in 1/32-inch increments or a dial caliper. If the head was sent out for service work, the installed height should be correct (but don't automatically assume that it is). The measurement is taken from the top of each spring seat or shim(s) to the bottom of the retainer **(see illustration)**. If the height is greater than specified, shims can be added under the springs to correct it. **Caution:** *Don't, under any circumstances, shim the springs to the point where the installed height is less than specified.*

9   Apply moly-base grease to the rocker arm faces and the camshaft, then install the camshaft, rocker arms, springs and shafts.

10   Reinstall the distributor case, using a new O-ring.

12   Pistons/connecting rods – removal

Refer to illustrations 12.1, 12.3 and 12.6

Note: *Prior to removing the piston/connecting rod assemblies, remove the cylinder head, the oil pan and the oil pickup by referring to the appropriate Sections in Chapter 2.*

1   Use your fingernail to feel if a ridge has formed at the upper limit of ring travel (about 1/4-inch down from the top of each cylinder). If carbon deposits or cylinder wear have produced ridges, they must be completely removed with a special tool **(see illustration)**. Follow the manufacturer's instructions provided with the tool. Failure to remove the ridges before attempting to remove the piston/connecting rod assemblies may result in piston breakage.

2   After the cylinder ridges have been removed, turn the engine upside-down so the crankshaft is facing up.

3   Before the connecting rods are removed, check the end play with feeler gauges. Slide them between the first connecting rod and the crankshaft throw until the play is removed **(see illustration)**. The end play is equal to the thickness of the feeler gauge(s). If the end play exceeds the service limit, new connecting rods will be required. If new rods (or a new crankshaft) are installed, the end play may fall under the specified minimum (if it does, the rods will have to be machined to restore it – consult an automotive machine shop for advice if necessary). Repeat the procedure for the remaining connecting rods.

4   Check the connecting rods and caps for identification marks. If they aren't plainly marked, use a small center punch to make the appropriate number of indentations on each rod and cap (1, 2, 3, 4, depending on the cylinder they're associated with).

5   Loosen each of the connecting rod cap nuts 1/2-turn at a time until they can be removed by hand. Remove the number one connecting rod cap and bearing insert. Don't drop the bearing insert out of the cap.

6   Slip a short length of plastic or rubber hose over each connecting rod

12.1   A ridge reamer is required to remove the ridge from the top of the cylinder – do this before removing the pistons!

12.3   Check the connecting rod end play with a feeler gauge as shown

12.6   To prevent damage to the crankshaft journals and cylinder walls, slip section of hose over the rod bolts before removing the pistons

13.1   Checking crankshaft endplay with a dial indicator

cap bolt to protect the crankshaft journal and cylinder wall as the piston is removed **(see illustration)**.

7   Remove the bearing insert and push the connecting rod/piston assembly out through the top of the engine. Use a wooden hammer handle to push on the upper bearing surface in the connecting rod. If resistance is felt, double-check to make sure that all of the ridge was removed from the cylinder.

8   Repeat the procedure for the remaining cylinders.

9   After removal, reassemble the connecting rod caps and bearing inserts in their respective connecting rods and install the cap nuts finger tight. Leaving the old bearing inserts in place until reassembly will help prevent the connecting rod bearing surfaces from being accidentally nicked or gouged.

10   Don't separate the pistons from the connecting rods (see Section 17 for additional information).

13   Crankshaft – removal

Refer to illustrations 13.1, 13.3, 13.4a and 13.4b

Note: *The crankshaft can be removed only after the engine has been removed from the vehicle. It's assumed that the flywheel or driveplate,* *crankshaft pulley, timing belt, oil pan, oil pump and piston/connecting rod assemblies have already been removed. The rear oil seal housing must be unbolted and separated from the block before proceeding with crankshaft removal.*

1   Before the crankshaft is removed, check the end play. Mount a dial indicator with the stem in line with the crankshaft and just touching one of the crank throws **(see illustration)**.

2   Push the crankshaft all the way to the rear and zero the dial indicator. Next, pry the crankshaft to the front as far as possible and check the reading on the dial indicator. The distance that it moves is the end play. If it's greater than specified, check the crankshaft thrust surfaces for wear. If no wear is evident, new thrust bearings should correct the end play.

3   If a dial indicator isn't available, feeler gauges can be used. Gently pry or push the crankshaft all the way to the front of the engine. Slip feeler gauges between the crankshaft and the front face of the thrust bearing to determine the clearance **(see illustration)**. The thrust bearings are located on both sides of the third main bearing saddle (not on the bearing cap).

4   Check the main bearing caps to see if they're marked to indicate their locations. They should be numbered consecutively from the front of the engine to the rear. If they aren't, mark them with number stamping dies or a center punch **(see illustration)**. Main bearing caps generally have a cast-

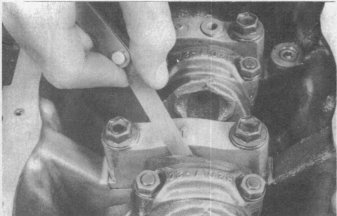

13.3   Checking crankshaft endplay with a feeler gauge

13.4a   Use a center punch or number stamping dies to mark the main bearing caps to ensure that they're reinstalled in their original locations on the block (make the punch marks near one of the bolt heads)

13.4b The arrow on the main bearing cap indicates the front of the engine

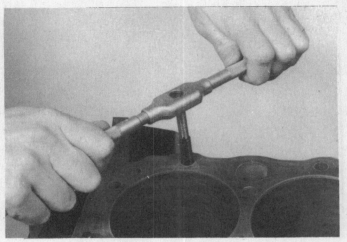

14.8 All bolt holes in the block – particularly the main bearing cap and head bolt holes – should be cleaned and restored with a tap (be sure to remove debris from the holes after this is done)

in arrow, which points to the front of the engine **(see illustration)**. Loosen the main bearing cap bolts 1/4-turn at a time each, until they can be removed by hand. Note if any stud bolts are used and make sure they're returned to their original locations when the crankshaft is reinstalled.

5   Gently tap the caps with a soft-face hammer, then separate them from the engine block. If necessary, use the bolts as levers to remove the caps. Try not to drop the bearing inserts if they come out with the caps.

6   Carefully lift the crankshaft out of the engine. It may be a good idea to have an assistant available, since the crankshaft is quite heavy. With the bearing inserts in place in the engine block and main bearing caps, return the caps to their respective locations on the engine block and tighten the bolts finger tight.

14 Engine block – cleaning

Refer to illustration 14.8

Caution: *The core plugs (also known as freeze or soft plugs) may be difficult or impossible to retrieve if they're driven into the block coolant passages.*

1   Remove the engine mount brackets and any other components still attached to the engine block.

2   Using a gasket scraper, remove all traces of gasket material from the engine block. Be very careful not to nick or gouge the gasket sealing surfaces.

3   Remove the main bearing caps and separate the bearing inserts from the caps and the engine block. Tag the bearings, indicating which cylinder they were removed from and whether they were in the cap or the block, then set them aside.

4   Remove all of the threaded oil gallery plugs from the block. The plugs are usually very tight – they may have to be drilled out and the holes re-tapped. Use new plugs when the engine is reassembled.

5   If the engine is extremely dirty it should be taken to an automotive machine shop to be steam cleaned or hot tanked.

6   After the block is returned, clean all oil holes and oil galleries one more time. Brushes specifically designed for this purpose are available at most auto parts stores. Flush the passages with warm water until the water runs clear, dry the block thoroughly and wipe all machined surfaces with a light, rust preventive oil. If you have access to compressed air, use it to speed the drying process and to blow out all the oil holes and galleries. **Warning:** *Wear eye protection when using compressed air!*

7   If the block isn't extremely dirty or sludged up, you can do an adequate cleaning job with hot soapy water and a stiff brush. Take plenty of time and do a thorough job. Regardless of the cleaning method used, be sure to clean all oil holes and galleries very thoroughly, dry the block completely and coat all machined surfaces with light oil.

8   The threaded holes in the block must be clean to ensure accurate torque readings during reassembly. Run the proper size tap into each of the holes to remove rust, corrosion, thread sealant or sludge and restore damaged threads **(see illustration)**. If possible, use compressed air to clear the holes of debris produced by this operation. Now is a good time to clean the threads on the head bolts and the main bearing cap bolts as well.

9   Reinstall the main bearing caps and tighten the bolts finger tight.

10   Apply non-hardening sealant (such as Permatex no. 2 or Teflon pipe sealant) to the new oil gallery plugs and thread them into the holes in the block. Make sure they're tightened securely.

11   If the engine isn't going to be reassembled right away, cover it with a large plastic trash bag to keep it clean.

15 Engine block – inspection

Refer to illustrations 15.4a, 15.4b, 15.4c and 15.13

1   Before the block is inspected, it should be cleaned as described in Section 14.

2   Visually check the block for cracks, rust and corrosion. Look for stripped threads in the threaded holes. It's also a good idea to have the block checked for hidden cracks by an automotive machine shop that has the special equipment to do this type of work. If defects are found, have the block repaired, if possible, or replaced.

3   Check the cylinder bores for scuffing and scoring.

4   Measure the diameter of each cylinder at the top (just under the ridge area), center and bottom of the cylinder bore, parallel to the crankshaft axis **(see illustrations)**.

5   Next, measure each cylinder's diameter at the same three locations across the crankshaft axis. Compare the results to the Specifications.

6   If the required precision measuring tools aren't available, the piston-to-cylinder clearances can be obtained, though not quite as accurately, using feeler gauge stock. Feeler gauge stock comes in 12-inch lengths and various thicknesses and is generally available at auto parts stores.

7   To check the clearance, select a feeler gauge and slip it into the cylinder along with the matching piston. The piston must be positioned exactly as it normally would be. The feeler gauge must be between the piston and cylinder on one of the thrust faces (90-degrees to the piston pin bore).

8   The piston should slip through the cylinder (with the feeler gauge in place) with moderate pressure.

9   If it falls through or slides through easily, the clearance is excessive and a new piston will be required. If the piston binds at the lower end of the cylinder and is loose toward the top, the cylinder is tapered. If tight spots are encountered as the piston/feeler gauge is rotated in the cylinder, the cylinder is out-of-round.

10   Repeat the procedure for the remaining pistons and cylinders.

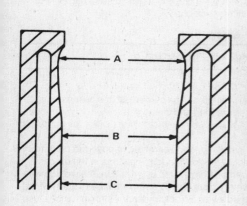

15.4a   Measure the diameter of each cylinder just under the wear ridge (A), at the center (B) and at the bottom (C)

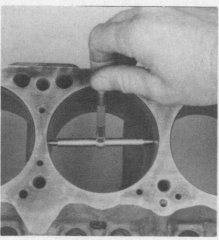

15.4b   The ability to "feel" when the telescoping gauge is at the correct point will be developed over time, so work slowly and repeat the check until you're satisfied that the bore measurement is accurate

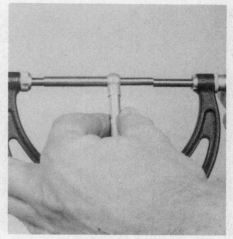

15.4c   The gauge is then measured with a micrometer to determine the bore size

2B

11   If the cylinder walls are badly scuffed or scored, or if they're out-of-round or tapered beyond the limits given in the Specifications, have the engine block rebored and honed at an automotive machine shop. If a re-bore is done, oversize pistons and rings will be required.

12   If the cylinders are in reasonably good condition and not worn to the outside of the limits, and if the piston-to-cylinder clearances can be maintained properly, then they don't have to be rebored. Honing is all that's necessary (Section 16).

13   Engines are originally fitted with either of two sizes of standard pistons. The engine blocks are stamped with number codes to indicate the size that was installed at the factory (see illustration). Consult the Specifications for dimensions.

---

16   Cylinder honing

Refer to illustrations 16.3a and 16.3b

1   Prior to engine reassembly, the cylinder bores must be honed so the

new piston rings will seat correctly and provide the best possible combustion chamber seal. **Note:** *If you don't have the tools or don't want to tackle the honing operation, most automotive machine shops will do it for a reasonable fee.*

2   Before honing the cylinders, install the main bearing caps and tighten the bolts to the specified torque.

3   Two types of cylinder hones are commonly available – the flex hone or "bottle brush" type and the more traditional surfacing hone with spring-loaded stones. Both will do the job, but for the less experienced mechanic the "bottle brush" hone will probably be easier to use. You'll also need some kerosene or honing oil, rags and an electric drill motor. Proceed as follows:

a)   Mount the hone in the drill motor, compress the stones and slip it into the first cylinder (see illustration). Be sure to wear safety goggles or a face shield!

b)   Lubricate the cylinder with plenty of honing oil, turn on the drill and move the hone up-and-down in the cylinder at a pace that will produce a fine crosshatch pattern on the cylinder walls. Ideally, the crosshatch lines should intersect at approximately a 60-degree

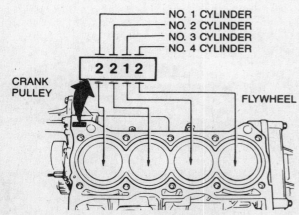

15.13   The engine block is stamped near the front of the head gasket – the numbers indicate the piston size fitted in the respective cylinders

16.3a   A "bottle brush" hone will produce better results if you've never done cylinder honing before

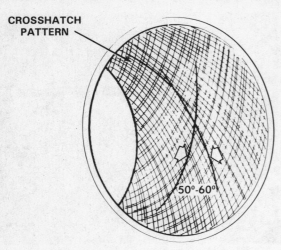

CROSSHATCH
PATTERN

50°-60°

**16.3b   The cylinder hone should leave a smooth,
crosshatch pattern with the lines intersecting at
approximately a 60-degree angle**

angle **(see illustration)**. Be sure to use plenty of lubricant and don't take off any more material than is absolutely necessary to produce the desired finish. **Note:** *Piston ring manufacturers may specify a smaller crosshatch angle than the traditional 60-degree – read and follow any instructions included with the new rings.*

c) Don't withdraw the hone from the cylinder while it's running. Instead, shut off the drill and continue moving the hone up-and-down in the cylinder until it comes to a complete stop, then compress the stones and withdraw the hone. If you're using a "bottle brush" type hone, stop the drill motor, then turn the chuck in the normal direction of rotation while withdrawing the hone from the cylinder.

d) Wipe the oil out of the cylinder and repeat the procedure for the remaining cylinders.

4   After the honing job is complete, chamfer the top edges of the cylinder bores with a small file so the rings won't catch when the pistons are installed. Be very careful not to nick the cylinder walls with the end of the file.

5   The entire engine block must be washed again very thoroughly with warm, soapy water to remove all traces of the abrasive grit produced during the honing operation. **Note:** *The bores can be considered clean when a lint-free white cloth – dampened with clean engine oil – used to wipe them out doesn't pick up any more honing residue, which will show up as gray areas on the cloth.* Be sure to run a brush through all oil holes and galleries and flush them with running water.

6   After rinsing, dry the block and apply a coat of light rust preventive oil to all machined surfaces. Wrap the block in a plastic trash bag to keep it clean and set it aside until reassembly.

17   Pistons/connecting rods – inspection

Refer to illustrations 17.4a, 17.4b, 17.10, 17.11a and 17.11b

1   Before the inspection process can be carried out, the piston/connecting rod assemblies must be cleaned and the original piston rings removed from the pistons. **Note:** *Always use new piston rings when the engine is reassembled.*

2   Using a piston ring installation tool, carefully remove the rings from the pistons. Be careful not to nick or gouge the pistons in the process.

3   Scrape all traces of carbon from the top of the piston. A handheld wire brush or a piece of fine emery cloth can be used once the majority of the deposits have been scraped away. Do not, under any circumstances, use a wire brush mounted in a drill motor to remove deposits from the pistons. The piston material is soft and may be eroded away by the wire brush.

4   Use a piston ring groove cleaning tool to remove carbon deposits from the ring grooves. If a tool isn't available, a piece broken off the old ring will do the job. Be very careful to remove only the carbon deposits – don't remove any metal and do not nick or scratch the sides of the ring grooves **(see illustrations)**.

5   Once the deposits have been removed, clean the piston/rod assemblies with solvent and dry them with compressed air (if available). Make sure the oil return holes in the back sides of the ring grooves are clear.

6   If the pistons and cylinder walls aren't damaged or worn excessively, and if the engine block is not rebored, new pistons won't be necessary. Normal piston wear appears as even vertical wear on the piston thrust surfaces and slight looseness of the top ring in its groove. New piston rings, however, should always be used when an engine is rebuilt.

7   Carefully inspect each piston for cracks around the skirt, at the pin bosses and at the ring lands.

8   Look for scoring and scuffing on the thrust faces of the skirt, holes in the piston crown and burned areas at the edge of the crown. If the skirt is scored or scuffed, the engine may have been suffering from overheating and/or abnormal combustion, which caused excessively high operating temperatures. The cooling and lubrication systems should be checked thoroughly. A hole in the piston crown is an indication that abnormal combustion (preignition) was occurring. Burned areas at the edge of the piston crown are usually evidence of spark knock (detonation). If any of the above problems exist, the causes must be corrected or the damage will occur again. The causes may include intake air leaks, incorrect fuel/air mixture, incorrect ignition timing and EGR system malfunctions.

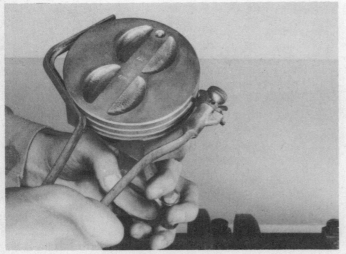

**17.4a   The piston ring grooves can be cleaned with a
special tool, as shown here, . . .**

17.4b . . . or a section of a broken ring

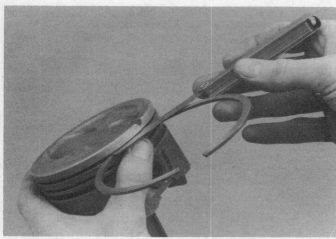

17.10   Check the ring side clearance with a feeler gauge at several points around the groove

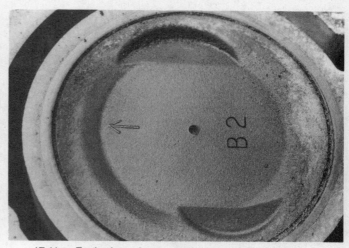

17.11a   Each piston has a number stamped in the top (1 or 2) – the arrow points to front of the engine and the letter (B) is a production code

9   Corrosion of the piston, in the form of small pits, indicates that coolant is leaking into the combustion chamber and/or the crankcase. Again, the cause must be corrected or the problem may persist in the rebuilt engine.

10   Measure the piston ring side clearance by laying a new piston ring in each ring groove and slipping a feeler gauge in beside it **(see illustration)**. Check the clearance at three or four locations around each groove. Be sure to use the correct ring for each groove – they are different. If the side clearance is greater than specified, new pistons will have to be used.

11   Check the piston-to-bore clearance by measuring the bore (see Section 15) and the piston diameter. Either of two standard size pistons may be fitted at the factory. Each piston has a number stamped on top **(see illustration)**. There are also numbers stamped on the block **(see illustration 15.13)**. The numbers (either 1 or 2) on the pistons and block designate the bore size. Make sure the pistons and bores are correctly matched. Measure the piston across the skirt, at a 90-degree angle to the piston pin, the specified distance up from the bottom edge of the skirt **(see illustration)**. Subtract the piston diameter from the bore diameter to obtain the clearance. If it's greater than specified, the block will have to be rebored and new pistons and rings installed.

12   Check the piston-to-rod clearance by twisting the piston and rod in opposite directions. Any noticeable play indicates excessive wear, which must be corrected. The piston/connecting rod assemblies should be taken to an automotive machine shop to have the pistons and rods resized and

new pins installed.

13   If the pistons must be removed from the connecting rods for any reason, they should be taken to an automotive machine shop. While they are there have the connecting rods checked for bend and twist, since automotive machine shops have special equipment for this purpose. **Note:** *Unless new pistons and/or connecting rods must be installed, do not disassemble the pistons and connecting rods.*

14   Check the connecting rods for cracks and other damage. Temporarily remove the rod caps, lift out the old bearing inserts, wipe the rod and cap bearing surfaces clean and inspect them for nicks, gouges and scratches. After checking the rods, replace the old bearings, slip the caps into place and tighten the nuts finger tight. **Note:** *If the engine is being rebuilt because of a connecting rod knock, be sure to install new rods.*

18   Crankshaft – inspection

Refer to illustrations 18.1, 18.3, 18.4, 18.6 and 18.8

1   Clean the crankshaft with solvent and dry it with compressed air (if available). Be sure to clean the oil holes with a stiff brush **(see illustration)** and flush them with solvent.

2   Check the main and connecting rod bearing journals for uneven wear, scoring, pits and cracks.

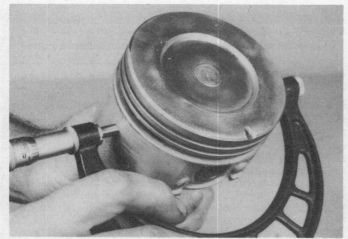

17.11b   Measure the piston diameter at a 90-degree angle to the piston pin and make sure the micrometer is positioned the specified distance from the bottom edge of the skirt

18.1   Use a wire or stiff bristle brush to clean the oil holes in the crankshaft

2B

18.3   Rubbing a penny across each journal will reveal their condition – if copper rubs off and adheres to the crankshaft, the journals should be reground

18.4   The oil holes should be chamfered so sharp edges don't gouge or scratch the new bearings

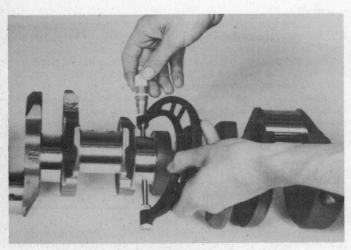

18.6   Measure the diameter of each crankshaft journal at several points to detect taper and out-of-round conditions

18.8   If the seals have worn grooves in the crankshaft journals, or if the seal contact surfaces are nicked or scratched, the new seals will leak

3   Rub a penny across each journal several times (**see illustration**). If a journal picks up copper from the penny, it's too rough and must be reground.

4   Remove all burrs from the crankshaft oil holes with a stone, file or scraper (**see illustration**).

5   Check the rest of the crankshaft for cracks and other damage. It should be magnafluxed to reveal hidden cracks – an automotive machine shop will handle the procedure.

6   Using a micrometer, measure the diameter of the main and connecting rod journals and compare the results to the Specifications (**see illustration**). By measuring the diameter at a number of points around each journal's circumference, you'll be able to determine whether or not the journal is out-of-round. Take the measurement at each end of the journal, near the crank throws, to determine if the journal is tapered.

7   If the crankshaft journals are damaged, tapered, out-of-round or worn beyond the limits given in the Specifications, have the crankshaft reground by an automotive machine shop. Be sure to use the correct size bearing inserts if the crankshaft is reconditioned.

8   Check the oil seal journals at each end of the crankshaft for wear and damage. If the seal has worn a groove in the journal, or if it's nicked or scratched (**see illustration**), the new seal may leak when the engine is reassembled. In some cases, an automotive machine shop may be able to

repair the journal by pressing on a thin sleeve. If repair isn't feasible, a new or different crankshaft should be installed.

9   Refer to Section 19 and examine the main and rod bearing inserts.

---

19   Main and connecting rod bearings – inspection and selection

Inspection

Refer to illustration 19.1

1   Even though the main and connecting rod bearings should be replaced with new ones during the engine overhaul, the old bearings should be retained for close examination, as they may reveal valuable information about the condition of the engine (**see illustration**).

2   Bearing failure occurs because of lack of lubrication, the presence of dirt or other foreign particles, overloading the engine and corrosion. Regardless of the cause of bearing failure, it must be corrected before the engine is reassembled to prevent it from happening again.

3   When examining the bearings, remove them from the engine block, the main bearing caps, the connecting rods and the rod caps and lay them out on a clean surface in the same general position as their location in the engine. This will enable you to match any bearing problems with the corresponding crankshaft journal.

19.1   Typical bearing failures

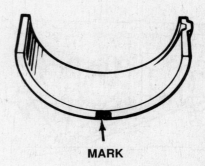

19.9   Standard size main bearings have one paint mark; undersize bearings have two paint marks – the colors indicate the bearing thickness at the center of the bearings

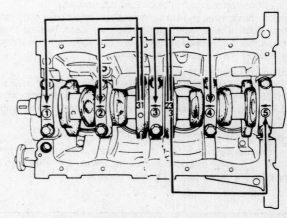

19.10   The crankshaft webs on both sides of the number three main bearing are stamped with numerals (1, 2 or 3) to indicate the size of each main bearing journal – the arrows in this drawing show which bearing each numeral is associated with

4   Dirt and other foreign particles get into the engine in a variety of ways. It may be left in the engine during assembly, or it may pass through filters or the PCV system. It may get into the oil, and from there into the bearings. Metal chips from machining operations and normal engine wear are often present. Abrasives are sometimes left in engine components after reconditioning, especially when parts are not thoroughly cleaned using the proper cleaning methods. Whatever the source, these foreign objects often end up embedded in the soft bearing material and are easily recognized. Large particles will not embed in the bearing and will score or gouge the bearing and journal. The best prevention for this cause of bearing failure is to clean all parts thoroughly and keep everything spotlessly clean during engine assembly. Frequent and regular engine oil and filter changes are also recommended.

5   Lack of lubrication (or lubrication breakdown) has a number of interrelated causes. Excessive heat (which thins the oil), overloading (which squeezes the oil from the bearing face) and oil leakage or throw off (from excessive bearing clearances, worn oil pump or high engine speeds) all contribute to lubrication breakdown. Blocked oil passages, which usually are the result of misaligned oil holes in a bearing shell, will also oil starve a bearing and destroy it. When lack of lubrication is the cause of bearing failure, the bearing material is wiped or extruded from the steel backing of the bearing. Temperatures may increase to the point where the steel backing turns blue from overheating.

6   Driving habits can have a definite effect on bearing life. Full throttle, low speed operation (lugging the engine) puts very high loads on bearings, which tends to squeeze out the oil film. These loads cause the bearings to flex, which produces fine cracks in the bearing face (fatigue failure). Eventually the bearing material will loosen in pieces and tear away from the steel backing. Short trip driving leads to corrosion of bearings because insufficient engine heat is produced to drive off the condensed water and corrosive gases. These products collect in the engine oil, forming acid and sludge. As the oil is carried to the engine bearings, the acid attacks and corrodes the bearing material.

7   Incorrect bearing installation during engine assembly will lead to bearing failure as well. Tight fitting bearings leave insufficient bearing oil clearance and will result in oil starvation. Dirt or foreign particles trapped behind a bearing insert result in high spots on the bearing which lead to failure.

Selection
Refer to illustrations 19.9, 19.10, 19.11 and 19.12

8   If the original bearings are worn or damaged, or if the oil clearances are incorrect (Section 22 or 24), the following procedures should be used to select the correct new bearings for engine reassembly. However, if the crankshaft has been reground, new undersize bearings must be installed – the following procedure should not be used if undersize bearings are required! The automotive machine shop that reconditions the crankshaft will provide or help you select the correct size bearings. Regardless of how the bearing sizes are determined, use the oil clearance, measured with Plastigage, as a guide to ensure the bearings are the right size.

Main bearings
9   If you need to use a STANDARD size main bearing, install one that has the same color code as the original bearing (**see illustration**).

10   If the color code on the original main bearing has been obscured, first locate the number on the crankshaft web that designates the crankshaft journal diameter (**see illustration**).

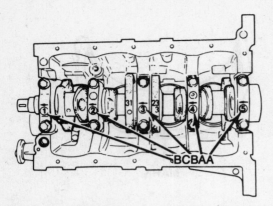

19.11   The letters (A, B or C) stamped in the oil pan mating surface indicate the sizes of the main bearing bores in the block – again, the arrows show which bearing each letter is associated with

		NUMERAL STAMPED ON CRANK WEB (JOURNAL DIAMETER)		
		1	2	3
Letter stamped on mating surface	A	Green	Black	Colorless
	B	Black	Colorless	Yellow
	C	Colorless	Yellow	Blue
		New standard bearing to be installed.		

19.12   Use this table to find the correct bearing color code

11   Next, locate the main bearing bore grade letters stamped into the oil pan mating surface on the engine block **(see illustration)**.

12   Use the accompanying chart to determine the correct color code **(see illustration)**. **Note:** *The actual main bearing bore sizes, bearing thicknesses and journal diameters designated by the number, letter and color codes are listed in this Chapter's Specifications.*

Connecting rod bearings

13   Two kinds of rod bearings are available from your dealer; standard size and a 0.25 mm (0.0098 in) undersize bearing. The undersize bearing has "US025" stamped on its back. Standard size bearings have no marking.

All bearings

14   Remember, the oil clearance is the final judge when selecting new bearing sizes. If you have any questions or are unsure which bearings to use, get help from a dealer parts or service department.

---

20   Engine overhaul – reassembly sequence

Refer to illustrations 20.2a, 20.2b and 20.2c

1   Before beginning engine reassembly, make sure you have all the necessary new parts, gaskets and seals as well as the following items on hand:

> Common hand tools
> A 1/2-inch drive torque wrench
> Piston ring installation tool
> Piston ring compressor
> Short lengths of rubber or plastic hose
>   to fit over connecting rod bolts
> Plastigage
> Feeler gauges
> A fine-tooth file
> New engine oil
> Engine assembly lube or moly-base grease
> Gasket sealant
> Thread locking compound

2   In order to save time and avoid problems, engine reassembly must be done in the following general order **(see illustrations)**:

> Piston rings
> Crankshaft and main bearings
> Rear main oil seal and housing
> Piston/connecting rod assemblies
> Oil pump
> Camshaft, rocker arms and shafts
> Oil pan

20.2a   Carburetor equipped engine – left side view

Cylinder head
Timing belt and sprockets
Timing belt cover
Intake and exhaust manifolds
Camshaft cover
Engine rear plate
Flywheel/driveplate

---

21   Piston rings – installation

Refer to illustrations 21.3, 21.4, 21.5, 21.9a, 21.9b, 21.12a and 21.12b

1   Before installing the new piston rings, the ring end gaps must be checked. It's assumed that the piston ring side clearance has been checked and verified correct (Section 17).

2   Lay out the piston/connecting rod assemblies and the new ring sets so the ring sets will be matched with the same piston and cylinder during the end gap measurement and engine assembly.

3   Insert the top (number one) ring into the first cylinder and square it up with the cylinder walls by pushing it in with the top of the piston **(see illustration)**. The ring should be near the bottom of the cylinder, at the lower limit of ring travel.

4   To measure the end gap, slip feeler gauges between the ends of the ring until a gauge equal to the gap width is found **(see illustration)**. The

20.2b   Carburetor equipped engine – front view

20.2c   Carburetor equipped engine – right side view

2B

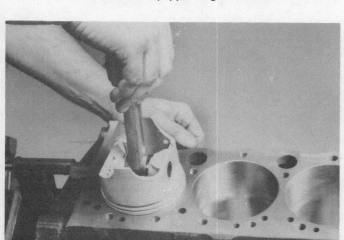

21.3   When checking piston ring end gap, the ring must be square in the cylinder bore (this is done by pushing the ring down with the top of a piston as shown)

21.4   With the ring square in the cylinder, measure the end gap with a feeler gauge

21.5   If the end gap is too small, clamp a file in a vise and file the ring ends (from the outside in only) to enlarge the gap slightly

feeler gauge should slide between the ring ends with a slight amount of drag. Compare the measurement to the Specifications. If the gap is larger or smaller than specified, double-check to make sure you have the correct rings before proceeding.

5   If the gap is too small, it must be enlarged or the ring ends may come in contact with each other during engine operation, which can cause serious damage to the engine. The end gap can be increased by filing the ring ends very carefully with a fine file. Mount the file in a vise equipped with soft jaws, slip the ring over the file with the ends contacting the file face and slowly move the ring to remove material from the ends. When performing this operation, file only from the outside in **(see illustration)**.

6   Excess end gap isn't critical unless it's greater than 0.040-inch. Again, double-check to make sure you have the correct rings for your engine.

7   Repeat the procedure for each ring that will be installed in the first cylinder and for each ring in the remaining cylinders. Remember to keep rings, pistons and cylinders matched up.

8   Once the ring end gaps have been checked/corrected, the rings can be installed on the pistons.

9   The oil control ring (lowest one on the piston) is usually installed first. It's composed of three separate components. Slip the spacer/expander

21.9a   Installing the spacer/expander in the oil control ring groove

21.9b   DO NOT use a piston ring installation tool when installing the oil ring side rails

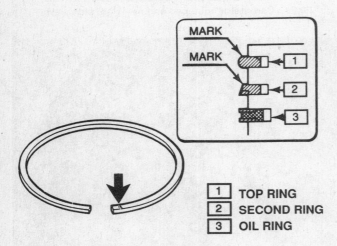

MARK

MARK

1

2

3

1 TOP RING
2 SECOND RING
3 OIL RING

21.12a   Earlier models have marks on both compression rings to indicate the top; later models may not have marks on the top rings – always follow the piston ring manufacturer's instructions when installing the rings

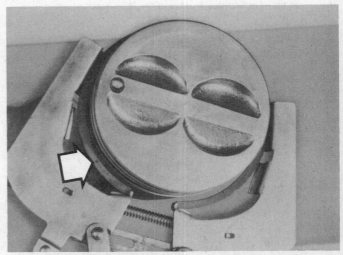

21.12b   Installing the compression rings with a ring expander – the mark (if applicable) must face up (arrow)

into the groove **(see illustration)**. If an anti-rotation tang is used, make sure it's inserted into the drilled hole in the ring groove. Next, install the lower side rail. Don't use a piston ring installation tool on the oil ring side rails, as they may be damaged. Instead, place one end of the side rail into the groove between the spacer/expander and the ring land, hold it firmly in place and slide a finger around the piston while pushing the rail into the groove **(see illustration)**. Next, install the upper side rail in the same manner.

10   After the three oil ring components have been installed, check to make sure that both the upper and lower side rails can be turned smoothly in the ring groove.

11   The number two (middle) ring is installed next. It's usually stamped with a mark which must face up, toward the top of the piston. **Note:** *Always follow the instructions printed on the ring package or box – different manufacturers may require different approaches. Do not mix up the top and middle rings, as they have different cross sections.*

12   Use a piston ring installation tool and make sure the identification mark is facing the top of the piston, then slip the ring into the middle groove on the piston **(see illustrations)**. Don't expand the ring any more than necessary to slide it over the piston.

13   Install the number one (top) ring in the same manner. Make sure the mark is facing up. Be careful not to confuse the number one and number two rings. **Note:** *Later model engines may not have a mark on the top ring. These unmarked rings can be installed with either side facing up. See Suzuki Service Bulletin ST-043-8 at your dealer for further information.*

14   Repeat the procedure for the remaining pistons and rings.

22   Crankshaft – installation and main bearing oil clearance check

Refer to illustrations 22.5, 22.6, 22.11 and 22.15

1   Crankshaft installation is the first step in engine reassembly. It's assumed at this point that the engine block and crankshaft have been cleaned, inspected and repaired or reconditioned.

2   Position the engine with the bottom facing up.

3   Remove the main bearing cap bolts and lift out the caps. Lay them out in the proper order to ensure correct installation.

4   If they're still in place, remove the original bearing inserts from the

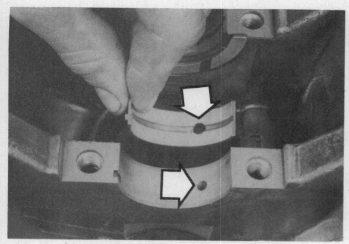

22.5   Ensure that the oil holes (arrows) align

22.6   Install the thrust bearings on both sides of the bearing saddle in the block; be sure the oil grooves face out

2B

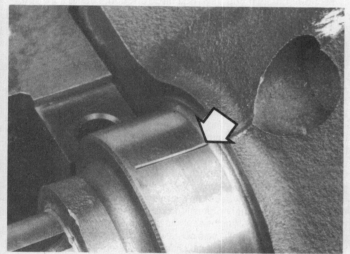

22.11   Lay the Plastigage strips (arrow) on the main bearing journals, parallel to the crankshaft centerline

22.15   Compare the width of the crushed Plastigage to the scale on the envelope to determine the main bearing oil clearance (always take the measurement at the widest point of the Plastigage); be sure to use the correct scale – standard and metric scales are included

block and the main bearing caps. Wipe the bearing surfaces of the block and caps with a clean, lint-free cloth. They must be kept spotlessly clean.

Main bearing oil clearance check

5   Clean the back sides of the new main bearing inserts and lay one in each main bearing saddle in the block. If one of the bearing inserts from each set has a large groove in it, make sure the grooved insert is installed in the block. Lay the other bearing from each set in the corresponding main bearing cap. Make sure the tab on the bearing insert fits into the recess in the block or cap. **Caution:** *The oil holes in the block must line up with the oil holes in the bearing insert* **(see illustration)**. *Do not hammer the bearing into place and don't nick or gouge the bearing faces. No lubrication should be used at this time.*

6   The flanged thrust bearings must be installed in the number three (center) saddle **(see illustration)**.

7   Clean the faces of the bearings in the block and the crankshaft main bearing journals with a clean, lint-free cloth.

8   Check or clean the oil holes in the crankshaft, as any dirt here can go only one way – straight through the new bearings.

9   Once you're certain the crankshaft is clean, carefully lay it in position

in the main bearings.

10   Before the crankshaft can be permanently installed, the main bearing oil clearance must be checked.

11   Cut several pieces of the appropriate size Plastigage (they must be slightly shorter than the width of the main bearings) and place one piece on each crankshaft main bearing journal, parallel with the journal axis **(see illustration)**.

12   Clean the faces of the bearings in the caps and install the caps in their respective positions (don't mix them up) with the arrows pointing toward the front of the engine. Don't disturb the Plastigage.

13   Starting with the center main and working out toward the ends, tighten the main bearing cap bolts, in three steps, to the specified torque. Don't rotate the crankshaft at any time during this operation.

14   Remove the bolts and carefully lift off the main bearing caps. Keep them in order. Don't disturb the Plastigage or rotate the crankshaft. If any of the main bearing caps are difficult to remove, tap them gently from side-to-side with a soft-face hammer to loosen them.

15   Compare the width of the crushed Plastigage on each journal to the scale printed on the Plastigage envelope to obtain the main bearing oil clearance **(see illustration)**. Check the Specifications to make sure it's correct.

23.3   After removing the housing from the block, support it on a couple of wood blocks and drive out the old seal with a hammer and punch

23.4   Drive the new seal into the housing with a block of wood or a section of pipe, if you have one large enough – make sure you don't cock the seal in the bore

16   If the clearance is not as specified, the bearing inserts may be the wrong size (which means different ones will be required). Before deciding that different inserts are needed, make sure that no dirt or oil was between the bearing inserts and the caps or block when the clearance was measured. If the Plastigage was wider at one end than the other, the journal may be tapered (refer to Section 18).

17   Carefully scrape all traces of the Plastigage material off the main bearing journals and/or the bearing faces. Use your fingernail or the edge of a credit card – don't nick or scratch the bearing faces.

Final crankshaft installation

18   Carefully lift the crankshaft out of the engine.

19   Clean the bearing faces in the block, then apply a thin, uniform layer of moly-base grease or engine assembly lube to each of the bearing surfaces and the thrust bearings.

20   Make sure the crankshaft journals are clean, then lay the crankshaft back in place in the block.

21   Clean the faces of the bearings in the caps, then apply lubricant to them.

22   Install the caps in their respective positions with the arrows pointing toward the front of the engine.

23   Install the bolts.

24   Tighten all except the thrust bearing cap bolts to the specified torque (work from the center out and approach the final torque in three steps).

25   Tighten the thrust bearing cap bolts to 10-to-12 ft-lbs.

26   Tap the ends of the crankshaft forward and backward with a lead or brass hammer to line up the thrust bearing and crankshaft thrust surfaces.

27   Retighten all main bearing cap bolts to the specified torque, starting with the center main and working out toward the ends.

28   On manual transmission equipped models, install a new pilot bearing in the end of the crankshaft (see Chapter 8).

29   Rotate the crankshaft a number of times by hand to check for any obvious binding.

30   The final step is to check the crankshaft endplay with a feeler gauge or a dial indicator as described in Section 13. The endplay should be correct if the crankshaft thrust faces aren't worn or damaged and new bearings have been installed.

---

23   Rear main oil seal installation

Refer to illustrations 23.3 and 23.4

1   All models are equipped with a one-piece seal that fits into a housing attached to the block. The crankshaft must be installed first and the main

bearing caps bolted in place, then the new seal should be installed in the housing and the housing bolted to the block.

2   Before installing the seal and housing, check the seal contact surface very carefully for scratches and nicks that could damage the new seal lip and cause oil leaks. If the crankshaft is damaged, the only alternative is a new or different crankshaft.

3   The old seal can be removed from the housing with a hammer and punch by driving it out from the back side **(see illustration)**. Be sure to note how far it's recessed into the housing bore before removing it; the new seal will have to be recessed an equal amount. Be very careful not to scratch or otherwise damage the bore in the housing or oil leaks could develop.

4   Make sure the housing is clean, then apply a thin coat of engine oil to the outer edge of the new seal. The seal must be pressed squarely into the housing bore, so hammering directly on it is not recommended. If you don't have access to a press, tap the seal into place with a hammer and a block of wood **(see illustration)**. The block of wood must be thick enough to distribute the force evenly around the entire circumference of the seal. Work slowly and make sure the seal enters the bore squarely.

5   The seal lips must be lubricated with moly-base grease or engine assembly lube before the seal/housing is slipped over the crankshaft and bolted to the block. Use a new gasket – no sealant is required – and make sure the dowel pins are in place before installing the housing.

6   Tighten the bolts a little at a time to the torque specified in this Chapter.

---

24   Pistons/connecting rods – installation and rod bearing oil clearance check

Refer to illustrations 24.5, 24.9, 24.11, 24.13 and 24.17

1   Before installing the piston/connecting rod assemblies, the cylinder walls must be perfectly clean, the top edge of each cylinder must be chamfered, and the crankshaft must be in place.

2   Remove the cap from the end of the number one connecting rod (refer to the marks made during removal). Remove the original bearing inserts and wipe the bearing surfaces of the connecting rod and cap with a clean, lint-free cloth. They must be kept spotlessly clean.

Connecting rod bearing oil clearance check

3   Clean the back side of the new upper bearing insert, then lay it in place in the connecting rod. Make sure the tab on the bearing fits into the recess in the rod. Don't hammer the bearing insert into place and be very careful not to nick or gouge the bearing face. Don't lubricate the bearing at this time.

4   Clean the back side of the other bearing insert and install it in the rod cap. Again, make sure the tab on the bearing fits into the recess in the cap,

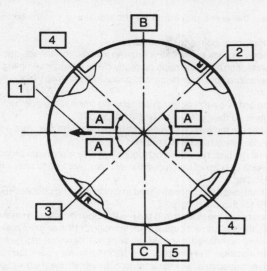

24.5   Position the ring end gaps as shown here before installing the piston/connecting rod assemblies in the engine

A	45-degrees	2	First ring end gap
B	Intake side	3	Second ring end gap
C	Exhaust side	4	Oil ring rail gaps
1	Arrow mark	5	Oil ring spacer gap

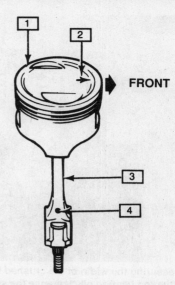

24.9   The arrow on the piston must point to the front (crankshaft pulley) end of the engine and the oil hole in the connecting rod must be on the intake manifold side

1	Piston	3	Connecting rod
2	Arrow mark	4	Oil hole

2B

and don't apply any lubricant. It's critically important that the mating surfaces of the bearing and connecting rod are perfectly clean and oil free when they're assembled.

5   Position the piston ring gaps around the piston as shown (see illustration).

6   Slip a section of plastic or rubber hose over each connecting rod cap bolt.

7   Lubricate the piston and rings with clean engine oil and attach a piston ring compressor to the piston. Leave the skirt protruding about 1/4-inch to guide the piston into the cylinder. The rings must be compressed until they're flush with the piston.

8   Rotate the crankshaft until the number one connecting rod journal is at BDC (bottom dead center) and apply a coat of engine oil to the cylinder walls.

9   With the arrow on top of the piston (see illustration) facing the front of the engine, gently insert the piston/connecting rod assembly into the number one cylinder bore and rest the bottom edge of the ring compressor on

the engine block.

10   Tap the top edge of the ring compressor to make sure it's contacting the block around its entire circumference.

11   Gently tap on the top of the piston with the end of a wooden or plastic hammer handle (see illustration) while guiding the end of the connecting rod into place on the crankshaft journal. The piston rings may try to pop out of the ring compressor just before entering the cylinder bore, so keep some downward pressure on the ring compressor. Work slowly, and if any resistance is felt as the piston enters the cylinder, stop immediately. Find out what's hanging up and fix it before proceeding. Do not, for any reason, force the piston into the cylinder – you might break a ring and/or the piston.

12   Once the piston/connecting rod assembly is installed, the connecting rod bearing oil clearance must be checked before the rod cap is permanently bolted in place.

13   Cut a piece of the appropriate size Plastigage slightly shorter than the width of the connecting rod bearing and lay it in place on the number one connecting rod journal, parallel with the journal axis (see illustration).

24.11   The piston can be driven (gently) into the cylinder bore with the end of a wooden or plastic hammer handle

24.13   Lay the Plastigage strips on each rod bearing journal, parallel to the crankshaft centerline

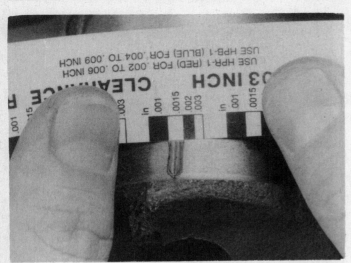

24.17   Measuring the width of the crushed Plastigage to determine the rod bearing oil clearance (be sure to use the correct scale – standard and metric scales are included)

14   Clean the connecting rod cap bearing face, remove the protective hoses from the connecting rod bolts and install the rod cap. Make sure the mating mark on the cap is on the same side as the mark on the connecting rod.

15   Install the nuts and tighten them to the specified torque, working up to it in three steps. **Note:** *Use a thin-wall socket to avoid erroneous torque readings that can result if the socket is wedged between the rod cap and nut. If the socket tends to wedge itself between the nut and the cap, lift up on it slightly until it no longer contacts the cap. Do not rotate the crankshaft at any time during this operation.*

16   Remove the nuts and detach the rod cap, being very careful not to disturb the Plastigage.

17   Compare the width of the crushed Plastigage to the scale printed on the Plastigage envelope to obtain the oil clearance **(see illustration)**. Compare it to the Specifications to make sure the clearance is correct.

18   If the clearance is not as specified, the bearing inserts may be the wrong size (which means different ones will be required). Before deciding that different inserts are needed, make sure that no dirt or oil was between the bearing inserts and the connecting rod or cap when the clearance was measured. Also, recheck the journal diameter. If the Plastigage was wider at one end than the other, the journal may be tapered (refer to Section 18).

Final connecting rod installation

19   Carefully scrape all traces of the Plastigage material off the rod journal and/or bearing face. Be very careful not to scratch the bearing – use your fingernail or the edge of a credit card.

20   Make sure the bearing faces are perfectly clean, then apply a uniform layer of clean moly-base grease or engine assembly lube to both of them. You'll have to push the piston into the cylinder to expose the face of the bearing insert in the connecting rod – be sure to slip the protective hoses over the rod bolts first.

21   Slide the connecting rod back into place on the journal, remove the protective hoses from the rod cap bolts, install the rod cap and tighten the nuts to the specified torque. Again, work up to the torque in three steps.

22   Repeat the entire procedure for the remaining pistons/connecting rods.

23   The important points to remember are . . .
  a) Keep the back sides of the bearing inserts and the insides of the connecting rods and caps perfectly clean when assembling them.
  b) Make sure you have the correct piston/rod assembly for each cylinder.
  c) The arrow on the piston must face the front of the engine.
  d) Lubricate the cylinder walls with clean oil.
  e) Lubricate the bearing faces when installing the rod caps after the oil clearance has been checked.

24   After all the piston/connecting rod assemblies have been properly installed, rotate the crankshaft a number of times by hand to check for any obvious binding.

25   As a final step, the connecting rod end play must be checked. Refer to Section 12 for this procedure.

26   Compare the measured end play to the Specifications to make sure it's correct. If it was correct before disassembly and the original crankshaft and rods were reinstalled, it should still be right. If new rods or a new crankshaft were installed, the end play may be inadequate. If so, the rods will have to be removed and taken to an automotive machine shop for resizing.

27   Install the remaining components in the reverse order of removal. Refer to Section 20 and Part A of this Chapter for additional information.

---

25   Initial start-up and break-in after overhaul

Warning: *Have a fire extinguisher handy when starting the engine for the first time.*

1   Once the engine has been installed in the vehicle, double-check the engine oil and coolant levels.

2   With the spark plugs out of the engine and the ignition system disabled (see Section 3), crank the engine until oil pressure registers on the gauge.

3   Install the spark plugs, hook up the plug wires and restore the ignition system functions (Section 3).

4   Start the engine. It may take a few moments for the fuel system to build up pressure, but the engine should start without a great deal of effort. **Note:** *If backfiring occurs through the carburetor or throttle body, recheck the valve timing and ignition timing.*

5   After the engine starts, it should be allowed to warm up to normal operating temperature. While the engine is warming up, make a thorough check for fuel, oil and coolant leaks.

6   Shut the engine off and recheck the engine oil and coolant levels.

7   Drive the vehicle to an area with minimum traffic, accelerate at full throttle from 30 to 50 mph, then allow the vehicle to slow to 30 mph with the throttle closed. Repeat the procedure 10 or 12 times. This will load the piston rings and cause them to seat properly against the cylinder walls. Check again for oil and coolant leaks.

8   Drive the vehicle gently for the first 500 miles (no sustained high speeds) and keep a constant check on the oil level. It is not unusual for an engine to use oil during the break-in period.

9   At approximately 500 to 600 miles, change the oil and filter.

10   For the next few hundred miles, drive the vehicle normally. Do not pamper it or abuse it.

11   After 2000 miles, change the oil and filter again and consider the engine broken in.

Chapter 3   Cooling, heating and air conditioning systems

Contents

3

Specifications

General

Coolant capacity	See Chapter 1
Radiator pressure cap rating	13 psi
Thermostat rating (starts to open)	
Standard	179-degrees F
Optional	190-degrees F

Torque specifications

	Ft-lbs
Thermostat housing cover bolts	7 to 12
Water pump-to-block bolts	7 to 9
Fan clutch-to-water pump nuts	6 to 8.5

1   General information

Refer to illustrations 1.2 and 1.3

Engine cooling system

All vehicles covered by this manual employ a pressurized engine cooling system with thermostatically controlled coolant circulation. An impeller type water pump mounted on the front of the block pumps coolant through the engine. The coolant flows around each cylinder and toward the rear of the engine. Cast-in coolant passages direct coolant around the intake and exhaust ports, near the spark plug areas and in close proximity to the exhaust valve guides.

A wax pellet type thermostat is located in a housing near the front of the engine. During warm up, the closed thermostat prevents coolant from circulating through the radiator. As the engine nears normal operating

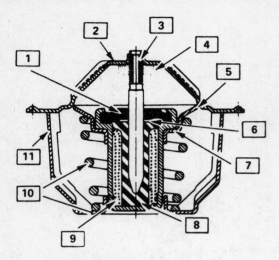

1.2   Wax pellet type thermostat

1	Flange seal	5	Valve seat	9	Wax pellet
2	Flange	6	Teflon seal	10	Coil spring
3	Piston	7	Valve	11	Frame
4	Nut	8	Rubber diaphragm		

VACUUM RELIEF   **PRESSURE RELIEF**

1.3   Pressure-type radiator cap

temperature, the thermostat opens and allows hot coolant to travel through the radiator, where it's cooled before returning to the engine (**see illustration**).

The cooling system is sealed by a pressure type radiator cap, which raises the boiling point of the coolant and increases the cooling efficiency of the radiator. If the system pressure exceeds the cap pressure relief value, the excess pressure in the system forces the spring-loaded valve inside the cap off its seat and allows the coolant to escape through the overflow tube into a coolant reservoir. When the system cools the excess coolant is automatically drawn from the reservoir back into the radiator (**see illustration**).

The coolant reservoir does double duty as both the point at which fresh coolant is added to the cooling system to maintain the proper fluid level and as a holding tank for overheated coolant.

This type of cooling system is known as a closed design because coolant that escapes past the pressure cap is saved and reused.

Heating system

The heating system consists of a blower fan and heater core located in the heater box, the hoses connecting the heater core to the engine cooling system and the heater/air conditioning control head on the dashboard. Hot engine coolant is circulated through the heater core. When the heater mode is activated, a flap door opens to expose the heater box to the passenger compartment. A fan switch on the control head activates the blower motor, which forces air through the core, heating the air.

Air conditioning system

The air conditioning system consists of a condenser mounted in front of the radiator, an evaporator mounted adjacent to the heater core, a compressor mounted on the engine, a filter-drier which contains a high pressure relief valve and the plumbing connecting all of the above components.

A blower fan forces the warmer air of the passenger compartment through the evaporator core (sort of a radiator-in-reverse), transferring the heat from the air to the refrigerant. The liquid refrigerant boils off into low pressure vapor, taking the heat with it when it leaves the evaporator.

2   Antifreeze – general information

Warning: *Do not allow antifreeze to come in contact with your skin or painted surfaces of the vehicle. Rinse off spills immediately with plenty of*

water. *NEVER leave antifreeze lying around in an open container or in a puddle in the driveway or on the garage floor. Children and pets are attracted by it's sweet smell. Antifreeze is fatal if ingested.*

The cooling system should be filled with a water/ethylene glycol based antifreeze solution, which will prevent freezing down to at least –20 degrees F, or lower if local climate requires it. It also provides protection against corrosion and increases the coolant boiling point.

The cooling system should be drained, flushed and refilled at the specified intervals (see Chapter 1). Old or contaminated antifreeze solutions are likely to cause damage and encourage the formation of rust and scale in the system. Use distilled water with the antifreeze.

Before adding antifreeze, check all hose connections, because antifreeze tends to leak through very minute openings. Engines don't normally consume coolant, so if the level goes down, find the cause and correct it.

The exact mixture of antifreeze-to-water which you should use depends on the relative weather conditions. The mixture should contain at least 50 percent antifreeze, but should never contain more than 70 percent antifreeze. Consult the mixture ratio chart on the antifreeze container before adding coolant. Hydrometers are available at most auto parts stores to test the coolant. Use antifreeze which meets the vehicle manufacturer's specifications.

3   Thermostat – check and replacement

Warning: *Do not remove the radiator cap, drain the coolant or replace the thermostat until the engine has cooled completely.*

Check

1   Before assuming the thermostat is to blame for a cooling system problem, check the coolant level, drivebelt tension (see Chapter 1) and temperature gauge operation.

2   If the engine seems to be taking a long time to warm up (based on heater output or temperature gauge operation), the thermostat is probably stuck open. Replace the thermostat with a new one.

3   If the engine runs hot, use your hand to check the temperature of the upper radiator hose. If the hose isn't hot, but the engine is, the thermostat is probably stuck closed, preventing the coolant inside the engine from escaping to the radiator. Replace the thermostat. **Caution:** *Don't drive the vehicle without a thermostat. The computer may stay in open loop and emissions and fuel economy will suffer.*

3.10   Unsnap the mixture control valve (if equipped) from its bracket, then remove the thermostat housing cover bolts (and wiring bracket on some models)

A   Mixture control valve   B   Thermostat housing cover bolts

3.13   Install the thermostat, with the spring end down, into the stepped seat in the housing

4   If the upper radiator hose is hot, it means that the coolant is flowing and the thermostat is open. Consult the Troubleshooting Section at the front of this manual for cooling system diagnosis.

Replacement
Refer to illustrations 3.10 and 3.13
5   Disconnect the negative battery cable from the battery.
6   Drain the cooling system (see Chapter 1). If the coolant is relatively new or in good condition (see Chapter 1), save it and reuse it.
7   Follow the upper radiator hose to the engine to locate the thermostat housing.
8   Loosen the hose clamp, then detach the hose from the fitting. If it's stuck, grasp it near the end with a pair of adjustable pliers and twist it to break the seal, then pull it off. If the hose is old or deteriorated, cut it off and install a new one.
9   If the outer surface of the large fitting that mates with the hose is deteriorated (corroded, pitted, etc.) it may be damaged further by hose removal. If it is, the thermostat housing cover will have to be replaced.
10   Remove the bolts and detach the housing cover **(see illustration)**. If the cover is stuck, tap it with a soft-face hammer to jar it loose. Be prepared for some coolant to spill as the gasket seal is broken.
11   Note how it's installed (which end is facing up), then remove the thermostat.
12   Stuff a rag into the engine opening, then remove all traces of old gasket material and sealant from the housing and cover with a gasket scraper. Remove the rag from the opening and clean the gasket mating surfaces with lacquer thinner or acetone.
13   Install the new thermostat in the housing. Make sure the correct end faces up – the spring end is directed into the engine **(see illustration)**.
14   Apply a thin, uniform layer of RTV sealant to both sides of the new gasket and position it on the housing.
15   Install the cover and bolts. Tighten the bolts to the torque listed in this Chapter's Specifications.
16   Reattach the hose to the fitting and tighten the hose clamp securely.
17   Refill the cooling system (see Chapter 1).
18   Start the engine and allow it to reach normal operating temperature, then check for leaks and proper thermostat operation (as described in Steps 2 through 4).

---

4   Engine cooling fan and clutch – check and replacement

Warning: *To avoid possible injury or damage, DO NOT operate the engine with a damaged fan. Do not attempt to repair fan blades – replace a damaged fan with a new one.*

Check
Auxiliary electric fan (air conditioned models only)
1   To test the motor, unplug the electrical connector at the motor and use jumper wires to connect the fan directly to the battery. If the fan still doesn't work, replace the motor.
2   If the motor tested OK, the fault lies in the condenser fan motor relay, the dual switch, the air conditioner amplifier or the wiring which connects the components (see the wiring diagrams in Chapter 12). Carefully check all wiring and connections. If no obvious problems are found, further diagnosis should be done by a dealer service department or repair shop.

Belt-driven fan with viscous clutch
Refer to illustration 4.3
3   Disconnect the negative battery cable and rock the fan back and forth by hand to check for excessive play in the fan clutch **(see illustration)**.
4   With the engine cold, turn the fan blades by hand. The fan should turn freely.
5   Visually inspect for substantial fluid leakage from the clutch assembly. If problems are noted, replace the clutch assembly.
6   With the engine completely warmed up, turn off the ignition switch and disconnect the negative battery cable from the battery. Turn the fan by hand. Some drag should be evident. If the fan turns easily, replace the fan clutch.

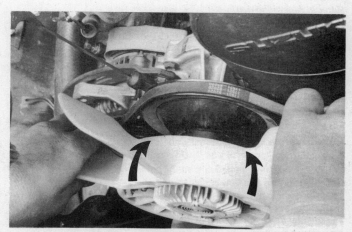

4.3   Rock the fan back and forth to check for play in the fan clutch

3

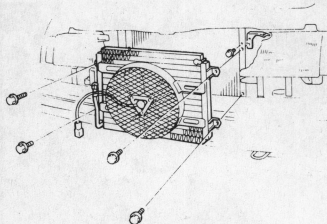

4.10   Auxiliary electric fan mounting details – the fan can be removed along with the condenser or by itself

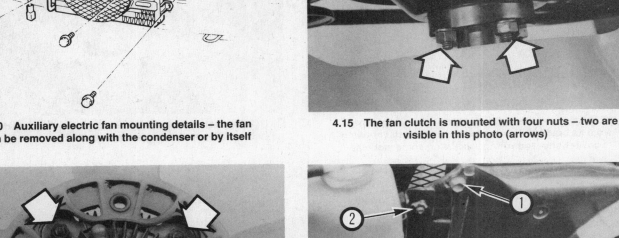

4.15   The fan clutch is mounted with four nuts – two are visible in this photo (arrows)

4.18   If you intend to replace the fan or clutch, remove the mounting nuts (arrows)

5.5a   Unbolt the fan shroud – the bolts are located at each corner

1   Shroud bolts   *2   Radiator mounting bolts*

Removal and installation

Auxiliary electric fan (air conditioned models only)
Refer to illustration 4.10

7   Disconnect the negative battery cable from the battery.
8   Remove the front bumper and grille (see Chapter 11).
9   Insert a small screwdriver into the connector to lift the lock tab and un-plug the fan wire harness.
10   Unbolt the fan bracket and shroud assembly **(see illustration)**, then carefully lift it out of the vehicle.
11   To detach the fan from the motor, remove the motor shaft fastener.
12   To remove the bracket from the fan motor, remove the mounting nuts.
13   Installation is the reverse of removal.

Belt-driven fan with viscous clutch
Refer to illustrations 4.15 and 4.18

14   Disconnect the negative battery cable. Remove the fan shroud mounting screws and detach the shroud.
15   Remove the bolts/nuts attaching the fan/clutch assembly to the water pump hub **(see illustration)**.
16   Lift the fan/clutch assembly (and shroud, if necessary) out of the engine compartment.
17   Carefully inspect the fan blades for damage and defects. Replace it if necessary.

18   At this point, the fan may be unbolted from the clutch, if necessary **(see illustration)**. If the fan clutch is stored, position it with the radiator side facing down.
19   Installation is the reverse of removal Be sure to tighten the fan and clutch mounting nuts/bolts evenly and securely.

5   Radiator – removal and installation

Refer to illustrations 5.5a, 5.5b, 5.6 and 5.8
Warning: *Wait until the engine is completely cool before beginning this procedure.*

1   Disconnect the negative battery cable from the battery.
2   Drain the cooling system (see Chapter 1). If the coolant is relatively new or in good condition, save it and reuse it.
3   Loosen the hose clamps, then detach the radiator hoses from the fittings. If they're stuck, grasp each hose near the end with a pair of Channel-lock pliers and twist it to break the seal, then pull it off – be careful not to distort the radiator fittings! If the hoses are old or deteriorated, cut them off and install new ones.
4   Disconnect the reservoir hose from the radiator filler neck.
5   Remove the bolts that attach the shroud to the radiator and slide the shroud toward the engine **(see illustrations)**.

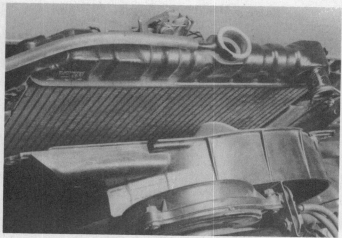

5.5b Lift the fan shroud back over the fan to provide clearance for radiator removal.

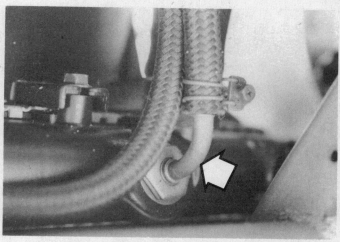

5.6 On automatic transmission equipped models, disconnect the cooling line (arrow) from each side of the bottom of the radiator

5.8 Air conditioned models have the radiator mounting bolts on the ends (arrow)

6.2 The coolant reservoir slips off/onto the bracket

6   If the vehicle is equipped with an automatic transmission, disconnect the cooler lines from the radiator (see illustration). Use a drip pan to catch spilled fluid.
7   Plug the lines and fittings.
8   Remove the radiator mounting bolts (see illustration).
9   Carefully lift out the radiator. Don't spill coolant on the vehicle or scratch the paint.
10 With the radiator removed, it can be inspected for leaks and damage. If it needs repair, have a radiator shop or dealer service department perform the work as special techniques are required.
11 Bugs and dirt can be removed from the radiator with compressed air and a soft brush. Don't bend the cooling fins as this is done.
12 Check the radiator mounts for deterioration and make sure there's nothing in them when the radiator is installed.
13 Installation is the reverse of the removal procedure.
14 After installation, fill the cooling system with the proper mixture of antifreeze and water. Refer to Chapter 1 if necessary.
15 Start the engine and check for leaks. Allow the engine to reach normal operating temperature, indicated by the upper radiator hose becoming hot. Recheck the coolant level and add more if required.
16 If you're working on an automatic transmission equipped vehicle, check and add fluid as needed.

6   Coolant reservoir – removal and installation

Refer to illustration 6.2
1   Detach the reservoir cap.
2   Remove the mounting bolt located on the bottom of the reservoir (if equipped) and lift the reservoir straight up from its mounting bracket (see illustration).
3   Pour the contents of the reservoir into a clean container.
4   Installation is the reverse of removal.
5   Refill the container with the proper mixture of antifreeze and water. Refer to Chapter 1 if necessary.

7   Water pump – check

Refer to illustrations 7.4 and 7.5
1   A failure in the water pump can cause serious engine damage due to overheating.
2   There are three ways to check the operation of the water pump while it's installed on the engine. If the pump is defective, it should be replaced with a new or rebuilt unit.

7.4   The water pump weep hole (arrow) will drip coolant when the seal on the pump shaft fails (pulley removed for clarity)

7.5   Try to rock the shaft up and down to check for play

8.8   Water pump mounting bolts (arrows) – when installing the pump, insert new rubber seals in the ridge gaps at the top and bottom of the pump

3   With the engine running at normal operating temperature, squeeze the upper radiator hose. If the water pump is working properly, a pressure surge should be felt as the hose is released. **Warning:** *Keep your hands away from the fan blades!*

4   Water pumps are equipped with weep or vent holes. If a failure occurs in the pump seal, coolant will leak from the hole. In most cases you'll need a flashlight to find the hole on the water pump from underneath to check for leaks **(see illustration)**.

5   If the fan or water pump shaft bearings fail there may be a howling sound at the front of the engine while it's running. Shaft wear can be felt if the fan or water pump pulley is rocked up and down **(see illustration)**. Don't mistake drivebelt slippage, which causes a squealing sound, for water pump bearing failure.

8   Water pump – replacement

Refer to illustration 8.8
Warning: *Wait until the engine is completely cool before beginning this procedure. On air conditioned vehicles, do not disconnect any refrigerant lines/fittings unless the system has been depressurized by a service station.*

1   Disconnect the negative battery cable from the battery.
2   Drain the cooling system (see Chapter 1). If the coolant is relatively new or in good condition, save it and reuse it.
3   Loosen the clamps and detach the hoses from the water pump. If they're stuck, grasp each hose near the end with a pair of adjustable pliers and twist it to break the seal, then pull it off. If the hoses are deteriorated, cut them off and install new ones.
4   Remove the cooling fan and shroud (see Sections 4 and 5).
5   Remove the drivebelt(s) (see Chapter 1) and the pulley at the end of the water pump shaft.
6   Remove all accessory brackets from the water pump. When removing the power steering pump and air conditioning compressor, (if equipped) don't disconnect the hoses. Tie the units aside with the hoses attached.
7   Remove the timing belt and idler assembly (see Chapter 2A).
8   Remove the bolts and detach the water pump from the engine **(see illustration)**. Note the locations of the various lengths and different types of bolts as they're removed to ensure correct installation.
9   Clean the bolt threads and the threaded holes in the engine to remove corrosion and sealant.
10   Compare the new pump to the old one to make sure they're identical.
11   Remove all traces of old gasket material from the engine with a gasket scraper.
12   Clean the engine and new water pump mating surfaces with lacquer thinner or acetone. Install new rubber seals in the ridge gaps at the top and bottom of the pump.
13   Apply a thin coat of RTV sealant to the engine side of the new gasket.
14   Apply a thin layer of RTV sealant to the gasket mating surface of the new pump, then carefully mate the gasket and the pump. Slip a couple of bolts through the pump mounting holes to hold the gasket in place.
15   Carefully attach the pump and gasket to the engine and thread the bolts into the holes finger tight.
16   Install the remaining bolts (if they also hold an accessory bracket in place, be sure to reposition the bracket at this time). Tighten them to the specified torque in 1/4-turn increments. Don't overtighten them or the pump may be distorted.
17   Reinstall all parts removed for access to the pump.
18   Refill the cooling system and check the drivebelt tension (see Chapter 1). Run the engine and check for leaks.

9   Coolant temperature sending unit – check and replacement

Refer to illustration 9.1
Warning: *Wait until the engine is completely cool before beginning this procedure.*

9.1   The coolant temperature sending unit is located just below the thermostat housing (arrow) – upper radiator hose removed for clarity

1   The coolant temperature indicator system is composed of a temperature gauge mounted in the instrument panel and a coolant temperature sending unit mounted on the engine **(see illustration)**. Some vehicles have more than one sending unit, but only one is used for the indicator system. **Warning:** *If the vehicle is equipped with an auxiliary electric cooling fan, stay clear of the fan blades, which can come on at any time.*
2   If an overheating indication occurs, check the coolant level in the system and then make sure the wiring between the gauge and the switch is secure and all fuses are intact.
3   Test the circuit by grounding the wire to the switch while the ignition is on (engine not running for safety). If the gauge deflects full scale, replace the sending unit.
4   If the sending unit must be replaced, simply unscrew it from the engine and install the replacement. Use sealant on the threads. Make sure the engine is cool before removing the defective sending unit. There will be some coolant loss as the unit is removed, so be prepared to catch it. Check the level after the replacement has been installed.

10   Blower unit – removal and installation

Refer to illustrations 10.2 and 10.4

1   Locate the main heater unit, which is readily accessible beneath the dashboard of the vehicle. On Samurai models, the blower is above and to the right of the throttle pedal; Sidekicks and Trackers have the unit mounted below the glove box.
2   Disconnect the blower motor electrical connector and hose, if equipped **(see illustration)**.
3   Remove the three screws holding the blower motor to the heater unit housing.
4   If you are replacing the motor, detach the fan and transfer it to the new motor **(see illustration)**.
5   Installation procedures are the reverse of those for removal. Run the fan and check for proper operation.

11   Heater core – removal and installation

Refer to illustrations 11.6 and 11.7

1   Disconnect the negative cable from the battery.
2   Drain the cooling system (see Chapter 1).
3   Working in the engine compartment, disconnect the heater hoses where they enter the firewall.
4   Remove the instrument panel and the center console, if equipped (see Chapter 11).
5   Remove the heater controls (see Section 12).
6   Label and detach the air ducts, wiring and controls still attached to the heater housing **(see illustration)**.
7   Unbolt the heating unit **(see illustration)** and lift it from the vehicle.
8   Remove the screws and clips and separate the two halves of the housing. Take out the old heater core and install the new unit.
9   Reassemble the heater unit and check the operation of the air control flaps. If any parts bind, correct the problem before installation.
10 Reinstall the remaining parts in the reverse order of removal.
11 Refill the cooling system, reconnect the battery and run the engine. Check for leaks and proper system operation.

12   Air conditioning and heater control assembly – removal and installation

Refer to illustrations 12.3a, 12.3b, 12.3c, 12.4a, 12.4b, 12.4c and 12.6

1   Disconnect the negative cable from the battery.
2   Remove the radio, if equipped (see Chapter 12).

3

10.2   Unplug the electrical connector from the motor, remove the three screws, then maneuver the blower unit out from under the dash

10.4   The fan is attached to the motor shaft with a nut (arrow)

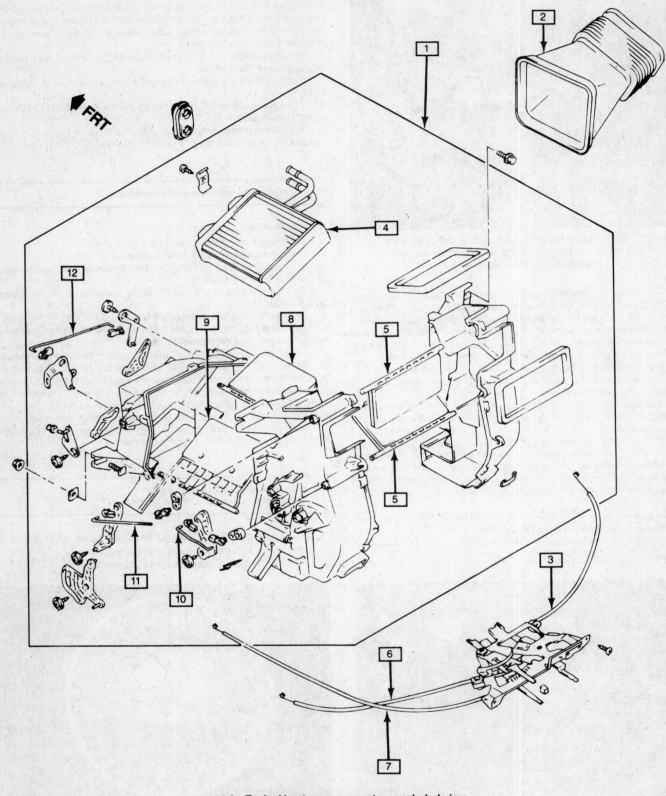

11.6   Typical heater components – exploded view

1	Heater unit	5	Damper	9	Damper
2	Heater duct (without A/C)	6	Cool-hot control cable	10	Shaft
3	Cir-fresh control cable	7	Mode control cable	11	Shaft
4	Heater core	8	Damper	12	Shaft

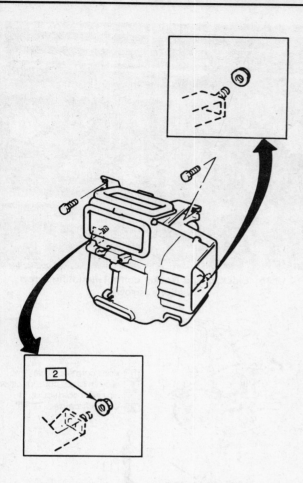

11.7   Typical heater housing mounting details

12.3a   On Samurai models, slip an L–hook through the slotted openings and gently pull the faceplate off, . . .

12.3b . . . then reach behind the faceplate and remove the light socket

3   Pull off the control knobs and faceplate (**see illustrations**).
4   Remove the mounting screws located on the front of the control assembly (**see illustrations**). On Samurai models, push the control assembly back into the dash and lower it out the bottom (**see illustration**).
5   Pull the control out slightly. On Sidekick and Tracker models it may be necessary to disconnect the cables at the operating ends before this is possible.
6   Clearly mark the positions of the cable housings relative to the adjustment clips, detach the cables and wiring from the control assembly (**see illustration**) and lift the assembly from the dash.
7   To install the unit, reverse the above procedure.
8   To adjust the cables, remove the adjustment clips at the lever ends and move the cable housings to the positions marked previously. Fasten the clips and check for stiffness or binding through the full range of operation.
9   Run the engine and check for proper functioning of the heater (and air conditioning, if equipped).

13   Air conditioning system – check and maintenance

Refer to illustrations 13.7, 13.9, 13.10 and 13.13
Warning: *The air conditioning system is under high pressure. Do not loosen any hose fittings or remove any components until after the system has been discharged by a dealer service department or service station. Always wear eye protection when disconnecting or charging air conditioning system fittings.*

12.3c   On Sidekick and Tracker models, gently grip the trim panel (arrows) and pull it off

1   The following maintenance checks should be performed on a regular basis to ensure the air conditioner continues to operate at peak efficiency.
  a) Check the compressor drivebelt. If it's worn or deteriorated, replace it (see Chapter 1).
  b) Check the drivebelt tension and, if necessary, adjust it (see Chapter 1).

12.4a   Samurai control mounting screw locations (arrows)

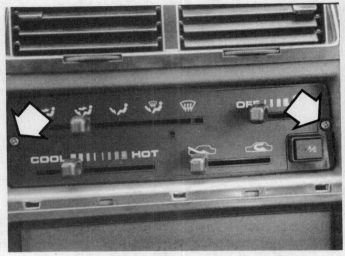

12.4b   Sidekick and Tracker control mounting screw locations (arrows)

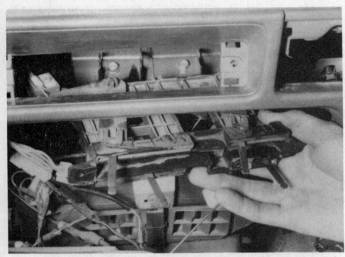

12.4c   On Samurai models, lower the control out the bottom of the dash

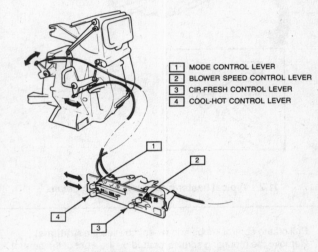

1	MODE CONTROL LEVER
2	BLOWER SPEED CONTROL LEVER
3	CIR-FRESH CONTROL LEVER
4	COOL-HOT CONTROL LEVER

12.6   Typical heater control connections

13.7   The sight glass is located on the top of the receiver-drier (arrow)

c) Check the system hoses. Look for cracks, bubbles, hard spots and deterioration. Inspect the hoses and all fittings for oil bubbles and seepage. If there's any evidence of wear, damage or leaks, replace the hose(s).

d) Inspect the condenser fins for leaves, bugs and other debris. Use a "fin comb" or compressed air to clean the condenser.

e) Make sure the system has the correct refrigerant charge.

2   It's a good idea to operate the system for about 10 minutes at least once a month, particularly during the winter. Long term non-use can cause hardening, and subsequent failure, of the seals.

3   Because of the complexity of the air conditioning system and the special equipment necessary to service it, in-depth troubleshooting and repairs are not included in this manual. However, simple checks and component replacement procedures are provided in this Chapter.

4   The most common cause of poor cooling is simply a low system refrigerant charge. If a noticeable drop in cool air output occurs, one of the following quick checks will help you determine if the refrigerant level is low.

5   Warm the engine up to normal operating temperature.

6   Place the air conditioning temperature selector at the coldest setting and put the blower at the highest setting. Open the doors (to make sure the air conditioning system doesn't cycle off as soon as it cools the passenger compartment).

14.3 Receiver/drier mounting details

1   Pressure switch connector   2   Mounting bracket pinch bolt

15.5 Never remove the refrigerant lines-to-compressor bolts (arrows) unless the system has been discharged by a service technician

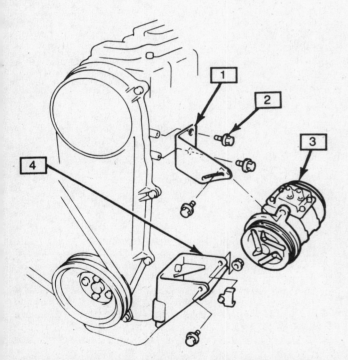

15.6 Typical air conditioning compressor mounting details

1 Upper mounting bracket	3 Compressor	
2 Bolts	4 Lower mounting bracket	

7   With the compressor engaged – the clutch will make an audible click and the center of the clutch will rotate – inspect the sight glass **(see illustration)**. If the refrigerant looks foamy, it's low. Have a dealer service department or automotive air conditioning shop charge the system.

8   If there's no sight glass, feel the inlet and outlet pipes at the compressor. One side should be cold and one hot. If there's no perceptible difference between the two pipes, there's something wrong with the compressor or the system. It might be a low charge. It might be something else. Take the vehicle to a dealer service department or an automotive air conditioning shop.

14   Air conditioning system receiver/drier – removal and installation

Refer to illustration 14.3

Warning: The air conditioning system is under high pressure. DO NOT disassemble any part of the system (hose, compressor, line fittings, etc.) until after the system has been depressurized by a dealer service department or service station.

1   Have the air conditioning system discharged (see Warning above).
2   Disconnect the negative battery cable from the battery.
3   Unplug the electrical connector from the pressure switch near the top of the receiver/drier **(see illustration)**.
4   Remove the bolts and disconnect the refrigerant lines from the top of the receiver/drier.
5   Plug the open fittings to prevent entry of dirt and moisture.
6   Loosen the mounting bracket pinch bolt and lift the receiver/drier out.
7   If a new receiver/drier is being installed, remove the Schrader valve and pour the oil out into a measuring cup, noting the amount. Add fresh refrigerant oil to the new receiver/drier equal to the amount removed from the old unit, plus one ounce.
8   Installation is the reverse of removal.
9   Take the vehicle back to the shop that discharged it. Have the air conditioning system evacuated, charged and leak tested.

15   Air conditioning system compressor – removal and installation

Refer to illustrations 15.5 and 15.6

Warning: The air conditioning system is under high pressure. DO NOT disassemble any part of the system (hoses, compressor, line fittings, etc.) until after the system has been depressurized by a dealer service department or service station.

Note: The receiver/drier (see Section 14) should be replaced whenever the compressor is replaced.

1   Have the A/C system discharged (see Warning above).
2   Disconnect the negative battery cable from the battery.
3   Disconnect the compressor clutch wiring harness.
4   Remove the drivebelt (see Chapter 1).
5   Disconnect the refrigerant lines from the top of the compressor **(see illustration)**. Plug the open fittings to prevent entry of dirt and moisture.
6   Unbolt the compressor from the mounting brackets and lift it out of the vehicle **(see illustration)**.
7   If a new compressor is being installed, follow the directions with the compressor regarding the draining of excess oil prior to installation.

3

8   The clutch may have to be transferred from the original to the new compressor.

9   Installation is the reverse of removal. Replace all O-rings with new ones specifically made for A/C system use and lubricate them with refrigerant oil.

10   Have the system evacuated, recharged and leak tested by the shop that discharged it.

16   Air conditioning system condenser – removal and installation

Warning: *The air conditioning system is under high pressure. DO NOT disassemble any part of the system (hoses, compressor, line fittings, etc.) until after the system has been depressurized by a dealer service department or service station.*

Note: *The receiver/drier (see Section 14) should be replaced whenever the condenser is replaced.*

1   Have the air conditioning system discharged (see Warning above).

2   Disconnect the negative cable from the battery.

3   Remove the grille and front bumper (see Chapter 11)

4   Disconnect the refrigerant lines from the condenser **(see illustration)**.

5   Remove the auxiliary electric fan (see Section 4).

6   Remove the mounting bolts from the condenser brackets **(see Illustration 4.10)**.

7   Lift the condenser out of the vehicle and plug the lines to keep dirt and moisture out.

8   If the original condenser will be reinstalled, store it with the line fittings on top to prevent oil from draining out.

9   If a new condenser is being installed, pour one ounce of refrigerant oil into it prior to installation.

10   Reinstall the components in the reverse order of removal. Be sure the rubber insulator pads are in place.

11   Have the system evacuated, recharged and leak tested by the shop that discharged it.

Notes:

Chapter 4 Fuel and exhaust systems

Contents

Specifications

Carburetor

Choke plate-to-bore clearance
   At 77-degrees F (25-degrees C) ambient temperature .... 0.004 to 0.023 in (0.1 to 0.6 mm)
   At 104-degrees F (40-degrees C) ambient temperature ...... 0.05 to 0.11 in (1.3 to 2.8 mm)

Throttle Body fuel Injected (TBI) models

Fuel pressure at idle .... 24 to 30 psi
Fuel injector coil resistance .... 1.0 to 2.0 ohms (at 68-degrees F, 20-degrees C)
Fuel injector leakage rate .... One drop per minute or less
TPS resistance
   Between terminals C and D
      Throttle plate closed .... 0 to 500 ohms
      Throttle plate wide open .... Infinity
   Between terminals A and D .... 3.5k to 6.5k ohms
   Between terminals B and D
      Throttle plate closed .... 0 to 2k ohms
      Throttle plate wide open .... 2 to 6.5k ohms
ISC solenoid valve resistance .... 5.4 to 6.6 ohms (at 68-degrees F, 20-degrees C)

Multi-Port Fuel Injected (MPFI) models

Fuel pressure (engine idling, vacuum hose connected to
   pressure regulator) .... 29 to 37 psi
Fuel injector resistance .... 12.0 to 17.0 ohms

Fuel injector leakage rate	One drop per minute or less
Throttle position sensor resistance	
Between terminals A and B	
Throttle lever-to-stop screw clearance 0.020 in (0.5 mm) ...	0 to 500 ohms
Throttle lever-to-stop screw clearance 0.031 (0.8 mm)	Infinity ohms
Between terminals A and D	3.5k to 6.5k ohms
Between terminals A and C	
Throttle valve at idle	0.3 to 2k ohms
Throttle plate wide open	2 to 6.5k ohms
IAC solenoid valve resistance	11 to 14 ohms

Throttle cable freeplay

Carbureted models	
Cold engine	3/8 to 5/8 in (10 to 15 mm)
Warm engine	1/8 to 3/16 in (3 to 5 mm)
Throttle Body fuel-Injected (TBI) models	3/8 to 5/8 in (10 to 15 mm)
Multi-Port Fuel Injected (MPFI) models	
Accelerator pedal freeplay	5/64 to 9/32 in (2 to 7 mm)
Throttle stop clearance	1/32 to 5/64 in (0.5 to 2.0 mm)

Torque specifications

	Ft-lbs
Fuel pump-to-cylinder head nuts	7.0 to 11.5
Carburetor or throttle body mounting nuts/bolts	13.5 to 20
Exhaust pipe-to-exhaust manifold bolts	37

1 General information

The fuel system consists of a rear mounted tank, combination metal and rubber fuel hoses, an engine-mounted mechanical pump or an in-tank electric pump, and either a two-stage, two-venturi carburetor or an electronic fuel injection system. Throttle Body fuel Injection (TBI) is used on most fuel-injected models, while some 1992 and later models are equipped with Multi-Port Fuel Injection (MPFI).

The exhaust system is composed of an exhaust manifold or manifolds, the catalytic converter and a combination muffler and tailpipe assembly.

The emissions control systems modify the functions of both the exhaust and fuel systems. There may be some cross-references throughout this Chapter to Sections in Chapter 6 because the emissions control systems are integral to the induction and exhaust systems.

Extreme caution should be exercised when dealing with either the fuel or the exhaust system. Fuel is a primary element for combustion. Be very careful! The exhaust system is also an area for exercising caution as it operates at very high temperatures. Serious burns can result from even momentary contact with any part of the exhaust system and the fire potential is ever present.

2 Fuel pressure relief procedure

Warning: *Gasoline is extremely flammable, so extra precautions must be taken when working on any part of the fuel system. Do not smoke or allow open flames or bare light bulbs in the work area. Also, do not work in a garage if a natural gas-type appliance that has a pilot light is present. Always keep a dry chemical (Class B) fire extinguisher near the work area.*

1   Before servicing any component on the fuel system, relieve the residual fuel pressure to minimize the risk of fire and personal injury.

2   Disconnect the cable from the negative terminal of the battery.

Carbureted vehicles

3   Unscrew the fuel filler cap to release the pressure caused by fuel vapor.

1990 and earlier fuel-injected models

Refer to illustration 2.5

4   Perform Step 2, then raise the vehicle and support it securely on jackstands.

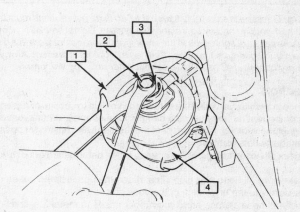

2.5 To relieve the fuel system pressure on 1990 and earlier fuel injected models, loosen the plug bolt on the fuel filter union bolt-wear eye protection while doing this

1	Rag	3	Fuel filter union bolt
2	Plug bolt	4	Fuel filter

5   Position a container under the fuel filter. Cover the fuel filter with a rag and, using a backup wrench to prevent the fuel filter union bolt from turning, slowly loosen the plug bolt and allow the pressurized fuel to escape **(see illustration)**.

6   When the pressure has been relieved completely, tighten the plug bolt securely.

7   Reconnect the battery cable only after all work to the fuel system has been completed, then start the engine and check the fittings for leaks.

1991 and later fuel-injected models

Refer to illustrations 2.9a and 2.9b

8   This procedure must be performed with the engine cold (to prevent damage to the catalytic converter) and the transmission in Park (automatic) or Neutral (manual).

9   Unplug the electrical connector from the fuel pump relay located next to the ECM under the left (Sidekick/Tracker) or right (Samurai) side of the instrument panel **(see illustrations)**.

10   Remove the fuel tank cap to release the pressure in the tank, then reinstall it.

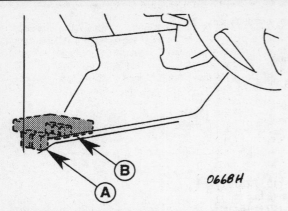

2.9a On 1991 and later Sidekick/Tracker models, unplug the fuel pump relay wire (A) located next to the ECM (B)

11   Start the engine and let it run until it stalls from lack of fuel. Crank the starter two or three times in short (three-second) bursts to release any residual fuel pressure.

3   Fuel lines and fittings-inspection and replacement

Warning: *Gasoline is extremely flammable, so extra precautions must be taken when working on any part of the fuel system. Do not smoke or allow open flames or bare light bulbs in the work area. Also, do not work in a garage if a natural gas-type appliance that has a pilot light is present. Always keep a dry chemical (Class B) fire extinguisher near the work area.*

Inspection

1   Once in a while, you will have to raise the vehicle to service or replace some component (an exhaust pipe hanger, for example). Whenever you work under the vehicle, always inspect the fuel lines and fittings for possible damage or deterioration.
2   Check all hoses and pipes for cracks, kinks, deformation or obstructions.
3   Make sure all hose and pipe clips attach their associated hoses or pipes securely to the underside of the vehicle.
4   Verify all hose clamps attaching rubber hoses to metal fuel lines or pipes are snug enough to assure a tight fit between the hoses and pipes.

Replacement

5   If you must replace any damaged sections, use original equipment replacement hoses or pipes constructed from exactly the same material as the section you are replacing. Do not install substitutes constructed from inferior or inappropriate material or you could cause a fuel leak or a fire.
6   Always, before detaching or disassembling any part of the fuel line system, note the routing of all hoses and pipes and the orientation of all clamps and clips to assure that replacement sections are installed in exactly the same manner.
7   Before detaching any part of the fuel system, be sure to relieve the fuel tank pressure (Section 2).
8   While you're under the vehicle, it's a good idea to check the condition of the fuel filter-make sure that it's not clogged or damaged (see Chapter 1).

4   Fuel pump – check

Warning: *Gasoline is extremely flammable, so extra precautions must be taken when working on any part of the fuel system. Do not smoke or allow open flames or bare light bulbs in the work area. Also, do not work in a garage if a natural gas-type appliance that has a pilot light is present. Always keep a dry chemical (Class B) fire extinguisher near the work area.*
Note: *The following checks assume the fuel filter is in good condition. If you doubt it's condition, install a new one (see Chapter 1).*

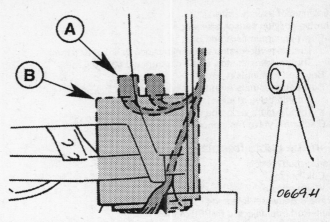

2.9b On 1991 and later fuel-injected Samurai models, unplug the fuel pump relay connector (A) found above the ECM (B)

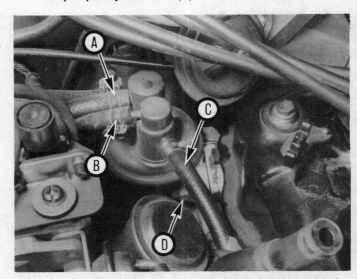

4.3 The fuel pump on carburetor-equipped models is mounted on the right rear corner of the cylinder head

A *Fuel inlet hose*	C *Fuel outlet hose*
B *Fuel return hose*	D *Mounting nut (1 of 2)*

1   Check that there is adequate fuel in the fuel tank. If you doubt the reading on the gauge, insert a long wooden dowel at the filler opening; it will serve as a dipstick.

Mechanical pump (carbureted vehicles)

Refer to illustration 4.3

2   Raise the vehicle and support it securely on jackstands. With the engine running, examine all fuel lines between the fuel tank and fuel pump for leaks, loose connections, kinks or flattening in the rubber hoses. Do this quickly, before the engine gets hot. Air leaks upstream of the fuel pump can seriously affect the pump's output. Shut off the engine.
3   Check the body of the pump for leaks **(see illustration)**.
4   Remove the fuel filler cap to relieve the fuel tank pressure. Disconnect the fuel line at the carburetor. Disconnect the primary wiring connector to the ignition coil so the engine can be cranked without it firing. Place an approved gasoline container at the end of the detached fuel line and have an assistant crank the engine for several seconds. There should be a strong spurt of gasoline from the line on every second revolution.
5   If little or no gasoline emerges from the line during engine cranking, either the fuel line is clogged or the fuel pump is not working properly. Disconnect the fuel feed line from the pump and blow air through it to be sure that the line is clear. If the line is not clogged, then the pump is suspect and needs to be replaced with a new one.

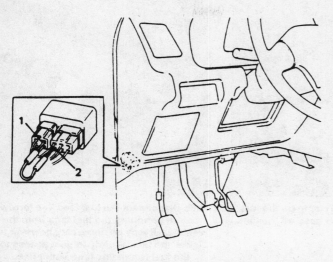

4.8 To check the fuel pump relay, jump terminals 1 and 2 of the relay connector and turn the ignition switch to On (earlier models)

Electric pump (fuel injected vehicles)

General check

Refer to illustration 4.8

6   Although the best way to check the operation of the fuel pump is with a fuel pressure gauge (see step 10), to do so on these fuel injected vehicles requires the use of special adapters not normally available to the home mechanic. It is possible, however, to determine if the fuel pump is receiving power and rotating, which is usually a pretty good indication that it is pumping fuel.

7   Turn the ignition key to the ON position, but don't crank the engine. Remove the fuel filler cap, put your ear next to the opening and listen for the fuel pump working, which is characterized by a whirring sound. After listening, turn the ignition switch to OFF.

8   If the fuel pump is not working, check the fuse. If the fuse is okay, find the fuel pump relay, which is located under the left (earlier models) or right (later models) side of the dash **(see illustration)**. Using a jumper wire, bridge the indicated terminals. **Note:** *On later models where the fuel pump relay has only four terminals, connect the jumper wire between the wires connected to the fuel pump relay's A and B terminals (usually, one wire is blue with a black tracer and one wire is pink with a black tracer). Turn the ignition switch to ON. If the fuel pump now works, replace the fuel pump relay.*

9   If the fuel pump is still not working, a problem could exist with the wiring harness to the pump or the pump itself.

Fuel pressure check

10   Relieve the fuel pressure (see Section 2).

11   Install a fuel pressure gauge. On models with MPFI, disconnect the fuel feed line from the fuel rail and install the gauge using a special hose and adapter (Suzuki special tools 09912-58431 and 09919-46010 or equivalent). On models with TBI, disconnect the fuel inlet fitting from the fuel filter and install the gauge using a banjo-type connector (Suzuki fuel pressure gauge kit 09912-58412 or equivalent).

12   Turn the ignition switch to ON. The fuel pump should run for about two seconds. Turn the key off and on about four times (pausing about two seconds each time) until the fuel pressure reading on the gauge stabilizes. It should be about 3 to 10 psi above the range listed in this Chapter's Specifications.

13   Start the engine and let it idle at normal operating temperature. The pressure should be within the range listed in this Chapter's Specifications. If all the pressure readings are within the limits listed in this Chapter's Specifications, the system is operating normally.

14   On MPFI models, if the pressure did not drop by 3 to 10 psi after starting the engine, apply 12 to 14 inches of vacuum to the pressure regulator. If the pressure now drops, repair the vacuum source to the pressure regulator. If the pressure does not drop, replace the regulator.

15   If the pressure is higher than specified, check for a faulty fuel pressure regulator or a pinched or clogged fuel return hose or pipe.

16   If the pressure is lower than specified, check the following:
 a) Inspect the fuel filter-make sure it's not clogged.
 b) Look for a pinched or clogged fuel hose between the fuel tank and fuel rail.
 c) Check the pressure regulator for a malfunction.
 d) Look for leaks in the fuel feed line/hose.
 e) Check for leaking injectors.
 f) Check the in-tank fuel pump check valve.

17   If the fuel pressure is low, there are no problems with any of the above-listed components and the fuel pump is operating (see Step 6), the problem is one of the following:
 a) The fuel pump is not receiving sufficient voltage (check the battery and charging system-see Chapter 5).
 b) There is a poor electrical connection in the fuel pump circuit (a bad ground connection is very likely).
 c) The fuel pump itself is faulty.

18   Turn off the engine and note the reading on the gauge. After one minute, the pressure should not drop to less than 21 psi on TBI models or 25 psi on MPFI models. If the fuel pressure drops rapidly after turning off the engine, there's a leak in the fuel system. If there are no external leaks, the leak is probably at the fuel pump (likely a leaking outlet check valve) or at the fuel injector(s).

19   After the testing is done, relieve the fuel pressure (see Section 2) and remove the fuel gauge.

---

5   Fuel pump – removal and installation

Warning: *Gasoline is extremely flammable, so extra precautions must be taken when working on any part of the fuel system. Do not smoke or allow open flames or bare light bulbs in the work area. Also, do not work in a garage if a natural gas-type appliance that has a pilot light is present. Always keep a dry chemical (Class B) fire extinguisher near the work area.*

1   Disconnect the cable from the negative terminal of the battery.

2   Relieve the fuel system pressure (see Section 2).

Mechanical pump (carbureted vehicles)

3   Relieve the fuel tank pressure by removing the fuel filler cap.

4   Locate the fuel pump mounted on the right rear corner of the cylinder head **(see illustration 4.3).** Place rags underneath the pump to catch any spilled fuel.

5   Loosen the hose clamps and slide them down the hoses, past the fittings. Disconnect the hoses from the pump, using a twisting motion as you pull them from the fittings. Immediately plug the hoses to prevent leakage of fuel and the entry of dirt.

6   Unscrew the fasteners that retain the pump to the cylinder head, then detach the pump from the head. Remove the pump pushrod and inspect it for wear, replacing it if necessary. Coat it with clean engine oil before installing it.

7   Using a gasket scraper or putty knife, remove all traces of old gasket material from the mating surfaces on the cylinder head (and the fuel pump, if the same one will be reinstalled). While scraping, be careful not to gouge the soft aluminum surfaces.

8   Installation is the reverse of the removal procedure, but be sure to use a new gasket and tighten the mounting fasteners to the specified torque.

Electric pump (fuel injected vehicles)

Refer to illustration 5.10

9   Remove the fuel tank following the procedure described in Section 6.

10   Unscrew the ring that secures the fuel pump, then lift the assembly out of the fuel tank **(see illustration)**.

11   Remove the pump from its bracket and disconnect the electrical connectors, noting their positions.

4

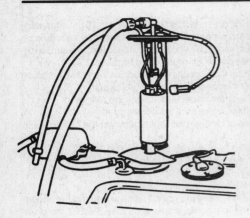

5.10 Once the pump unit securing ring has been unscrewed, the assembly can be lifted straight out of the fuel tank

6.6a Loosen the hose clamp on the fuel filler neck and slide the hose off the tank

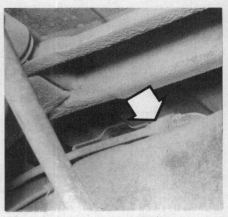

6.6b Disconnect the fuel feed line (arrow) before unbolting the fuel tank from the vehicle – it may be necessary, however, to lower the tank slightly to gain access to the fuel return line (and vapor line, if equipped)

12   Push the nozzle of the new pump into the coupling hose, then insert the bottom of the pump into its bracket. Connect the wires to the proper terminals. If the filter at the bottom of the pump appears dirty, replace it.

13   The remainder of installation is the reverse of the removal procedure. Be sure to replace the pump unit sealing O-ring if it shows any signs of deterioration.

---

6   Fuel tank-removal and installation

Refer to illustrations 6.6a, 6.6b, 6.6c and 6.8

Note: *The following procedure is much easier to perform if the fuel tank is empty. Some tanks have a drain plug for this purpose. If the tank does not have a drain plug, simply run the engine until the tank is empty.*

Warning: *Gasoline is extremely flammable, so extra precautions must be taken when working on any part of the fuel system. Do not smoke or allow open flames or bare light bulbs near the work area. Also, do not work in a garage if a natural gas-type appliance with a pilot light is present. When performing any work on the fuel tank, wear safety glasses and to have a dry chemical (Class B) fire extinguisher on hand. If you spill any fuel on your skin, rinse it off immediately with soap and water.*

1   Remove the fuel tank filler cap to relieve fuel tank pressure.
2   Relieve the fuel system pressure (see Section 2).
3   Detach the cable from the negative terminal of the battery.
4   If the tank has a drain plug, remove it and allow the fuel to collect in an approved gasoline container.
5   Raise the vehicle and place it securely on jackstands.
6   Disconnect the fuel lines, the vapor return line and the fuel filler neck **(see illustrations). Note:** *The fuel feed and return lines and the vapor return line are three different diameters, so reattachment is simplified. If you have any doubts, however, clearly label the lines and the fittings. Be sure to plug the hoses to prevent leakage and contamination of the fuel system.*

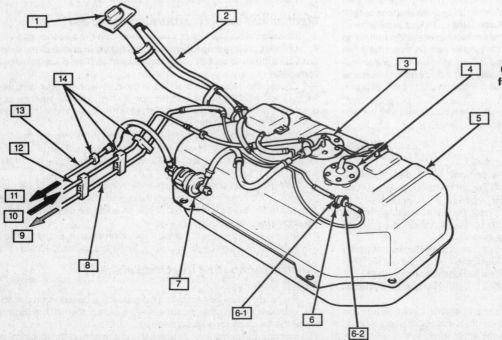

6.6c Fuel tank details (TBI fuel-injected model shown, others similar

1	Fuel filler cap
2	Breather hose
3	Fuel pump assembly
4	Fuel level sending unit
5	Fuel tank
6	Two-way check valve
6-1	Black side
6-2	Orange side
7	fuel filter
8	Fuel vapor line
9	Vapor line to canister
10	Fuel return line
11	Fuel feed line (to TBI unit)
12	Return line
13	Fuel feed line
14	Hose clamps

6.8 The fuel tank and skid plate are secured to the underside of the vehicle with four bolts (one at each corner)

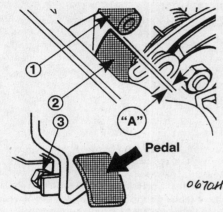

8.9 On MPFI models, check the clearance (A) between the lever stop (1) and the lever (2) – if it's not correct, adjust the throttle pedal stop bolt (3)

7   Support the fuel tank and skid plate (if equipped) with a floor jack. Position a piece of wood between the jack head and the fuel tank to protect the tank.
8   Remove the four fuel tank and skid plate bolts **(see illustration)**.
9   Lower the tank and skid plate enough to disconnect the electrical wires and ground strap from the fuel pump/fuel gauge sending unit, if you have not already done so.
10   Remove the tank from the vehicle.
11   Installation is the reverse of removal.

7   Fuel tank cleaning and repair – general information

1   All repairs to the fuel tank or filler neck should be carried out by a professional who has experience in this critical and potentially dangerous work. Even after cleaning and flushing of the fuel system, explosive fumes can remain and ignite during repair of the tank.
2   If the fuel tank is removed from the vehicle, it should not be placed in an area where sparks or open flames could ignite the fumes coming out of the tank. Be especially careful inside garages where a natural gas-type appliance is located, because the pilot light could cause an explosion.

8   Air cleaner assembly – removal and installation

Carbureted vehicles
Refer to illustration 8.1
1   Unlatch the clips that secure the top of the air cleaner to the main housing **(see illustration)**.

8.1 Air cleaner installation details (carbureted models)
A   Clips   B   Air cleaner mounting fasteners

2   Remove the nut that secures the air intake case to the carburetor, then lift off the case and disconnect the vacuum line from the underside. Unplug the breather hose from the rocker arm cover and remove the air intake case.
3   Disconnect the hot and fresh air intake hoses from the air cleaner. Remove the three mounting nuts and washers that secure the air cleaner to the inner fender panel **(see illustration 8.1)** and remove the air cleaner from the vehicle.
4   Installation is the reverse of the removal procedure.

Fuel injected vehicles
5   Remove the air filter element (see Chapter 1).
6   Unbolt the air cleaner case from the inner fender panel.
7   Unbolt the air intake case from the throttle body and the bracket on the camshaft cover, then remove the air intake duct.
8   Installation is the reverse of the removal procedure.
9   On MPFI models, have an assistant push the accelerator pedal all way to the floor (against the stop bolt). In the engine compartment, measure the clearance between the throttle lever and the stop **(see illustration)**. Check this measurement against this Chapter's Specifications. Adjust the throttle stop clearance by turning the pedal stop bolt.

9   Throttle cable – removal, installation and adjustment

Refer to illustrations 9.2, 9.4 and 9.7
Removal
1   Disconnect the cable from the negative terminal of the battery.
2   Unscrew the locknut on the threaded portion of the throttle cable at the carburetor or throttle body **(see illustration)**.
3   Pass the cable through the slot in the throttle lever and slide the cable end from the lever.
4   Working inside the vehicle, disconnect the cable from the accelerator pedal by passing the cable through the slot at the top of the pedal linkage **(see illustration)**.
5   Pull the cable through the firewall into the engine compartment.

Installation and adjustment
6   Installation is the reverse of the removal procedure, but it is important to adjust the cable to obtain the correct amount of free play.
7   Lightly push on the cable between the throttle lever and the cable bracket **(see illustration)**. Measure the amount the cable deflects and compare it with the figure listed in the Specifications section. To adjust cable free play, screw the adjuster nut up or down on the threaded portion of the cable casing, as necessary, to obtain the correct amount of freeplay. If you adjust the cable when the engine is cold, be sure to recheck the adjustment after it has reached normal operating temperature.

4

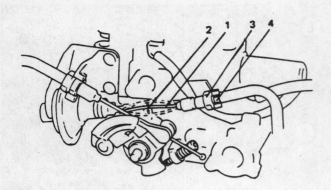

9.2 Throttle cable installation details (fuel-injected model shown, carbureted models similar)

1	Cable	3	Locknut
2	Cable free play	4	Adjusting nut

9.7 Push on the cable and measure the free play-it should be as listed in this Chapter's Specifications

9.4 Pass the cable through the slot (arrow) and slide the cable end out of the accelerator pedal linkage

10.2 Using a feeler gauge (arrow), check the clearance of the choke plate to the carburetor bore

10.5 With the idle-up actuator removed, rotate the fast idle cam to align the hole in the cam with the hole in the bracket – insert a punch through the two holes to hold the cam in this position – the choke lever can now be adjusted with a pair of pliers

10   Carburetor – check and adjustment

Warning: *Gasoline is extremely flammable, so extra precautions must be taken when working on any part of the fuel system. Do not smoke or allow open flames or bare light bulbs in the work area. Also, do not work in a garage if a natural gas-type appliance that has a pilot light is present. Always keep a dry chemical (Class B) fire extinguisher near the work area.*

Note: *If your vehicle's engine is hard to start or does not start at all, has an unstable idle or poor driveability and you suspect the carburetor is malfunctioning, it's best to first take the vehicle to a dealer service department that has the equipment necessary to diagnose this highly complicated system. The following procedures are intended to help the home mechanic verify proper operation of components, make minor adjustments, and replace some components. They are not intended as troubleshooting procedures.*

Choke check and adjustment
Refer to illustrations 10.2 and 10.5

1   Remove the air intake case (see Section 8 if necessary). With the engine stopped and cold, hold the throttle open and depress the choke plate with your finger – it should move smoothly. The choke should be almost fully closed if the ambient air temperature is below 77-degrees F (25-degrees C) and the engine is cold.

2   Check the clearance between the choke plate and the carburetor bore **(see illustration)** and compare your reading with those listed in the Specifications section. If the clearances are too small or too large, lubricate the choke linkage and take another measurement.

3   Start the engine and allow it to warm to normal operating temperature. Depress and release the accelerator once. The choke should now be fully open. If it's not, and the plate-to-bore clearance is correct, there's a problem with the choke linkage or operating mechanism.

4   If the plate-to-bore clearance is not as specified, remove the carburetor (Section 11) and adjust the choke lever as follows.

5   Remove the idle-up actuator from the carburetor, turn the fast idle cam counter-clockwise and insert a pin into the cam and bracket to lock them into place **(see illustration)**.

10.10 With the carburetor cool, make sure the mark on the fast idle cam is in alignment with the center of the cam follower

6   Using a pair of pliers, bend the choke lever up or down until the choke-to-bore clearance is set to the specified amount. Bending the tab up causes the choke valve to close, while bending it down allows it to open a little more **(see illustration 10.5)**.

7   Reinstall the carburetor and check the choke again.

Accelerator pump

8   Remove the air intake case (Section 8). With the engine Off, operate the throttle linkage through its full range of travel while looking down the throat of the carburetor (you may have to hold the choke plate open). A healthy stream of fuel should squirt out of the pump discharge nozzle. If fuel just dribbles out or there is no squirt at all, the accelerator pump is defective or the discharge passage is clogged. In either case, an overhaul of the carburetor is required.

Fast idle adjustment

Refer to illustrations 10.10 and 10.11

9   Allow the engine to cool for at least four hours, then remove the carburetor and let it cool off for another hour. The ambient temperature should be between 71 and 82-degrees F.

10   After the carburetor has cooled, check to see that the mark on the fast idle cam and the center of the cam follower are in alignment **(see illustration)**.

11   Disconnect the hose from the idle-up actuator and connect a hand-held vacuum pump to the port. Apply a vacuum of approximately 16-in Hg. and measure the clearance between the actuator rod and the idle-up adjusting screw **(see illustration)**. It should be 0.10 to 0.12 in (2.5 to 3.0 mm). If it isn't, turn the idle-up adjusting screw accordingly. Reinstall the carburetor.

Idle-up adjustment

12   Run the engine until it reaches normal operating temperature. Connect a tachometer and verify that the idle speed is as specified (see Chapter 1).

13   Turn the parking lamps On and check to see that the idle-up actuator rod moves down. Now turn the headlights On and check the engine rpm (the heater fan, rear defogger and air conditioner must be turned Off). It should increase to 900-1000 rpm. If it doesn't increase, turn the adjusting screw **(see illustration 10.11)**.

11   Carburetor-removal and installation

Warning: *Gasoline is extremely flammable so extra precautions must be taken when working on any part of the fuel system. DO NOT smoke or allow open flames or bare light bulbs in or near the work area. Also, don't work in a garage if a natural gas appliance such as a water heater or clothes dryer is present. Always keep a dry chemical (Class B) fire extinguisher near the work area.*

Removal

1   Remove the fuel filler cap to relieve fuel tank pressure.

10.11 Apply vacuum to the idle-up actuator and measure the clearance between the actuator rod and the idle up adjusting screw

A   *Actuator rod*   B   *Idle-up adjusting screw*

2   Remove the air cleaner from the carburetor. Be sure to label all vacuum hoses attached to the air cleaner housing.

3   Disconnect the throttle cable from the throttle lever (see Section 9).

4   If the vehicle is equipped with an automatic transmission, disconnect the TV cable from the throttle lever.

5   Clearly label all vacuum hoses and fittings, then disconnect the hoses.

6   Disconnect the fuel line from the carburetor.

7   Label the wires and terminals, then unplug all wire harness connectors.

8   Remove the mounting fasteners and detach the carburetor from the intake manifold. Remove the carburetor mounting gasket. Stuff a shop rag into the intake manifold openings.

Installation

9   Use a gasket scraper to remove all traces of gasket material and sealant from the intake manifold (and the carburetor, if it's being reinstalled), then remove the shop rag from the manifold openings. Clean the mating surfaces with lacquer thinner or acetone.

10   Place a new gasket on the intake manifold.

11   Position the carburetor on the gasket and install the mounting fasteners.

12   To prevent carburetor distortion or damage, tighten the fasteners to the specified torque in a criss-cross pattern, 1/4-turn at a time.

13   The remaining installation steps are the reverse of removal.

14   Check and, if necessary, adjust the idle speed (Chapter 1).

15   If the vehicle is equipped with an automatic transmission, refer to Chapter 7B for the kickdown cable adjustment procedure.

16   Start the engine and check carefully for fuel leaks.

12   Carburetor-diagnosis and overhaul

Refer to illustration 12.6

Warning: *Gasoline is extremely flammable, so extra precautions must be taken when working on any part of the fuel system. DO NOT smoke or allow open flames or bare light bulbs in or near the work area. Also, don't work in a garage if a natural gas appliance with a pilot light is present. Always keep a dry chemical (Class B) fire extinguisher near the work area.*

Diagnosis

1   A thorough road test and check of carburetor adjustments should be done before any major carburetor service work. Follow the procedures in Section 10. Specifications for some adjustments are listed on the Vehicle Emissions Control Information (VECI) label found in the engine compartment.

12.6 Before buying a carburetor rebuild kit, look for a number like this and write it down – it will ensure that you get the correct rebuild kit for the carburetor

2   Carburetor problems usually show up as flooding, hard starting, stalling, severe backfiring and poor acceleration. A carburetor that's leaking fuel and/or covered with wet looking deposits definitely needs attention.

3   Some performance complaints directed at the carburetor are actually a result of loose, out-of-adjustment or malfunctioning engine or electrical components. Others develop when vacuum hoses leak, are disconnected or are incorrectly routed. The proper approach to analyzing carburetor problems should include the following items:

   a) Inspect all vacuum hoses and actuators for leaks and correct installation (see Chapters 1 and 6).
   b) Tighten the intake manifold and carburetor mounting nuts/bolts to the torques specified in this Chapter and Chapter 2A.
   c) Perform a cylinder compression test (see Chapter 2B).
   d) Clean or replace the spark plugs as necessary (see Chapter 1).
   e) Check the spark plug wires (see Chapter 1).
   f) Inspect the ignition primary wires.
   g) Check the ignition timing (follow the instructions printed on the Emissions Control Information label).
   h) Check the fuel pump (see Chapter 4).
   i) Check the heat control valve in the air cleaner for proper operation (see Chapter 1).
   j) Check/replace the air filter element (see Chapter 1).
   k) Check the PCV system (see Chapter 6).
   l) Check/replace the fuel filter (see Chapter 1). Also, the strainer in the tank could be restricted.
   m) Check for a plugged exhaust system.
   n) Check EGR valve operation (see Chapter 1).
   o) Check the choke – it should be completely open at normal engine operating temperature (see Section 10).
   p) Check for fuel leaks and kinked or dented fuel lines (see Chapters 1 and 4)
   q) Check accelerator pump operation with the engine off (remove the air cleaner cover and operate the throttle as you look into the carburetor throat – you should see a stream of gasoline enter the carburetor).
   r) Check for incorrect fuel or bad gasoline.
   s) Check the valve clearances (see Chapter 1)
   t) Have a dealer service department or repair shop check the electronic engine and carburetor controls.

4   Diagnosing carburetor problems may require that the engine be started and run with the air cleaner off. While running the engine without the air cleaner, backfires are possible. This situation is likely to occur if the carburetor is malfunctioning, but just the removal of the air cleaner can lean the fuel/air mixture enough to produce an engine backfire. **Warning:** *Do not position any part of your body, especially your face, directly over the carburetor during inspection and servicing procedures. Wear eye protection!*

Overhaul

5   Once it's determined that the carburetor needs an overhaul, several options are available. If you're going to attempt to overhaul the carburetor yourself, first obtain a good quality carburetor rebuild kit (which will include all necessary gaskets, internal parts, instructions and a parts list). You'll also need some special solvent and a means of blowing out the internal passages of the carburetor with air.

6   An alternative is to obtain a new or rebuilt carburetor. They are readily available from dealers and auto parts stores. Make absolutely sure the exchange carburetor is identical to the original. A tag is usually attached to the top of the carburetor or a number is stamped on the float bowl **(see illustration)**. It will help determine the exact type of carburetor you have. When obtaining a rebuilt carburetor or a rebuild kit, make sure the kit or carburetor matches your application exactly. Seemingly insignificant differences can make a large difference in engine performance.

7   If you choose to overhaul your own carburetor, allow enough time to disassemble it carefully, soak the necessary parts in the cleaning solvent (usually for at least one-half day or according to the instructions listed on the carburetor cleaner) and reassemble it, which will usually take much longer than disassembly. When disassembling the carburetor, match each part with the illustration in the carburetor kit and lay the parts out in order on a clean work surface. Overhauls by inexperienced mechanics can result in an engine which runs poorly or not at all. To avoid this, use care and patience when disassembling the carburetor so you can reassemble it correctly.

8   Because carburetor designs are constantly modified by the manufacturer in order to meet increasingly more stringent emissions regulations, it isn't feasible to include a step-by-step overhaul of each type. You'll receive a detailed, well illustrated set of instructions with any carburetor overhaul kit; they will apply in a more specific manner to the carburetor on your vehicle.

13   Throttle Body Injection (TBI) – general information

Most fuel-injected models are equipped with a Throttle Body fuel Injection (TBI) system. This system provides optimum mixture ratios at all stages of combustion and offers immediate throttle response characteristics. It also enables the engine to run at the leanest possible air/fuel mixture ratio, reducing exhaust gas emissions.

A Throttle Body Injection (TBI) unit replaces a conventional carburetor atop the intake manifold. It is controlled by the Electronic Control Module (ECM), which monitors engine performance and adjusts the air/fuel mixture accordingly (see Chapter 6 for a complete description of the fuel control system).

An electric fuel pump – located in the fuel tank with the fuel gauge sending unit-pumps fuel to the fuel injection system through the fuel feed line and an inline fuel filter. A pressure regulator keeps fuel available at a constant pressure. Fuel in excess of injector needs is returned to the fuel tank by a separate line.

The basic TBI unit is made up of the throttle body housing, a fuel injector, a fuel pressure regulator, the throttle opener (which controls the throttle valve opening so that it's a little bit wider when the engine is starting than when it's at an idle), the throttle position sensor, an air valve (which lets an additional amount of air past the throttle plate during cold engine operation) and the idle speed control solenoid valve (which controls the idle speed according to the ECM).

The fuel injector is a solenoid operated device controlled by the ECM. The ECM turns on the solenoid, which lifts a normally closed needle valve off its seat. The fuel, which is under pressure, is injected in a conical spray pattern at the walls of the throttle body bore above the throttle valve. The fuel which is not used by the injector passes through the pressure regulator before being returned to the fuel tank.

14   Throttle body injection (TBI) unit-removal and installation

Refer to illustration 14.6
Warning: *Gasoline is extremely flammable, so extra precautions must be taken when working on any part of the fuel system. Do not smoke or allow open flames or bare light bulbs in the work area. Also, do not work in a garage if a natural gas-type appliance that has a pilot light is present. Always keep a dry chemical (Class B) fire extinguisher near the work area.*

14.6   Throttle body injection unit mounting details

1   Throttle body
2   Throttle body gasket
3   PTC heater (some models with automatic transmission)
4   PVC valve
5   Intake manifold gasket
6   Coolant temperature gauge sending unit
7   Coolant temperature sensor
8   Intake air temperature sensor
9   Intake manifold

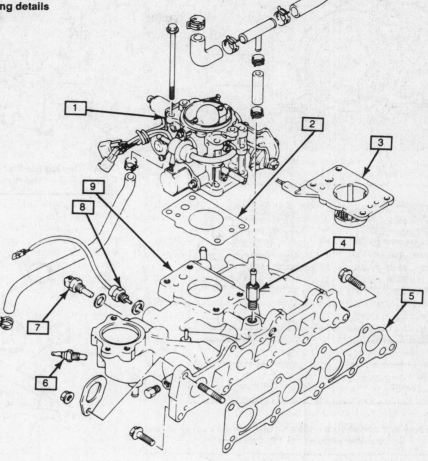

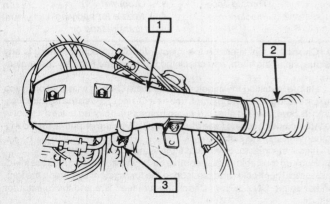

15.1 Air intake case installation details

1   Air intake case
2   Air cleaner outlet hose   3   PCV hose

Removal

1   Disconnect the cable from the negative terminal of the battery.
2   Relieve the fuel system pressure (Section 2).

3   Following the procedure described in Section 9, disconnect the throttle cable from the throttle lever at the TBI unit.
4   Disconnect the fuel feed and return lines from the TBI unit.
5   Label and disconnect any electrical connectors and vacuum hoses.
6   Remove the attaching bolts and lift the TBI unit from the intake manifold **(see illustration)**. On automatic transmission models, also remove the PTC heater from underneath the TBI unit and check the condition of the heating element (grid). If it is burned or has holes in it, replace it with a new one.

Installation

7   Using a gasket scraper or a putty knife, remove all traces of old gasket material and sealant from the intake manifold (and throttle body, if the same one will be installed). While scraping, be careful not to gouge the soft aluminum surfaces.
8   Installation is the reverse of the removal procedure, but be sure to use a new TBI unit base gasket, and tighten the bolts to the specified torque.

15   Throttle body injection (TBI) system – component check and replacement

Warning: *Gasoline is extremely flammable, so extra precautions must be taken when working on any part of the fuel system. Do not smoke or allow open flames or bare light bulbs in the work area. Also, do not work in a garage if a natural gas-type appliance that has a pilot light is present. Always keep a dry chemical (Class B) fire extinguisher near the work area.*

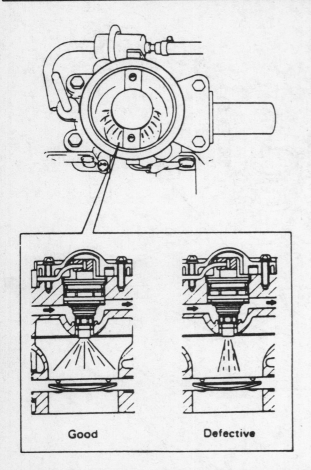

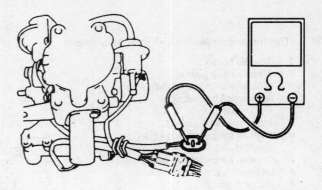

15.4   Unplug the fuel injector electrical connector and measure the resistance across the terminals

Good   Defective

15.2   The fuel injector should emit a strong, conical spray of fuel against the walls of the TBI unit bore

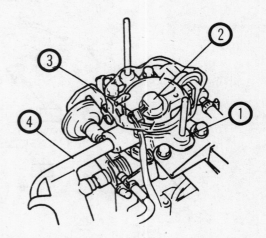

15.9   Apply compressed air (85 psi maximum) to the fuel inlet port to aid in injector removal

1	Throttle body	3	Grommet
2	Injector	4	Nozzle for applying compressed air

Fuel injector

Refer to illustrations 15.1, 15.2, 15.4, 15.9 and 15.11

1   Unbolt the air intake case from the top of the throttle body (see illustration) and move it aside.

2   Start the engine and carefully peer down into the throttle body (wear safety goggles), checking the injector spray pattern. It should be an even, conical pattern (see illustration) – if it isn't, the injector must be replaced with a new one.

3   Shut off the engine and make sure the injection of fuel stops as well. The injector should not leak more than one drop per minute-if it does, replace it.

4   Disconnect the electrical connector from the injector and, using an ohmmeter, measure the resistance across the injector coils (see illustration). If the resistance measured is not as listed in the Specifications section, replace the injector.

5   To replace the fuel injector, begin by relieving the fuel system pressure (Section 2).

6   Disconnect the cable from the negative terminal of the battery.

7   Disconnect the fuel feed line from the throttle body. Remove the two injector cover screws and lift the cover from the injector.

8   Disconnect the injector electrical connector, release the harness clamp and dislodge the grommet from the throttle body housing.

9   To remove the injector from the throttle body, carefully direct compressed air into the fuel inlet port while pulling up on the injector (see illustration). **Caution:** *Apply the compressed air gradually, using only enough to ease the injector out of the throttle body. Do not exceed 85 psi, or damage to the injector and other components may occur. Also, once the injector has been removed, handle it carefully and don't immerse it in solvent to clean it.*

10   Check the fuel filters on the injector for dirt particles. If there is any residue, clean the filters and check the fuel tank and lines for contamination.

11   Before installing the injector, lubricate the O-rings with light oil (if you are reinstalling the same injector, use new O-rings). Push the injector firmly into its bore, making sure the wiring harness is pointing toward its slot in the throttle body housing (see illustration). Push the grommet on the wiring harness into the slot.

12   Install the injector cover and tighten the screws securely.

13   Hook up the cable to the negative battery terminal. Connect the injector electrical connector and pressurize the fuel system by turning the ignition key to the ON position. Check the fuel feed line and the injector for leakage.

14   Install the air intake case.

Fuel pressure regulator

Refer to illustration 15.17

Note: *Since checking the fuel pressure requires the use of some special adapters not normally available to the home mechanic, the fuel pressure should be checked by a dealer service department or other service facility with the necessary hardware. If the regulator has been determined to be faulty, replace it using the following procedure.*

15   Disconnect the cable from the negative terminal of the battery.

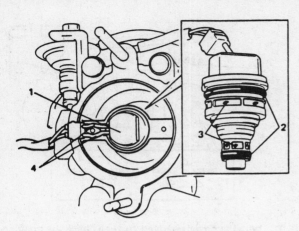

15.11 Fuel injector installation details

1	Injector	3	Filter
2	O-rings	4	Wire harness

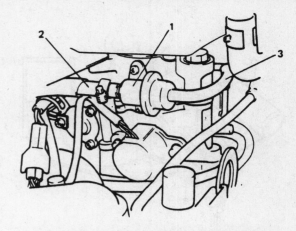

15.17 Fuel pressure regulator mounting details

1	Fuel pressure regulator	3	Vacuum hose
2	Fuel return hose		

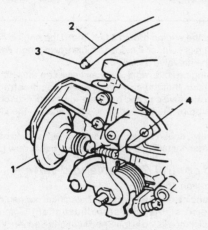

15.22 Throttle opener details

1	Throttle opener	3	Plug
2	Vacuum hose	4	Throttle opener adjusting screw

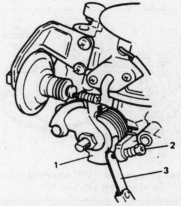

15.32 Using a feeler gauge, block the throttle lever open the specified amount

1	Throttle lever	3	Feeler gauge
2	Idle speed adjusting screw		

16   Relieve the fuel system pressure (Section 2).

17   Loosen the hose clamp on the fuel return hose and disconnect the hose from the pressure regulator **(see illustration)**. Also disconnect the vacuum hose from its port on the regulator.

18   Remove the screws that secure the regulator to the throttle body, then pull the regulator straight out.

19   Coat the O-ring on the new fuel pressure regulator with light oil and push the regulator straight into the throttle body to install it. Tighten the screws securely.

20   Install the fuel return line, tightening the hose clamp securely. Connect the vacuum hose to its port on the regulator.

21   Connect the cable to the negative battery terminal, pressurize the fuel system by turning the ignition switch to ON and check around the regulator for fuel leaks.

Throttle opener
Refer to illustration 15.22

22   To check the throttle opener, disconnect the vacuum hose from it and connect a hand-held vacuum pump. Apply vacuum and verify that the plunger retracts **(see illustration)**.

23   If the throttle opener diaphragm does not hold vacuum or the plunger doesn't retract, replace it.

24   To replace the throttle opener, detach it along with its bracket by removing the two screws securing the bracket to the throttle body assembly. Position the new throttle opener and bracket on the throttle body and install the screws, tightening them securely.

25   To adjust the throttle opener, start the engine and allow it to warm up to normal operating temperature. Make sure all electrical accessories are turned off.

26   Connect a tachometer to the engine, following the manufacturer's instructions.

27   Disconnect the vacuum hose from the throttle opener diaphragm and plug it. Check the engine rpm – it should be approximately 1700 to 1800 rpm. If it isn't, adjust the rpm by turning the opener adjusting screw **(see illustration 15.22)**. Reconnect the vacuum hose.

Throttle position sensor (TPS)
Refer to illustrations 15.32 and 15.33

28   Disconnect the cable from the negative terminal of the battery.

29   Unplug the TPS electrical connector and, referring to the Specifications section, check the resistance between the terminals when the throttle is fully open and fully closed. If the readings aren't as specified, adjust the throttle position sensor. If the correct readings cannot be obtained even after adjustment, then replace the sensor.

30   To adjust the sensor, disconnect the vacuum hose from the throttle

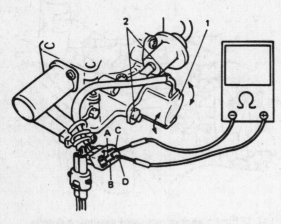

15.33   Turn the TPS clockwise completely, then turn it counterclockwise until the ohmmeter reading changes from infinity to zero

1	TPS	2	Securing bolts

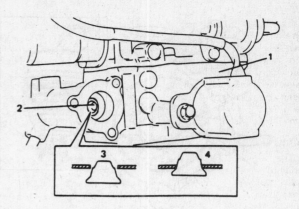

15.37   With the cover removed you can check the position of the air valve – it should be open when the engine is cool and closed when it's hot

1	Throttle body	3	Air valve open position
2	Air valve	4	Air valve closed position

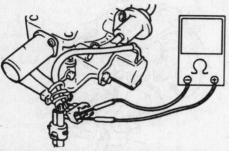

15.40   Check the resistance of the ISC solenoid valve – if it isn't as specified, replace it

opener and connect a hand-held vacuum pump. Apply enough vacuum to retract the plunger to the idle position **(see illustration 15.22)**.

31   Loosen the idle speed screw (Chapter 1) so there is clearance between the screw and the throttle lever. Write down how many turns the screw was loosened. Now turn the screw in until it just contacts the throttle lever, again counting the number of turns. Subtract this number from the number of turns that the screw was loosened and you will end up with the number of turns that the screw was actually loosened from the idle position. This can be used as a guide when returning it to its original position after the TPS sensor adjustment is performed.

32   If the vehicle has a manual transmission, insert a 2.2 mm (0.086 in) feeler gauge between the idle speed screw and the throttle lever **(see illustration)**. If the vehicle has an automatic transmission, use a 2.4 mm (0.094 in) gauge.

33   Connect an ohmmeter between terminals C and D of the throttle position sensor electrical connector **(see illustration)**. Loosen the sensor bolts and turn the sensor clockwise completely. Now turn the sensor counter-clockwise slowly until the ohmmeter needle changes from infinity to zero. Tighten the bolts securely then remove the feeler gauge.

34   Reconnect the vacuum hose to the throttle opener, then connect the cable to the negative battery terminal. Connect the TPS electrical connector.

35   Return the idle speed screw to its previous position and check the idle speed following the procedure in Chapter 1.

Air valve

Refer to illustration 15.37

36   The air valve permits an additional amount of air to bypass the throttle plate when the engine is cold (when the coolant is less than 140-degrees

F). This raises the engine rpm to a fast idle. If the engine doesn't run at a fast idle when it is cold, or if it doesn't idle down when warm, check the operation of the air valve as follows.

37   With the engine cold, remove the air valve cap from the TBI unit. Look inside and confirm that the air valve is open **(see illustration)**.

38   Install the air valve cap and run the engine until it reaches normal operating temperature. Remove the cap once again – the valve should be closed.

39   If the air valve doesn't operate as described, it should be replaced with a new one. When installing the air valve cap, use a new gasket.

Idle speed control (ISC) solenoid valve

Refer to illustration 15.40

40   With the engine off, unplug the ISC electrical connector and connect an ohmmeter across the terminals **(see illustration)**. Compare your reading with the resistance listed in the Specifications Section. If the resistance doesn't fall within the specified range, replace the ISC solenoid valve.

41   Unbolt the ISC solenoid valve from the throttle body. Using jumper wires connected to a 12-volt source, energize the ISC solenoid and verify operation. **Caution:** *Don't energize the solenoid for more than 1 second at a time. If the check must be repeated, wait at least 10 seconds before checking it again.*

42   If no clicking sounds can be heard during the test, replace the ISC solenoid valve.

16   Multi-Port Fuel Injection (MPFI) system – general information

Some 1992 and later models are equipped with a Multi-Port Fuel Injection (MPFI) system. The MPFI system is composed of three basic sub systems: fuel system, air induction system and electronic control system.

Fuel system

An electric fuel pump located inside the fuel tank supplies fuel under constant pressure to the fuel rail, which distributes pressurized fuel evenly to all injectors. From the fuel rail, fuel is injected into the intake ports, just above the intake valves, by four fuel injectors. The amount of fuel supplied by the injectors is precisely controlled by an Electronic Control Module (ECM). The ECM opens each injector, during its associated cylinder's intake stroke, for the precise amount of time necessary to produce the optimum air/fuel mixture for the existing operating conditions. conditions. A pressure regulator controls system pressure in relation to intake manifold vacuum. A fuel filter between the fuel pump and the fuel rail filters fuel to protect the components of the system.

Air induction system

The air system consists of an air filter housing, a mass airflow (MAF) sensor and a throttle body. The MAF sensor is an information gathering device for the ECM that measures the amount of air flowing into the engine. This information helps the ECM determine the amount of fuel to be injected by the injectors (open-time duration of the injectors). The throttle plate inside the throttle body is controlled by the driver. As the throttle plate opens, the amount of air that can pass through the system increases, so the MAF sensor directs the ECM to increase the amount of fuel delivered to the intake ports.

Electronic control system

The Computer Control System controls the fuel injection and other systems by means of an Electronic Control Module (ECM), which employs a microcomputer. The ECM receives signals from a number of information sensors which monitor such variables as intake air volume (MAF sensor), intake air temperature, coolant temperature, engine rpm, acceleration/deceleration and exhaust oxygen content. These signals help the ECM determine the injection duration necessary for the optimum air/fuel ratio. Some of these sensors and their corresponding ECM-controlled relays are not contained within EFI components, but are located throughout the engine compartment. For further information regarding the ECM and its relationship to the engine electrical and ignition system, see Chapter 6.

17 Multi-port fuel injection (MPFI) system – check

Warning: *Gasoline is extremely flammable, so extra precautions must be taken when working on any part of the fuel system. Do not smoke or allow open flames or bare light bulbs near the work area. Also, do not work in a garage if a natural gas-type appliance with a pilot light is present. While performing any work on the fuel system, wear safety glasses and have a dry chemical (Class B) fire extinguisher on hand. If you spill any fuel on your skin, rinse it off immediately with soap and water.*

1   Check the ground wire connections for tightness. Check all wiring and electrical connectors that are related to the system. Loose electrical connectors and poor grounds can cause many problems that resemble more serious malfunctions.
2   Check to see that the battery is fully charged, as the control unit and sensors depend on an accurate supply voltage in order to properly meter the fuel.
3   Check the air filter element – a dirty or partially blocked filter will severely impede performance and economy (see Chapter 1).
4   If a blown fuse is found, replace it and see if it blows again. If it does, search for a grounded wire in the harness related to the system.
5   Check the air intake duct from the MAF sensor to the intake manifold for leaks, which will result in an excessively lean mixture. Also check the condition of the vacuum hoses connected to the intake manifold.
6   Remove the air intake duct from the throttle body and check for dirt, carbon, sludge or other residue build-up. Deposits usually form in the throttle plate area. These deposits frequently cause driveability problems. Open the throttle plate by hand and clean any deposits in the throttle bore with a toothbrush and aerosol carburetor cleaner. Be sure the cleaner is safe for use with oxygen sensors and catalytic converters.
7   With the engine running, place a screwdriver or a stethoscope against each injector, one at a time, and listen through the handle for a clicking sound, indicating operation.
8   If an injector isn't operating (or sounds different than the others), turn off the engine and unplug the electrical connector from the injector. Check the resistance across the terminals of the injector and compare your reading with the resistance value listed in this Chapter's Specifications. If the resistance isn't as specified, replace the injector with a new one.
9   Check the fuel pump and fuel pressure (see Section 4).
10 Clogged fuel injectors frequently cause driveability problems. Many repair shops have the equipment necessary to pressure-clean injectors and will perform this service at a reasonable cost. Several companies sell gasoline additives that help prevent injector clogs and, in some cases, can clean small clogs from injectors. Fuel additives are available inexpensively from auto parts stores.

11 The remainder of the system checks should be left to a dealer service department or other qualified repair shop, as there is a chance that the control unit may be damaged if not performed properly.

18 Multi-Port Fuel Injection (MPFI) system – component check and replacement

Warning: *Gasoline is extremely flammable, so extra precautions must be taken when working on any part of the fuel system. Do not smoke or allow open flames or bare light bulbs near the work area. Also, do not work in a garage if a natural gas-type appliance with a pilot light is present. While performing any work on the fuel system, wear safety glasses and have a dry chemical (Class B) fire extinguisher on hand. If you spill any fuel on your skin, rinse it off immediately with soap and water.*
Note: *For check and replacement procedures for the oxygen sensor, coolant temperature sensor, Manifold Air Temperature (MAT) sensor and crank angle sensor, see Chapter 6.*

Throttle body

Check
1   Verify that the throttle linkage operates smoothly.
2   Check the throttle bore for deposits and clean, as necessary (see the previous Section). With the engine at idle, check for vacuum leaks at the throttle body base gasket, vacuum connections and at the throttle shaft by spraying aerosol carburetor cleaner in these areas. If the idle speed increases and smoothes out when spraying in one of these areas, you've located a vacuum leak (the carburetor cleaner temporarily seals the leak). Replace the base gasket or throttle body or repair the faulty vacuum connection, as necessary.

Removal and installation
3   Detach the cable from the negative terminal of the battery.
4   Drain the radiator (see Chapter 1).
5   Loosen the hose clamps and remove the air intake duct.
6   Detach the accelerator cable from the throttle lever arm (see Section 9), then detach the throttle cable bracket and set it aside (it's not necessary to detach the throttle cable from the bracket).
7   If your vehicle is equipped with an automatic transmission, detach the kickdown cable from the throttle linkage (see Chapter 7B), detach the cable brackets from the engine and set the cable and brackets aside.
8   Clearly label, then detach, all vacuum and coolant hoses from the throttle body.
9   Unplug the electrical connector from the throttle position sensor.
10 Remove the throttle body mounting bolts and detach the throttle body and gasket from the air intake chamber.
11 Using compressed air, thoroughly clean the throttle body casting, then blow out all passages with compressed air. **Caution:** *Do not clean the throttle position sensor or other components with anything. Just use compressed air or wipe them off carefully with a clean soft cloth. Do not use drill bits or wire to clean the passages in the casting.*
12 Installation of the throttle body is the reverse of removal. Be sure to tighten the throttle body mounting bolts to the torque listed in the Specifications Section at the beginning of this Chapter.

Throttle position sensor
Note: *For further information on the throttle position sensor, see Chapter 6.*

Check
Refer to illustrations 18.14a and 18.14b
13 Unplug the electrical connector from the throttle position sensor.
14 Referring to the Specifications section, use an ohmmeter to check the resistance between terminals A and D (**see illustration**). Then check the resistance between A and C when the throttle is at idle and fully open. Finally, check the resistance between terminals A and B with the specified feeler gauges between the throttle stop screw and the lever (**see illustration**). If the correct readings cannot be obtained even after adjustment, then replace the sensor.

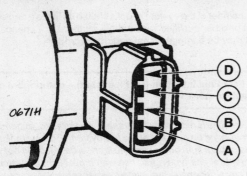

18.14a TPS terminal identification

Adjustment

15   Disconnect the battery negative cable and insert a 0.026 inch (0.65 mm) feeler gauge between the throttle stop screw and the lever (**see illustration 8.14b**), connect the ohmmeter between the A and B terminals, then loosen the sensor mounting screws and slowly turn the sensor counterclockwise until the ohmmeter needle moves from continuity to no continuity.

16   Use the ohmmeter to check that the continuity between terminals A and B is as specified in Step 14. Tighten the TPS screws securely.

Replacement

17   If adjustment doesn't bring the throttle position sensor within specifications, unplug it, remove the screws and replace it with a new one, then adjust it as described above.

Fuel pressure regulator

Check

18   Refer to the fuel pump/fuel pressure check procedure (see Section 4).

Removal and Installation

19   Relieve the fuel pressure (Section 2) and detach the cable from the negative terminal of the battery.

20   Detach the vacuum sensing hose.

21   Place a metal container or shop towel under the fuel return line. Also cover the line with a rag to catch any fuel that may spray out.

22   Loosen the hose clamp and detach the fuel return hose from the fuel pressure regulator pipe.

23   Remove the pressure regulator mounting bolts and detach the pressure regulator and return pipe rearward from the fuel rail.

24   Installation is the reverse of removal. Be sure to use a new O-ring and make sure that the pressure regulator is installed properly on the fuel rail.

Idle Air Control (IAC) valve

Check

Refer to illustrations 18.25

25   With the ignition switch Off, unplug the IAC electrical connector and measure the resistance between the two terminals (**see illustration**). Compare this reading with the one listed in the Specifications section.

26   If the resistance is not as specified, replace the IAC valve.

27   If the resistance is as specified, disconnect the IAC valve hose and blow into it to make sure that air will not pass easily.

28   Using fused jumper wires, connect battery voltage to the two IAC valve terminals (**see illustration 18.25**). Check that air can now be blown into the hose.

29   If it fails any of the above tests, replace the valve.

Removal and Installation

30   Disconnect the battery negative cable.

31   Remove the throttle cover.

32   Disconnect the IAC air hose and valve coupler.

33   With the engine cold, remove the radiator cap and disconnect the water hoses from the valve.

34   Remove the bolts and detach the valve from the intake manifold.

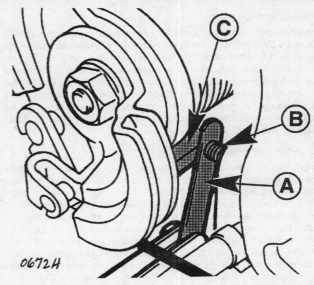

18.14b Insert the feeler gauge (A) between the lever (C) and stop screw (B)

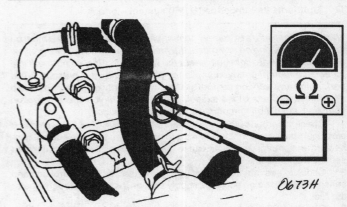

18.25 Checking the resistance across the IAC connector terminals – connect the battery to the same terminals when checking IAC valve operation

35   Installation of the IAC valve is the reverse of removal. Be sure to use a new gasket when installing the IAC valve.

Fuel rail and fuel injectors

Check

36   Refer to Section 17.

Replacement

Refer to illustration 18.45

37   Relieve the fuel pressure (Section 2).

38   Detach the cable from the negative terminal of the battery.

39   Remove the throttle cover.

40   Remove the air cleaner intake pipe and hose assembly.

41   Remove the bracket and surge tank from the intake manifold.

42   Unplug the four fuel injector electrical connectors and set the injector wire harness aside.

43   Remove the fuel pressure regulator.

44   Remove the three fuel rail mounting bolts and detach the fuel rail/injector assembly from the cylinder head by pulling on it while wiggling it back and forth.

45   Remove the fuel injectors from the fuel rail, set them aside in a clearly labeled storage container, then remove the four fuel rail insulators from the cylinder head and set them aside as well (**see illustration**).

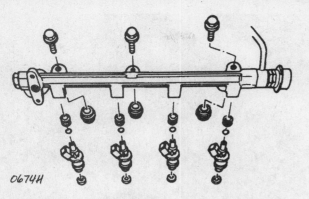

18.45 Fuel rail and injector components-exploded view

18.48 The Mass Airflow (MAF) sensor is attached to the air cleaner upper case and connected to the throttle body by a long rubber duct

4

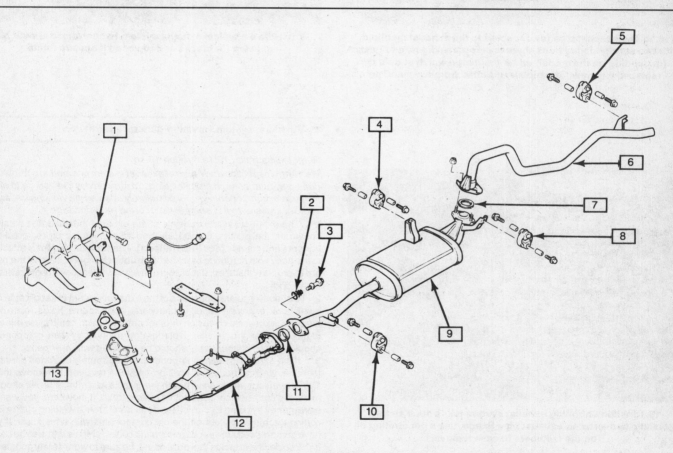

19.1a   Exploded view of the exhaust system (Sidekick and Tracker shown, Samurai similar)

1	Exhaust manifold	6	Tail pipe	10	Rubber hanger
2	Spring	7	Gasket	11	Sealing ring
3	Bolt	8	Rubber hanger	12	Catalytic converter
4	Rubber hanger	9	Muffler	13	Gasket
5	Rubber hanger				

46   If you are replacing the injector(s), discard the old injector, the grommet and the O-ring. If you are simply replacing leaking injector O-rings and intend to re-use the same injectors, remove the old grommet and O-ring and discard them. Installation is the reverse of removal.

Mass Airflow (MAF) sensor
Refer to illustration 18.48

Check
47   Inspect the intake air duct from the MAF sensor to the throttle body. Any air leaks between the sensor and throttle body will cause the engine to run poorly.
48   Visually inspect the sensor for cracks and other damage (see illustration). Make sure the electrical connection is tight and clean.

19.1b The exhaust pipe is connected to the exhaust manifold with two spring-loaded bolts-there is also a sealing ring or gasket (depending on the model) under the flange which should be replaced whenever the pipe is unbolted from the manifold

19.1c Here's a typical exhaust system hanger-these should be inspected for cracks and replaced if any are found

19.1d When unbolting exhaust system joints such as this catalytic converter-to-exhaust pipe flange, use a penetrating oil on the fasteners to ease removal

49   A malfunction in the MAF sensor circuit will frequently set diagnostic code 33 or 34 (see Chapter 6). If you suspect an intermittent malfunction in the MAF sensor that does not set a code, try tapping gently on the MAF sensor housing with a small wrench while the engine is idling. If the engine runs poorly when the MAF sensor is tapped, the sensor is probably faulty.

Replacement
50   Disconnect the negative cable from the battery.
51   Disconnect the electrical connector and intake air duct from the MAF sensor.
52   Remove the MAF sensor with the air cleaner upper case.
53   Disconnect the MAF sensor from the air cleaner upper case.
54   Installation is the reverse of removal. Be sure to replace the MAF sensor-to-air cleaner upper case seal.

19   Exhaust system servicing-general information

Refer to illustration 19.1a through 19.1d
Warning: *Inspection and repair of exhaust system components should be done only after enough time has elapsed after driving the vehicle to allow the system components to cool completely. Also, when working under the vehicle, make sure it is securely supported on jackstands.*

1   The exhaust system consists of the exhaust manifold, the catalytic converter, the muffler, the tailpipe and all connecting pipes, brackets, hangers and clamps (**see illustrations**). The exhaust system is attached to the body with mounting brackets and rubber hangers. If any of the parts are improperly installed, excessive noise and vibration will be transmitted to the body.
2   Conduct regular inspections of the exhaust system to keep it safe and quiet. Look for any damaged or bent parts, open seams, holes, loose connections, excessive corrosion or other defects which could allow exhaust fumes to enter the vehicle. Deteriorated exhaust system components should not be repaired; they should be replaced with new parts.
3   If the exhaust system components are extremely corroded or rusted together, welding equipment will probably be required to remove them. The convenient way to accomplish this is to have a muffler repair shop remove the corroded sections with a cutting torch. If, however, you want to save money by doing it yourself (and you don't have a welding outfit with a cutting torch), simply cut off the old components with a hacksaw. If you have compressed air, special pneumatic cutting chisels can also be used. If you do decide to tackle the job at home, be sure to wear safety goggles to protect your eyes from metal chips and work gloves to protect your hands.
4   Here are some simple guidelines to follow when repairing the exhaust system:
   a) Work from the back to the front when removing exhaust system components.
   b) Apply penetrating oil to the exhaust system component fasteners to make them easier to remove.
   c) Use new gaskets, hangers and clamps when installing exhaust systems components.
   d) Apply anti-seize compound to the threads of all exhaust system fasteners during reassembly.
   e) Be sure to allow sufficient clearance between newly installed parts and all points on the underbody to avoid overheating the floor pan and possibly damaging the interior carpet and insulation. Pay particularly close attention to the catalytic converter and heat shield.

Chapter 5   Engine electrical systems

Contents

5

Specifications

Ignition coil

1990 and earlier models
  Primary resistance . . . . 1.35 to 1.65 ohms
  Secondary resistance . . . . 11.0 to 14.5 k-ohms
1991 and later models
  Primary resistance . . . . 0.72 to 8.88 ohms
  Secondary resistance . . . . 10.2 to 14.0 k-ohms

Distributor

1990 and earlier models
  Igniter (pickup coil) resistance . . . . 130 to 190 ohms
  Signal rotor air gap . . . . 0.008 to 0.016 in (0.2 to 0.4 mm)
1991 and later models (igniter continuity check)
  Tracker and Sidekick
    No voltage applied to G and IB terminals . . . . No continuity
    Voltage applied to G and IB terminals . . . . Continuity
  Samurai . . . . Specifications not available

Alternator

Standard charging voltage . . . . 14.2 to 14.8 volts
  Brush length
    Samurai
      Standard . . . . 0.43 in (11 mm)
      Minimum . . . . 0.20 in (5 mm)
    Sidekick/Tracker
      Standard . . . . 0.63 in (16 mm)
      Minimum . . . . 0.08 in (2 mm)

1   General information

The engine electrical systems include all ignition, charging and starting components. Because of their engine-related functions, these components are covered separately from chassis electrical devices such as the lights, instruments, etc. (which are included in Chapter 12).

Always observe the following precautions when working on the electrical systems:

a) Be extremely careful when servicing engine electrical components. They're easily damaged if checked, connected or handled improperly.
b) Never leave the ignition switch on for long periods of time with the engine off.
c) Don't disconnect the battery cables while the engine is running.
d) Maintain correct polarity when connecting a battery cable from another vehicle during jump starting.
e) Always disconnect the negative cable first and hook it up last or the battery may be shorted by the tool being used to loosen the cable clamps.

It's also a good idea to review the safety-related information regarding the engine electrical systems located in the Safety first! Section near the front of this manual before beginning any operation included in this Chapter.

2   Battery – emergency jump starting

Refer to the Booster battery (jump) starting procedure at the front of this manual.

3   Battery – removal and installation

Refer to illustration 3.2
Caution: *Always disconnect the negative cable first and hook it up last or the battery may be shorted by the tool being used to loosen the cable clamps.*
1   Disconnect both cables from the battery terminals.
2   Remove the battery hold down clamp or strap **(see illustration)**.
3   Lift out the battery. Be careful – it's heavy.
4   While the battery is out, inspect the carrier (tray) for corrosion (see Chapter 1).

3.2   **Unscrew the nuts (arrows), then pull the hold down clamp off the battery**

5   If you're replacing the battery, make sure you get one that's identical to the original, with the same dimensions, amperage rating, cold cranking rating, etc.
6   Installation is the reverse of removal.

4   Battery cables – check and replacement

1   Periodically inspect the entire length of each battery cable for damage, cracked or burned insulation and corrosion. Poor battery cable connections can cause starting problems and decreased engine performance.
2   Check the cable-to-terminal connections at the ends of the cables for cracks, loose wire strands and corrosion. The presence of white, fluffy deposits under the insulation at the cable terminal connection is a sign the cable is corroded and should be replaced. Check the terminals for distortion, missing mounting bolts and corrosion.
3   When removing the cables, always disconnect the negative cable first and hook it up last or the battery may be shorted by the tool used to loosen the cable clamps. Even if only the positive cable is being replaced, be sure to disconnect the negative cable from the battery first (see Chapter 1 for further information regarding battery cable removal).
4   Disconnect the old cables from the battery, then trace each of them to their opposite ends and detach them from the starter solenoid and ground terminals. Note the routing of each cable to ensure correct installation.
5   If you're replacing either or both of the cables, take the old ones along when buying new cables. It's very important to replace the cables with identical parts. Cables have characteristics that make them easy to identify: positive cables are usually red, larger in cross-section and have a larger diameter battery post clamp; ground cables are usually black, smaller in cross-section and have a slightly smaller diameter clamp for the negative post.
6   Clean the threads of the solenoid or ground connection with a wire brush to remove corrosion. Apply a light coat of battery terminal corrosion inhibitor, or petroleum jelly, to the threads to prevent future corrosion.
7   Attach the cable to the solenoid or ground connection and tighten the mounting nut/bolt securely.
8   Before connecting a new cable to the battery, make sure it reaches the battery post without having to be stretched.
9   Connect the positive cable first, followed by the negative cable.

5   Ignition system – general information and precautions

The ignition system includes the ignition switch, the battery, the coil, the primary (low voltage) and secondary (high voltage) wiring circuits, the distributor and the spark plugs.

When working on the ignition system, take the following precautions:
a) Don't keep the ignition switch on for more than 10 seconds if the engine won't start.
b) Always connect a tachometer by following the manufacturer's instructions. Some tachometers may be incompatible with the ignition system. Consult a dealer service department before buying a tachometer.
c) Never ground the ignition coil terminals. Grounding the coil could result in damage to the igniter and/or the ignition coil.
d) Don't disconnect the battery when the engine is running.
e) Make sure the igniter is properly grounded.

6   Ignition system – check

1   Attach an inductive timing light to each plug wire, one at a time, and crank the engine.
a) If the light flashes, voltage is reaching the plug.
b) If the light doesn't flash, proceed to the next Step.
2   Inspect the spark plug wire(s), distributor cap, rotor and spark plug(s) (see Chapter 1).

7.3a   With the primary wiring electrical connector (arrow) unplugged, check the resistance across the primary terminals (1990 and earlier models)

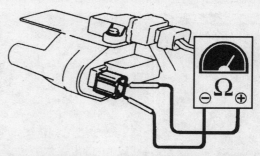

7.3b Measuring the coil primary resistance on 1991 and later models (Sidekick/Tracker shown, Samurai similar) – to measure secondary resistance, measure between one of the primary terminals shown here and the secondary terminal (the terminal where the coil-to-distributor cap wire connects)

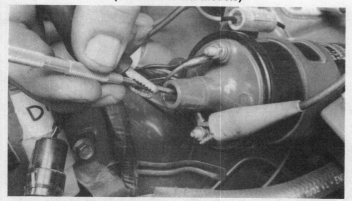

7.4   When measuring the secondary coil resistance, insert a probe into the coil tower and connect the other lead to the positive (+) primary terminal (1990 and earlier models)

3   If the engine still won't start, check the ignition coil (see Section 7).
4   If the coil is functioning properly, proceed to check the igniter and generator (Section 11).

7   Ignition coil – check and replacement

Refer to illustrations 7.3, 7.4 and 7.8

Check

Note: *These checks should be done when the engine is cold so the coil is also cold.*

1   Disconnect the cable from the negative terminal of the battery.
2   On 1990 and earlier models, follow the primary wiring harness from the ignition coil up to the electrical connector, then unplug the connector. If you can't find the electrical connector, detach the wires right at the coil by removing the nuts from the terminals. On 1991 and later models disconnect the electrical connector at the coil. On all model, disconnect the high tension lead from the coil tower.
3   Using an ohmmeter, measure the resistance across the primary terminals **(see illustrations)** and compare it to the figures listed in this Chapter's Specifications. If the resistance is not as specified, replace the coil.
4   Now measure the secondary resistance of the coil. Insert a pointed metal tool into the coil tower and attach one of the ohmmeter leads to it **(see the accompanying illustration or illustration 7.3b)**. Connect the other lead to the positive primary terminal on the coil and read the meter. Compare the results to this Chapter's Specifications. If it isn't within the specified range, replace the coil.
5   Inspect the area around the coil tower for carbon tracking, which looks like fine pencil-drawn lines. This indicates an electrical shorting condition – if any carbon tracking is found, the coil must be replaced and the secondary wiring should be checked for excessive resistance (see Chapter 1).

7.8   The coil is attached to the firewall with two screws (1990 and earlier models)

Replacement

6   Disconnect the cable from the negative battery terminal.
7   Label and disconnect the primary wires from the coil. Pull the high tension lead out of the coil tower.
8   Remove the coil bracket-to-firewall screws **(see illustration)** and detach the coil.
9   To install the coil, reverse the removal procedure. If the new coil doesn't come with a bracket, loosen the clamp screw on the old bracket and slide it off the coil. Slide the new coil into the bracket and tighten the clamp screw securely. When mounting the coil on the firewall, be sure to install the condenser, if equipped, under the upper mounting screw.

8   Distributor – removal and installation

Refer to illustrations 8.5a and 8.5b

Removal

1   Unplug the distributor primary lead wire (from the coil).
2   Unplug the electrical connector for the igniter. Follow the wires as they exit the distributor to find the connector.
3   Look for a raised "1" on the distributor cap. This marks the location for the number one cylinder spark plug wire terminal. If the cap doesn't have a mark for the number one terminal, locate the number one spark plug and trace the wire back to the terminal on the cap.
4   Remove the distributor cap (see Chapter 1) and turn the engine over until the rotor is pointing at the number one spark plug terminal (refer to the locating TDC procedure in Chapter 2).
5   Make a mark on the edge of the distributor body directly below the rotor tip and in line with it **(see illustration)**. Also, mark the distributor base

5

8.5a   Before removing the distributor, use chalk or a felt-tip pen to make an alignment mark on the edge of the distributor base directly beneath the rotor tip – DO NOT use a lead pencil

8.5b   Mark the relationship of the distributor to the gear case as well

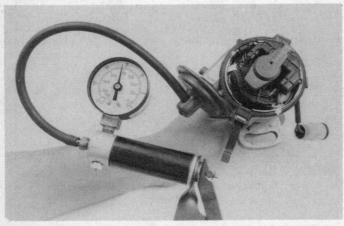

9.3   Use a vacuum pump to check the operation of the vacuum advance unit

9.5   The vacuum advance arm is secured to the pin on the generator base plate with an E-clip (internal distributor components removed for clarity)

| | B | Advance mechanism |
| A | E-clip | mounting screw |

and the gear case to ensure the distributor is reinstalled correctly (see illustration).
6   Remove the distributor hold down bolt and clamp, then pull the distributor straight out to remove it. Caution: *DO NOT turn the crankshaft while the distributor is out of the engine – if you do, the alignment marks will be useless.*

Installation

Note: *If the crankshaft has been moved while the distributor is out, the number one piston must be repositioned at TDC. This can be done by feeling for compression pressure at the number one plug hole as the crankshaft is turned. Once compression is felt, align the ignition timing zero mark with the pointer.*

7   Insert the distributor into the engine in exactly the same position it was when removed.
8   To mesh the helical gears on the camshaft and distributor, it may be necessary to turn the rotor slightly. Recheck the alignment marks on the distributor base and gear case to verify the distributor is in the same position it was before removal. Also check the rotor to see if it's aligned with the mark on the edge of the distributor base.
9   Place the hold down clamp in position and loosely install the bolt.
10   Install the distributor cap.
11   Plug in the electrical connectors.
12   Reattach the spark plug wires to the plugs (if removed).
13   Connect the cable to the negative terminal of the battery.
14   Check the ignition timing (refer to Chapter 1) and tighten the distributor hold down bolt securely.

9   Vacuum advance unit – check and replacement (1990 and earlier models)

Refer to illustrations 9.3 and 9.5

Check

1   Disconnect the cable from the negative terminal of the battery.
2   Remove the distributor cap.
3   Disconnect the vacuum hose from the vacuum advance unit and connect a hand-held vacuum pump (see illustration). Apply vacuum and watch the generator base plate – it should rotate counterclockwise slightly. The needle on the vacuum pump gauge should also remain steady, indicating the diaphragm inside the advance unit is in good condition.
4   If the generator base plate doesn't move and the vacuum diaphragm doesn't hold vacuum, replace the advance unit. If the generator base plate doesn't move but the advance unit does hold vacuum, disconnect the advance unit arm from the pin on the generator base plate and attempt to turn the plate. If it moves smoothly, replace the advance unit. If the plate is stuck or doesn't move smoothly, replace it (Section 13).

Replacement

5   Using a small screwdriver or scribe, pry off the E-clip that retains the vacuum advance arm to the generator base plate (see illustration). Lift up on the advance arm and turn the generator base plate to disconnect the arm from the plate.

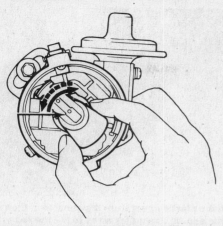

10.3 If the centrifugal advance mechanism is functioning properly, the rotor should snap back to its original position after being turned clockwise

6   Remove the screw that secures the advance unit to the distributor body (see illustration 9.5). Slide the advance unit out of the distributor body, using a twisting motion if it's stuck.
7   Installation is the reverse of the removal procedure.

10   Centrifugal advance mechanism – check (1990 and earlier models)

Refer to illustration 10.3
1   Disconnect the cable from the negative terminal of the battery.
2   Remove the distributor cap.
3   Turn the rotor clockwise and see if it snaps back **(see illustration)**. It should turn smoothly, but you should be able to feel some spring resistance. If the distributor has been removed, you'll have to hold the distributor drive gear.
4   If the rotor won't turn, snap back to its original position or if it's sticky, the distributor must be replaced (individual centrifugal advance parts aren't available separately, at least not at the time of this writing – check with a dealer parts department or a parts store before removing any parts).

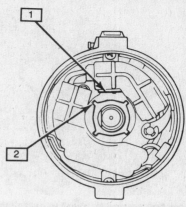

11.1 The teeth on the signal rotor must be positioned as shown, in relation to the terminal on the igniter, when testing the ignition primary circuit (1990 and earlier models)

1   *Igniter (pickup coil)*   2   *Signal rotor tooth*

11   Igniter, pick-up assembly and generator – check and replacement

1990 and earlier models

Refer to illustrations 11.1, 11.2, 11.3, 11.5, 11.6, 11.7 and 11.8
1   Remove the distributor cap and rotor and look at the relationship of the signal rotor to the igniter terminal. For the purposes of this test, the terminal on the igniter should be pointing between two of the teeth on the signal rotor **(see illustration)**. If it isn't, turn the crankshaft until it is.
2   Connect the positive lead of a voltmeter to the negative terminal on the coil. Connect the negative terminal of the voltmeter to a good ground. Disconnect the high tension coil wire from the distributor and clip it to a good ground also **(see illustration)**.
3   Turn the ignition switch to the On position, but don't crank the engine. Pass a standard screwdriver between the igniter terminal and a tooth on the signal rotor several times while looking at the voltmeter **(see illustration)**. The needle on the meter should fluctuate a little bit – about 0.5 to 1 volt – from normal battery voltage. If it does, the generator and igniter are working properly.
4   If there's no voltage fluctuation, remove the distributor (Section 8).

5

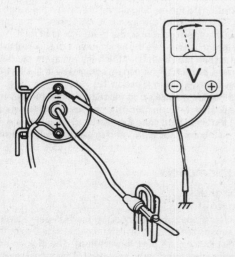

11.2 Connect a voltmeter to the coil as shown, unplug the coil wire from the distributor cap and ground it, ...

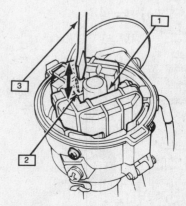

11.3 then pass a screwdriver between the igniter and a tooth on the signal rotor – the voltage on the meter should fluctuate if the primary circuit is functioning properly (1990 and earlier models)

1   *Signal rotor*   3   *Screwdriver*
2   *Igniter*

11.5   Remove the two screws (arrows) to detach the generator from the distributor body (1990 and earlier models)

11.6   Detach the plastic cover from the generator, then remove the screws that secure the igniter wires to it – the red or orange wire goes to the positive terminal and the white wire goes to the negative terminal (mark them if there's any uncertainty) (1990 and earlier models)

11.7   Measure the resistance of the igniter – if it isn't as specified, replace it (1990 and earlier models)

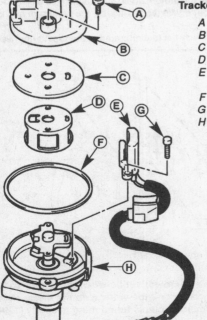

11.11   An exploded view of the distributor used on 1991 and later models (Samurai model shown, Sidekick and Tracker similar)

A   Rotor screw
B   Rotor
C   Shield cover
D   Signal rotor
E   Pick-up assembly
F   Seal
G   Screw
H   Distributor housing

11.8   The igniter is held to the generator base plate with two screws (1990 and earlier models)

5   Remove the two screws that retain the generator to the distributor body (see illustration), push the rubber grommet on the wiring harness up and out of the groove, then lift the generator out of the distributor.

6   Unclip the plastic cover on the generator, then remove the screws that secure the igniter wiring to the generator (see illustration).

7   Using an ohmmeter, measure the resistance across the igniter terminals (see illustration). If the reading doesn't fall within the range listed in this Chapter's Specifications, the igniter is defective. If the resistance reading is within the specified range, the generator is at fault.

8   To replace the igniter, remove the two screws that secure it to the generator base plate (see illustration). Attach the igniter to the base plate with the two screws, but don't tighten them completely until after the signal rotor air gap has been adjusted (Section 12).

9   When installing the generator, connect the orange (or red) wire from the igniter to the positive (+) terminal on the generator and the white wire to the negative (–) terminal, then snap the plastic cover into place.

10   Install the distributor (Section 8) and adjust the ignition timing (see Chapter 1).

1991 and later models

General information

Refer to illustration 11.11

11   1991 and later models are equipped with a Hall-effect-type pick-up assembly that senses the passing of a shutter-type signal rotor that is attached to the distributor shaft (see illustration). The pick-up assembly senses the passing of each of the four shutters of the signal rotor (one for each engine cylinder) and sends a signal to the igniter and ECM that triggers ignition. The igniter amplifies the pick-up assembly's signal. It is mounted externally and is normally attached to the ignition coil.

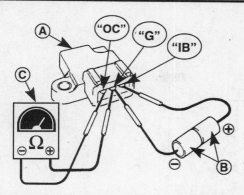

11.14 Checking the igniter on 1991 and later models with two 1.5-volt batteries and an ohmmeter (Sidekick and Tracker models)

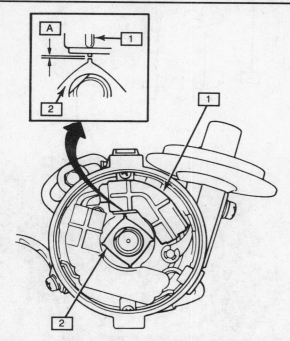

12.2 Align a tooth on the signal rotor with the igniter terminal and insert a brass feeler gauge between them to check the air gap

A   Air gap
1   Igniter terminal
2   Signal rotor

12.3 The air gap can be adjusted by loosening the two igniter screws, inserting a screwdriver into the slot in the igniter and turning the screwdriver to pry the igniter toward or away from the signal rotor

Check (igniter only)
Refer to illustration 11.14
Note: *The following procedure applies to Sidekick and Tracker models only. On 1991 and later Samurai models, take the vehicle to a dealer service department or other qualified shop. Also, checking the pick-up assembly on all 1991 and later models is beyond the scope of the home mechanic. Take the vehicle to a dealer service department or other qualified shop.*

12   Disconnect the electrical connector from the igniter, which is attached to the ignition coil.
13   Remove the igniter from the coil bracket.
14   Connect two 1.5 volt batteries in series so that their total output voltage is around 3 volts. Connect the positive terminal of an ohmmeter to the G terminal of the igniter and the negative terminal to the OC terminal. Apply the 3 volts between the G and IB terminal and make sure that there is continuity on the ohmmeter (**see illustration**). With no voltage applied, there should be no continuity. If the continuity is not as specified, replace the igniter.

Replacement
15   To replace the igniter, disconnect the electrical connector, remove the mounting screws and lift the igniter from the coil bracket. Installation is the reverse of removal.
16   To replace the pick-up assembly, remove the distributor cap and rotor, lift off the shield cover or dust cover, then remove the signal rotor. If the signal rotor is damaged or bent, replace it.
17   Disconnect the electrical connector, remove the mounting screw and lift off the pick-up assembly. Installation is the reverse or removal.

12   Signal rotor air gap – adjustment (1990 and earlier models)

Refer to illustrations 12.2 and 12.3
1   Any time you replace the igniter – or remove it to get at the generator base plate – be sure to adjust the air gap before reinstalling the generator.
2   Remove the generator and loosen the igniter mounting screws. Place a BRASS feeler gauge of the specified thickness between one of the four projections on the signal rotor and the igniter (**see illustration**).
3   Gently pry the igniter toward the signal rotor until it's a snug – not tight – fit against the feeler gauge (**see illustration**).
4   Tighten the igniter mounting screws.
5   Check the adjustment by noting the amount of drag on the feeler gauge when you pull it out of the gap between the signal rotor and igniter. You should feel a slight amount of drag. If you feel excessive drag on the gauge, the gap is probably too small. If you don't feel any drag on the gauge when you pull it out, the air gap is too large.
6   Install the generator.

13   Distributor – disassembly and reassembly (1990 and earlier models)

Refer to illustrations 13.5a, 13.5b, 13.5c and 13.6
Note: *On 1991 and later models, the manufacturer does not recommend disassembling the distributor. If the distributor is damaged or the shaft is worn, replace the distributor as a unit.*
1   Disconnect the cable from the negative terminal of the battery.
2   Remove the distributor (Section 8).
3   Remove the generator and igniter (Section 11).
4   Remove the vacuum advance unit (Section 9).
5   Remove the two screws that retain the generator base plate to the distributor body, then lift the plate out (**see illustrations**). Check the plate for smooth rotation – if it's stuck or doesn't turn smoothly, replace it.
6   To remove the distributor drive gear, grind off the ends of the set pin (**see illustration**), then knock the pin out with a hammer and punch. The gear should now slide off the shaft. If it's stuck, a small gear puller can be used to remove it.

5

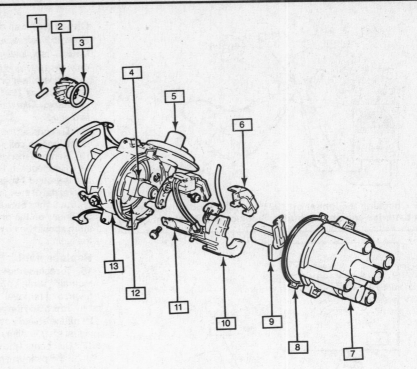

13.5a Exploded view of the distributor components

1   Set pin
2   Distributor drive gear
3   O-ring
4   Signal rotor
5   Vacuum advance assembly
6   Generator dust cover
7   Distributor cap
8   Seal
9   Rotor
10 Igniter dust cover
11 Igniter
12 Generator base plate
13 Distributor housing

13.5b   When removing the generator base plate screws, be careful not to lose the small hold down plates

13.5c   When lifting the generator base plate out of the distributor body, be careful not to nick the signal rotor teeth

13.6   Before attempting to knock the drive gear set pin out, grind off the ends

7   To install the gear, slide it onto the distributor shaft and align the set pin holes. Tap the new pin into place, then peen each end of the pin by hitting it with a hammer and punch while the other end is resting against a solid surface. This will prevent the pin from working its way out during engine operation.

8   Install the generator base plate – the four spring clips around the outer edge of the plate must line up with the four grooves in the distributor housing before the plate will drop down into position. Make sure the pin for the vacuum advance arm is located properly.

9   To reassemble the remainder of the distributor, reverse the disassembly sequence. Don't forget to adjust the signal rotor air gap following the procedure in Section 12.

14   Charging system – general information and precautions

The charging system includes the alternator, an internal voltage regulator, a charge indicator, the battery, a fusible link and the wiring between all the components. The charging system supplies electrical power for the ignition system, lights, radio, etc. The alternator is driven by a belt at the front of the engine.

The purpose of the voltage regulator is to limit the alternator's output

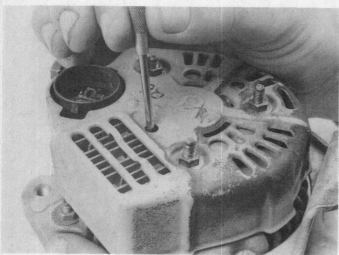

15.6 If the charging voltage is low, insert a metal tool into the test hole in the rear of the alternator and take a voltage reading at the B+ terminal on the alternator – if the voltage rises, the regulator is faulty (alternator removed for clarity)

16.3 Alternator mounting details (Samurai shown, others similar)

A   Electrical connector   C   Adjusting bolt (pivot bolt on underside
B   B+ terminal   of alternator isn't visible in this photo)

to a preset value. This prevents power surges, circuit overloads, etc., during peak voltage output.

The fusible link is a short length of insulated wire integral with the engine compartment wiring harness. The link is four wire gauges smaller than the wire in the circuit it protects. Production fusible links and their identification flags are identified by the flag color. See Chapter 12 for additional information on the fusible links.

The charging system doesn't ordinarily require periodic maintenance. However, the drivebelt, battery and wires and connections should be inspected at the intervals outlined in Chapter 1.

The dashboard warning light should come on when the ignition key is turned to Start, then go off immediately. If it remains on, there's a malfunction in the charging system (see Section 15). Some vehicles are also equipped with a voltmeter. If the voltmeter indicates abnormally high or low voltage, check the charging system (see Section 15).

Be very careful when making electrical test connections on a vehicle equipped with an alternator and note the following:

a) When reconnecting wires to the alternator from the battery, be sure to note the polarity.
b) Before using arc welding equipment to repair any part of the vehicle, disconnect the wires from the alternator and the battery terminals.
c) Never start the engine with a battery charger connected.
d) Always disconnect both battery cables before using a battery charger.
e) The alternator is turned by an engine drivebelt which could cause serious injury if hands, hair or clothes become entangled in it with the engine running.
f) Because the alternator is connected directly to the battery, it could arc or cause a fire if overloaded or shorted out.
g) Wrap a plastic bag over the alternator and secure it with rubber bands before steam cleaning the engine.
h) Never disconnect the battery while the engine is running.

15 Charging system – check

Refer to illustration 15.6

1   If a malfunction occurs in the charging system, don't automatically assume the alternator is causing the problem. First check the following items:

a) Check the drivebelt tension and condition (Chapter 1). Replace it if it's worn or deteriorated.

b) Make sure the alternator mounting and adjustment bolts are tight.
c) Inspect the alternator wiring harness and the connectors at the alternator. They must be in good condition and tight.
d) Check the fusible link (if equipped) located between the battery and the alternator. If it's burned, determine the cause, repair the circuit and replace the link (the battery won't charge and/or the accessories won't work if the fusible link blows). Sometimes a fusible link may look good, but still be bad. If in doubt, remove it and check it for continuity.
e) Start the engine and check the alternator for abnormal noises (a shrieking or squealing sound indicates a bad bearing).
f) Check the specific gravity of the battery electrolyte. If it's low, charge the battery (doesn't apply to maintenance free batteries).
g) Make sure the battery is fully charged (one bad cell in a battery can cause overcharging by the alternator).
h) Disconnect the battery cables (negative first, then positive). Inspect the battery posts and the cable clamps for corrosion. Clean them thoroughly if necessary (see Chapter 1). Reconnect the cable to the negative terminal.
i) With the key off, connect a test light between the negative battery post and the disconnected negative cable clamp.
   1) If the test light doesn't come on, reattach the clamp and proceed to Step 3.
   2) If the test light comes on, there's a short (drain) in the electrical system of the vehicle. The short must be repaired before the charging system can be checked.
   3) Disconnect the alternator wiring harness.
      (a) If the light goes out, the alternator is bad.
      (b) If the light stays on, pull each fuse until the light goes out (this will tell you which circuit is shorted).

2   Using a voltmeter, check the battery voltage with the engine off. If should be approximately 12-volts.

3   Start the engine and check the battery voltage again. It should now be approximately 14-to-15 volts.

4   Turn on the headlights. The voltage should drop, and then come back up, if the charging system is working properly.

5   If the voltage reading is more than the specified charging voltage, replace the voltage regulator (refer to Section 17). If the voltage is less, the alternator diode(s), stator or rectifier may be bad or the voltage regulator may be malfunctioning.

6   To isolate the problem component, insert a scribe or small screwdriver into the test hole in the rear of the alternator (**see illustration**), then start the engine. Measure the output voltage at terminal B (the large threaded

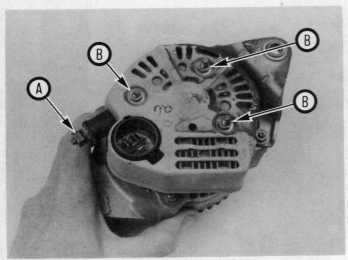

17.2   The alternator rear end cover is attached to the frame with three nuts (Samurai)

A   B+ terminal (nuts must be loosened and   B   Nuts
insulator pulled away from the cover)

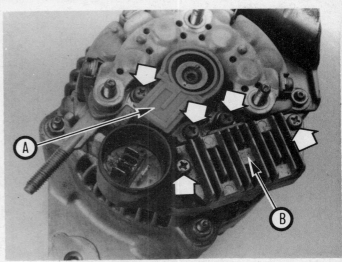

17.3   The brush holder and voltage regulator are attached to the rear end frame with screws (Samurai)

A   Brush holder   B   Voltage regulator

terminal on the alternator) – if the indicated voltage is higher than the standard charging value, replace the regulator.

7   If the indicated voltage is less than the standard charging value, the problem lies elsewhere in the alternator. It would be cheaper and easier to replace the alternator with a rebuilt unit rather than attempt to repair the problem.

16   Alternator – removal and installation

Refer to illustration 16.3

1   Detach the cable from the negative terminal of the battery.
2   Detach the electrical connectors from the alternator.
3   Loosen the alternator adjustment and pivot bolts and detach the drivebelt (see illustration).
4   Remove the bolts and separate the alternator from the engine.
5   If you're replacing the alternator, take the old one with you when purchasing a replacement unit. Make sure the new/rebuilt unit looks identical to the original. Look at the terminals – they should be the same in number, size and location as the terminals on the old alternator. Finally, look at the identification numbers – they'll be stamped into the housing or printed on a tag attached to the housing. Make sure the numbers are the same on both alternators.
6   Many new/rebuilt alternators DO NOT have a pulley installed, so you may have to switch the pulley from the old unit to the new/rebuilt one. When buying an alternator, find out the shop's policy regarding pulleys – some shops will perform this service free of charge.
7   Installation is the reverse of removal.
8   After the alternator is installed, adjust the drivebelt tension (see Chapter 1).
9   Check the charging voltage to verify proper operation of the alternator (see Section 14).

17   Voltage regulator and brushes – replacement

1   Remove the alternator from the vehicle (see Section 16).

Samurai

Refer to illustrations 17.2, 17.3 and 17.4

2   Loosen the nuts on the B+ terminal and remove the three nuts that secure the rear end cover to the alternator end frame (see illustration). Lift off the cover.

17.4   If the brushes are worn down below the minimum length, replace them with new ones

3   Remove the screws securing the voltage regulator and brush holder to the rear end frame (see illustration), then remove the regulator and brush holder.
4   Measure the length of each brush (see illustration). If they're worn below the minimum length listed in this Chapter's Specifications, replace the brush and holder assembly.
5   Installation of the components is the reverse of the removal procedure.

Sidekick/Tracker

Refer to illustrations 17.7, 17.8a, 17.8b, 17.10, 17.11 and 17.13

6   Mark the relationship of the end frames to ensure they're reassembled correctly.
7   Remove the four housing screws (see illustration).
8   Using a 200 watt soldering iron, apply heat to the bearing box area on the alternator rear housing (see illustration). When the temperature

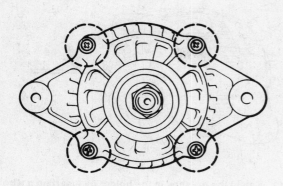

17.7   The two halves of the alternator are held together with these four screws (Tracker/Sidekick)

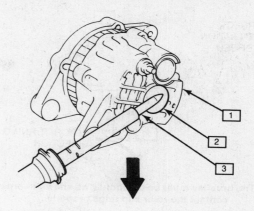

17.8a   The alternator rear bearing must be heated before separating the two halves (Tracker/Sidekick)

1   Rear end frame   3   Soldering iron (200W)
2   Bearing box

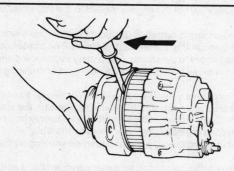

17.8b   Once the bearing box is hot enough, pry the two halves of the alternator apart (Tracker/Sidekick)

reaches 122-to-140 degrees F, pry the front housing from the stator core **(see illustration)**.

9   Remove the nut from the B+ post, remove the stator-to-rear frame screws and detach the stator from the rear frame.

10   Separate the regulator/brush holder from the end frame **(see illustration)**. Remove the wire cover from the brush holder, then unsolder the leads from the brushes. Measure the brushes as described in Step 4 (replace them if they're worn excessively).

11   Install the brushes by reversing the removal procedure. Make sure the brushes are installed in the correct relationship to the slip rings **(see illustration)**.

12   If the regulator is faulty, replace it along with a new set of brushes. Set the new regulator/brush holder in position, lower the stator into the end frame and install the screws.

5

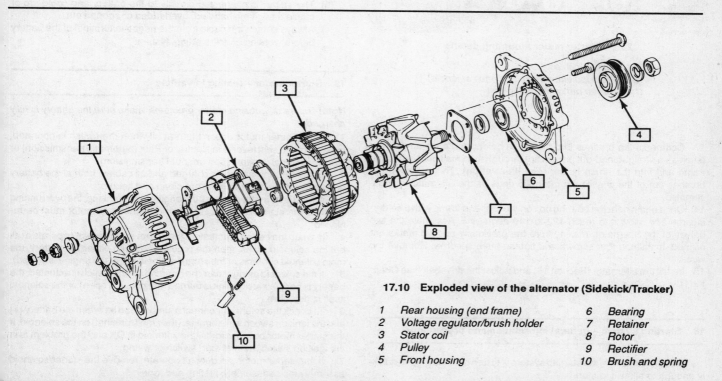

17.10   Exploded view of the alternator (Sidekick/Tracker)

1   Rear housing (end frame)   6   Bearing
2   Voltage regulator/brush holder 7   Retainer
3   Stator coil   8   Rotor
4   Pulley   9   Rectifier
5   Front housing   10   Brush and spring

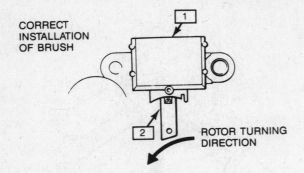

CORRECT
INSTALLATION
OF BRUSH

1

2

ROTOR TURNING
DIRECTION

**17.11 The brushes must be positioned as shown in order to
contact the rotor slip rings properly**

1   Brush holder   2   Brush

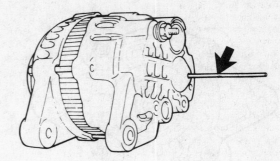

**17.13 Retain the brushes in the holder by inserting a wire
(arrow) through the small hole in the rear end frame provided for
this purpose**

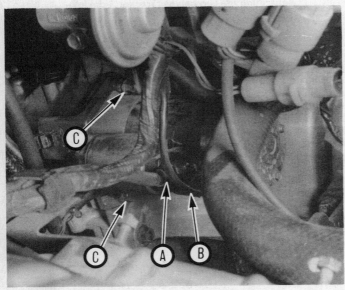

20.2   Starter motor mounting details

A   Battery cable
B   From ignition switch (activates solenoid)
C   Starter motor mounting bolt

13   Compress the brushes into the brush holder and pass a rigid wire (such as a straightened-out paper clip) through the small hole in the end frame and into the brush holder **(see illustration)**. This will keep the brushes out of the way of the rotor slip rings as the alternator is reassembled.
14   Once again heat the bearing box on the rear end frame with a soldering iron and allow it to reach 122-to-140 degrees F. Assemble the two halves of the alternator, making sure the previously applied marks are aligned. Install the four screws and tighten them securely. Remove the wire.
15   Install the alternator (Section 16) and adjust the drivebelt (see Chapter 1).

18   Starting system – general information and precautions

The sole function of the starting system is to turn over the engine quickly enough to allow it to start.

The starting system consists of the battery, the starter motor, the starter solenoid and the wires connecting them. The solenoid is mounted directly on the starter motor. The solenoid/starter motor assembly is installed on the lower part of the engine, bolted to the transmission bellhousing.
When the ignition key is turned to the Start position, the starter solenoid is actuated through the starter control circuit. The starter solenoid then connects the battery to the starter. The battery supplies the electrical energy to the starter motor, which does the actual work of cranking the engine.
The starter motor on a vehicle equipped with a manual transmission can only be operated when the clutch pedal is depressed; the starter on a vehicle equipped with an automatic transmission can only be operated when the transmission selector lever is in Park or Neutral.
Always observe the following precautions when working on the starting system:
a) Excessive cranking of the starter motor can overheat it and cause serious damage. Never operate the starter motor for more than 30 seconds at a time without pausing to allow it to cool for at least two minutes.
b) The starter is connected directly to the battery and could arc or cause a fire if mishandled, overloaded or shorted out.
c) Always detach the cable from the negative terminal of the battery before working on the starting system.

19   Starter motor – testing in vehicle

Note: *Before diagnosing starter problems, make sure the battery is fully charged.*
1   If the starter motor doesn't turn at all when the switch is operated, make sure the shift lever is in Neutral or Park (automatic transmission) or the clutch pedal is depressed (manual transmission).
2   Make sure the battery is charged and all cables, both at the battery and starter solenoid terminals, are clean and secure.
3   If the starter motor spins but the engine isn't cranking, the overrunning clutch in the starter motor is slipping and the starter motor must be replaced.
4   If, when the switch is actuated, the starter motor doesn't operate at all but the solenoid clicks, then the problem lies with either the battery, the main solenoid contacts or the starter motor itself (or the engine is seized).
5   If the solenoid plunger can't be heard when the switch is actuated, the battery is bad, the fusible link is burned (the circuit is open) or the solenoid itself is defective.
6   To check the solenoid, connect a jumper lead between the battery (+) and the ignition switch wire terminal (the small terminal) on the solenoid. If the starter motor now operates, the solenoid is OK and the problem is in the ignition switch, neutral start switch or wiring.
7   If the starter motor still doesn't operate, remove the starter/solenoid assembly for disassembly, testing and repair.

8   If the starter motor cranks the engine at an abnormally slow speed, first make sure the battery is charged and all terminal connections are tight. If the engine is partially seized, or has the wrong viscosity oil in it, it will crank slowly.

9   Run the engine until normal operating temperature is reached, then disconnect the coil wire from the distributor cap and ground it on the engine.

10   Connect a voltmeter positive lead to the positive battery post and connect the negative lead to the negative post.

11   Crank the engine and take the voltmeter readings as soon as a steady figure is indicated. Don't allow the starter motor to turn for more than 30 seconds at a time. A reading of 9 volts or more, with the starter motor turning at normal cranking speed, is normal. If the reading is 9 volts or more but the cranking speed is slow, the motor is faulty. If the reading is less than 9 volts and the cranking speed is slow, the solenoid contacts are probably burned, the starter motor is bad, the battery is discharged or there's a bad connection.

20   Starter motor – removal and installation

Refer to illustration 20.2

1   Detach the cable from the negative terminal of the battery.

2   Clearly label, then disconnect the wires from the terminals on the starter solenoid **(see illustration)**.

3   Remove the mounting bolts and detach the starter.

4   Installation is the reverse of removal.

21   Starter solenoid – removal and installation

Refer to illustrations 21.3 and 21.4

1   Detach the cable from the negative terminal of the battery.

2   Remove the starter motor (see Section 20).

3   Disconnect the strap from the solenoid to the starter motor terminal **(see illustration)**.

4   Remove the screws that secure the solenoid to the starter motor **(see illustration)**.

5   Pull the solenoid off the starter body flange.

6   Installation is the reverse of removal.

21.3   To separate the solenoid from the starter motor, remove the nut and detach the lead (arrow), . . .

21.4   . . . then remove the solenoid mounting screws (arrows) and pull the solenoid straight off the starter flange

5

Chapter 6 Emissions control systems

Contents

Specifications

General

Positive Temperature Co-efficient (PTC) heater resistance ...... 0.5 to 3.0 ohms

1 General information

Refer to illustrations 1.1a, 1.1b and 1.7

To prevent pollution of the atmosphere from incompletely burned and evaporating gases, and to maintain good driveability and fuel economy, a number of emission control systems are incorporated (**see illustrations**). They include the:

  Positive Crankcase Ventilation (PCV) system
  Fuel evaporative emission control system
  Electronic engine control system
  Fuel feedback system
  Hot Idle Compensator (HIC)
  Deceleration mixture control system
  Exhaust Gas Recirculation (EGR) system
  Thermostatically Controlled Air Cleaner (TCAC)
  Positive Temperature Co-efficient (PTC) system
  Catalytic converter

All of these systems are linked, directly or indirectly, to the computerized emission control system.

The Sections in this Chapter include general descriptions, checking procedures within the scope of the home mechanic and component replacement procedures (when possible) for each of the systems listed above.

Before assuming an emissions control system is malfunctioning, check the fuel and ignition systems carefully. The diagnosis of some emission control devices requires specialized tools, equipment and training. If checking and servicing become too difficult, or if a procedure is beyond your ability, consult a dealer service department. Remember, the most frequent cause of emissions problems is simply a loose or broken vacuum hose or wire, so always check the hose and wiring connections first.

This doesn't mean, however, that emission control systems are particularly difficult to maintain and repair. You can quickly and easily perform many checks and do most of the regular maintenance at home with common tune-up and hand tools. **Note:** *Because of a Federally mandated extended warranty which covers the emission control system components, check with a dealer service department about warranty coverage before working on any emissions-related systems. Once the warranty has expired, you may wish to perform some of the component checks and/or replacement procedures in this Chapter to save money.*

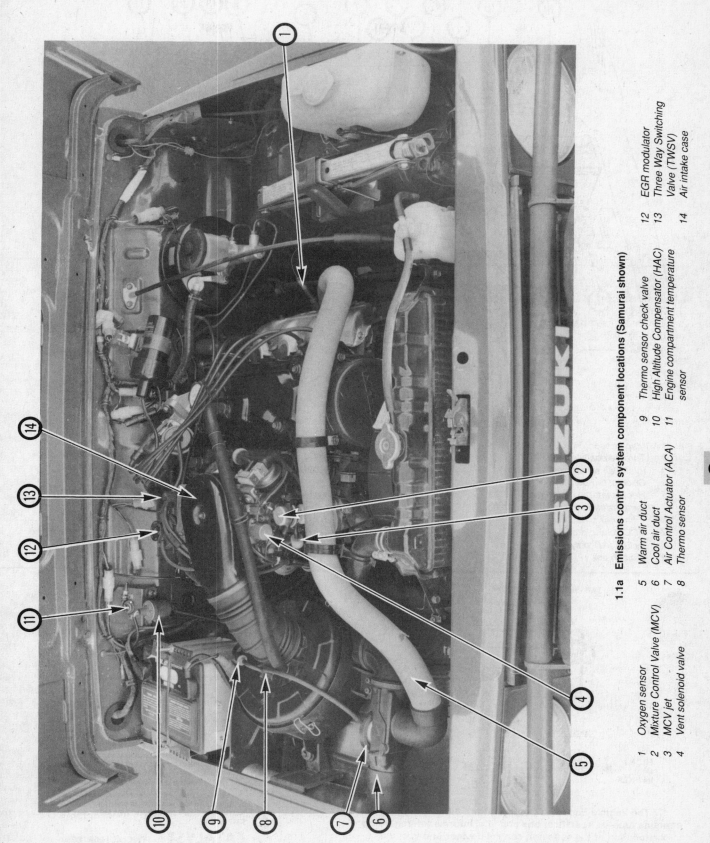

1.1a   Emissions control system component locations (Samurai shown)

1   Oxygen sensor
2   Mixture Control Valve (MCV)
3   MCV jet
4   Vent solenoid valve
5   Warm air duct
6   Cool air duct
7   Air Control Actuator (ACA)
8   Thermo sensor
9   Thermo sensor check valve
10   High Altitude Compensator (HAC)
11   Engine compartment temperature sensor
12   EGR modulator
13   Three Way Switching Valve (TWSV)
14   Air intake case

6

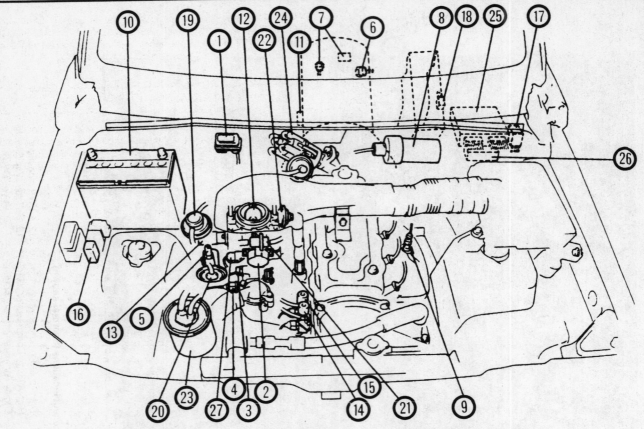

1.1b Emissions control system component locations (TBI fuel injected vehicles)

1   Map sensor
2   Throttle position sensor
3   Intake air temperature sensor
4   Coolant temperature sensor
5   Recirculated exhaust gas
    temperature sensor (California only)
6   Fifth gear switch (M/T only)
7   TCC solenoid/oil pressure
    switch (A/T only)
8   Ignition coil

9   Oxygen sensor
10   Battery
11   Shift switch (A/T only)
12   Injector
13   ISC solenoid valve
14   Throttle opener VSV (brown)
15   EGR VSV (blue)
16   PTC heater relay (A/T only)
17   Control relay
18   TCC relay (A/T only)

19   EGR modulator
20   EGR valve
21   Fuel pressure regulator
22   Throttle opener
23   Canister
24   Distributor
25   ECM
26   Fuse box (diagnostic terminal)
27   PTC heater (A/T only)

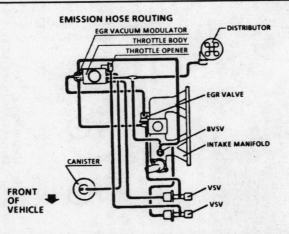

1.7 The Vehicle Emission Control Information (VECI) label contains tune-up specifications and vital information regarding the location of the emission control devices and vacuum hose routing

EMISSION CONTROL INFORMATION
SUZUKI MOTOR CO., LTD.

ENGINE DISPLACEMENT:	97 CU. IN.
ENGINE FAMILY IDENTIFICATION:	KSK1.6T5FFC5

THE ENGINE TUNE-UP AND ADJUSTMENT
SPECIFICATIONS ARE APPLICABLE AT BOTH
LOW AND HIGH ALTITUDES:

ALL ADJUSTMENTS ARE TO BE PERFORMED
WITH THE TRANSMISSION IN NEUTRAL

IDLE SPEED:		800 RPM
IGNITION TIMING:		8° BTDC/800 RPM
SPARK PLUG GAP:		0.028 IN.
VALVE LASH (COLD):	INTAKE	0.006 IN.
	EXHAUST	0.007 IN.
(HOT):	INTAKE	0.010 IN.
	EXHAUST	0.011 IN.

TURN THE IDLE SPEED ADJUSTING SCREW TO OBTAIN
THE CORRECT IDLE SPEED WITH ENGINE AT NORMAL
OPERATING TEMPERATURE, AIR VALVE FULLY CLOSED,
AIR CLEANER INSTALLED AND AIR CONDITIONING OFF.

THIS VEHICLE CONFORMS TO CALIFORNIA REGULATIONS
APPLICABLE TO 1989 MODEL YEAR NEW LIGHT-DUTY
TRUCKS AND TO U.S.EPA REGULATIONS APPLICABLE TO
CALIFORNIA.

CATALYST   TWC / CL / EGR / EGS

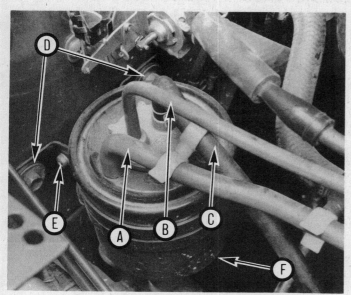

3.2a Charcoal canister mounting details (carburetor equipped vehicles)

A Vent solenoid valve (port D)
B To intake manifold (port B)
C To fuel tank (port A)
D Mounting bolts
E Bracket clamp bolt
F Port C (on bottom of canister, hidden from view)

Pay close attention to any special precautions outlined in this Chapter. It should be noted that the illustrations of the various systems may not exactly match the system installed on your vehicle because of changes made by the manufacturer during production or from year-to-year.

A Vehicle Emissions Control Information label is located in the engine compartment **(see illustration)**. The label contains important emissions specifications and adjustment information, as well as a vacuum hose schematic with emissions components identified. When servicing the engine or emissions systems, the VECI label in your particular vehicle should always be checked for up-to-date information.

2 Positive Crankcase Ventilation (PCV) system

1 The Positive Crankcase Ventilation (PCV) system reduces hydrocarbon emissions by scavenging crankcase vapors. It does this by circulating fresh air from the air cleaner through the crankcase, where it mixes with blow-by gases and is then rerouted through a PCV valve to the intake manifold.

2 The main components of the PCV system are the PCV valve, a fresh air filtered inlet and the vacuum hoses connecting these two components with the engine.

3 To maintain idle quality, the PCV valve restricts the flow when the intake manifold vacuum is high. If abnormal operating conditions (such as piston ring problems) arise, the system is designed to allow excessive amounts of blow-by gases to flow back through the crankcase vent tube into the air cleaner to be consumed by normal combustion.

4 Checking and replacement of the PCV valve is covered in Chapter 1.

3 Fuel evaporative emissions control system

Refer to illustrations 3.2a, 3.2b, 3.4 and 3.9

General description

1 This system is designed to prevent hydrocarbons from being released into the atmosphere, by trapping and storing fuel vapor from the fuel tank, the carburetor or the fuel injection system.

2 The serviceable parts of the system include a charcoal filled canister, a two-way check valve (fuel injected models), the fuel tank filler cap and the lines between the fuel tank and the rest of the system **(see illustrations)**.

6

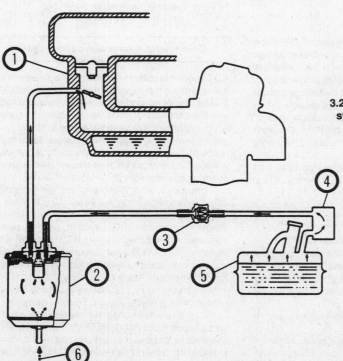

3.2b Fuel evaporative emissions control system diagram – fuel injected vehicles

1 Throttle body
2 Charcoal canister
3 Two-way check valve
4 Vapor/liquid separator
5 Fuel tank
6 Fresh air

3.4   Location of the vent solenoid valve (arrow)

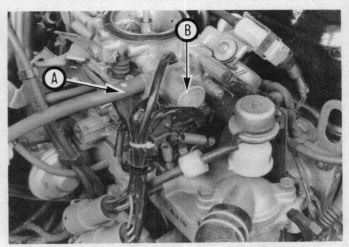

3.9   The hose from the vent solenoid valve goes directly to the canister

A   To canister   B   Vent solenoid valve

3   Vapor trapped in the gas tank is vented through a line in the top of the tank. The vapor leaves the tank through the line and is routed to a carbon canister located in the engine compartment where it's stored until the next time the engine is started.

4   The canister outlet is connected to an electrically actuated vent solenoid valve in the carburetor **(see illustration)**. The vent solenoid valve is normally closed. When the engine is started, the solenoid is energized by a signal from the ECM and allows intake vacuum to open the line between the canister and a port on the carburetor, which draws vapor stored in the canister through the carburetor and into the engine where it's burned. On fuel injected models, the system operates continually – there is no solenoid valve.

Check

Warning: *When performing checks that require you to blow air into a hose or port, be extremely careful not to inhale or suck on the hose or port – fuel vapor is harmful.*

Charcoal canister

5   Except for the check valve(s), there are no moving parts and nothing to wear in the canister. Check for loose, missing, cracked or broken fittings and inspect the canister for cracks and other damage. If the canister is damaged, replace it (refer to Step 12). Never attempt to wash the canister.

6   Disconnect the cable from the negative terminal of the battery and detach the hoses from the canister. On carburetor equipped models, cover port C and D with your fingers and blow into port A – air should come out of port B **(see illustration 3.2a)**. When you blow into port B, air shouldn't come out of any of the other ports. When air is blown into port C, it should come out all of the other ports.

7   On fuel injected models, blow into port A **(see illustration 3.2a)** – air should exit ports B and C. When air is blown into port B, no air should escape from the other ports.

8   If the canister doesn't check out as described above, replace it (Step 12).

Vent solenoid valve (carburetor equipped models only)

9   Pull the hose off the vent solenoid valve outlet on the carburetor **(see illustration)** and connect another length of hose to the port. With the engine off, blow air into the hose – the air should flow through the valve freely. The results of this check should be the same with the ignition switch in the Off and On positions.

10   Start the engine and let it idle. Blow into the hose again – air should not pass through the valve.

11   If the vent solenoid valve doesn't operate as described, either the valve is defective or there's a problem with the electrical circuit or ECM, which will require diagnosis by a dealer service department to pinpoint.

Component replacement

Charcoal canister

12   Locate the canister in the engine compartment. On carburetor equipped models it's mounted on the firewall, below the battery. On fuel injected vehicles, it's mounted on the right inner fender panel.

13   Disconnect the hoses from the canister and remove the mounting bolts **(see illustration 3.2a)**. Remove the canister from the engine compartment.

14   Installation is the reverse of removal.

All other components

15   Referring to the appropriate vacuum hose and vacuum valve schematics in this Section and on the VECI label in the vehicle, locate the component to be replaced.

16   Label the hoses and fittings, then detach the hoses and remove the component.

17   Installation is the reverse of removal.

---

4   Computerized emission control system

The computerized emission control system (the electronic engine control system on fuel injected models and the fuel feedback system on carburetor equipped models) monitors various engine operating conditions and alters the fuel/air mixture and engine idle speed to promote better fuel economy, improve driveability and reduce exhaust emissions. Diagnosis and service of the computerized emission control system is beyond the scope of the home mechanic. Each of the complex systems used on the various models covered by this manual includes a computer and dozens of information sensors and output actuators.

Fortunately, all of these systems are protected by a Federally mandated, extended warranty (5 years/ 50,000 miles, whichever comes first, at the time this manual was written). This warranty covers all emission control components (EGR system, oxygen sensor, catalytic converter, fuel evaporative control system, PCV system, etc.). It also covers emissions related parts like the carburetor, certain fuel injection components, exhaust manifold and major ignition system components (the distributor, ignition wires, coil, spark plugs, etc.). Contact a dealer service department – they're required by Federal law to provide a detailed list of the emission related parts protected by the Federal warranty.

Therefore, we strongly discourage any attempt to test or repair the emission control system while it's under warranty. And, because of the specialized and expensive diagnostic equipment required and the complex testing procedures necessary to check it, we don't recommend attempting to service the system once it's out of warranty either.

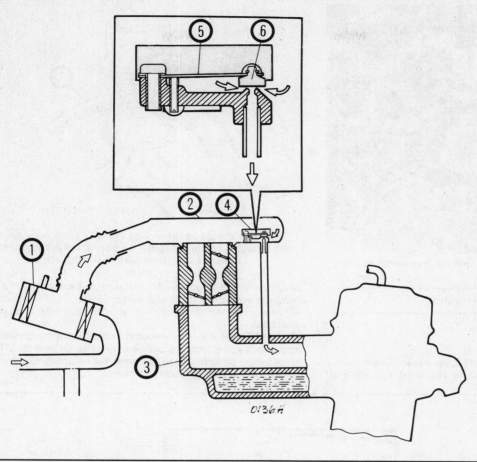

5.1 The Hot Idle Compensator, located in the air intake case, stabilizes the engine idle by leaning-out the fuel/air mixture

1 Air cleaner
2 Air intake case
3 Intake manifold
4 HIC
5 Bi-metal strip
6 HIC valve

5 Hot Idle Compensator (HIC) (carburetor equipped vehicles)

Refer to illustration 5.1

General description

1   The Hot Idle Compensator helps to maintain a stable idle speed during hot operation, when the mixture becomes rich under high intake manifold vacuum conditions. A bi-metallic valve, located in the top of the air intake case and connected to the intake manifold with a hose **(see illustration)** begins to open when the engine heat in the air intake case exceeds approximately 131-degrees F (55-degrees C). This creates a controlled vacuum leak which leans out the fuel/air mixture and stabilizes the idle. It becomes fully open at 158-degrees F (70-degrees C).

Check

2   Unbolt the air intake case from the carburetor. Follow the hose from the HIC valve in the air intake case down to the intake manifold and disconnect it from the manifold. Attach a hand-held vacuum pump to the hose. With the engine cold, apply vacuum to the valve – the gauge on the pump should indicate vacuum and the needle should remain steady.

3   Plug the open port on the manifold, install the air intake case and start the engine, allowing it to warm up. When the temperature in the air intake case reaches 150-degrees F, operate the vacuum pump – the gauge should not show vacuum, indicating the HIC valve is open. If the valve doesn't operate as described, replace it.

Component replacement

4   Remove the air intake case from the carburetor. Remove the screw from the under side of the case that retains the HIC valve and detach the valve. Installation is the reverse of the removal procedure.

6 Deceleration mixture control system (carburetor equipped vehicles)

Refer to illustrations 6.3a and 6.3b

General description

1   This system reduces the excessive HC and CO emissions that are generated during rapid deceleration conditions. It consists of a Mixture Control Valve (MCV), a jet and the necessary vacuum hoses.

2   The MCV contains a pressure balancing orifice and a check valve in the diaphragm. When manifold vacuum is constant, the valve remains closed. Under rapid deceleration, the valve opens and allows an additional amount of air into the intake manifold, which leans out the fuel/air mixture.

Check

3   Start the engine and allow it to reach normal operating temperature. Disconnect the small hose from the valve, then reconnect it. At the same time, hold a strip of paper close to the under side of the valve – the paper should be drawn up to the valve, indicating air is passing through it **(see illustrations)**.

4   Disconnect the hoses from the jet and blow into the gray side – air should pass through. If the valve is clogged, replace it – be sure to install it with the gray side toward the MCV.

5   If the valve doesn't operate as described in Step 3, check the hoses for cracks, holes and kinks, replacing them if necessary. If the hoses are in good condition, replace the valve.

Component replacement

6   Disconnect the hoses from the valve and unclip the valve from the mount. Installation is the reverse of the removal procedure.

6.3a   The MCV clips into a bracket near the thermostat housing

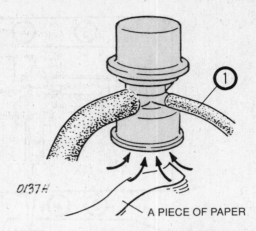

6.3b   Air should be drawn into the MCV when hose no. 1 is disconnected and reinstalled – it's normal for the engine to run rough or stall when performing this check

7   Exhaust Gas Recirculation (EGR) system

General description

Refer to illustrations 7.1a and 7.1b

1   The Exhaust Gas Recirculation (EGR) system **(see illustrations)** is designed to reduce oxides of nitrogen in the engine exhaust. The EGR system recirculates a portion of the exhaust gas back into the intake manifold to be burned with the fuel/air mixture, which in turn brings down the temperature in the combustion chamber and reduces the oxides of nitrogen output.

2   The EGR valve is vacuum operated, controlled by the modulator. The modulator is operated by exhaust backpressure and allows the EGR valve to open wider under high-load conditions, but reduces or closes the EGR valve opening under light-load conditions.

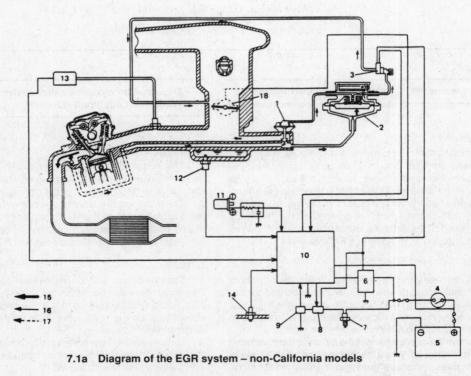

7.1a   Diagram of the EGR system – non-California models

1	EGR Valve	7	Brake light switch	13	Pressure sensor
2	EGR modulator	8	Lock-up relay (A/T only)	14	Fifth gear switch (M/T only)
3	Vacuum Switching Valve (VSV)	9	Lock-up solenoid (A/T only)	15	Exhaust gas
4	Main switch	10	ECM	16	Vacuum
5	Battery	11	Ignition coil	17	Air
6	Control relay	12	Coolant sensor	18	Throttle Position Sensor (TPS)

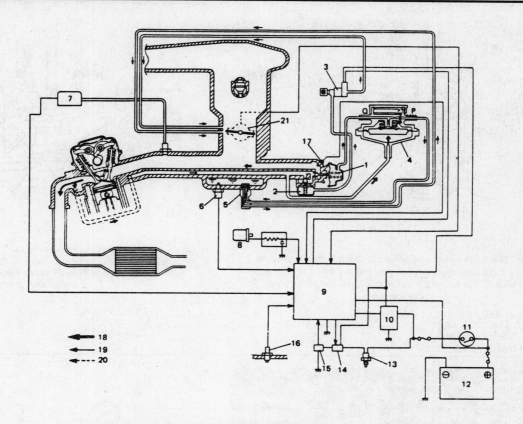

7.1b   Diagram of the EGR system – TBI fuel injected California models

1	Main EGR valve	6	Coolant temperature	11	Main switch	17	Recirculation Exhaust Gas
2	Sub-EGR valve		sensor	12	Battery		Temperature Sensor (REGTS)
3	Vacuum Switching Valve (VSV)	7	Pressor sensor	13	Brake light switch	18	Exhaust gas
4	EGR modulator	8	Ignition coil	14	Lock-up relay (A/T only)	19	Vacuum
5	Bi-metal Vacuum Switching	9	ECM	15	Lock-up selenoid (A/T only)	20	Air
	Valve (BVSV)	10	Control relay	16	Fifth gear switch (M/T only)	21	TPS

3   Fuel injected vehicles destined for the California market also employ a sub-EGR valve, which regulates the flow of exhaust gas to the main EGR valve. The sub-EGR valve is regulated by an ECM controlled Vacuum Switching Valve (VSV), much like the Three Way Solenoid Valve (TWSV) on carburetor equipped models.

4   Under certain conditions, the ECM, Three Way Solenoid Valve (TWSV) or Vacuum Switching Valve (VSV) and the Bi-metal Vacuum Switching Valve (BVSV) can overide the vacuum modulator (for instance, during low coolant temperatures when fifth gear is engaged and the High Altitude Compensator is turned on).

5   If the EGR system is malfunctioning and the following checks don't indicate a problem, have the system diagnosed by a dealer service department or a repair shop.

Check

EGR valve

Refer to illustrations 7.6, 7.9a and 7.9b

Warning: *The EGR valve becomes very hot during engine operation – wear gloves when checking the valve to avoid burning your fingers. If this check is being performed on a carburetor equipped vehicle at an altitude of 4000 feet or higher, the High Altitude Compensator (HAC) electrical connector must be disconnected (see illustration 1.1b at the beginning of this Chapter).*

6   The first check must be performed when the engine is cool, or under 131-degrees F (55-degrees C) (carburetor equipped models) or 113-degrees F (45-degrees C) (fuel injected models). Start the engine and rev it

up a little while touching the valve diaphragm with your finger **(see illustration)** – the diaphragm shouldn't move.

7   Allow the engine to warm up to normal operating temperature and repeat the check – the diaphragm should now move when the engine speed is increased.

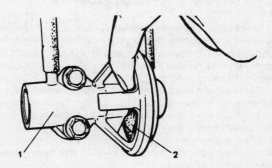

7.6 Check for movement of the EGR diaphragm with your finger, but be careful – the valve can get EXTREMELY hot!

1	EGR valve	2	Diaphragm

6

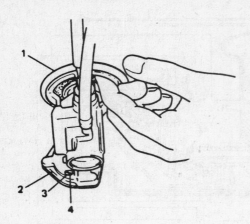

7.9a   The EGR valve on California models is checked in essentially the same manner, but you must also look through the small hole in the sub-EGR valve to check the movement of its diaphragm

1	Main EGR valve	3	Inspection hole
2	Sub-EGR valve	4	Diaphragm

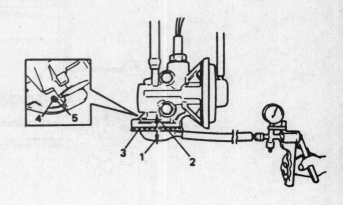

7.9b   Check the sub-EGR valve diaphragm with a hand-held vacuum pump

1	Apply vacuum	4	Hole
2	No vacuum	5	Diaphragm support
3	Diaphragm		

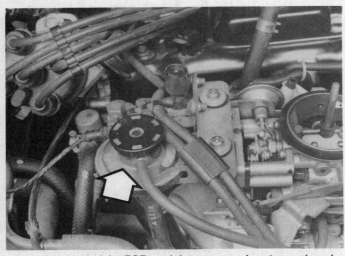

7.11   Location of the EGR modulator on a carburetor equipped vehicle (arrow)

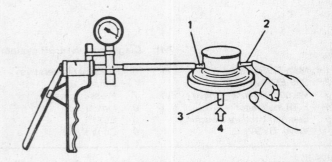

7.13   The EGR modulator should hold vacuum when it's applied to port P, port Q is plugged and air is blown into port A

1	Port P	3	Port A
2	Port Q	4	Air

8   If the diaphragm doesn't move, disconnect the vacuum hose to the valve and connect a hand-held vacuum pump to it. Apply vacuum – the diaphragm should move and the gauge on the pump should indicate vacuum. If it doesn't, replace the valve (Step 16). If the valve works, proceed with the following checks.

9   If the vehicle is a fuel injected California model, the sub-EGR diaphragm must be checked too. Look through the small inspection hole in the sub-EGR valve **(see illustration)** while revving the engine as in the EGR valve check – the diaphragm of the sub-EGR valve should move when the engine is warm, but not when it's cold. The sub-EGR valve can also be checked with a hand-held vacuum pump **(see illustration)**, just like the main EGR valve.

Hoses
Refer to illustration 7.11

10   Check all of the hoses associated with the EGR system for cracks, holes and signs of general deterioration, replacing them if necessary.

11   Mark the hoses at the modulator, then disconnect them. Unclip the modulator from the bracket **(see illustration)**.

EGR modulator
Refer to illustration 7.13

12   Plug one of the vacuum ports on the side of the valve and blow into the other port. Air should pass through the valve and come out the filter at the top of the valve.

13   Connect a vacuum pump to the modulator **(see illustration)**, plug the other vacuum port with your finger then blow into the port on the bottom. Operate the pump – the modulator should hold vacuum as long as air is being blown into the bottom port.

14   If the modulator doesn't operate as described, replace it.

Bi-metal Vacuum Switching Valve (BVSV)

15   With the engine cool, disconnect the hoses from the valve (located adjacent to the EGR vacuum modulator). Connect a length of hose to the top port on the valve and blow into it – no air should come out of the bottom port.

16   Warm up the engine to normal operating temperature and repeat the check – air should now come out of the bottom port. If the valve doesn't check out as described, replace it (Step 23).

7.17a   The TWSV (sometimes called the Vacuum Switching Valve [VSV]) is fastened to a bracket on the rear of the carburetor

7.17b   When the TWSV or VSV is not energized, air should pass through the valve when blown into hose 1 – when the valve is energized, air should come out of the filter

1	Hose to EGR valve
2	Hose to EGR modulator
3	Filter
4	Air
5	TWSV

Three-way Solenoid Valve (TWSV) (carburetor equipped models) or Vacuum Switching Valve (VSV) (fuel injected models)

Refer to illustrations 7.17a and 7.17b

17   Disconnect the hose from the EGR valve and the hose from the EGR modulator to the TWSV or VSV **(see illustrations)**. Blow into the hose that was connected to the EGR valve – air should pass through the valve and come out the other hose.

18   Unplug the electrical connector from the valve. Using jumper wires connected to the battery, energize the valve and blow into the hose again – air should come out of the filter now, not the hose. If the valve doesn't operate as described, replace it.

Component replacement

EGR valve

Refer to illustration 7.19

19   Unscrew the threaded fitting that connects the EGR pipe to the EGR valve, disconnect the vacuum hose and remove the two mounting bolts **(see illustration)**. Remove the valve and clean the mating surface on the intake manifold. If the passage in the manifold is clogged or restricted by exhaust deposits, clean it out before installing the valve.

20   Position the EGR valve and gasket against the intake manifold and install the bolts, but don't tighten them completely yet.

21   Start the EGR pipe fitting by hand to avoid cross-threading it. Tighten the two EGR valve bolts securely.

22   Tighten the EGR pipe fitting securely and connect the vacuum hose.

Bi-metal Vacuum Switching Valve (BVSV)

Refer to illustration 7.25

Warning: *This procedure must be done with the engine cool.*

23   Remove the radiator cap, squeeze the upper radiator hose, then install the cap. This will create a slight vacuum in the cooling system and will allow removal of the BVSV without draining the coolant first.

24   Prepare the new valve by wrapping the threads with teflon tape.

25   Disconnect the hoses from the valve, then unscrew it from the intake manifold **(see illustration)**.

26   Quickly install the new valve in the manifold (to avoid excessive coolant loss) and tighten it securely. Reconnect the hoses.

6

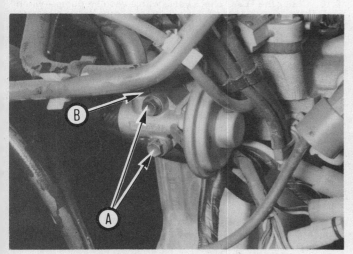

7.19   The EGR valve is mounted on the rear of the intake manifold

A   *Mounting bolts*   B   *EGR pipe fitting*

7.25   The BVSV on carburetor equipped vehicles is screwed into the intake manifold, below the carburetor

8.4   Pull the warm air duct off the air intake housing and feel the damper door – it should be shut with the engine off

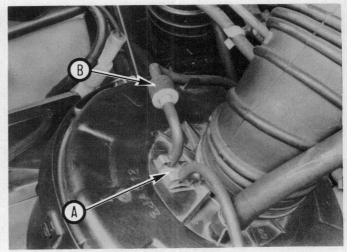

8.7   The TCAC thermo sensor is mounted in the air cleaner cover and retained by a spring clip

 A Thermo sensor   *B Check valve*

Three Way Solenoid Valve (TWSV) (carburetor equipped models) or Vacuum Switching Valve (VSV) (fuel injected models)

27 Mark and disconnect the hoses from the TWSV, then unplug the electrical connector **(see illustrations 1.1b and 7.17a)**.
28 Remove the screws that retain the valve and detach it from the bracket.
29 Installation is the reverse of removal.

8 Thermostatically Controlled Air Cleaner (TCAC) (carburetor equipped vehicles)

Refer to illustrations 8.4, 8.7 and 8.10

General description

1 This system is designed to improve driveability and reduce emissions in cold weather, as well as to maintain a constant inlet air temperature during all driving conditions to improve fuel vaporization.
2 The incoming air can enter the air cleaner two ways – through the fresh air duct (cold air) or past the exhaust manifold cover, through a duct and into the air cleaner (warm air). A thermo sensor, located in the air filter, regulates vacuum to the Air Control Actuator (ACA) which operates a damper in the air intake housing. The ACA opens or closes the damper as necessary, mixing the required amounts of hot and cold air to come up with the desired temperature intake air charge.
3 An improperly functioning TCAC system can result in poor cold or hot driveability and excessive emissions.

Check

Air Control Actuator (ACA) and damper valve

4 With the engine off, disconnect the warm air hose from the air intake housing and feel the damper valve **(see illustration)** – it should be shut (covering the warm air inlet duct).
5 Start the engine. If the air cleaner is cold, the damper door should now open up. Allow the engine to warm up to normal operating temperature – the door should begin to close, allowing cool air to pass into the air intake housing.
6 If the damper valve doesn't move as described above, disconnect the vacuum hose to the ACA and connect a hand-held vacuum pump to it. Apply vacuum and feel for the damper valve to open – if it doesn't, replace the ACA.

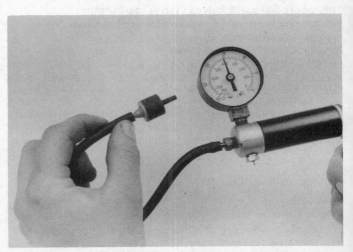

8.10   Check the TCAC check valve with a vacuum pump – when the pump is connected to the orange side of the valve, it should hold vacuum

Thermo sensor

7 If the damper valve does open, check the thermo sensor. Disconnect the two hoses from the sensor, which is located on the air cleaner lid **(see illustration)**.
8 Measure the air temperature around the sensor and write it down. Attach a length of hose to one side of the sensor, cover the other port with your finger and blow into the hose. If the recorded temperature is above 104-degrees F (40-degrees C), air should bleed out of the valve, indicating the valve is open.
9 If the temperature is below 77-degrees F (25-degrees C), no air should come out. If the thermo sensor doesn't work as described, replace it.

Check valve

10 Disconnect the hoses from the check valve, located between the thermo sensor and the intake manifold. Connect a vacuum pump to the orange side of the valve and apply vacuum **(see illustration)** – the needle on the gauge should indicate vacuum and the valve shouldn't leak.
11 Now connect the pump to the black side of the valve and apply vacuum – the valve should leak. If the valve doesn't work as described, replace it. **Note:** *When installing the valve, the orange side must connect to the hose coming from the thermo sensor.*

Component replacement

Air control actuator (ACA)

12   Pull the warm air duct out of the outlet on the air intake housing. Disconnect the vacuum hose from the ACA.

13   Rotate the ACA to align the retaining clip with the slot in the air intake housing, then pull the ACA out. Lift the ACA to disconnect the rod from the damper door.

14   When installing the ACA, position the rod with the bent end pointing down, push in on the damper door, then engage the rod with the hole in the damper door. A small mirror and flashlight will be helpful when doing this.

15   Clip the ACA into the hole, making sure the ends of the clip are securely fastened around the edges of the hole.

16   Reconnect the vacuum hose and the warm air duct.

Thermo sensor

17   Unplug the vacuum hoses from the sensor. Remove the top of the air cleaner, along with the air intake case, from the carburetor.

18   Pry the spring clip off the ports on the thermo sensor and remove the sensor from the under side of the air cleaner lid.

19   Installation is the reverse of the removal procedure.

---

9   Positive Temperature Co-efficient (PTC) system (fuel injected vehicles)

Refer to illustrations 9.2 and 9.7

General description

1   The PTC system is designed to heat the fuel/air mixture to improve cold start performance. When the engine coolant is below 86-degrees F (30-degrees C), the PTC heater is energized for up to ten seconds.

2   The system consists of the PTC heater (see illustration), located between the throttle body unit and the intake manifold, the PTC heater relay, the ECM and the coolant sensor.

3   An improperly functioning PTC could result in hard starting and/or stumbling and stalling when cold (no PTC operation) or sluggish performance and/or overheating when hot (PTC stays on).

Check

Note: *The engine must be cool for this check.*

4   Unplug the electrical connector from the PTC heater. Using an ohm meter, measure the resistance between the PTC heater side of the electrical connector and ground, comparing your reading with the value listed in this Chapter's Specifications. If the resistance isn't as specified, replace the PTC heater.

5   Due to the fairly complex procedures for testing the rest of the system, all further diagnostic procedures should be left to a dealer service department or a repair shop.

Component replacement

6   Following the procedure in Chapter 4, remove the TBI unit from the intake manifold.

7   Unplug the PTC electrical connector and detach the heater from the intake manifold (see illustration). Clean all traces of old gasket material off the manifold, TBI unit and PTC heater (if it's going to be reinstalled).

8   Installation is the reverse of the removal procedure.

---

10   Catalytic converter

Note: *Because of a Federally mandated extended warranty which covers emissions-related components such as the catalytic converter, check with a dealer service department before replacing the converter at your own expense.*

General description

1   The catalytic converter is an emission control device added to the exhaust system to reduce pollutants in the exhaust gas stream. There are two types of converters. The conventional oxidation catalyst reduces the levels of hydrocarbon (HC) and carbon monoxide (CO). The three-way catalyst lowers the levels of oxides of nitrogen (NOx) as well as hydrocarbons (HC) and carbon monoxide (CO).

Check

2   The test equipment for a catalytic converter is expensive and highly sophisticated. If you suspect the converter is malfunctioning, take the vehicle to a dealer service department or authorized emissions inspection facility for diagnosis and repair.

3   Whenever the vehicle is raised for servicing of underbody components, check the converter for leaks, corrosion, dents and other damage.

6

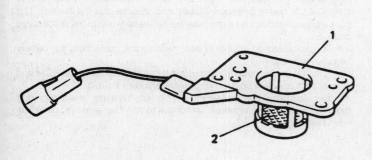

9.2   The positive Temperature Co-efficient (PTC) heater warms the fuel/air mixture during cold start conditions

1	*Insulator*	2	*Heating element*

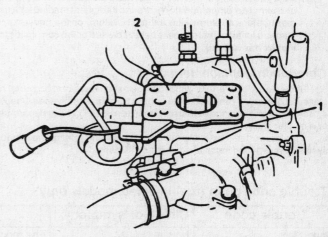

9.7   PTC heater mounting details

1	*Intake manifold*	2	*PTC heater*

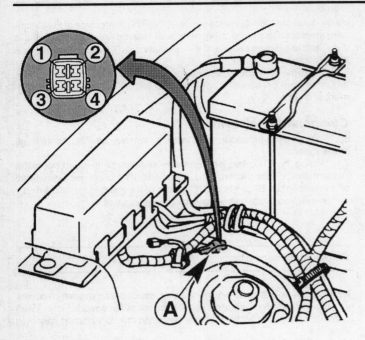

11.5 Obtain the codes on later models by using a jumper wire between the 2 and 3 terminals of the test connector (A) located next to the battery

1	*Duty check terminal*	3	*Ground terminal*
2	*Diagnostic test terminal*	4	*Test switch terminal*

Check the welds/flange bolts that attach the front and rear ends of the converter to the exhaust system. If damage is discovered, the converter should be replaced.

4   Although catalytic converters don't break too often, they do become plugged. The easiest way to check for a restricted converter is to use a vacuum gauge to diagnose the effect of a blocked exhaust on intake vacuum.
a) Open the throttle until the engine speed is about 2000 RPM.
b) Release the throttle quickly.
c) If there's no restriction, the gauge will quickly drop to not more than 2 in-Hg or more above its normal reading.
d) If the gauge doesn't show 5 in-Hg or more above its normal reading, or seems to momentarily hover around its highest reading for a moment before it returns, the exhaust system, or the converter, is plugged (or an exhaust pipe is bent or dented or the core inside the muffler has shifted).

Component replacement

5   Because the converter is welded to the exhaust system, converter replacement requires removal of the exhaust pipe assembly (see Chapter 4). Take the vehicle, or the exhaust system, to a dealer service department or a muffler shop.

6   If the converter is bolted to the exhaust system, refer to the exhaust system removal and installation section in Chapter 4.

---

11   Diagnosis system – general information and obtaining code output

Note: *This procedure applies to fuel-injected models only.*

General information

1   The Electronic Control Module (ECM) (computer) contains a built-in self-diagnosis system which detects and identifies malfunctions occurring in the engine management system. When the ECM detects a problem, three things happen: the Check Engine light comes on, the trouble is identified and a diagnostic code is recorded and stored. The ECM stores the failure code assigned to the specific problem area until the diagnosis system is canceled by removing the diagnostic fuse on models so equipped or by removing the tail lamp fuse from the fuse block (later models).

2   The Check Engine warning light, which is located on the instrument panel, comes on when the ignition switch is turned to On and the engine is not running. When the engine is started, the warning light should go out. If the light remains on, the diagnosis system has detected a malfunction in the system.

Obtaining diagnosis code output

Refer to illustration 11.5

3   To obtain an output of diagnostic codes, verify first that the battery voltage is above 11 volts, the throttle is fully closed, the transmission is in Neutral, the accessory switches are off and the engine is at normal operating temperature.

4   Turn the ignition switch to OFF. Do not start the engine. **Caution:** *The ignition key must be in the OFF position when disconnecting or reconnecting power to the ECM.*

5   On 1990 and earlier Sidekick/Tracker models and all Samurai models, insert the spare fuse into the diagnostic terminal of the fuse block. On 1991 and later Sidekick and Tracker models, connect a jumper wire between the number 2 and 3 terminals of the Check connector located adjacent to the battery (**see illustration**).

6   Turn the ignition key ON. Read the diagnosis code as indicated by the number of flashes of the "Check Engine" light on the dash (see the accompanying chart). Normal system operation is indicated by Code 12 (no malfunctions) for all models. The "Check Engine" light displays a Code 12 by blinking the corresponding pattern one time only.

7   If there are any malfunctions in the system, their corresponding trouble codes are stored in computer memory and the light will blink the requisite number of times for the indicated trouble codes. If there's more than one trouble code in the memory, they'll be displayed in numerical order (from lowest to highest) with a pause interval between each one. After the code with the largest number flashes has been displayed, there will be another pause and then the sequence will begin all over again.

8   To ensure correct interpretation of the blinking "Check Engine" light, watch carefully for the interval between the end of one code and the beginning of the next (otherwise, you will become confused by the relative length of the pause between flashes and misinterpret the codes). The pause between codes is longer than the pause between digits of the same code.

9   To cancel stored trouble codes, remove the cable from the battery negative terminal.

10   If the diagnosis code is not canceled it will be stored by the ECM and appear with any new codes in the event of future trouble.

11   Should it become necessary to work on engine components requiring removal of the battery terminal, first check to see if a diagnostic code has been recorded.

Trouble code chart (fuel-injected models only)

Trouble code	Circuit or symptom	Probable cause
Code 12 (1 flash, pause, 2 flashes)	Normal	This code will flash whenever the diagnostic terminal in the fuse block is activated, the ignition is switched to ON and there are no other codes stored in the ECM.
Code 13 (1 flash, pause, 3 flashes)	Oxygen sensor circuit (open circuit)	Check the wiring and connectors from the oxygen sensor. Replace the oxygen sensor.*

Trouble code chart (continued) (fuel-injected models only)

Code 14 (1 flash, pause, 4 flashes)	Coolant sensor circuit (low temperature)	Check all wiring and connectors associated with the coolant temperature sensor. Replace the coolant temperature sensor.
Code 15 (1 flash, pause, 5 flashes)	Coolant sensor circuit (high temperature)	If the engine is experiencing overheating problems, the problem must be rectified before continuing. Then check the wiring connections at the ECM.
Code 21 (2 flashes, pause, 1 flash)	Throttle Position Sensor (TPS)	Check the TPS adjustment and connection (see Chapter 4). Check the ECM connector. Replace the TPS.*
Code 22 (2 flashes, pause, 2 flashes)	Throttle position sensor	Check the TPS adjustment and connection (see Chapter 4). Check the ECM connector. Replace the TPS.*
Code 23 (2 flashes, pause, 3 flashes)	Intake Air Temperature sensor	Check the IAT sensor, wiring and connectors for an open sensor circuit. Replace the IAT sensor.*
Code 24 (2 flashes, pause, 4 flashes)	Vehicle Speed Sensor (VSS)	A fault in this circuit should be indicated only when the vehicle is in motion. Check and repair the speedometer if it is functioning.
Code 25 (2 flashes, pause, 5 flashes)	Intake Air Temperature sensor	Check the IAT sensor, wiring and connectors for an open sensor circuit. Replace the IAT sensor.*
Code 31 (3 flashes, pause, 1 flash)	MAP sensor (TBI models)	Check the circuit for bare wire (stripped insulation) or damaged electrical connectors. Check the vacuum hose connection. Replace the MAP sensor if necessary.
Code 32 (3 flashes, pause, 2 flashes)	MAP sensor (TBI models)	Check the circuit for bare wire (stripped insulation) or damaged electrical connectors. Check the vacuum hose connection. Replace the MAP sensor if necessary.
Code 33 (3 flashes, pause, 3 flashes)	Mass Airflow (MAF) sensor (MPFI models)	Check the MAF sensor and electrical connections (see Chapter 4). Replace the MAF sensor, if necessary.
Code 34 (3 flashes, pause, 4 flashes)	Mass Airflow (MAF) sensor (MPFI models)	Check the MAF sensor and electrical connections (see Chapter 4). Replace the MAF sensor, if necessary.
Code 41 (4 flashes, pause, 1 flash)	Ignition signal	Inspect and repair any damaged electrical connectors and wire in the harness.
Code 42 (4 flashes, pause, 2 flashes)	Crank angle sensor (pick-up assembly)	Check for a faulty connector or circuit. Also check for an improper air gap in the distributor (see Chapter 5). Replace the sensor (pick-up assembly), if necessary.
Code 44 (4 flashes, pause, 4 flashes)	Throttle Position Sensor (TPS) idle switch circuit	Check the TPS and its adjustment, as described in Chapter 4. Replace the TPS, if necessary.
Code 45 (4 flashes, pause, 5 flashes)	Throttle Position Sensor (TPS) idle switch circuit	Check the TPS and its adjustment, as described in Chapter 4. Replace the TPS, if necessary.
Code 51 (5 flashes, pause, 1 flash)	Exhaust Gas Recirculation (EGR) system	Check for a faulty connector or circuit. Also check for high resistance in the EGR solenoid coil.
Code 53 (5 flashes, pause, 3 flashes)	Ground circuit	Poor ground connection at the ECM or engine block. Also, possibly a faulty ECM.

6

12   Information sensors – check and replacement

Note: *Most of the components described in this section are protected by a Federally-mandated extended warranty (5 years or 50,000 miles at the time of publication). See your dealer for the details regarding your vehicle. It therefore makes little sense to either check or replace any of these parts yourself as long as they are still under warranty. However, once the warranty has expired, you may wish to perform some of the component checks and/or replacement procedures in this Chapter to save money.*

Oxygen sensor

General description
1   The oxygen sensor is mounted in the exhaust system where it can monitor the oxygen content of the exhaust gas stream. By monitoring the voltage output of the oxygen sensor, the ECM will know what fuel mixture command to give the fuel system.
2   The oxygen sensor produces no voltage when it's below its normal operating temperature of about 600-degrees F. During this initial period before warm-up, the ECM operates in open loop mode.
3   In normal operation, when the oxygen sensor has been warmed by hot exhaust (about 2 minutes after start-up), the oxygen sensor will normally produce a signal voltage that varies between 1.0-volt (rich limit) and 0.1 volt (lean limit).

4   An open in the oxygen sensor circuit on fuel-injected models will normally set a diagnostic code 13.

Check
5   The sensor can be checked with a high-impedance digital voltmeter. Warm up the engine to normal operating temperature, then turn the engine off. Unplug the oxygen sensor electrical connector and connect the positive probe of the voltmeter to the sensor side of the connector. **Note:** *If the sensor has three wires connected to it, it is a heated-type sensor. Connect the voltmeter to the wire that's routed to the ECM (usually a yellow wire with a blue tracer).* **Caution:** *Don't let the sensor wire or the voltmeter lead touch the exhaust pipe or manifold. Ground the negative probe of the meter, turn the meter to the millivolt setting and start the engine.*
6   The reading on the voltmeter should fluctuate between 100 and 1,000 millivolts (0.1 and 1.0 volts). If the meter reading doesn't fluctuate, the sensor is probably bad (although a fuel system problem could be the cause).

Replacement
7   Refer to Chapter 1 for the oxygen sensor replacement procedure.

Coolant temperature sensor

General description
8   The coolant sensor is a thermistor (a resistor which varies the value of its voltage output in accordance with temperature changes) and is located in the side of the intake manifold. A failure in the coolant sensor circuit

should set either a Code 14 or a Code 15. These codes indicate a failure in the coolant temperature circuit, so the appropriate solution to the problem will be either repair of a wire or replacement of the sensor.

Check

9   Unplug the electrical connector and use an ohmmeter to measure the resistance across the sensor terminals with the engine cold. Warm the engine up and take another measurement. If the difference in resistance readings is not approximately 500 ohms, the sensor is probably bad.

Replacement

10   To remove the sensor, release the locking tab, unplug the electrical connector, then carefully unscrew the sensor. **Caution:** *Handle the coolant sensor with care. Damage to this sensor will affect the operation of the entire fuel system.*

11   Before installing the new sensor, wrap the threads with Teflon sealing tape to prevent leakage and thread corrosion.

12   Installation is the reverse of removal.

Manifold Air Temperature (MAT) sensor

13   The manifold air temperature (MAT) sensor used on fuel-injected models is a thermistor which constantly measures the temperature of the air entering the intake manifold (TBI models) or air cleaner housing (MPFI models). As air temperature varies, the ECM, by monitoring the MAT sensor, adjusts the amount of fuel according to the air temperature. A failure in the MAT sensor or circuit will often set a diagnostic code 23. The diagnosis of the MAT sensor should be left to a dealer service department.

Manifold Absolute Pressure (MAP) sensor

General description

15   The Manifold Absolute Pressure (MAP) sensor used on TBI models monitors the intake manifold pressure changes resulting from changes in engine load and speed and converts the information into a voltage output. The ECM uses the MAP sensor to control fuel delivery and ignition timing.

16   Other than checking the vacuum hose and electrical connector for proper connection and damage, inspection of the MAP sensor should be left to a dealer service department, since the sensor could be damaged unless checked properly.

Replacement

17   To replace the sensor, detach the vacuum hose, unplug the electrical connector and remove the mounting screws. Installation is the reverse of removal.

Mass Airflow (MAF) sensor

18   The MAF sensor measures the volume of air flowing into the engine. This information is used by the ECM to help calculate the correct air-fuel ratio for the Multi-Port Fuel Injection (MPFI) system. A MAF sensor failure will often set diagnostic code 33 or 34.

19   Basic checks and MAF sensor replacement are covered in Chapter 4. Complete checking of this sensor should be left to a dealer service department or other qualified shop.

Throttle Position Sensor (TPS)

20   The Throttle Position Sensor (TPS) is located on the throttle shaft at the throttle body.

21   By monitoring the output voltage from the TPS, the ECM can determine fuel delivery based on throttle valve angle (driver demand). A broken or loose TPS can cause intermittent bursts of fuel from the injector and an unstable idle because the ECM thinks the throttle is moving.

22   A problem in any of the TPS circuits will set either a Code 21 or 22. Once a trouble code is set, the ECM will use an artificial default value for TPS and some vehicle performance will return.

23   Checking and replacement procedures for the TPS are contained in Chapter 4.

Vehicle Speed Sensor (VSS)

General description

24   The Vehicle Speed Sensor (VSS) consists of the lead switch and magnet that's built into the speedometer As the magnet turns with the speedometer cable, its magnetic force causes the lead switch to turn on and off. This pulsing voltage signal is sent to the ECM and is converted into miles per hour. If a failure occurs, a code 24 will be set. Diagnosis and repair should be left to a dealer service department.

25   The Vehicle Speed Sensor (VSS) consists of the lead switch and magnet that's built into the speedometer As the magnet turns with the speedometer cable, its magnetic force causes the lead switch to turn on and off. This pulsing voltage signal is sent to the ECM which is converted into miles per hour. If a failure occurs, a code 24 will be set. Diagnosis and repair should be left to a dealer service department.

Crank angle sensor

26   The Crank Angle Sensor is located in the distributor and serves a dual purpose by also being the pick-up assembly for the ignition system (see Chapter 5). It consists of a signal generator and signal rotor. As the signal rotor turns, pulsing AC voltage is generated in the pick-up assembly. This pulse signal is sent to the ECM where it is used to calculate the engine speed and also as one of the signals to control various devices. If a failure occurs, a code 42 will be set. Diagnosis and repair should be left to a dealer service department.

Chapter 7 Part A Manual transmission

Contents

7A

Specifications

Torque specifications

Ft-lbs (unless otherwise specified)

Oil check/fill and drain plugs	See Chapter 1
Transmission-to-engine bolts/nuts	
Samurai	16 to 25
Sidekick/Tracker	51 to 72
Input shaft bearing retainer bolts	14 to 20
Shift lever retainer bolts (Samurai)	36 to 60 in-lbs

---

1 General information

All vehicles covered in this manual come equipped with either a five-speed manual transmission or an automatic transmission. All information on the manual transmission is included in this Part of Chapter 7. Information on the automatic transmission can be found in Part B of this Chapter.

Due to the complexity, unavailability of replacement parts and the special tools necessary, internal repair by the home mechanic is not recommended. The information in this Chapter is limited to general information and removal and installation of the transmission.

Depending on the expense involved in having a faulty transmission overhauled, it may be a good idea to replace the unit with either a new or rebuilt one. Your local dealer or transmission shop should be able to sup-

ply you with information concerning cost, availability and exchange policy. Regardless of how you decide to remedy a transmission problem, you can still save a lot of money by removing and installing the unit yourself.

---

2 Oil seal replacement

Refer to illustrations 2.3, 2.4, 2.6, 2.12 and 2.13

Front oil seal

1   Remove the transmission as described in Section 6.
2   Remove the release bearing as described in Chapter 8.
3   Make a mark on the clutch release arm before removing it from the pivot shaft **(see illustration)**.

2.3   Mark the relationship of the clutch release arm to the pivot shaft to insure proper alignment during installation

2.4   Use needle-nose pliers to release the end of the spring clip from the shaft

2.6   The transmission front oil seal is located in the front cover – to remove it, carefully pry it out with a screwdriver

2.12   The rear oil seal can be removed by prying it out with a seal remover (Samurai)

4   Release the end of the return spring from the shaft on the inside of the bellhousing (see illustration).

5   Remove the bolts that retain the input shaft bearing retainer to the case, then lift off the retainer.

6   Being careful not to nick or damage the bearing retainer, pry out the front oil seal (see illustration).

7   Drive the new seal into the retainer using a seal driver or a large socket.

8   Apply a light coat of gear oil to the seal lips and the transmission input shaft, then reinstall the bearing retainer. Tighten the retainer bolts to the torque listed in this Chapter's Specifications.

9   Reinstall the remaining components in the reverse order of removal.

Rear oil seal – Samurai

10   Remove the driveshaft as described in Chapter 8.

11   On later models it may be necessary to remove the dust cover for access to the oil seal.

12   Being careful not to damage the output shaft of the transmission housing, use a seal remover to pry out the old seal (see illustration).

13   Apply a coat of gear oil to the lips of the new seal and drive it into place using a seal driver or an appropriately-sized socket (see illustration).

14   Reinstall the driveshaft.

2.13   A large socket and extension can be used to drive the seal into place – make sure the seal is installed squarely in the bore

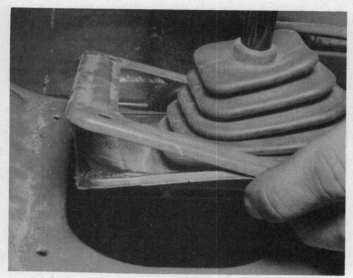

3.3   Remove the bolts that secure the shift lever boot and lift the boot off the floor

3.4   Pull the small inner boot up off the lever retainer

3.7   Check the lower portion of the shift lever for excessive wear

3   Manual transmission shift lever (Samurai) – removal and installation

Refer to illustrations 3.3, 3.4 and 3.7

1   Place the shift lever in Neutral.

2   Remove the carpet from around the shifter area.

3   Remove the bolts that secure the shift lever boot and lift the boot off the floor **(see illustration)**.

4   Slide the small inner boot up toward the knob **(see illustration)**.

5   Remove the three bolts that secure the shift lever retainer to the transmission.

6   Pull the the shift lever out of the case.

7   Check the lower portion of the shift lever for excessive wear **(see illustration)**. Also check the boot for damage.

8   Apply grease to the pivot portions and the seat. Install the shift lever into the case.

9   Tighten the shift lever retainer bolts to the torque listed in this Chapter's Specifications.

10   The remainder of the installation procedure is the reverse of removal.

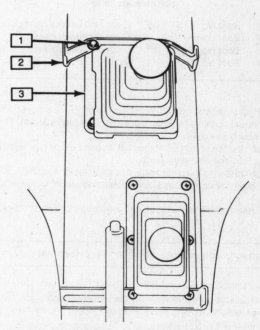

4.2   Remove the console bracket bolts

1	Bolt	2	Console box bracket
		3	Boot cover

4   Manual transmission shift lever (Sidekick/Tracker) – removal and installation

Refer to illustrations 4.2 and 4.4

Note: *The transfer case shift lever can also be removed using this procedure.*

1   Using an Allen wrench and a small Phillips screwdriver, remove the two screws at the front and the two clips at the rear of the console box and pull the console box up.

2   Remove the bolts that secure the console box bracket and lift up the boot cover **(see illustration)**.

3   Remove the boot clamp that attaches to the small inner boot then pull the boot up and away from the gear shift assembly.

7A

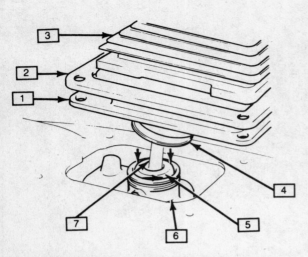

4.4   With your fingers, push the gear shift control case cover down while simultaneously turning it counterclockwise

1 *Boot No. 2*	5 *Gear shift control case cover*
2 *Boot cover*	6 *Gear shift lever case*
3 *Boot No. 3*	7 *Gear shift control lever*
4 *Boot No. 1*	

4   With your fingers, push the gear shift control case cover down while simultaneously turning it counterclockwise **(see illustration)**. The shift lever can now be removed.

5   Check the lower portion of the shift lever for excessive wear and boot damage. Replace any worn parts.

6   Apply grease to the pivot areas and seat. Install the shift lever into the housing, push the control case cover down and turn it clockwise to lock it in place.

7   The remainder of installation is the reverse of the removal procedure.

5   Transmission mount – check and replacement

Refer to illustrations 5.2 and 5.3

1   Insert a large screwdriver or pry bar into the space between the transmission extension housing and the crossmember and try to pry the transmission up slightly.

2   The transmission should not move away from the mount much at all **(see illustration)**.

3   To replace the mount, remove the bolts attaching the mount to the crossmember and the bolt attaching the mount to the transmission **(see illustration)**.

4   Raise the transmission slightly with a jack and remove the mount.

5   Installation is the reverse of the removal procedure. Be sure to tighten the bolts securely.

6   Manual transmission – removal and installation

Samurai
Removal
Refer to illustrations 6.8, 6.11a, 6.11b and 6.13

1   Disconnect the negative cable from the battery.

2   Drain the oil from the transmission and transfer case (see Chapter 1).

3   Remove the transfer case (see Chapter 7C).

5.2   Using a screwdriver, try to pry the transmission up and away from the rubber mount – replace the mount if the play is excessive

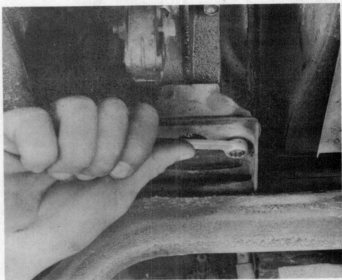

5.3   Remove the bolts that secure the transmission mount to the crossmember

4   Working inside the vehicle, remove the transmission shift lever (see Section 3).

5   Raise the vehicle and support it securely on jackstands.

6   Remove the exhaust system components as necessary for clearance (see Chapter 4).

7   Support the engine. This can be done from above with an engine hoist, or by placing a jack (with a wood block as an insulator) under the engine oil pan. The engine should remain supported at all times while the transmission is out of the vehicle.

8   Remove the distributor (see Chapter 2) and place a wood block between the distributor housing and firewall to prevent damage to the housing and firewall **(see illustration)**.

9   Support the transmission with a jack – preferably a special jack made for this purpose. Safety chains will help steady the transmission on the jack.

10   Remove the starter (see Chapter 5).

6.8 Insert a wood block behind the distributor housing to prevent damage to the housing and firewall

6.11a Remove the transmission rear support-to-crossmember nuts and bolts (Samurai)

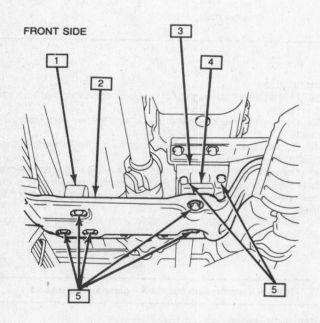

6.11b Remove the rear transmission support to crossmember nuts and bolts (Sidekick/Tracker)

1	Rubber snubber	4	Rear engine mount
2	Engine rear mounting crossmember	5	Bolt
3	Mounting bracket	6	Torque stopper bracket

11 Remove the rear transmission support-to-crossmember nuts and bolts **(see illustrations)**

12 Raise the transmission slightly and remove the crossmember.

13 Remove the front crossmember **(see illustration).**

14 Remove the front and rear driveshafts (see Chapter 8)

15 Disconnect the clutch cable from the release arm.

16 Remove the transmission-to-engine bolts.

17 Make a final check that all wires and hoses have been disconnected from the transmission, then move the transmission and jack toward the rear of the vehicle until the transmission input shaft is clear of the clutch pressure plate. Keep the transmission level as this is being done.

18 Once the input shaft is clear, lower the transmission and remove it from under the vehicle.

19 The clutch components can be inspected after removing them from the engine (see Chapter 8). In most cases, new clutch components should be routinely installed if the transmission is removed.

7A

6.13   The front crossmember is attached by two bolts (Samurai)

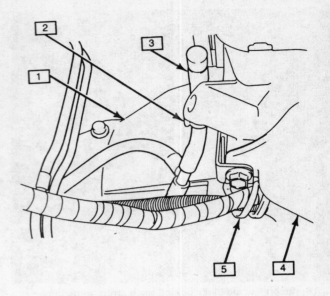

6.35   Disconnect the breather clamp and wiring harness clamp (Sidekick/Tracker)

1	Transmission	4	Intake manifold
2	Breather clamp	5	Wiring harness clamp
3	Breather hose		

Installation

20   If removed, install the clutch components (see Chapter 8).

21   Position the transmission on the jack.

22   With the transmission secured to the jack as on removal, raise it into position and carefully slide it forward, engaging the input shaft with the clutch plate hub. Do not use excessive force to install the transmission – if the input shaft does not slide into place, readjust the angle of the transmission so it is level and/or turn the input shaft so the splines engage properly with the clutch hub.

23   Install the transmission-to-engine bolts. Tighten the bolts to the torque listed in this Chapter's Specifications.

24   Install the crossmembers and transmission support. Tighten all nuts and bolts securely.

25   Remove the jacks supporting the transmission and the engine.

26   Install the transfer case.

27   Install the various items removed previously, referring to Chapter 8 for the installation of the driveshaft, the installation and adjustment of the clutch cable and Chapter 4 for information regarding the exhaust system components.

28   Make a final check that all wires, hoses and the speedometer cable have been connected and that the transmission and transfer case has been filled with lubricant to the proper level (Chapter 1). Lower the vehicle.

29   Working inside the vehicle, install the shift lever (see Section 3).

30   Connect the negative battery cable. Road test the vehicle for proper operation and check for leakage.

Sidekick and Tracker

Removal

Refer to illustration 6.35

31   Disconnect the negative cable from the battery.

32   Working inside the vehicle, remove the transfer case shift lever (see Section 4).

33   Remove the transmission shift lever (see Section 4).

34   Drain the lubricant from the transmission/transfer case unit (see Chapter 1).

35   Disconnect the breather hose from the clamp at the rear end of the cylinder head **(see illustration)**.

36   Disconnect the wiring harness clamp at the rear end of the intake manifold to free the wiring harness **(see illustration 6.35)**.

37   Follow Steps 5 through 19 of this Section (see illustration 6.11b for crossmember removal). **Note:** *The Sidekick and Tracker are equipped with a transmission/transfer case unit.*

Installation

38   Follow Steps 20 through 27 of this Section, ignoring the Steps which don't apply.

39   Connect the breather hose to the clamp at the rear end of the cylinder head.

40   Connect the wiring harness clamp at the rear end of the intake manifold to the wiring harness.

41   Make a final check that all wires, hoses and the speedometer cable have been connected and that the transmission/transfer case unit has been filled with lubricant to the proper level (see Chapter 1). Lower the vehicle.

42   Connect the negative battery cable. Road test the vehicle for proper operation and check for leakage.

7   Manual transmission overhaul – general information

Refer to illustration 7.4

Overhauling a manual transmission is a difficult job for the do-it-yourselfer. It involves the disassembly and reassembly of many small parts. Numerous clearances must be precisely measured and, if necessary, changed with select fit spacers and snap-rings. As a result, if transmission problems arise, it can be removed and installed by a competent do-it-yourselfer, but overhaul should be left to a transmission repair shop. Rebuilt transmissions may be available – check with your dealer parts department and auto parts stores. At any rate, the time and money involved in an overhaul is almost sure to exceed the cost of a rebuilt unit.

Nevertheless, it's not impossible for an inexperienced mechanic to rebuild a transmission if the special tools are available and the job is done in a deliberate step-by-step manner so nothing is overlooked.

The tools necessary for an overhaul include internal and external snap-ring pliers, a bearing puller, a slide hammer, a set of pin punches, a dial indicator and possibly a hydraulic press. In addition, a large, sturdy workbench and a vise or transmission stand will be required.

During disassembly of the transmission, make careful notes of how each piece comes off, where it fits in relation to other pieces and what holds it in place. An exploded view is included **(see illustration)** to show where the parts go – but actually noting how they are installed when you remove the parts will make it much easier to get the transmission together.

Before taking the transmission apart for repair, it will help if you have some idea what area of the transmission is malfunctioning. Certain problems can be closely tied to specific areas in the transmission, which can make component examination and replacement easier. Refer to the *Troubleshooting* Section at the front of this manual for information regarding possible sources of trouble.

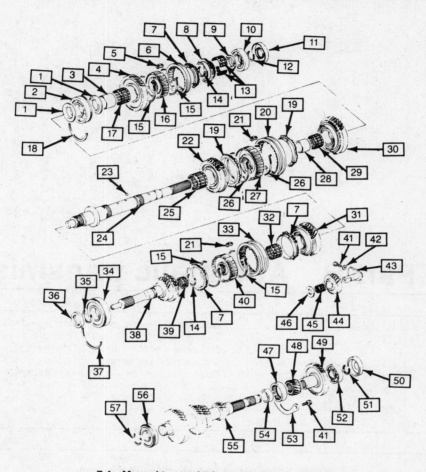

7.4 Manual transmission exploded view (typical)

1	Bearing washer	20	Low speed sleeve	39	Needle bearing
2	Main shaft bearing	21	Synchronizer key	40	High speed hub
3	Main shaft reverse gear bushing	22	Main shaft second gear	41	Bolt
4	Main shaft reverse gear	23	Main shaft washer ball	42	Washer
5	Synchronizer key	24	Transmission main shaft	43	Reverse gear shaft
6	Reverse sleeve	25	Second gear bearing	44	Reverse idle gear
7	High speed ring	26	Low speed spring	45	Reverse idle gear bearing
8	Main shaft fifth gear	27	Low speed hub	46	Thrust washer
9	Fifth gear washer	28	Low gear bushing	47	Countershaft center bearing
10	Main shaft rear bearing	29	Low gear bearing	48	Reverse gear
11	Main shaft oil seal	30	Main shaft low gear	49	Countershaft fifth gear
12	Rear bearing circlip	31	Main shaft third gear	50	Countershaft plug
13	Fifth gear bearing	32	Third gear bearing	51	Rear bearing circlip
14	High speed and reverse hub circlip	33	High speed sleeve	52	Countershaft rear bearing
15	High speed spring	34	Input shaft bearing	53	Bearing plate
16	Reverse hub	35	Bearing circlip	54	Center bearing bushing
17	Main shaft reverse gear bearing	36	Input shaft oil seal	55	Transmission countershaft
18	Bearing C-ring	37	Bearing C-ring	56	Countershaft front bearing
19	Low speed ring	38	Input shaft	57	Front bearing circlip

7A

Chapter 7 Part B Automatic transmission

Contents

Specifications

Torque specifications
Ft-lb (unless otherwise specified)

Transmission-to-engine bolts and nuts	62
Torque converter-to-driveplate bolt	40
Oil pan bolts	See Chapter 1

1 General information

All vehicles covered in this manual come equipped with either a five-speed manual transmission or an automatic transmission. The automatic transmission is composed of a fully automatic three-speed mechanism with a four element hydraulic torque converter including a torque converter clutch (TCC). All information on the automatic transmission is included in this Part of Chapter 7. Information for the manual transmission can be found in Part A of this Chapter.

Due to the complexity of the automatic transmissions covered in this manual and the need for specialized equipment to perform most service operations, this Chapter contains only general diagnosis, routine maintenance, adjustment and removal and installation procedures.

If the transmission requires major repair work, it should be left to a dealer service department or an automotive or transmission repair shop. You can, however, remove and install the transmission yourself and save the expense, even if the repair work is done by a transmission shop.

2 Diagnosis – general

Note: *Automatic transmission malfunctions may be caused by four general conditions: poor engine performance, improper adjustments, hydraulic malfunctions or mechanical malfunctions. Diagnosis of these problems should always begin with a check of the easily repaired items: fluid level and condition (see Chapter 1), shift linkage adjustment and throttle linkage adjustment. Next, perform a road test to determine if the problem has been corrected or if more diagnosis is necessary. If the problem persists after the preliminary tests and corrections are completed, additional diagnosis should be done by a dealer service department or transmission repair shop. Refer to the Troubleshooting Section at the front of this manual for transmission problem diagnosis.*

Preliminary checks

1   Drive the vehicle to warm the transmission to normal operating temperature.
2   Check the fluid level as described in Chapter 1:
 a) If the fluid level is unusually low, add enough fluid to bring the level within the designated area of the dipstick, then check for external leaks.
 b) If the fluid level is abnormally high, drain off the excess, then check the drained fluid for contamination by coolant. The presence of engine coolant in the automatic transmission fluid indicates that a failure has occurred in the internal radiator walls that separate the coolant from the transmission fluid (see Chapter 3).
 c) If the fluid is foaming, drain it and refill the transmission then check for coolant in the fluid or a high fluid level.
3   Check the engine idle speed. **Note:** *If the engine is malfunctioning, do not proceed with the preliminary checks until it has been repaired and runs normally.*
4   Check the kickdown cable for freedom of movement. Adjust it if necessary (see Section 5). **Note:** *The kickdown cable may function properly when the engine is shut off and cold, but it may malfunction once the engine is hot. Check it cold and at normal engine operating temperature.*
5   Inspect the shift control cable (see Section 3). Make sure that it's properly adjusted and that the linkage operates smoothly.

Fluid leak diagnosis

6   Most fluid leaks are easy to locate visually. Repair usually consists of replacing a seal or gasket. If a leak is difficult to find, the following procedure may help.
7   Identify the fluid. Make sure it's transmission fluid and not engine oil or brake fluid (automatic transmission fluid is a deep red color).
8   Try to pinpoint the source of the leak. Drive the vehicle several miles, then park it over a large sheet of cardboard. After a minute or two, you should be able to locate the leak by determining the source of the fluid dripping onto the cardboard.
9   Make a careful visual inspection of the suspected component and the area immediately around it. Pay particular attention to gasket mating surfaces. A mirror is often helpful for finding leaks in areas that are hard to see.
10   If the leak still cannot be found, clean the suspected area thoroughly with a degreaser or solvent, then dry it.
11   Drive the vehicle for several miles at normal operating temperature and varying speeds. After driving the vehicle, visually inspect the suspected component again.
12   Once the leak has been located, the cause must be determined before it can be properly repaired. If a gasket is replaced but the sealing flange is bent, the new gasket will not stop the leak. The bent flange must be straightened.
13   Before attempting to repair a leak, check to make sure that the following conditions are corrected or they may cause another leak. **Note:** *Some of the following conditions cannot be fixed without highly specialized tools and expertise. Such problems must be referred to a transmission shop or a dealer service department.*

Gasket leaks

14   Check the pan periodically. Make sure the bolts are tight, no bolts are missing, the gasket is in good condition and the pan is flat (dents in the pan may indicate damage to the valve body inside).
15   If the pan gasket is leaking, the fluid level or the fluid pressure may be too high, the vent may be plugged, the pan bolts may be too tight, the pan sealing flange may be warped, the sealing surface of the transmission housing may be damaged, the gasket may be damaged or the transmission casting may be cracked or porous. If sealant instead of a gasket has been used to form a seal between the pan and the transmission housing, it may be the wrong sealant.

Seal leaks

16   If a transmission seal is leaking, the fluid level or pressure may be too high, the vent may be plugged, the seal bore may be damaged, the seal itself may be damaged or improperly installed, the surface of the shaft protruding through the seal may be damaged or a loose bearing may be causing excessive shaft movement.
17   Make sure the dipstick tube seal is in good condition and the tube is properly seated. Periodically check the area around the speedometer gear or sensor for leakage. If transmission fluid is evident, check the O-ring for damage. Also inspect the side gear shaft oil seals for leakage.

Case leaks

18   If the case itself appears to be leaking, the casting is porous and will have to be repaired or replaced.
19   Make sure the oil cooler hose fittings are tight and in good condition.

Fluid comes out vent pipe or fill tube

20   If this condition occurs, the transmission is overfilled, there is coolant in the fluid, the case is porous, the dipstick is incorrect, the vent is plugged or the drain back holes are plugged.

---

3   Shift linkage – adjustment

Refer to illustrations 3.4 and 3.6

1   This adjustment should not be considered routine and is not required unless there is wear in the shift cable or a new cable has been installed.
2   Raise the front of the vehicle and support it securely on jack stands.
3   Locate the shift cable on the passenger side of the transmission. Clean the threads and nuts on the end of the cable.
4   Loosen the locknut on the end of the shift cable (**see illustration**). Turn the adjusting nut so it is closer to the rubber boot on the cable. Put the manual select lever (on the transmission) in the N position. **Note:** *The N position is the third from the lowest (L) position.*
5   Remove the screws at the front and the clips at the rear of the console box, then lift the console box up. Remove the four bolts that secure the manual selector to the floor and raise the unit.
6   Place the shift lever inside the vehicle to the N position also, and insert an appropriately-sized pin into the hole in the shift mechanism (**see illustration**) to hold the lever in place.
7   Confirm the N position of the select lever on the transmission and turn the adjuster nut and the locknut until they each contact the boss on the lever, without moving the lever in either direction. Tighten the nuts against the lever boss securely, at the same time, to ensure correct positioning of the select lever.
8   Make sure the vehicle only starts in Park and Neutral.

---

4   Shift cable – removal and installation

Refer to illustration 4.3

Removal

1   Remove the screws at the front and the clips at the rear of the console box. Lift the console box up.
2   Remove the four bolts that secure the manual selector to the floor and raise the unit.
3   Remove the cable end clip, washer and outer cable E-ring, then disconnect the cable from the selector assembly (**see illustration**).
4   Raise the vehicle and support it securely on jack stands. Remove the lock nut from the cable end at the transmission (**see illustration 3.4**).
5   Pull down the manual select lever and disconnect the cable from the lever.
6   Remove the cable by taking the E-ring out of the shift cable bracket, then pull the cable from the vehicle.

Installation

7   Installation is the reverse of the removal procedure, but be sure to adjust the cable as described in the previous Section before installing the console box.
8   Confirm that the vehicle only starts in Park and Neutral.

7B

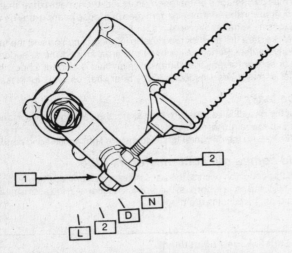

**3.4   Put the manual select lever in the N position – it's
the third from the lowest (L) position**

1   *Locknut*   2   *Adjust nut*

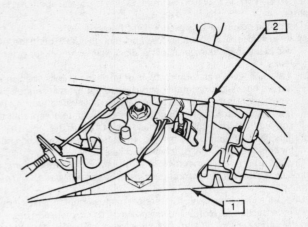

**3.6   Install a pin in the hole indicated to prevent the
selector from moving**

1   *Selector assembly*   2   *Pin*

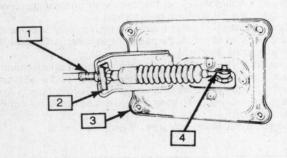

**4.3   Shift cable installation details
(passenger compartment end)**

1   *Select cable assembly*   3   *Manual selector assembly*
2   *E-ring*   4   *End clip*

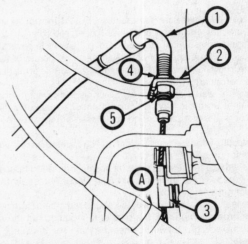

**5.1   Slide the plastic joint off the lever pin (in direction A),
then loosen the adjusting nut**

1   *Kickdown cable*   4   *Locknut*
2   *Bracket*   5   *Adjusting nut*
3   *Plastic joint*

---

5   Kickdown cable – removal, installation and adjustment

Refer to illustrations 5.1 and 5.5

Removal and installation

1   Locate the kickdown cable on the throttle lever of the carburetor or
TBI unit. Push the plastic joint on the cable end off the lever pin **(see illustration)**.
2   Remove the cable by loosening the adjusting nut at the bracket and by
pulling the cable through the slotted keyway of the bracket.
3   Remove the retaining plate from the cable bracket by unscrewing the
bolt.

4   Clean the right side of the transmission where the cable is connected.
5   Using a screwdriver, pry the cable from the transmission case and
disconnect the inner cable from the valve **(see illustration)**.
6   Install the cable by reversing the removal procedure. Be sure to route
the cable clear of any hot or moving parts.

Adjustment

7   Adjust the cable by loosening the kickdown cable locknut and adjusting nut.
8   Have an assistant depress the accelerator pedal to the floor, pulling
the kickdown cable in. Adjust the locknut-to-bracket clearance to
0.039-inch (1 mm) by turning the locknut. **Note:** *When adjusting the clearance, make sure the adjusting nut does not contact the bracket.*

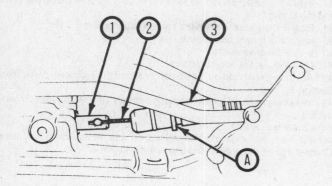

5.5 Pry the cable out of the transmission case with a screwdriver

A	Pry here	2	Inner cable
1	Kickdown valve	3	Kickdown cable

6.4 Loosen the adjusting nut on the cable and remove the cable from the bracket but not from the backdrive cam

1	Backdrive cable	4	Back drive cam
2	Locknut	5	Adjusting nut
3	Cable end clip		

9   Release the accelerator pedal and tighten the adjusting nut until it contacts the bracket, making sure the locknut doesn't turn. To accomplish this, pull the adjusting nut and kickdown cable away from the lock tabs of the bracket while you tighten it.

10   With adjusting nut positioned against the bracket, tighten the locknut securely.

6   Back drive system – adjustment

Refer to illustration 6.4

1   This system is a safety device to prevent the select lever from being released from the Park position without using the ignition key and to prevent the steering lock from engaging while driving. The system also prevents you from taking the key out of the ignition (which will prevent the steering wheel from locking) unless you have shifted the selector lever into Park.

2   Remove the center console box (see Chapter 11).

3   Turn the ignition switch to the Acc position.

4   Loosen the adjusting nut on the cable and remove the cable from the bracket but not from the backdrive cam **(see illustration)**.

5   Shift the selector to the P position and depress the push button all the way. Pull the cable tight and turn the adjusting nut so it contacts the bracket.

6   Release the push button and put a mark on the adjusting nut.

7   Tighten the adjusting nut one full rotation, then tighten the locknut.

8   Check to make sure the key cannot be turned to the Lock position (though it can be turned from On to Acc) when the select lever is in any other position than Park. The select lever shouldn't be able to be shifted from the Park position to other positions when key is in the Lock position or when the key is not in the key slot.

7   Automatic transmission – removal and installation

Removal

1   Disconnect the negative cable from the battery.

2   Remove the transfer shift control lever (see Chapter 7 Part A, *Manual transmission shift lever – removal and installation*).

3   Disconnect the wiring harness couplers, breather hose clamp, kick down cable and vacuum hoses.

4   Raise the vehicle and support it securely on jackstands.

5   Drain the transfer case fluid and transmission fluid (see Chapter 1), then reinstall the pan.

6   Remove the torque converter cover.

7   Mark the torque converter to the driveplate so they can be installed in the same position.

8   Remove the torque converter-to-driveplate bolts. Turn the crankshaft for access to each bolt. Turn the crankshaft in a clockwise direction only (as viewed from the front).

9   Remove the nut from the end of the select cable **(see illustration 3.4)** and the E-ring from the bracket to release the cable.

10   Detach the select cable bracket by removing the two bolts.

11   Loosen the clamps and disconnect the oil cooler hoses from the pipes. **Note:** *To avoid any leaking of transmission fluid, plug the open ends of the transmission cooler pipes and hoses.*

12   Remove the starter motor (see Chapter 5).

13   Remove the driveshafts (see Chapter 8).

14   Disconnect the speedometer cable.

15   On models so equipped, disconnect the vacuum hose from the modulator.

16   Remove any exhaust components which will interfere with transmission removal (see Chapter 4).

17   Support the engine with a jack. Use a block of wood under the oil pan to spread the load.

18   Support the transmission with a jack – preferably a jack made for this purpose. Safety chains will help steady the transmission on the jack.

19   Remove the rear mount to crossmember bolts and the crossmember-to-frame bolts.

20   Remove the two engine rear support-to-transmission extension housing bolts.

21   Raise the transmission enough to allow removal of the crossmember.

22   Remove the bolts securing the transmission to the engine.

23   Lower the transmission slightly.

24   Remove the transmission dipstick tube.

25   Move the transmission to the rear to disengage it from the engine block dowel pins and make sure the torque converter is detached from the driveplate. Secure the torque converter to the transmission so it won't fall out during removal.

Installation

26   Prior to installation, make sure the torque converter hub is securely engaged in the pump.

7B

27   With the transmission secured to the jack, raise it into position. Be sure to keep it level so the torque converter does not slide forward. Connect the transmission fluid cooler lines.

28   Turn the torque converter to line up the matchmark with the mark on the driveplate.

29   Move the transmission forward carefully until the dowel pins and the torque converter are engaged.

30   Install the transmission housing-to-engine bolts. Tighten them securely.

31   Install the torque converter-to-driveplate bolts. Tighten the bolts to the torque listed in this Chapter's Specifications.

32   Install the transmission mount crossmember bolts. Tighten the bolts and nuts securely.

33   Remove the jacks supporting the transmission and the engine.

34   Install the dipstick tube.

35   Install the starter motor (see Chapter 5).

36   Connect the vacuum hose(s) (if equipped).

37   Install the select cable into the select cable bracket. Install the bolts and the E-ring.

38   Plug in the transmission wire harness connectors.

39   Install the torque converter cover.

40   Install the driveshafts.

41   Connect the speedometer cable.

42   Adjust the shift linkage (see Section 3) and the kickdown cable (see Section 5).

43   Install any exhaust system components that were removed or disconnected.

44   Lower the vehicle.

45   Fill the transfer case and transmission with the specified fluid (see Chapter 1), run the engine and check for fluid leaks.

Chapter 7 Part C   Transfer case

Contents

7C

Specifications

Torque specifications

	Ft-lb (unless otherwise specified)
Transfer case-to-transmission nuts	20
Shift lever case center bolt	60 in-lbs
Shift lever case bolts	
Sidekick	144 in-lbs
Tracker	20

1   General information

The transfer case is a device which passes the power from the engine and transmission to the front and rear driveshafts.

This auxiliary transmission selects between four wheel drive (engaging the front and rear axles) and two wheel drive (rear axle), and between High and Low for four wheel drive.

2   Shift lever (Samurai) – removal and installation

Refer to illustration 2.3

Note: *The transfer case shift lever removal and installation procedure for Sidekick and Tracker models can be found in Chapter 7 Part A (it's the same as the manual transmission shift lever procedure).*

2.3   Push down on the lever guide while simultaneously
twisting it counterclockwise

3.9a   Remove the transfer case rear
support-to-crossmember nuts and bolts (Samurai)

Removal

1   Carefully pull the carpet away from the shift lever and remove the bolts that connect the boot to the floor.
2   Loosen the clamp and slide the boot up the transfer case shift lever.
3   Remove the retaining clip and the small inner boot, then twist the shift lever guide counterclockwise while pushing it down (see illustration). This will unlock the lever from the transfer case.
4   Pull the shift lever out of the case.

Installation

5   Check the lower portion of the lever for excessive wear (see illustration 3.7 in Chapter 7A) and also inspect the boot for damage. Replace parts as necessary.
6   Apply grease to the pivot portions and lever seat. Insert the shift lever into the case, then push down on the guide clockwise to lock it in place.
7   The remainder of installation is the reverse of the removal procedure.

---

3   Transfer case – removal and installation

Samurai

Removal

Refer to illustrations 3.9a and 3.9b

1   Disconnect the negative cable from the battery.
2   Raise the vehicle and support it securely on jackstands.
3   Drain the transfer case lubricant and the transmission lubricant (see Chapter 1).
4   Disconnect the speedometer cable, shift lever, and the 4WD switch at the electrical connector.
5   Remove the driveshafts (see Chapter 8).
6   Remove the exhaust system components as necessary for clearance (see Chapter 4).
7   Support the transmission with a floor jack. The transmission must remain supported at all times while the transfer case is out of the vehicle. **Note:** *Place a wood block between the distributor housing and the firewall to prevent damage when the engine tilts.*
8   Support the transfer case with a floor jack. Safety chains will help steady the transfer case on the jack.
9   Remove the transfer case rear support-to-crossmember nuts and bolts **(see illustrations)**.
10   Raise the transfer case slightly and remove the crossmember.
11   Make a final check that all wires and hoses have been disconnected from the transfer case, then move the transfer case and jack toward the rear of the vehicle.

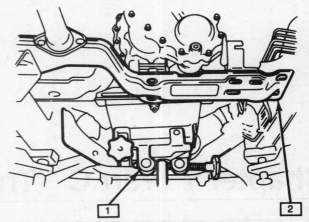

3.9b   Transfer case rear support and crossmember
installation details (Sidekick/Tracker)

1   *Transmission jack*   2   *Crossmember*

---

12   Remove the intermediate shaft with the transfer case. The shaft slides out of the transmission housing.
13   Lower the transfer case and remove it from under the vehicle.

Installation

14   With the transfer case secured to the jack as on removal, raise it into position behind the transmission and carefully slide it forward, engaging the intermediate shaft with the transmission output shaft. Do not use excessive force to install the transfer case if the intermediate shaft does not slide into place. Readjust the angle so it is level and/or turn the intermediate shaft so the splines engage properly.
15   Install the crossmember and transmission support. Tighten the fasteners securely.
16   Remove the jacks supporting the transmission and transfer case.
17   Install the various items removed previously, referring to Chapter 8 for the installation of the driveshafts and Chapter 4 for information regarding the exhaust system components.
18   Make a final check that all wires, hoses, and the speedometer cable have been connected and that the transmission and transfer case have been filled with lubricant to the proper level (see Chapter 1).
19   Connect the negative battery cable. Road test the vehicle for proper operation and check for leakage.

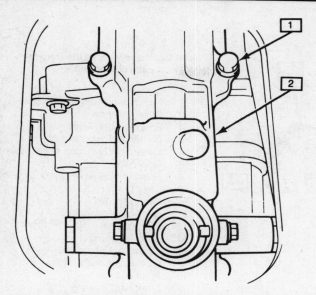

3.24 Remove the bolts that secure the shift lever case (Sidekick/Tracker)

1 Bolt   2 Shift lever case

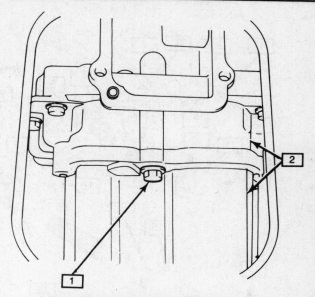

3.26 Remove the transfer case center bolt (Sidekick/Tracker)

1 Bolt   2 Transfer case

3.27 Remove the engine rear mounting assembly (Sidekick/Tracker)

1 Bolt
2 Engine rear mount
3 Transfer case assembly

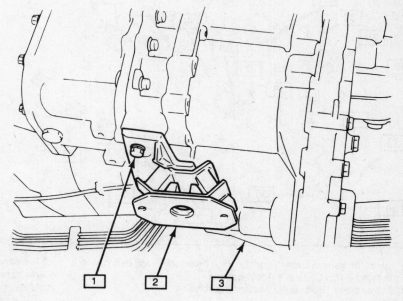

7C

Sidekick and Tracker

Removal

Refer to illustrations 3.24, 3.26 and 3.27

20 Disconnect the negative cable from the battery.
21 Remove the console box (see Chapter 11).
22 Remove the transmission shift lever (see Chapters 7A and 7B) and the transfer case shift lever (see Chapter 7A – it's the same procedure as for the transmission shift lever).
23 Follow steps 2 through 10 of this Section.
24 Inside the passenger compartment, remove the bolts that secure the gear shift lever case **(see illustration)**.

25 Slide the breather hose clamp forward and remove the hose.
26 Remove the gear shift lever case and then remove the transfer case center bolt **(see illustration)**.
27 Remove the transfer case/engine rear mounting assembly **(see illustration)**.
28 Remove the transfer case-to-transmission bolts.
29 With the transfer case assembly supported with a jack (preferably a transmission jack), slide it toward the rear of the vehicle and lower it.

Installation

30 With the transfer case secured to the jack, raise it into position behind the transmission and carefully slide it forward. Do not use excessive force to install the transfer case – make sure the splines are correctly aligned.

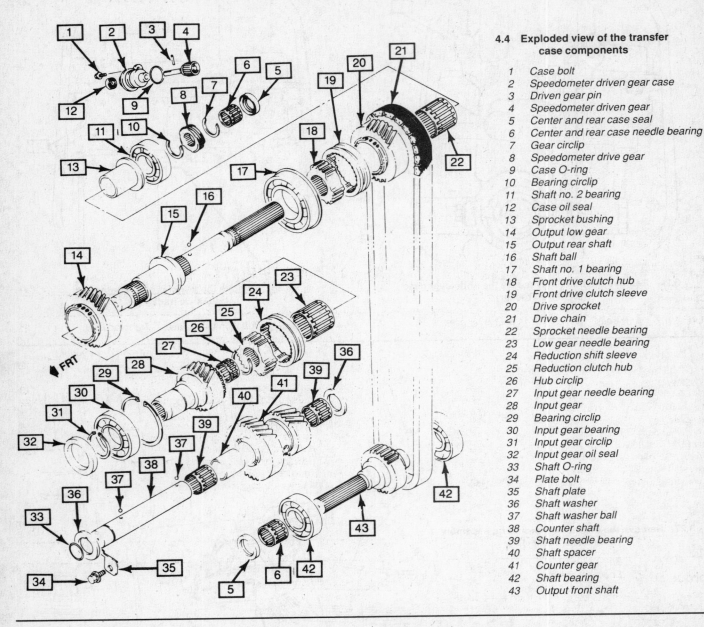

4.4 Exploded view of the transfer case components

1   Case bolt
2   Speedometer driven gear case
3   Driven gear pin
4   Speedometer driven gear
5   Center and rear case seal
6   Center and rear case needle bearing
7   Gear circlip
8   Speedometer drive gear
9   Case O-ring
10 Bearing circlip
11 Shaft no. 2 bearing
12 Case oil seal
13 Sprocket bushing
14 Output low gear
15 Output rear shaft
16 Shaft ball
17 Shaft no. 1 bearing
18 Front drive clutch hub
19 Front drive clutch sleeve
20 Drive sprocket
21 Drive chain
22 Sprocket needle bearing
23 Low gear needle bearing
24 Reduction shift sleeve
25 Reduction clutch hub
26 Hub circlip
27 Input gear needle bearing
28 Input gear
29 Bearing circlip
30 Input gear bearing
31 Input gear circlip
32 Input gear oil seal
33 Shaft O-ring
34 Plate bolt
35 Shaft plate
36 Shaft washer
37 Shaft washer ball
38 Counter shaft
39 Shaft needle bearing
40 Shaft spacer
41 Counter gear
42 Shaft bearing
43 Output front shaft

31   Install the transmission to transfer case bolts, tightening them to the torque listed in this Chapter's Specifications.
32   Follow steps 15 through 19 of this Section.

4   Transfer case overhaul – general information

Refer to illustration 4.4

Overhauling a transfer case is a difficult job for the do-it-yourselfer. It involves the disassembly and reassembly of many small parts. Numerous clearances must be precisely measured and, if necessary, changed with select fit spacers and snap-rings. As a result, if transfer case problems arise, it can be removed and installed by a competent do-it-yourselfer, but overhaul should be left to a transmission repair shop. Rebuilt transfer cases may be available – check with your dealer parts department and auto parts stores. At any rate, the time and money involved in an overhaul is almost sure to exceed the cost of a rebuilt unit.

Nevertheless, it's not impossible for an inexperienced mechanic to re-build a transfer case if the special tools are available and the job is done in a deliberate step-by-step manner so nothing is overlooked.

The tools necessary for an overhaul include internal and external snap-ring pliers, a bearing puller, a slide hammer, a set of pin punches, a dial indicator and possibly a hydraulic press. In addition, a large, sturdy workbench and a vise or transmission stand will be required.

During disassembly of the transfer case, make careful notes of how each piece comes off, where it fits in relation to other pieces and what holds it in place. An exploded view is included **(see illustration)** to show where the parts go – but actually noting how they are installed when you remove the parts will make it much easier to get the transfer case back together.

Before taking the transfer case apart for repair, it will help if you have some idea what area of the transfer case is malfunctioning. Certain prob-lems can be closely tied to specific areas in the transfer case, which can make component examination and replacement easier. Refer to the *Trou-bleshooting* Section at the front of this manual for information regarding possible sources of trouble.

Chapter 8   Clutch and drivetrain

Contents

Specifications

Torque specifications

	Ft-lbs (unless otherwise indicated)
Pressure plate-to-flywheel bolts	14 to 20
Driveshaft bolts and nuts	
Samurai	17 to 22
Sidekick/Tracker	36 to 43
Freewheeling hub	
Manual locking	
Hub body bolts	15 to 22
Hub cover bolts	72 to 109 in-lbs
Automatic locking hub body bolts	15 to 21
Kingpin bolts (Samurai)	15 to 22
Front wheel bearing nut (Samurai)	96 to 132 in-lbs
Front wheel bearing locknut (Samurai)	43 to 65
Driveaxle flange bolt and nut (Sidekick/Tracker)	29 to 43
Front axle housing mounting bolts (Sidekick/Tracker)	
Left side	37
Right side	37
Rear	37
Front wheel bearing locknut (Sidekick/Tracker)	89 to 148
Brake backing plate bolts/nuts	14 to 20
Differential carrier bolts	
Samurai	20
Sidekick/Tracker	41

1   General information

The information in this Chapter deals with the components from the rear of the engine to the wheels, except for the transmission and transfer case, which are dealt with in the previous Chapter. For the purposes of this Chapter, these components are grouped into four categories: Clutch, driveshaft, front axle and rear axle. Separate Sections within this Chapter offer general descriptions and checking procedures for components in each of the four groups.

Since nearly all the procedures covered in this Chapter involve working under the vehicle, make sure it's securely supported on sturdy jackstands or on a hoist where the vehicle can be easily raised and lowered.

2   Clutch – description and check

Refer to illustration 2.1

1   All vehicles with a manual transmission use a single dry plate, diaphragm spring type clutch **(see illustration)**. The clutch disc has a splined hub which allows it to slide along the splines of the transmission input shaft. The clutch and pressure plate are held in contact by spring pressure exerted by the diaphragm in the pressure plate.

2   The clutch release system is operated mechanically. The mechanical release system includes the clutch pedal, a clutch cable which actuates the clutch release lever and the release bearing.

3   When pressure is applied to the clutch pedal to release the clutch, pressure is exerted against the outer end of the clutch release lever. As the lever pivots the shaft fingers push against the release bearing. The bearing pushes against the fingers of the diaphragm spring of the pressure plate assembly, which in turn releases the clutch plate.

4   Terminology can be a problem when discussing the clutch components because common names are in some cases different from those used by the manufacturer. For example, the driven plate is also called the clutch plate or disc, and the clutch release bearing is sometimes called a throwout bearing.

5   Other than to replace components with obvious damage, some preliminary checks should be performed to diagnose clutch problems.

a) To check "clutch spin down time," run the engine at normal idle speed with the transmission in Neutral (clutch pedal up – engaged). Disengage the clutch (pedal down), wait several seconds and shift the transmission into Reverse. No grinding noise should be heard. A grinding noise would most likely indicate a problem in the pressure plate or the clutch disc.

b) To check for complete clutch release, run the engine (with the parking brake applied to prevent movement) and hold the clutch pedal approximately 1/2-inch from the floor. Shift the transmission between 1st gear and Reverse several times. If the shift is rough, component failure is indicated.

c) Visually inspect the pivot bushing at the top of the clutch pedal to make sure there is no binding or excessive play.

d) A clutch pedal that is difficult to operate is most likely caused by a faulty clutch cable. Check the cable where it enters the housing for frayed wires, rust and other signs of corrosion. If it looks good, lubricate the cable with penetrating oil. If pedal operation improves, the cable is worn out and should be replaced.

e) Crawl under the vehicle and make sure the clutch release arm is solidly clamped to the release shaft.

3   Clutch components – removal, inspection and installation

Warning: *Dust produced by clutch wear and deposited on clutch components may contain asbestos, which is hazardous to your health. DO NOT blow it out with compressed air and DO NOT inhale it. DO NOT use gasoline or petroleum-based solvents to remove the dust. Brake system cleaner should be used to flush the dust into a drain pan. After the clutch components are wiped clean with a rag, dispose of the contaminated rags and cleaner in a covered, marked container.*

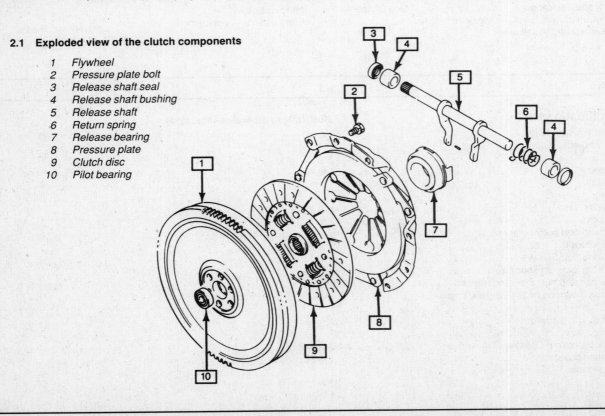

2.1 Exploded view of the clutch components

1   *Flywheel*
2   *Pressure plate bolt*
3   *Release shaft seal*
4   *Release shaft bushing*
5   *Release shaft*
6   *Return spring*
7   *Release bearing*
8   *Pressure plate*
9   *Clutch disc*
10   *Pilot bearing*

3.6   Mark the relationship of the pressure plate to the flywheel (arrow) (in case you are going to reuse the same pressure plate)

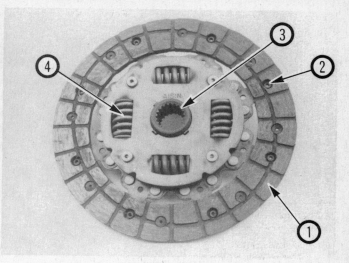

3.11   The clutch plate

1   Lining This will wear down in use
2   Rivets – These secure the lining and will damage the flywheel or pressure plate if allowed to contact the surfaces
3   Splined hub – the splines should not be worn and should slide smoothly on the input shaft splines
4   Springs – check for deformation

Removal

Refer to illustration 3.6

1   Access to the clutch components is normally accomplished by removing the transmission, leaving the engine in the vehicle. If, of course, the engine is being removed for major overhaul, then check the clutch for wear and replace worn components as necessary. However, the relatively low cost of the clutch components compared to the time and trouble spent gaining access to them warrants their replacement anytime the engine or transmission is removed, unless they are new or in near perfect condition. The following procedures are based on the assumption the engine will stay in place.

2   Remove the clutch cable (see Section 6).

3   Referring to Chapter 7, Part A, remove the transmission from the vehicle. Support the engine while the transmission is out. Preferably, an engine hoist should be used to support it from above. However, if a jack is used underneath the engine, make sure a piece of wood is positioned between the jack and oil pan to spread the load. **Caution:** *The pickup for the oil pump is very close to the bottom of the oil pan. If the pan is bent or distorted in any way, engine oil starvation could occur.*

4   The clutch fork and release bearing can remain attached to the housing for the time being.

5   To support the clutch disc during removal, install a clutch alignment tool through the clutch disc hub.

6   Carefully inspect the flywheel and pressure plate for indexing marks. The marks are usually an X, an O or a white letter. If they cannot be found, scribe marks yourself so the pressure plate and the flywheel will be in the same alignment during installation **(see illustration)**.

7   Turning each bolt only a little at a time, loosen the pressure plate-to-flywheel bolts. Work in a criss-cross pattern until all spring pressure is relieved. Then hold the pressure plate securely and completely remove the bolts, followed by the pressure plate and clutch disc.

Inspection

Refer to illustrations 3.11 and 3.13

8   Ordinarily, when a problem occurs in the clutch, it can be attributed to wear of the clutch driven plate assembly (clutch disc). However, all components should be inspected at this time.

9   Inspect the flywheel for cracks, heat checking, grooves and other obvious defects. If the imperfections are slight, a machine shop can machine the surface flat and smooth, which is highly recommended regardless of the surface appearance. Refer to Chapter 2 for the flywheel removal and installation procedure.

10   Inspect the pilot bearing (see Section 5).

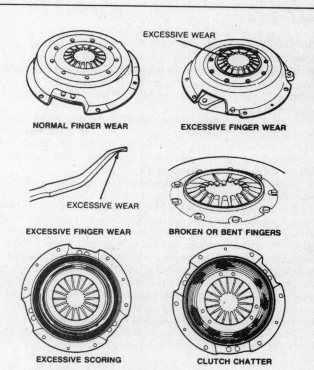

3.13   Replace the pressure plate if excessive wear is noted

11   Inspect the lining on the clutch disc. There should be at least 1/16-inch of lining above the rivet heads. Check for loose rivets, distortion, cracks, broken springs and other obvious damage **(see illustration)**. As mentioned above, ordinarily the clutch disc is routinely replaced, so if in doubt about the condition, replace it with a new one.

12   The release bearing should also be replaced along with the clutch disc (see Section 4).

3.15   Center the clutch disc in the pressure plate with an alignment tool before the bolts are tightened – a clutch alignment tool can be purchased at most auto parts stores and eliminates all guesswork when centering the clutch disc in the pressure plate

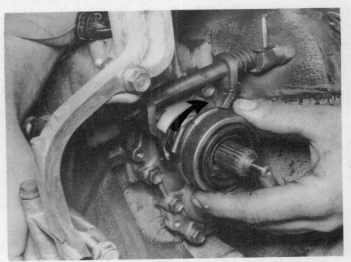

4.3   Turn the release bearing assembly in a clockwise direction to detach it from the release fork – when installing the bearing, make sure the pin on the fork is engaged with the slot in the release bearing

13   Check the machined surfaces and the diaphragm spring fingers of the pressure plate **(see illustration)**. If the surface is grooved or otherwise damaged, replace the pressure plate. Also check for obvious damage, distortion, cracking, etc. Light glazing can be removed with emery cloth or sandpaper. If a new pressure plate is required, new and factory-rebuilt units are available.

Installation

Refer to illustration 3.15

14   Before installation, clean the flywheel and pressure plate machined surfaces with lacquer thinner or acetone. It's important that no oil or grease is on these surfaces or the lining of the clutch disc. Handle the parts only with clean hands.

15   Position the clutch disc and pressure plate against the flywheel with the clutch held in place with an alignment tool **(see illustration)**. Make sure it's installed properly (most replacement clutch plates will be marked "flywheel side" or something similar – if not marked, install the clutch disc with the damper springs toward the transmission).

16   Tighten the pressure plate-to-flywheel bolts only finger tight, working around the pressure plate.

17   Center the clutch disc by ensuring the alignment tool extends through the splined hub and into the pilot bearing in the crankshaft. Wiggle the tool up, down or side-to-side as needed to bottom the tool in the pilot bearing. Tighten the pressure plate-to-flywheel bolts a little at a time, working in a criss-cross pattern to prevent distorting the cover. After all the bolts are snug, tighten them to the specified torque. Remove the alignment tool.

18   Using high temperature grease, lubricate the inner groove of the release bearing (see Section 4). Also place grease on the release lever contact areas and the transmission input shaft bearing retainer.

19   Install the clutch release bearing as described in Section 4.

20   Install the transmission and all components removed previously. Tighten all fasteners to the proper torque specifications.

---

4   Clutch release bearing – removal, inspection and installation

Refer to illustration 4.3

Warning: *Dust produced by clutch wear and deposited on clutch components may contain asbestos, which is hazardous to your health. DO NOT blow it out with compressed air and DO NOT inhale it. DO NOT use gasoline or petroleum-based solvents to remove the dust. Brake system cleaner should be used to flush the dust into a drain pan. After the clutch*

components are wiped clean with a rag, dispose of the contaminated rags and cleaner in a covered, marked container.

Removal

1   Disconnect the negative cable from the battery.

2   Remove the transmission (see Chapter 7).

3   Push the clutch release arm forward, then remove the bearing from the fork by turning the bearing assembly in a clockwise direction **(see illustration)**.

Inspection

4   Hold the center of the bearing and rotate the outer portion while applying pressure. If the bearing doesn't turn smoothly or if it's noisy, replace it with a new one. Wipe the bearing with a clean rag and inspect it for damage, wear and cracks. Don't immerse the bearing in solvent – it's sealed for life and to do so would ruin it.

Installation

5   Using high temperature grease, lightly lubricate the release fork and the input shaft where they contact the bearing. Fill the inner groove of the bearing with the same grease.

6   Attach the release bearing to the clutch lever by turning counterclockwise. Make sure the pin on the fork is engaged with the slot in the release bearing ear.

7   Install the transmission.

8   The remainder of installation is the reverse of the removal procedure. Tighten all bolts to the specified torque.

---

5   Pilot bearing – inspection and replacement

Refer to illustrations 5.5 and 5.9

1   The clutch pilot bearing is a roller type bearing which is pressed into the rear of the crankshaft. It is greased at the factory and does not require additional lubrication. Its primary purpose is to support the front of the transmission input shaft. The pilot bearing should be inspected whenever the clutch components are removed from the engine. Due to its inaccessibility, if you are in doubt as to its condition, replace it with a new one. **Note:** *If the engine has been removed from the vehicle, disregard the following steps which do not apply.*

2   Remove the transmission (see Chapter 7 Part A).

3   Remove the clutch components (see Section 3).

4   Inspect for any excessive wear, scoring, lack of grease, dryness or obvious damage. If any of these conditions are noted, the bearing should be replaced. A flashlight will be helpful to direct light into the recess.

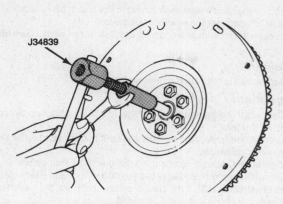

5.5   One method of removing the pilot bearing requires a special tool

5.9   Pack the recess behind the pilot bearing with heavy grease and force it out hydraulically with a steel rod slightly smaller than the bore in the bearing – when the hammer strikes the rod, the bearing will pop out of the crankshaft

5   Removal can be accomplished with a special puller (**see illustration**), but an alternative method also works very well.
6   Find a solid steel bar which is slightly smaller in diameter than the bearing. Alternatives to a solid bar would be a wood dowel or a socket with a bolt fixed in place to make it solid.
7   Check the bar for fit – it should just slip into the bearing with very little clearance.
8   Pack the bearing and the area behind it (in the crankshaft recess) with heavy grease. Pack it tightly to eliminate as much air as possible.
9   Insert the bar into the bearing bore and strike the bar sharply with a hammer which will force the grease to the back side of the bearing and push it out (**see illustration**). Remove the bearing and clean all grease from the crankshaft recess.
10   To install the new bearing, lightly lubricate the outside surface with lithium-based grease, then drive it into the recess with a soft-face hammer.
11   Install the clutch components, transmission and all other components removed previously, tightening all fasteners properly.

6   Clutch cable – replacement

Refer to illustrations 6.2 and 6.5

Removal
1   Disconnect the negative cable from the battery.

2   Remove the clutch cable joint nut and loosen the cable housing nuts (**see illustration**).
3   Remove the cable from the release arm and the cable bracket.
4   Follow the clutch cable up to the firewall and remove any clutch cable clamps.
5   Remove the two bolts holding the cable to the firewall (**see illustration**).
6   Disconnect the clutch cable hook at the clutch pedal and remove the cable from the vehicle.

Installation
7   Apply grease to the cable hook and the joint pin.
8   Position the cable in the vehicle and hook the cable end to the clutch pedal. Install the two cable housing-to-firewall bolts.
9   Install the clutch cable into the cable bracket and the release arm.
10   Refer to Chapter 1 for the clutch cable and pedal adjustments.
11   Connect the negative battery cable.
12   Check for proper clutch operation.

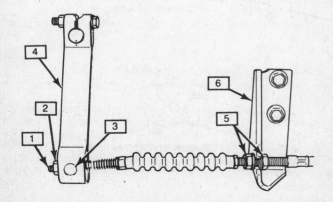

6.2   Typical clutch cable components (transmission end shown)

1	Inner cable	4	Clutch release arm
2	Joint nut	5	Cable housing nut
3	Joint pin	6	Clutch cable bracket

6.5   Remove the two bolts to disconnect the clutch cable from the firewall

8

7   Clutch pedal – removal and installation

Refer to illustration 7.1

Removal

1   Loosen the pedal shaft clamp bolt **(see illustration)**.
2   Remove the clutch pedal shaft arm.
3   Remove the clutch pedal spring while sliding the clutch pedal out.

Installation

4   Connect the clutch pedal spring while sliding the clutch pedal into position through the shaft bushing and the pedal bracket.
5   Install the clutch pedal shaft arm.
6   Tighten the clamp bolt securely.

8   Clutch start switch – removal, installation and adjustment

Refer to illustration 8.3

Removal

1   Apply the parking brake firmly and put the transmission in neutral.

2   Locate the clutch start switch next to the clutch pedal bracket under the dash. Disconnect the electrical connector.
3   Loosen the locknut and unscrew the clutch start switch **(see illustration)**.

Installation

4   Installation is the reverse of removal.

Adjustment

5   Depress the clutch pedal all the way and bring it back up two to three inches off the floor.
6   With an ohmmeter connected to the switch, slowly screw the switch in until there is continuity.
7   Tighten the locknut and connect the electrical connector.
8   Depress the clutch pedal all the way to the floor and check clearance B **(see illustration 8.3)**. If the clearance is not correct, the switch may be damaged.

9   Driveshafts, differentials and axles – general information

Refer to illustrations 9.1a and 9.1b

   Three different driveshaft assemblies are used on the vehicles covered in this manual **(see illustrations)**. Samurai models use three drive

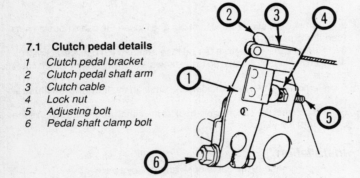

7.1   Clutch pedal details

1   *Clutch pedal bracket*
2   *Clutch pedal shaft arm*
3   *Clutch cable*
4   *Lock nut*
5   *Adjusting bolt*
6   *Pedal shaft clamp bolt*

8.3   Adjust gap B by turning the switch in its bracket, then tighten the lock nut

B   *0.02 to 0.04-inch (0.5 to 1.0 mm)*
1   *Locknut*
2   *Clutch start switch*
3   *Pedal bracket*

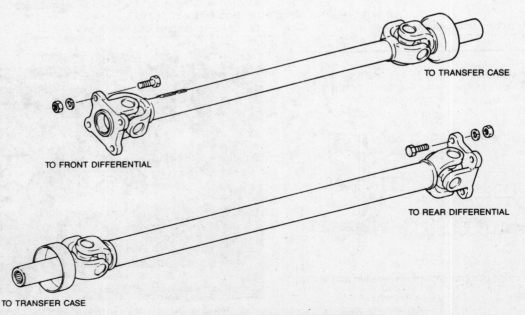

TO TRANSFER CASE

TO FRONT DIFFERENTIAL

TO REAR DIFFERENTIAL

TO TRANSFER CASE

9.1a   Sidekick and Tracker driveshafts

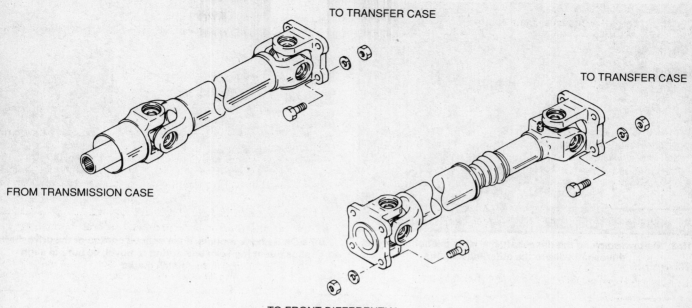

TO TRANSFER CASE

FROM TRANSMISSION CASE

TO TRANSFER CASE

TO FRONT DIFFERENTIAL

TO REAR DIFFERENTIAL

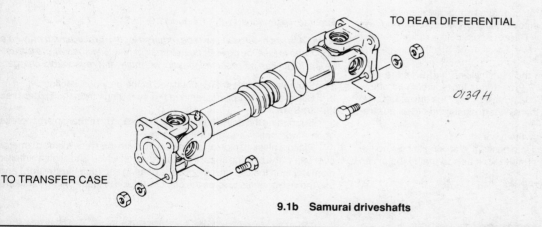

TO TRANSFER CASE

0139 H

9.1b Samurai driveshafts

shafts and Tracker and Sidekick models use only two. On the Samurai, a short driveshaft is used to transfer power from the transmission to the transfer case. On all models, a front and rear driveshaft transmit power from the transfer case to the front and rear axles. Since the transfer case on Tracker and Sidekick models is mounted to the rear of the transmission, the short driveshaft is not necessary.

All universal joints are of the solid type and can be replaced separate from the driveshaft.

The driveshafts are finely balanced during production and whenever they are removed or disassembled, they must be reassembled and reinstalled in the exact manner and positions they were originally in, to avoid excessive vibration.

The rear axle on all models (and the front axle on Samurai models) is of the semi-floating type, which is held in proper alignment with the body by the suspension.

Mounted in the center of the axle is the differential, which transfers the turning force of the driveshaft to the axleshafts.

The axleshafts are splined at their inner ends to fit into the splines in the differential gears; at the rear, outer support for the shaft is provided by the rear wheel bearing. Up front, the axles are supported by a bearing in the spindle.

Because of the complexity and critical nature of the differential adjustments, as well as the special equipment needed to perform the operations, we recommend any disassembly of the differential be done by a dealer service department or a repair shop.

10 Driveshafts – removal and installation

Refer to illustrations 10.3 and 10.7

Removal

1   Disconnect the negative cable from the battery.
2   Raise the vehicle and support it securely on jackstands. Place the transmission in Neutral with the parking brake off.
3   Using a scribe, paint or a hammer and punch, place marks on the driveshaft and the differential flange (and transfer case flange on Samurai models) in line with each other **(see illustration)**. This is to make sure the driveshaft is reinstalled in the same position to preserve the balance.
4   Remove the rear universal joint bolts and nuts. Turn the driveshaft (or tires) as necessary to bring the bolts into the most accessible position.

8

10.3   Before removing the driveshaft, mark the relationship of the driveshaft yoke to the differential flange

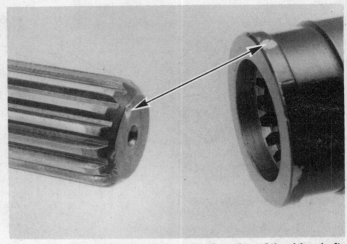

10.7   On Samurai models, if the splined portion of the driveshaft slips out of the yoke end during removal, be sure to align the match marks

5   Lower the rear of the driveshaft and slide the front out of the transmission. On some models it will be necessary to unbolt the driveshaft from the transmission.

6   To prevent loss of fluid and protect against contamination while the driveshaft is out, wrap a plastic bag over the transmission housing and hold it in place with a rubber band (Tracker and Sidekick models only).

Installation

7   Remove the plastic bag from the transmission and wipe the area clean. Inspect the oil seal carefully. Procedures for replacement of this seal can be found in Chapter 7. On Samurai models if the driveshaft slips apart, be sure to realign the match marks when reinstalling it (see illustration).

8   Slide the front of the driveshaft into the transmission.

9   Raise the rear of the driveshaft into position, checking to be sure the marks are in alignment. If not, turn the rear wheels to match the pinion flange and the driveshaft.

10   Tighten the bolts and nuts to the specified torque.

11   Universal joints – replacement

Refer to illustrations 11.2, 11.4 and 11.9

Note: *A press or large vise will be required for this procedure. It may be a good idea to take the driveshaft to a repair or machine shop where the universal joints can be replaced for you, normally at a reasonable charge.*

1   Remove the driveshaft as outlined in the previous Section.

2   Using snap-ring pliers, remove the snap-rings from the spider (see illustration).

3   Supporting the driveshaft, place it in position on either an arbor press or on a workbench equipped with a vise.

4   Place a piece of pipe or a large socket with the same inside diameter over one of the bearing caps. Position a socket which is of slightly smaller diameter than the cap on the opposite bearing cap (see illustration) and use the vise or press to force the cap out (inside the pipe or large socket),

11.2   Use snap-ring pliers to remove the snap-rings

11.4   To press the universal joint out of the driveshaft, set it up in a vise with the small socket (on the left) pushing the joint and bearing cap into the large socket

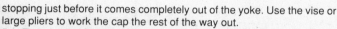

11.9 To relieve stress produced by pressing the bearing caps into the yokes, strike the yoke in the area shown

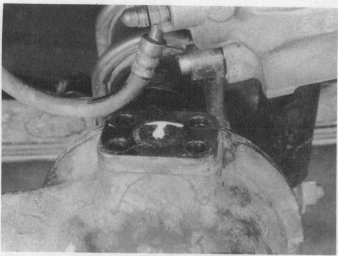

12.6 Before removing the kingpins be sure to mark them so they will be reinstalled in their original positions

stopping just before it comes completely out of the yoke. Use the vise or large pliers to work the cap the rest of the way out.

5   Transfer the sockets to the other side and press the opposite bearing cap out in the same manner.

6   Pack the new universal joint bearings with grease. Ordinarily, specific instructions for lubrication will be included with the universal joint servicing kit and should be followed carefully.

7   Position the spider in the yoke and partially install one bearing cap in the yoke. If the replacement spider is equipped with a grease fitting, be sure it's offset in the proper direction (toward the driveshaft).

8   Start the spider into the bearing cap and then partially install the other cap. Align the spider and press the bearing caps into position, being careful not to damage the dust seals.

9   Install the snap-rings. If difficulty is encountered in seating the snap-rings, strike the driveshaft yoke sharply with a hammer. This will spring the yoke ears slightly and allow the snap-rings to seat in the groove **(see illustration)**.

10   Install the grease fitting and fill the joint with grease. Be careful not to overfill the joint, as this could blow out the grease seals.

11   Install the driveshaft. Tighten the flange bolts and nuts to the specified torque.

---

12   Front axleshaft and steering knuckle (Samurai only) – removal, inspection and installation

Refer to illustrations 12.6, 12.8, 12.12 and 12.14

Removal

1   Loosen the wheel lug nuts, raise the front of the vehicle and support it securely on jackstands. Apply the parking brake. Remove the wheel.

2   Remove the disc brake caliper and carrier and hang them out of the way with a piece of wire (see Chapter 9).

3   Remove the brake disc (see Chapter 9).

4   Remove the freewheeling hub or automatic hub (see Section 21).

5   Remove the front wheel bearings and hub (see Section 22).

6   Loosen the upper and lower kingpin bolts but don't remove them at this time. Mark the upper and lower kingpins so they can be installed in their original positions **(see illustration)**.

7   Remove the disc brake dust cover.

8   Mark the relationship of the spindle to the steering knuckle and unbolt it **(see illustration)**.

9   Separate the tie-rod end from the steering knuckle (see Chapter 10).

8

12.8 Mark the spindle so it can be reinstalled in its original position

12.12 Remove the steering knuckle carefully, because the lower kingpin bearing could fall out

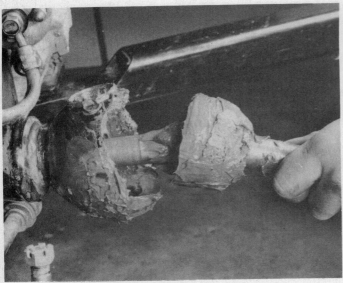

12.14   To remove the axleshaft, simply pull it out

13.2   Using a small prybar, pry the axle seal out of the housing

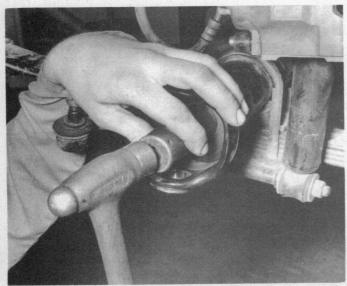

13.3   A socket with an outside diameter slightly smaller than the outside diameter of the seal can be used to install the seal

10   Remove the steering knuckle oil seal (see Chapter 1).
11   Remove the kingpins, noting the locations of any shims that may be present between the kingpins and the steering knuckle.
12   Remove the steering knuckle, taking care not to drop the kingpin bearing **(see illustration)**.
13   Drain the front differential lubricant (see Chapter 1).
14   Remove the axleshaft by pulling it straight out of the housing **(see illustration)**.

Inspection

15   Check all parts for cracks, distortion, dents, deformed splines and any other type of damage and replace as necessary.

Installation

16   Installation is the reverse of removal, but before installing the axleshaft, pack the constant velocity joint with chassis grease. Also, be sure to lubricate the kingpins and the kingpin bearing with the same grease.
17   Tighten all fasteners to the torque listed in this Chapter's Specifications.
18   Fill the front differential with the recommended lubricant (see Chapter 1).

---

13   Front axleshaft oil seal (Samurai only) – removal and installation

---

Refer to illustrations 13.2 and 13.3

1   Remove the front axleshaft (see Section 12).
2   Remove the seal with a seal remover tool or a small pry bar **(see illustration)**.
3   Lubricate the seal lip, then drive the seal into position with a seal installation tool, a piece of pipe, or socket with an outside diameter slightly smaller than the outside diameter of the seal **(see illustration)**.
4   Install the axleshaft (see Section 12).

---

14   Driveaxle (Sidekick/Tracker only) – removal and installation

---

Refer to illustrations 14.8 and 14.10

Removal

1   Loosen the lug nuts, raise the front of the vehicle and support it securely on jackstands. Remove the front wheel.
2   Drain the differential lubricant (see Chapter 1).
3   Remove the locking hub (see Section 21).
4   Remove the driveaxle snap-ring with a pair of snap-ring pliers.
5   Disconnect the stabilizer bar from the lower arm (see Chapter 10).
6   Remove the tie-rod ends (see Chapter 10).
7   Remove the caliper bolts and suspend the caliper with a piece of wire (see Chapter 9).

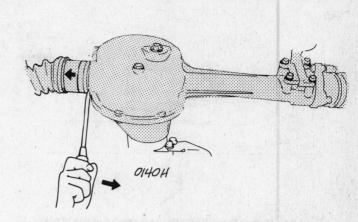

14.8   Support the lower arm with a jack positioned under the spring seat

| 1 | *Lower arm* | 2 | *Jack* |

14.10   Be careful when prying the inner end of the axleshaft out of the differential (the seal is very close to the edge of the joint and could be damaged if the prybar is inserted too far)

8   Loosen, but do not remove, the steering knuckle balljoint nut (see Chapter 10). Support the the lower arm with a jack **(see illustration)** and remove the balljoint nut.
9   Lower the jack slowly and swing the steering knuckle clear of the lower arm.

Right side
10   Pry the driveaxle out of the differential **(see illustration)**.
11   Remove the driveaxle from the hub, being careful not to damage the axle boots during removal.

Left side
12   Unbolt the three driveaxle bolts and remove the driveaxle, being careful not to damage the axle boots during removal. Removal of the differential side gear shaft can be accomplished by prying it out, using the technique described in Step 10.

Installation
13   Inspect all parts for damage, warpage, cracks, breakage and corrosion. Replace parts as necessary.
14   Installation is the reverse of the removal procedure. Tighten all fasteners to the torque values listed in this Chapter's Specifications.

---

15   Front axle housing – removal and installation

Removal
1   Loosen the front wheel lug nuts, raise the front of the vehicle and support it securely on jackstands positioned under the frame rails. Remove the front wheels.
2   Mark the relationship of the front driveshaft to the front differential pinion shaft yoke, then disconnect the driveshaft from the yoke (see Section 10). With a piece of wire, suspend the driveshaft up out of the way. **Note:** *On Tracker and Sidekick models, don't pull the driveshaft out of the transfer case unless you drain the transfer case lubricant first.*

Samurai
3   Unbolt the front brake calipers and hang them out of the way with a piece of wire – don't let the calipers hang by the brake hose (see Chapter 9).
4   Remove the brake pads, caliper holder and the brake discs (see Chapter 9).
5   Remove the stabilizer bar (See Chapter 10).
6   Disconnect the tie-rod ends from the steering knuckles (see Chapter 10). Position them out the way and hang them with pieces of wire from the underbody.

7   Position a hydraulic jack under the differential. If two jacks are available, place one under the right side axle tube to balance the assembly.
8   Unbolt the lower ends of the shock absorbers from the axle.
9   Remove the nuts from the leaf spring U-bolts (see Chapter 10).
10   Remove the leaf spring front mounting bolts and loosen the rear shackle bolts. Allow the leaf springs to swing down.
11   Slowly lower the assembly down and out from under the vehicle.

Sidekick/Tracker
Refer to illustrations 15.13, 15.14 and 15.16
12   Remove the differential breather hose.
13   Remove the four bolts from the left hand mounting bracket and the three bolts and nuts from the driveaxle flange **(see illustration)**. Separate the driveaxle from the flange and hang it from the underbody with a piece of wire.

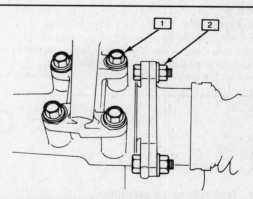

15.13   Remove the left driveaxle bolts and nuts (2) then unscrew the four mounting bolts (1)

---

14   Remove the two bolts from the differential rear mounting bracket **(see illustration)**.
15   Place a jack under the differential housing – a transmission jack is preferred, as the unit can be secured to the jack with a chain.
16   Remove the three right side mounting bolts **(see illustration)**.
17   Using a prybar, pry the right side driveaxle from the housing. As this is done, the axle housing will move to the left considerably, so make sure the jack is allowed to roll with it so it doesn't fall off. Also, don't let the driveaxle fall as it comes out of the housing – support it with a piece of wire.
18   Slowly lower the jack and remove the housing from the vehicle.

8

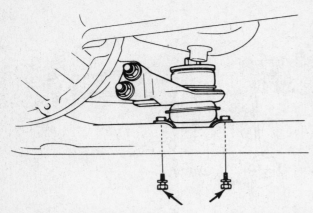

15.14   Unbolt the differential rear mount at the bracket

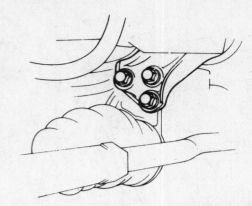

15.16   Remove the three right hand mounting bolts when removing the front axle housing

Installation

19   Installation is the reverse of the removal procedure. On Samurai models, make sure the leaf springs are positioned properly on the axle housing (see Chapter 10). Tighten all fasteners the torque values listed in this Chapter's Specifications.

16   Driveaxle boot – replacement

Note: *Some auto parts stores carry "split" type replacement boots, which can be installed without removing the driveaxle from the vehicle. This is a convenient alternative; however, it's recommended that the driveaxle be removed and the CV joints cleaned to ensure that the joint is free from contaminants such as moisture and dirt, which will accelerate CV joint wear.*

Inner CV joint and boot

Disassembly

Refer to illustrations 16.3, 16.4a, 16.4b, 16.5, 16.6 and 16.7

1   Remove the driveaxle from the vehicle (see Section 14).
2   Mount the driveaxle in a vise. The jaws of the vise should be lined with wood or rags to prevent damage to the axleshaft.
3   Pry the boot clamp retaining tabs up with a small screwdriver and

16.3   Pry the boot clamp retaining tabs up with a small screwdriver and slide the clamps off the boot

slide the clamps off the boot **(see illustration)**.
4   Slide the boot back on the axleshaft and pry the wire ring ball retainer from the outer race **(see illustrations)**.

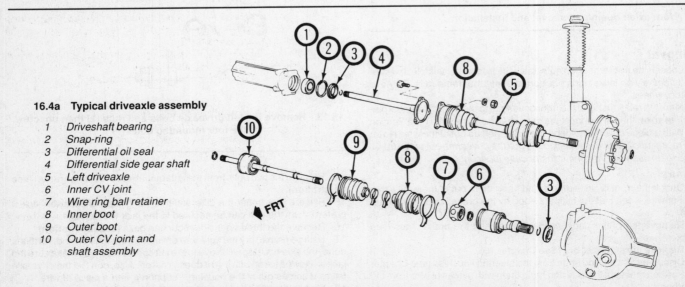

16.4a   Typical driveaxle assembly

1   Driveshaft bearing
2   Snap-ring
3   Differential oil seal
4   Differential side gear shaft
5   Left driveaxle
6   Inner CV joint
7   Wire ring ball retainer
8   Inner boot
9   Outer boot
10   Outer CV joint and shaft assembly

FRT

16.4b   Pry the wire ring ball retainer out of the outer race

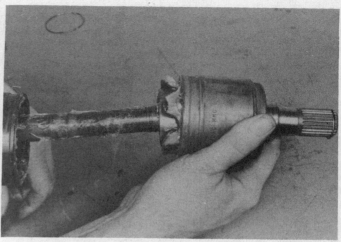

16.5   Slide the outer race off the inner bearing assembly

16.6   Remove the snap-ring from the end of the axle

16.7   Apply match marks to the bearing to identify which side faces out during reassembly

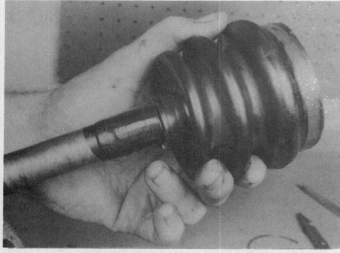

16.10   Wrap the splined area of the axle with tape to prevent damage to the boot when installing it

5   Pull the outer race off the inner bearing assembly (see illustration).
6   Remove the snap-ring from the groove in the axleshaft with a pair of snap-ring pliers (see illustration).
7   Mark the inner bearing assembly to ensure that it is reassembled with the correct side facing out (see illustration).
8   Slide the inner bearing assembly off the axleshaft.

Inspection

9   Clean the components with solvent to remove all traces of grease. Inspect the cage, balls and races for pitting, score marks, cracks and other signs of wear and damage. Shiny, polished spots are normal and will not adversely affect CV joint performance.

Reassembly

Refer to illustrations 16.10, 16.13, 16.16, 16.17a and 16.17b

10   Wrap the axleshaft splines with tape to avoid damaging the boot. Slide the small boot clamp and boot onto the axleshaft, then remove the tape (see illustration).
11   Install the inner bearing assembly on the axleshaft with the larger diameter side or "bulge" of the cage (and the previously applied mark) facing the axleshaft end.
12   Install the snap-ring in the groove. Make sure it's completely seated by pushing on the inner bearing assembly.

8

16.13   Pack the inner bearing assembly full of CV joint grease (also note that the larger diameter side, or "bulge", is facing the axleshaft end)

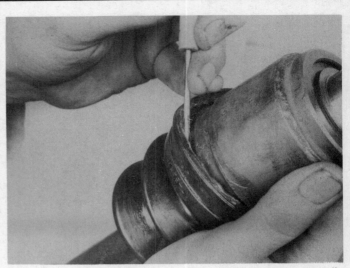

16.16   Equalize the pressure inside the boot by inserting a small, dull screwdriver between the boot and the outer race

16.17a   To install the new clamps, bend the tang down and . . .

16.17b   . . . fold the tabs over to hold it in place

13   Fill the outer race and boot with the specified type and quantity of CV joint grease (normally included with the new boot kit). Pack the inner bearing assembly with grease, by hand, until grease is worked completely into the assembly (see illustration).

14   Slide the outer race down onto the inner race and install the wire ring retainer.

15   Wipe any excess grease from the axle boot groove on the outer race. Seat the small diameter of the boot in the recessed area on the axleshaft. Push the other end of the boot onto the outer race.

16   Equalize the pressure in the boot by inserting a dull screwdriver between the boot and the outer race (see illustration). Don't damage the boot with the tool.

17   Install the boot clamps (see illustrations).

18   If you are working on the right side driveaxle, install a new circlip on the inner CV joint stub axle.

19   Install the driveaxle as described in Section 14.

Outer CV joint and boot

Disassembly

20   Following Steps 1 through 8, remove the inner CV joint from the axleshaft.

21   Remove the outer CV joint boot clamps, using the technique described in Step 3. Slide the boot off the axleshaft.

Inspection

Refer to illustration 16.23

22   Thoroughly wash the inner and outer CV joints in clean solvent and blow them dry with compressed air, if available. **Note:** *Because the outer joint cannot be disassembled, it is difficult to wash away all the old grease and to rid the bearing of solvent once it's clean. But it is imperative that the job be done thoroughly, so take your time and do it right.*

23   Bend the outer CV joint housing at an angle to the driveaxle to expose

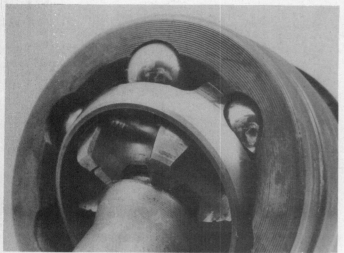

16.23 After the old grease has been rinsed away and the solvent has been blown out with compressed air, rotate the outer joint housing through its full range of motion and inspect the bearing surfaces for wear and damage – if any of the balls, the race or /he cage look damaged, replace the driveaxle and outer joint assembly

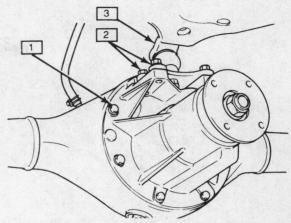

17.8 Rear differential mounting details – Sidekick and Tracker models

1 *Differential carrier-to-rear axle housing bolt*
2 *Upper arm-to-differential carrier bolt*
3 *Upper arm*

the bearings, inner race and cage (see illustration). Inspect the bearing surfaces for signs of wear. If the bearings are damaged or worn, replace the driveaxle.

Reassembly
24 Slide the new outer boot onto the driveaxle. It's a good idea to wrap vinyl tape around the spline of shaft to prevent damage to the boot **(see illustration 16.10)**. When the boot is in position, add the specified amount of grease (included in the boot replacement kit) to the outer joint and the boot (pack the joint with as much grease as it will hold and put the rest into the boot). Slide the boot on the rest of the way and install the new clamps **(see illustrations 16.17a and 16.17b)**.
25 Proceed to clean and install the inner CV joint and boot by following Steps 9 through 18, then install the driveaxle as outlined in Section 14.

---

17 Differential carrier assembly – removal and installation

Removal

All models
1 Loosen the front or rear wheel lug nuts and raise the front or rear of the vehicle, supporting it securely on jackstands. Remove the front or rear wheels.
2 Drain the differential lubricant (See Chapter 1).
3 Remove the front or rear axleshafts or driveaxles and side gear shaft (see Sections 12, 14 and 18).
4 Remove the driveshaft hang it up out of the way with a piece of wire (see Section 10).

Samurai (front and rear)
5 Remove the eight carrier-to-differential housing bolts.
6 Place a jack under the carrier, pull the carrier out of the housing and slowly lower the assembly.

Sidekick/Tracker
Front
7 The front differential carrier must be removed as a complete unit with the axle housing (see Section 15).
Rear
Refer to illustration 17.8
8 Place a jack under the differential, remove the four upper arm-to-

carrier bolts (see illustration) and lower the rear axle down onto a pair of jackstands or large blocks of wood.
9 Remove the eight differential bolts and, with the jack, lower the carrier assembly.

Installation (all models)
10 Clean the mating surfaces of the differential carrier and the rear axle housing and apply RTV sealant to them.
11 Installation is the reverse of removal.

---

18 Rear axleshaft and bearing assembly – removal and installation

---

Refer to illustrations 18.8 and 18.10
Note: *A slide hammer and an adapter may be needed to perform this procedure.*

Removal
1 Loosen the rear wheel lug nuts, raise the rear of the vehicle and support it securely on jackstands. Remove the wheels.
2 Remove the brake drum (see Chapter 1).
3 Drain the differential lubricant (see Chapter 1).
Samurai
4 Disconnect the parking brake cable from the rear brake assembly and backing plate (see Chapter 9).
5 Unscrew the brake line fitting from the wheel cylinder – don't pull the line away from the cylinder, as it may become kinked. When the axle and brake assembly are pulled from the housing, plug the line.
6 Remove the brake backing plate nuts from the axle housing.
7 Pull the axle and brake assembly away from the axle housing. If necessary, attach a slide hammer to the axle flange to accomplish this.
8 Slide the axle out of the housing, being careful not to damage the seal or the splines on the inner end **(see illustration)**.
Sidekick/Tracker
9 Remove the brake backing plate/wheel bearing retainer nuts from the axle housing.
10 Check to make sure there is enough clearance between the bearing retainer and the parking brake lever to allow the bearing retainer to pass through **(see illustration)**. If there isn't, pry the parking brake lever back while performing the next Step.

8

18.8   After breaking the axleshaft loose, detach the puller and slide the axle assembly out of the housing, being careful not to damage the axle seal or splines (Samurai)

11   Remove the axleshaft from the housing. If it won't come out, attach a slide hammer to the axle flange and pull the axle from the housing, being careful not to pull the brake backing plate along with the axleshaft.

Inspection

12   If the axle bearing must be replaced, take the assembly to a dealer service department or repair shop to have the old bearing removed and a new one pressed on. If a new bearing is installed, be sure to also replace the axleshaft oil seal (see Section 20).

Installation

13   Wipe the bearing bore in the axle housing clean. Apply a thin coat of grease to the outer surface of the bearing.
14   Smear the lips of the axleshaft seal with grease, then guide the axle straight into the axle housing, being careful not to damage the seal.
15   Installation is the reverse of the removal procedure. Be sure to tighten the brake backing plate/bearing retainer nuts to the torque listed in this Chapter's Specifications. On Samurai models, bleed the brakes as described in Chapter 9.

---

19   Rear axle housing – removal and installation

Refer to illustration 19.12

Removal

1   Loosen the rear wheel lug nuts, raise the vehicle and support it securely on jackstands placed underneath the frame. Remove the wheels.
2   Support the rear axle assembly with a floor jack placed underneath the differential.
3   Disconnect the driveshaft from the differential pinion shaft yoke and hang the rear of the driveshaft from the underbody with a piece of wire (see Section 10).
4   Disconnect the parking brake cables from the levers on the backing plates (Samurai) or from the equalizer (Sidekick/Tracker) (see Chapter 9).
5   Disconnect the flexible brake hose from the junction block on the rear axle housing. Plug the end of the hose or wrap a plastic bag tightly around it to prevent excessive fluid loss and contamination.

Samurai

6   Remove the shock absorber lower mounting nuts and compress the shocks to get them out of the way (see Chapter 10).
7   Remove the U-bolt nuts from the leaf spring plates (see Chapter 10).
8   Raise the rear axle assembly slightly, then unbolt the springs from the

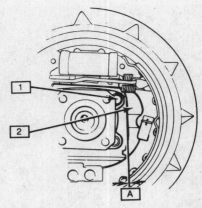

18.10   Before pulling the axleshaft be sure there is enough clearance between the wheel bearing retainer and parking brake lever – if there isn't, pry the lever back (Sidekick/Tracker)

A	Clearance	1	Bearing retainer
		2	Parking brake lever

shackles (see Chapter 10) and lower the rear ends of the springs to the floor.
9   Lower the jack and move the axle assembly out from under the vehicle.

Sidekick/Tracker

10   Disconnect the breather hose from the axle housing.
11   Unbolt the upper arm from the differential housing (**see illustration 17.8**).
12   Loosen the trailing rod nuts, but don't remove them yet (**see illustration**).
13   Remove the coil springs (see Chapter 10).
14   Remove the trailing rod nuts and bolts. Lower the jack and move the axle assembly out from under the vehicle.

Installation (all models)

15   Installation is the reverse of the removal procedure. Be sure to tighten the fasteners torque values listed in this Chapter's Specifications and the Chapter 10 Specifications, where applicable.

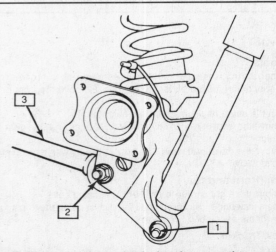

19.12   Trailing rod and rear shock absorber mounting arrangement

1   Rear shock absorber
2   Trailing rod-to-rear axle housing nut and bolt
3   Trailing rod

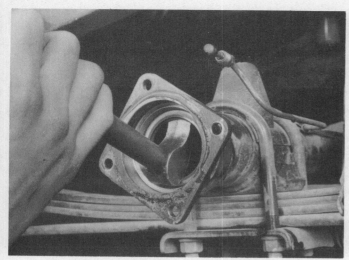

20.2   Pry out the seal, being careful not to damage the axle housing

20.4   To install the axle seal, use a large socket, piece of pipe or seal installation tool

21.2   Before removing the hub cover, apply match marks

21.4   Using snap-ring pliers, remove the snap-ring from the end of the axle

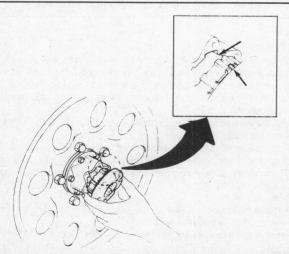

21.8   When installing the hub cover, make sure the two follower stopper nails fit freely into the grooves of the body assembly

20   Rear axle oil seal – replacement

Refer to illustrations 20.2 and 20.4

1   Remove the axleshaft (see Section 18).

2   Remove the axle seal with a pry bar or seal removal tool **(see illustration)**.

3   Wipe the seal bore in the axle housing clean, then apply a coat of grease to the seal lips.

4   Install the seal with a large socket or piece of pipe **(see illustration)**.

5   Install the axleshaft.

21   Freewheel hub – removal and installation

1   Raise the front of the vehicle and place it securely on jackstands.

Manual locking hubs

Refer to illustrations 21.2, 21.4 and 21.8

2   Set the hub cover to the Free position and apply match marks between the cover and hub body **(see illustration)**

3   Remove the hub cover mounting bolts and pull off the cover along with the clutch.

8

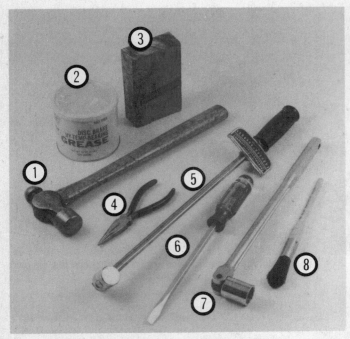

22.1   Tools and materials needed for front wheel bearing maintenance

1   *Hammer* – A common hammer will do just fine
2   *Grease* – High-temperature grease which is formulated specially for front wheel bearings should be used
3   *Wood block* – If you have a scrap piece of 2x4, it can be used to drive the new seal into the hub
4   *Needle-nose pliers* – Used to straighten and remove the cotter pin in the spindle
5   *Torque wrench* – This is very important in this procedure; if the bearing is too tight, the wheel won't turn freely – if it's too loose, the wheel will "wobble" on the spindle. Either way, it could mean extensive damage.
6   *Screwdriver* – Used to remove the seal from the hub (a long screwdriver would be preferred)
7   *Socket/breaker bar* – Needed to loosen the nut on the spindle if it's extremely tight
8   *Brush* – Together with some clean solvent, this will be used to remove old grease from the hub and spindle

4   Using snap-ring pliers, remove the snap-ring from the end of the axle **(see illustration)**.
5   Remove the mounting nuts from the freewheel hub body.
6   Pull the freewheel hub body from the wheel hub.
7   Installation is the reverse of the removal procedure. Use new gaskets and apply multi-purpose grease to the inner hub splines. The control handle should be set to the Free position and the cover should be attached to the body with the match marks aligned.
8   If match marks were not made or were wiped off during cleaning, align the cover to hub body so the two stopper nails fit freely into the wide slots in the hub body **(see illustration)**.

Automatic locking hubs

9   Remove the front hub cover.
10   Remove the circlip with a pair of snap-ring pliers **(see illustration 21.4)**.
11   Remove the bolts and remove the drive flange.
12   Installation is the reverse of removal.

22.7a   With a hammer and chisel, bend back the locking tabs

22.7b   Loosen the front wheel bearing locknut with a large socket

22   Front wheel bearing check, repack and adjustment

Check
Refer to illustration 22.1
1   In most cases the front wheel bearings will not need servicing until the brake pads are changed. However, the bearings should be checked whenever the front of the vehicle is raised for any reason. Several items, including a torque wrench and special grease, are required for this procedure **(see illustration)**.
2   With the vehicle securely supported on jackstands, spin each wheel and check for noise, rolling resistance and free play.
3   Grasp the top of each tire with one hand and the bottom with the other. Move the wheel in-and-out on the spindle. If there's any noticeable movement, the bearings should be checked and then repacked with grease or replaced if necessary.
4   Remove the wheel.
5   Remove the brake caliper and disc (see Chapter 9). Hang the caliper out of the way with a piece of wire.
6   Remove the freewheeling hub assembly (see Section 21).

Samurai
Refer to illustrations 22.7a, 22.7b, 22.8 and 22.11
7   Straighten the bent ends of the lock washer, then remove the wheel bearing locknut **(see illustrations)**.

22.8   Remove the wheel bearing locknut, lock washer, wheel bearing nut and spacer

22.11   Use a screwdriver to pry the grease seal out of the hub

8   Remove the wheel bearing nut and spacer from the end of the spindle **(see illustration)**.

9   Pull the hub assembly out slightly, then push it back into its original position. This should force the outer bearing off the spindle enough so it can be removed.

10   Pull the hub off the spindle.

11   Use a screwdriver to pry the seal out of the rear of the hub **(see illustration)**. As this is done, note how the seal is installed.

12   Remove the inner wheel bearing from the hub.

Sidekick/Tracker

Refer to illustrations 22.13 and 22.17

13   Remove the front wheel bearing lock plate by removing the four screws **(see illustration)**.

14   Remove the front wheel bearing locknut and thrust washer.

15   Remove the hub assembly from the spindle.

16   Use a screwdriver to pry out the inner wheel bearing seal.

17   Using a pair of snap-ring pliers, remove the wheel bearing snap-ring followed by the bearing assembly **(see illustration)**. It may be necessary to have the bearing assembly pressed from the hub.

Repack and adjustment

Samurai

Refer to illustration 22.20

18   Use solvent to remove all traces of the old grease from the bearings, hub and spindle. A small brush may prove helpful; however make sure no bristles from the brush break off inside the bearing. Allow the parts to air dry.

19   Carefully inspect the bearings for cracks, heat discoloration, worn rollers, etc. Check the bearing races inside the hub for wear and damage. If the bearing races are defective, the hubs should be taken to a machine shop with the facilities to remove the old races and press new ones in. Note that the bearings and races come as matched sets and old bearings should never be installed on new races.

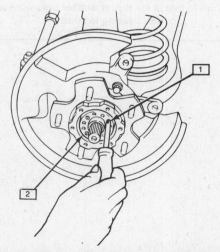

22.13   Remove the four screws to detach the front wheel bearing lock plate (Sidekick/Tracker)

1   *Screw*   2   *Bearing lock plate*

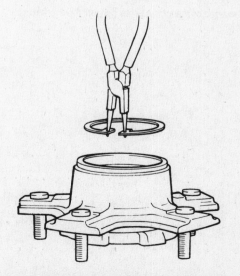

22.17   Remove the wheel bearing snap-ring

8

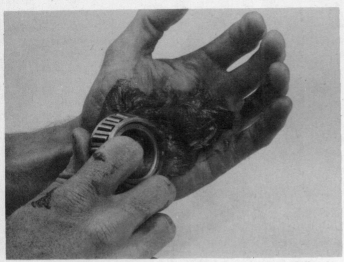

22.20 Work the grease into each bearing until it's full

20   Use high-temperature front wheel bearing grease to pack the bearings. Work the grease completely into the bearings, forcing it between the rollers, cone and cage from the back side **(see illustration)**.
21   Apply a thin coat of grease to the spindle at the outer bearing seat, inner bearing seat, shoulder and seal seat.
22   Put a small quantity of grease inboard of each bearing race inside the hub. Using your finger, form a dam at these points to provide extra grease availability and to keep thinned grease from flowing out of the bearing.
23   Place the grease-packed inner bearing into the rear of the hub.
24   Place a new seal over the inner bearing and tap the seal evenly into place with a hammer and block of wood or a large socket until it's flush with the hub.
25   Carefully place the hub assembly onto the spindle and push the grease-packed outer bearing into position.
26   Install the spacer and wheel bearing nut.
27   Tighten the nut to 57 ft-lbs while spinning the hub by hand. Spin the hub in a forward direction a few more times to seat the bearings and remove any grease or burrs which could cause excessive bearing play later.
28   Loosen the spindle nut until it's just loose, no more.
29   Using a torque wrench, tighten the nut to the torque listed in this Chapter's Specifications. Install the lock washer and the wheel bearing locknut.
30   Tighten the locknut to the torque listed in this Chapter's Specifications.
31   Bend the ends of the lock washer up until they're flat against the locknut.

Sidekick/Tracker
Refer to illustration 22.36
32   Lubricate the the wheel bearing assembly with high temperature wheel bearing grease. Install the bearing into the hub, followed by the snap-ring.
33   Install the hub seal and wheel bearing seal and coat the lips of the seals with wheel bearing grease.
34   Pack the area behind the seal lips with wheel bearing grease, and apply a light coat of the same grease to the spindle.
35   Install the hub assembly on the spindle.
36   Install the spindle thrust washer **(see illustration)**.
37   Install the wheel bearing locknut and tighten it to the torque listed in this Chapter's Specifications.
38   Install the bearing lock plate and screws. If the screw holes don't line up, tighten the wheel bearing nut a little more until they are aligned.

Installation (all models)
39   Install the brake disc and caliper (see Chapter 9).
40   Install the freewheeling hub (see Section 21).
41   Install the tire/wheel assembly on the hub and tighten the lug nuts to the torque listed in the Chapter 1 Specifications.
42   Grasp the top and bottom of the tire and check the bearings in the manner described earlier in this Section.
43   Lower the vehicle.

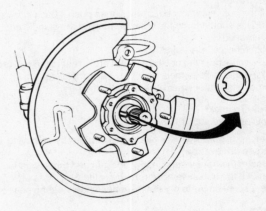

22.36   Be sure to install the thrust washer before installing the wheel bearing locknut

Chapter 9 Brakes

Contents

9

Specifications

General

Brake fluid type . . . . See Chapter 1
Brake light switch plunger clearance . . . . 1/64 to 1/32-inch (1/2 to 1 mm)

Disc brakes

Disc standard thickness . . . . 0.394 in (10.0 mm)
Disc minimum thickness* . . . . 0.315 in (8.0 mm)
Disc runout (maximum) . . . . 0.006 in (0.15 mm)
Brake pad minimum thickness . . . . See Chapter 1
* Refer to marks cast in the rotor (they supersede information printed here)

Drum brakes
Drum standard diameter . . . .   8.66 in (220 mm)
Drum maximum diameter* . . . .   8.74 in (222 mm)
Minimum brake lining thickness . . . .   See Chapter 1
Refer to marks cast in the drum (they supersede information printed here)

Parking brake lever travel
Samurai . . . .   3 to 8 clicks
Sidekick and Tracker . . . .   7 to 9 clicks

Power brake booster
Booster-to-master cylinder clearance . . . .   0.010 to 0.020 in (0.25 to 0.50 mm)
Booster pushrod length . . . .   4.94 to 4.98 in (125.5 to 126.5 mm)

Torque specifications   Ft-lbs
Brake bleeder screw   8
Power brake booster mounting nuts . . . .   7 to 12
Master cylinder mounting nuts . . . .   7 to 12
Caliper mounting bolts
    Samurai . . . .   18 to 20
    Sidekick and Tracker . . . .   36 to 57
Caliper holder bolts . . . .   29 to 43
Brake hose-to-caliper inlet fitting bolt . . . .   14 to 18
Wheel cylinder mounting bolts . . . .   6 to 9

1   General information

The vehicles covered by this manual are equipped with hydraulically operated front and rear brake systems. The front brakes are disc type and the rear brakes are drum type. Both the front and rear brakes are self adjusting. The front disc brakes automatically compensate for pad wear, while the rear drum brakes incorporate an adjustment mechanism which is activated as the brakes are applied when the vehicle is driven in reverse.

Hydraulic system
The hydraulic system consists of two separate circuits. The master cylinder has separate reservoirs for the two circuits and in the event of a leak or failure in one hydraulic circuit, the other circuit will remain operative. A visual warning of circuit failure or air in the system is given by a warning light activated by displacement of the piston in the pressure differential switch portion of the combination valve from its normal "in balance" position.

Proportioning and bypass valve (Samurai only)
A proportioning and bypass valve, located in the engine compartment below the master cylinder, consists of three sections providing the following functions. The metering section limits pressure to the front brakes until a predetermined front input pressure is reached and until the rear brakes are activated. There is no restriction at inlet pressures below 3 psi, allowing pressure equalization during non-braking periods. The proportioning section proportions outlet pressure to the rear brakes after a predetermined rear input pressure has been reached, preventing early rear wheel lock-up under heavy brake loads. The valve is also designed to assure full pressure to one brake system should the other system fail.

Load sensing proportioning valve (LSPV) – Sidekick and Tracker only
The LSPV is included within the hydraulic circuit which connects the master cylinder and the rear brakes. The LSPV controls the hydraulic pressure applied to the rear brakes according to the loaded state of the vehicle, preventing the rear wheels from locking prematurely.

If pressure drops in the front brake hydraulic circuit, the LSPV releases this control over the rear brake hydraulic pressure. This allows maximum braking effort at the rear if the front brakes fail.

Power brake booster
The power brake booster, utilizing engine manifold vacuum and atmospheric pressure to provide assistance to the hydraulically operated brakes, is mounted on the firewall in the engine compartment.

Parking brake
The parking brake operates the rear brakes only, through cable actuation. It's activated by a lever located between the front seats.

Service
After completing any operation involving disassembly of any part of the brake system, always test drive the vehicle to check for proper braking performance before resuming normal driving. When testing the brakes, perform the tests on a clean, dry flat surface. Conditions other than these can lead to inaccurate test results.

Test the brakes at various speeds with both light and heavy pedal pressure. The vehicle should stop evenly without pulling to one side or the other. Avoid locking the brakes because this slides the tires and diminishes braking efficiency and control of the vehicle.

Tires, vehicle load and front-end alignment are factors which also affect braking performance.

2   Disc brake pads – replacement (Samurai)

Refer to illustrations 2.5 and 2.6a through 2.6h
Warning: *Disc brake pads must be replaced on both front wheels at the same time – never replace the pads on only one wheel. Also, the dust created by the brake system may contain asbestos, which is harmful to your health. Never blow it out with compressed air and don't inhale any of it. An approved filtering mask should be worn when working on the brakes. Do not, under any circumstances, use petroleum-based solvents to clean brake parts. Use brake cleaner or denatured alcohol only!*
Note: *When servicing the disc brakes, use only high quality, nationally recognized name brand pads.*
1   Remove the cover from the brake fluid reservoir.
2   Loosen the wheel lug nuts, raise the front of the vehicle and support it securely on jackstands.

2.5 Using a large C-clamp, push the piston back into the caliper bore – note that one end of the clamp is on the flat area on the back side of the caliper and the other end (screw end) is pressing against the outer brake pad.

2.6a Before removing the caliper, wash off all traces of brake dust with brake system cleaner

2.6b Using a screwdriver, remove the anti-rattle clip

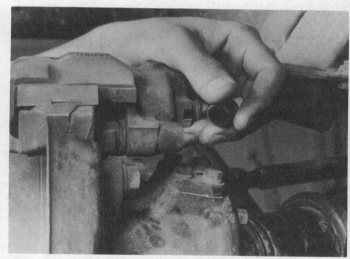

2.6c Remove the rubber caps to gain access to the caliper bolts

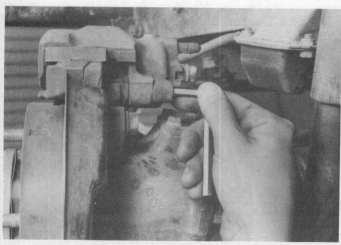

2.6d Using a 6 mm Allen wrench, unscrew the two caliper mounting bolts

3   Remove the front wheels. Work on one brake assembly at a time, using the assembled brake for reference if necessary.

4   Inspect the brake disc carefully as outlined in Section 5. If machining is necessary, follow the information in that Section to remove the disc, at which time the pads can be removed from the calipers as well.

5   Push the piston back into the bore to provide room for the new brake pads. A C-clamp can be used to accomplish this (see illustration). As the piston is depressed to the bottom of the caliper bore, the fluid in the master cylinder will rise. Make sure it doesn't overflow. If necessary, siphon off some of the fluid.

6   Follow the accompanying illustrations, beginning with 2.6a, for the actual pad replacement procedure. Be sure to stay in order and read the caption under each illustration. Before installing the new brake pads, it's a good idea to apply anti-squeal compound to the backing plates. Follow the manufacturer's instructions.

7   When reinstalling the caliper, be sure to tighten the mounting bolts to the specified torque. After the job has been completed, firmly depress the brake pedal a few times to bring the pads into contact with the disc.

8   Check for fluid leakage and make sure the brakes operate normally before driving in traffic.

9

2.6e   **Using a screwdriver, remove the pad protector clips and lift off the caliper**

2.6f   **Pull the inner pad straight out, disengaging the retainer spring from the caliper piston**

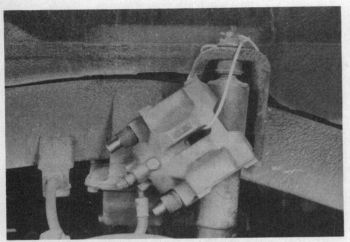

2.6g   **Hang the caliper with a piece of wire – DON'T let it hang by the brake hose**

2.6h   **Slide the outer brake pad out of the caliper holder – as you do this, note how it fits into the frame so you can install the new one the same way**

3   Disc brake pads – replacement (Sidekick/Tracker)

Refer to illustrations 3.6a through 3.6d

Warning: *Disc brake pads must be replaced on both front wheels at the same time – never replace the pads on only one wheel. Also, the dust created by the brake system may contain asbestos, which is harmful to your health. Never blow it out with compressed air and don't inhale any of it. An approved filtering mask should be worn when working on the brakes. Do not, under any circumstances, use petroleum-based solvents to clean brake parts. Use brake cleaner or denatured alcohol only!*

Note: *When servicing the disc brakes, use only high quality, nationally recognized name brand pads.*

1   Remove the cover from the brake fluid reservoir.
2   Loosen the wheel lug nuts, raise the front of the vehicle and support it securely on jackstands.
3   Remove the front wheels. Work on one brake assembly at a time, using the assembled brake for reference if necessary.
4   Inspect the brake disc carefully as outlined in Section 5. If machining is necessary, follow the information in that Section to remove the disc, at which time the pads can be removed from the calipers as well.
5   Push the piston back into the bore to provide room for the new brake pads. A C-clamp can be used to accomplish this **(see illustration 2.5)**. As the piston is depressed to the bottom of the caliper bore, the fluid in the

master cylinder will rise. Make sure it doesn't overflow. If necessary, siphon off some of the fluid.
6   Before removing the caliper, wash off all traces of brake dust with brake system cleaner **(see illustration 2.6a)**. Follow the accompanying

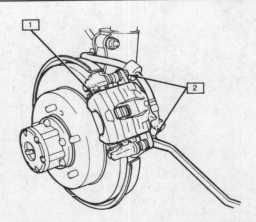

3.6a   **Using a box end wrench, unscrew the two caliper mounting bolts (2) and lift the caliper (1) off**

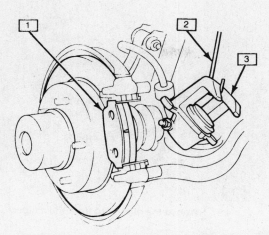

3.6b   Once the caliper is removed, hang it with a piece of wire – DON'T let it hang by the brake hose

1   Brake pad
2   Piece of wire
3   Caliper

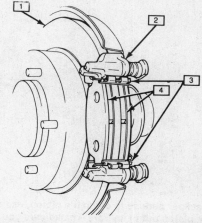

3.6c   Remove one pad at a time, noting how they are retained – check the anti-rattle clips for any damage and replace as necessary

1   Brake disc
2   Caliper mounting plate
3   Anti-rattle clips
4   Brake pads

illustrations, beginning with 3.6a, for the actual pad replacement procedure. Be sure to stay in order and read the caption under each illustration. Before installing the new brake pads, it's a good idea to apply anti-squeal compound to the backing plates. Follow the manufacturer's instructions.
7   When reinstalling the caliper, be sure to tighten the mounting bolts to the specified torque. After the job has been completed, firmly depress the brake pedal a few times to bring the pads into contact with the disc.
8   Check for fluid leakage and make sure the brakes operate normally before driving in traffic.

4   Disc brake caliper – removal, overhaul and installation

Warning: *Dust created by the brake system may contain asbestos, which is harmful to your health. Never blow it out with compressed air and don't inhale any of it. An approved filtering mask should be worn when working on the brakes. Do not, under any circumstances, use petroleum-based solvents to clean brake parts. Use brake cleaner or denatured alcohol only!*

Note: *If an overhaul is indicated (usually because of fluid leakage) explore all options before beginning the job. New and factory rebuilt calipers are available on an exchange basis, which makes this job quite easy. If it's decided to rebuild the calipers, make sure a rebuild kit is available before proceeding. Always rebuild the calipers in pairs – never rebuild just one of them.*

Removal
Refer to illustration 4.4
1   Remove the cover from the brake fluid reservoir, siphon off two-thirds of the fluid into a container and discard it.
2   Loosen the wheel lug nuts, raise the front of the vehicle and support it securely on jackstands. Remove the front wheels.
3   Bottom the piston in the caliper bore **(see illustration 2.5)**.
4   **Note:** *Do not remove the brake hose from the caliper if you are only removing the caliper.* Remove the brake hose inlet fitting bolt and detach the hose **(see illustration)**. Have a rag handy to catch spilled fluid and wrap a plastic bag tightly around the end of the hose to prevent fluid loss and contamination.
5   Remove the two mounting bolts and detach the caliper from the vehicle (refer to Section 2 or 3 if necessary).

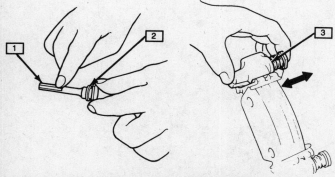

3.6d   Check to be sure the caliper guide pins slide in and out easily – if they don't, check for bending and corrosion – apply a little silicone grease to them so they'll slide more easily

1   Guide pin
2   Bushing
3   Caliper mounting plate

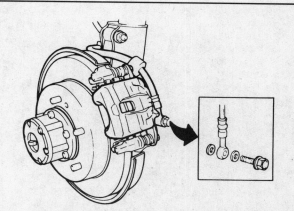

4.4   Location of the brake hose inlet fitting bolt – when reinstalling the bolt, be sure to use new sealing washers on each side of the fitting to prevent fluid leaks

9

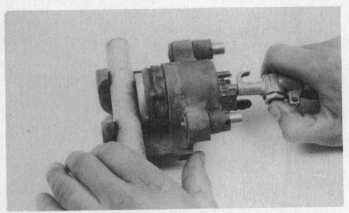

4.8 With the caliper padded to catch the piston, use compressed air to force the piston out of its bore – make sure your hands and fingers are not between the piston and caliper frame!

Overhaul

Refer to illustrations 4.8, 4.9, 4.10, 4.11, 4.15, 4.17 and 4.18

6   Refer to Section 2 and remove the brake pads from the caliper.
7   Clean the exterior of the caliper with brake cleaner or denatured alcohol. Never use gasoline, kerosene or petroleum-based cleaning solvents. Place the caliper on a clean workbench.
8   Position a wooden block or several shop rags in the caliper as a cushion, then use compressed air to remove the piston from the caliper (**see illustration**). Use only enough air pressure to ease the piston out of the bore. If the piston is blown out, even with the cushion in place, it may be damaged. **Warning:** *Never place your fingers in front of the piston in an attempt to catch or protect it when applying compressed air, as serious injury could occur.*
9   Carefully remove the dust boot from the caliper bore (**see illustration**).
10 Using a wood or plastic tool, remove the piston seal from the groove in the caliper bore (**see illustration**). Metal tools may cause bore damage.
11 Remove the caliper bleeder screw, then remove and discard the bushings from the caliper ears. Discard all rubber parts (**see illustration**).
12 Clean the remaining parts with brake system cleaner or denatured alcohol then blow them dry with compressed air.
13 Carefully examine the piston for nicks and burrs and loss of plating. If surface defects are present, the parts must be replaced.
14 Check the caliper bore in a similar way. Light polishing with crocus cloth is permissible to remove light corrosion and stains. Discard the

4.9   Remove the dust boot from the caliper

4.10   The piston seal should be removed with a plastic or wooden tool to avoid damage to the bore and seal groove – a pencil will do the job

mounting bolts if they're corroded or damaged.
15 When assembling, lubricate the piston bores and seal with clean brake fluid. Position the seal in the caliper bore groove (**see illustration**).

4.11   Grab the ends of the mounting pin bushings with needle-nose pliers and, using a twisting motion, push them through the caliper ears

4.15   Push the new seal into the groove with your fingers, then check to see that it is not twisted or kinked

4.17   Position the piston squarely and push it straight into the caliper

4.18   Install the lip of the dust boot in the groove on the piston

5.3   The brake pads on this vehicle were obviously neglected, as they wore down to the rivets and cut deep grooves into the disc – wear this severe will require replacement of the disc

5.4a   Use a dial indicator to check disc runout – if the reading exceeds the maximum allowable runout limit, the disc will have to be machined or replaced

16   Lubricate the piston with clean brake fluid, then install a new boot in the piston groove with the fold toward the open end of the piston.
17   Insert the piston squarely into the caliper bore, then apply force to the piston and move it about half way down (see illustration).
18   Install the lip of the dust boot in the groove on the piston (see illustration). Make sure the boot is recessed evenly below the caliper face. Push the piston the rest of the way down.
19   Install the bleeder screw.
20   Lubricate the new bushings with silicone grease and install them in the mounting bolt holes.

Installation

21   Inspect the mounting bolts for excessive corrosion.
22   Place the caliper in position over the rotor and mounting bracket, install the bolts and tighten them to the specified torque.
23   Install the brake hose and inlet fitting bolt, using new copper washers, then tighten the bolt to the specified torque.
24   If the line was disconnected, be sure to bleed the brakes (Section 11).
25   Install the wheels and lower the vehicle.
26   After the job has been completed, firmly depress the brake pedal a few times to bring the pads into contact with the disc.
27   Check brake operation before driving the vehicle in traffic.

5   Brake disc – inspection, removal and installation

Refer to illustrations 5.3, 5.4a, 5.4b 5.5, 5.6 and 5.7

Inspection

1   Loosen the wheel lug nuts, raise the vehicle and support it securely on jackstands. Remove the wheel and install two lug nuts to hold the disc in place.
2   Remove the brake caliper as outlined in Section 4. It's not necessary to disconnect the brake hose. After removing the caliper bolts, suspend the caliper out of the way with a piece of wire.
3   Visually inspect the disc surface for score marks and other damage. Light scratches and shallow grooves are normal after use and may not always be detrimental to brake operation, but deep score marks – over 0.015-inch (0.38 mm) – require disc removal and refinishing by an automotive machine shop. Be sure to check both sides of the disc (see illustration). If pulsating has been noticed during application of the brakes, suspect disc runout. Be sure to check the wheel bearings to make sure they're properly adjusted.
4   To check disc runout, place a dial indicator at a point about 1/2-inch from the outer edge of the disc (see illustration). Set the indicator to zero

9

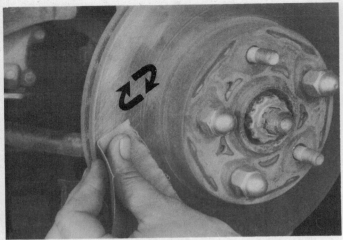

5.4b   Using a swirling motion, remove the glaze from the disc
surface with sandpaper or emery cloth

5.5   Use a micrometer to measure disc thickness

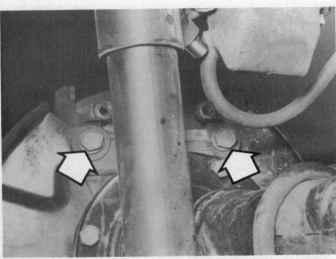

5.6   The caliper holder is secured to the steering knuckle with
two bolts (arrows)

5.7   To help free the disc, thread bolts of the appropriate size into
the two holes provided in the disc – alternate between the bolts,
turning them a little at a time, until the disc is free

and turn the disc. The indicator reading should not exceed the specified allowable runout limit. If it does, the disc should be refinished by an automotive machine shop. **Note:** *Professionals recommend resurfacing of brake discs regardless of the dial indicator reading (to produce a smooth, flat surface that will eliminate brake pedal pulsations and other undesirable symptoms related to questionable discs). At the very least, if you elect not to have the discs resurfaced, deglaze them with sandpaper or emery cloth (use a swirling motion to ensure a nondirectional finish)* **(see illustration)**.

5   The disc must not be machined to a thickness less than the minimum thickness cast into the inside of the disc. The disc thickness can be checked with a micrometer **(see illustration)**. If the minimum thickness is not cast into the disc, refer to this Chapter's Specifications.

Removal

6   Remove the two caliper holder-to-steering knuckle bolts and remove the holder **(see illustration)**.
7   Remove the two lug nuts which were put on to hold the disc in place and remove the disc from the hub. If the disc is stuck to the hub and won't come off, thread two bolts into the holes provided **(see illustration)**.

Installation

8   Place the disc in position over the threaded studs.
9   Install the caliper holder and tighten the bolts to the torque listed in this Chapter's Specifications.
10   Install the caliper and brake pad assembly over the disc and position it on the steering knuckle (refer to Section 4 for the caliper installation procedure, if necessary). Tighten the caliper bolts to the torque listed in this Chapter's Specifications.
11   Install the wheel, then lower the vehicle to the ground. Depress the brake pedal a few times to bring the brake pads into contact with the disc. Bleeding of the system will not be necessary unless the brake hose was disconnected from the caliper. Check the operation of the brakes carefully before placing the vehicle into normal service.

6   Drum brake shoes – replacement

Refer to illustrations 6.4a through 6.4u
Warning: *Drum brake shoes must be replaced on both wheels at the same time – never replace the shoes on only one wheel. Also, the dust*

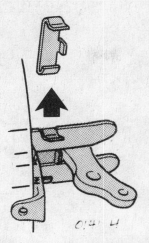

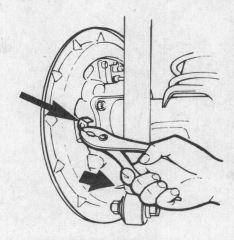

6.4a   To retract the brake shoes on Samurai models, disconnect the parking brake cable (Section 14), then remove the stopper plate, as shown

6.4b   To retract the brake shoes on Sidekick and Tracker models, pull the hold-down pin down about 1/4-inch (arrow)

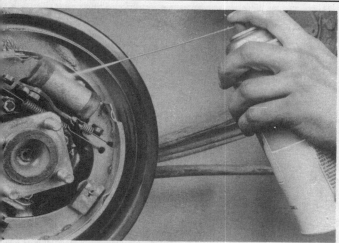

6.4c   Before removing anything, clean the brake assembly with brake cleaner and allow it to dry – position a drain pan under the brake to catch the fluid and residue – DO NOT USE COMPRESSED AIR TO BLOW THE DUST FROM THE PARTS!

created by the brake system may contain asbestos, which is harmful to your health. Never blow it out with compressed air and don't inhale any of it. An approved filtering mask should be worn when working on the brakes. Do not, under any circumstances, use petroleum-based solvents to clean brake parts. Use brake cleaner or denatured alcohol only!

Caution: Whenever the brake shoes are replaced, the retractor and hold-down springs should also be replaced. Due to the continuous heating/cooling cycle that the springs are subjected to, they lose their tension over a period of time and may allow the shoes to drag on the drum and wear at a much faster rate than normal. When replacing the rear brake shoes, use only high quality nationally recognized brand-name parts.

1   Loosen the wheel lug nuts, raise the rear of the vehicle and support it securely on jackstands. Block the front wheels to keep the vehicle from rolling.
2   Release the parking brake.
3   Remove the wheel. **Note:** All four rear brake shoes must be replaced at the same time, but to avoid mixing up parts, work on only one brake assembly at a time.
4   Follow the accompanying illustrations (6.4a through 6.4u) for the inspection and replacement of the brake shoes. Be sure to stay in order and read the caption under each illustration. **Note:** If the brake drum cannot be easily pulled off the axle and shoe assembly (see Chapter 1), make sure

9

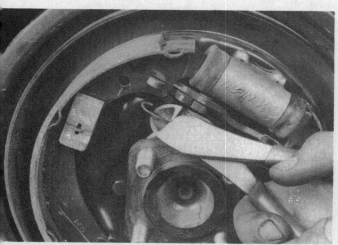

6.4d   Using a pair of pliers, unhook the long return spring from the front brake shoe, . . .

6.4e . . . then remove the short return spring

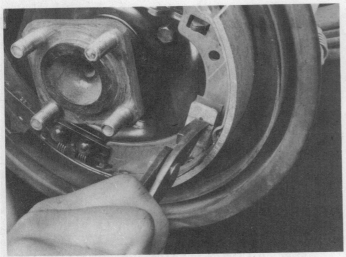

6.4f   On the rear shoe, using a pair of pliers, push in on the hold-down spring, turn it 90-degrees and release it

6.4g   Unhook the rear shoe from the brake strut rod (arrow)

that the parking brake is completely released, then apply some penetrating oil at the hub-to-drum joint. Allow the oil to soak in and try to pull the drum off. If the drum still cannot be pulled off, the brake shoes will have to be retracted. On Samurai models, to retract the brake shoes, disconnect the parking brake cable (Section 14) then remove the parking brake lever stopper plate (see illustration). On Sidekick and Tracker models, to retract the brake shoes, pull the shoe hold down pin about 1/4-inch (see illustration). The drum should now come off.

5   Before reinstalling the drum it should be checked for cracks, score marks, deep scratches and hard spots, which will appear as small discolored areas. If the hard spots cannot be removed with fine emery cloth or if any of the other conditions listed above exist, the drum must be taken to an automotive machine shop to have it turned. **Note:** Professionals recommend resurfacing the drums whenever a brake job is done. Resurfacing will eliminate the possibility of out-of-round drums. If the drums are worn so much that they can't be resurfaced without exceeding the maximum allowable diameter (stamped into the drum), then new ones will be required. At the very least, if you elect not to have the drums resurfaced, remove the glazing from the surface with medium-grit emery cloth using a swirling motion.

6.4h   Unhook the shoe return spring from the front brake shoe

6.4i   On Sidekick and Tracker models, grasp the end of the parking brake cable with a pair of pliers and pull it out of the parking brake lever

6.4j   On Sidekick and Tracker models, pry the C-washer apart and remove it to separate the parking brake lever and adjusting lever from the rear shoe

6.4k   Using a pair of pliers, remove the hold-down spring on the front shoe

6.4l   Unhook the front shoe from the brake strut

6.4m   Lubricate the brake shoe contact areas with high-temperature grease

6.4n   On Sidekick and Tracker models, assemble the parking brake lever and adjuster lever on the new rear shoe and crimp the C washer closed with a pair of pliers

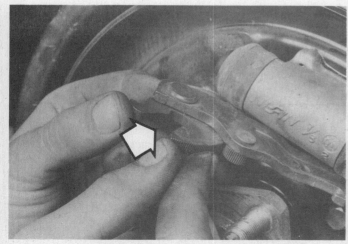

6.4o   Push the brake strut lever in about halfway

6.4p   Hook the new front shoe on the brake strut and install the hold-down spring

9

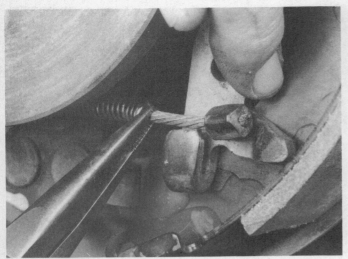

6.4q   On Sidekick and Tracker models, pull the parking brake cable spring back and hold it there with a pair of pliers, then place the cable into the hooked end of the parking brake lever

6.4r   Connect the shoe return spring to both shoes and make sure the spring and shoe is installed behind the anchor plate

6.4s   Hook the rear shoe to the brake strut and install the hold-down spring – hook the long and short return springs to both shoes

6.4t   If the brake drum won't go on after replacing the shoes, it may be necessary to retract the shoes – put a screwdriver between the two parts of the ratchet and push in – spring pressure will retract the shoes

6   Install the brake drum on the axle flange.
7   Mount the wheel, install the lug nuts, then lower the vehicle.
8   Make a number of forward and reverse stops to adjust the brakes until satisfactory pedal action is obtained.
9   Check brake operation before driving the vehicle in traffic.

7   Wheel cylinder – removal, overhaul and installation

Note: *If an overhaul is indicated (usually because of fluid leakage or sticky operation) explore all options before beginning the job. New wheel cylinders are available, which makes this job quite easy. If it's decided to rebuild the wheel cylinder, make sure that a rebuild kit is available before proceeding. Never overhaul only one wheel cylinder – always rebuild both of them at the same time.*

Removal
Refer to illustration 7.4

1   Raise the rear of the vehicle and support it securely on jackstands. Block the front wheels to keep the vehicle from rolling.

6.4u   Wiggle the brake assembly (arrows) to make sure it's seated properly against the backing plate

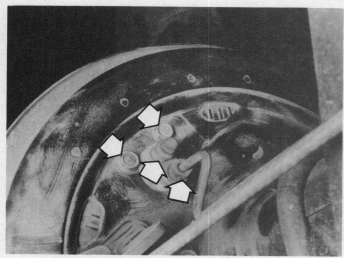

7.4 Remove the brake bleeder screw and the brake line fitting, then remove the two wheel cylinder bolts (arrows)

2 Remove the brake shoe assembly (Section 6).
3 Remove all dirt and foreign material from around the wheel cylinder.
4 Unscrew the bleeder screw and the brake line fitting (**see illustration**). Don't pull the brake line away from the wheel cylinder.
5 Remove the wheel cylinder mounting bolts.
6 Detach the wheel cylinder from the brake backing plate and place it on a clean workbench. Immediately plug the brake line to prevent fluid loss and contamination. **Note:** *If the brake shoe linings are contaminated with brake fluid, install new brake shoes.*

Overhaul

Refer to illustration 7.7
7 Remove the, cups, pistons, boots and spring assembly from the wheel cylinder body (**see illustration**).
8 Clean the wheel cylinder with brake fluid, denatured alcohol or brake system cleaner. **Warning:** *Do not, under any circumstances, use petroleum based solvents to clean brake parts!*
9 Use compressed air to remove excess fluid from the wheel cylinder and to blow out the passages.
10 Check the cylinder bore for corrosion and score marks. Crocus cloth can be used to remove light corrosion and stains, but the cylinder must be replaced with a new one if the defects cannot be removed easily, or if the bore is scored.
11 Lubricate the new cups with brake fluid.
12 Assemble the wheel cylinder components. Make sure the cup lips face in (**see illustration 7.7**).

Installation

13 Place the wheel cylinder in position and install the bolts. Tighten them to the torque listed in this Chapter's Specifications.
14 Connect the bleeder screw and the brake line and tighten the fitting. Install the brake shoe assembly.
15 Bleed the brakes (Section 11).
16 Check brake operation before driving the vehicle in traffic.

8 Master cylinder – removal, overhaul and installation

Refer to illustrations 8.4, 8.6, 8.8a, 8.8b, 8.9, 8.10, 8.11a, 8.11b and 8.11c
Note: *Before deciding to overhaul the master cylinder, check on the availability and cost of a new or factory rebuilt unit and also the availability of a rebuild kit.*

Removal

1 The master cylinder is located in the engine compartment, mounted to the power brake booster.

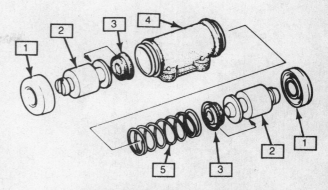

7.7 Exploded view of the wheel cylinder

1 Boot
2 Piston
3 Cups
4 Wheel cylinder body
5 Spring

2 Remove as much fluid as you can from the reservoir with a syringe.
3 Place rags under the fluid fittings and prepare caps or plastic bags to cover the ends of the lines once they are disconnected. **Caution:** *Brake fluid will damage paint. Cover all body parts and be careful not to spill fluid during this procedure.*
4 Loosen the tube nuts at the ends of the brake lines where they enter the master cylinder (**see illustration**). To prevent rounding off the flats on these nuts, the use of a flare nut wrench, which wraps around the nut, is preferred.
5 Pull the brake lines slightly away from the master cylinder and plug the ends to prevent contamination.
6 Disconnect the electrical connector at the master cylinder, then remove the two nuts attaching the master cylinder to the power booster (**see illustration**). Pull the master cylinder off the studs and out of the engine compartment. Again, be careful not to spill the fluid as this is done.

Overhaul

7 Before attempting the overhaul of the master cylinder, obtain the proper rebuild kit, which will contain the necessary replacement parts and also any instructions which may be specific to your model.

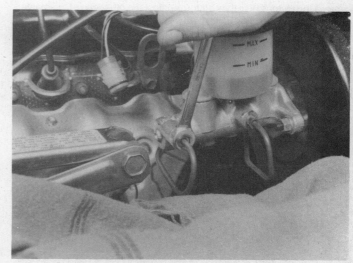

8.4 Disconnect the brake lines from the master cylinder – a flare nut wrench should be used

8.6   After disconnecting the electrical connector and the brake lines, remove the two master cylinder mounting nuts (arrows)

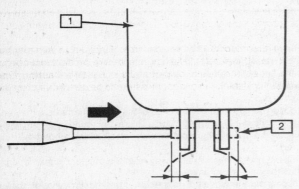

8.8b   On Sidekick and Tracker models, use a punch and hammer to knock out the connection pin

    1   *Reservoir*   2   *Connection pin*

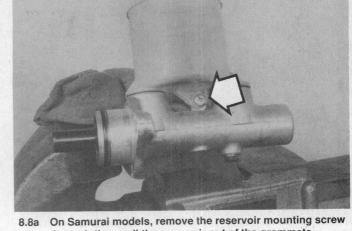

8.8a   On Samurai models, remove the reservoir mounting screw (arrow), then pull the reservoir out of the grommets

8.9   Push the pistons all the way in and remove the piston stop screw

8   Inspect the reservoir grommets for indications of leakage near the base of the reservoir. Remove the reservoir **(see illustrations)**.
9   Place the cylinder in a vise and use a punch or Phillips screwdriver to depress the pistons until they bottom against the other end of the master cylinder **(see illustration)**. Hold the pistons in this position and remove

the stop screw on the side of the master cylinder.
10   Carefully remove the snap-ring at the end of the master cylinder **(see illustration)**.
11   The internal components can now be removed from the cylinder bore **(see illustrations)**. Make a note of the proper order of the components so

8.10   While still holding the pistons in, use snap-ring pliers to remove the snap-ring

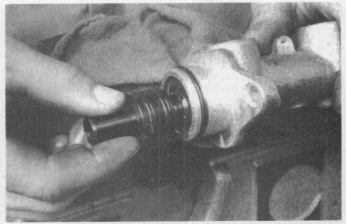

8.11a   Remove the primary piston assembly from the master cylinder bore

8.11b   To remove the secondary piston assembly, tap the master cylinder firmly against a block of wood

they can be returned to their original locations. **Note:** *The two springs are of different tension, so pay particular attention to their order. Also, do not disassemble the piston components – they are serviced as an assembly.*

12   Carefully inspect the bore of the master cylinder. Any deep scoring or other damage will mean a new master cylinder is required.

13   Replace all parts included in the rebuild kit, following any instructions in the kit. Clean all reused parts with clean brake fluid or denatured alcohol. Do not use any petroleum-based cleaners. During assembly, lubricate all parts liberally with clean brake fluid.

14   Push the assembled components into the bore, bottoming them against the end of the master cylinder, then install the stop screw. Be sure to install a new gasket on the stop screw.

15   Install the new snap-ring, making sure it is seated properly in the groove.

16   Before installing the master cylinder it should be bench bled. Because it will be necessary to apply pressure to the master cylinder piston and, at the same time, control flow from the brake line outlets, it is recommended that the master cylinder be mounted in a vise, with the jaws of the vise clamping on the mounting flange. The master cylinder is aluminum, so be careful not to damage it.

17   Insert threaded plugs into the brake line outlet holes and snug them down so that there will be no air leakage past them, but not so tight that they cannot be easily loosened.

18   Fill the reservoir with brake fluid of the recommended type (see Chapter 1).

19   Remove one plug and push the piston assembly into the master cylinder bore to expel the air from the master cylinder. A large Phillips screwdriver can be used to push on the piston assembly.

20   To prevent air from being drawn back into the master cylinder the plug must be replaced and snugged down before releasing the pressure on the piston assembly.

21   Repeat the procedure until only brake fluid is expelled from the brake line outlet hole. When only brake fluid is expelled, repeat the procedure with the other outlet hole and plug. Be sure to keep the master cylinder reservoir filled with brake fluid to prevent the introduction of air into the system.

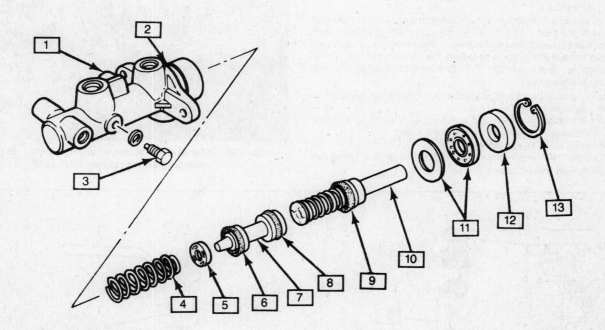

8.11c   Exploded view of the master cylinder components – Sidekick and Tracker models shown, Samurai models similar

1	Master cylinder body	6	Piston cup
2	O-ring	7	Secondary piston
3	Stop screw	8	Secondary piston pressure cup
4	Secondary piston return spring	9	Piston cup
5	Return spring secondary seat	10	Primary piston
		11	Cylinder cup and plate
		12	Piston stopper
		13	Snap-ring

9

22   Since high pressure is not involved in the bench bleeding procedure, an alternative to the removal and replacement of the plugs with each stroke of the piston assembly is available. Before pushing in on the piston assembly, remove the plug as described in Step 19. Before releasing the piston, however, instead of replacing the plug, simply put your finger tightly over the hole to keep air from being drawn back into the master cylinder. Wait several seconds for brake fluid to be drawn from the reservoir into the piston bore, then depress the piston again, removing your finger as brake fluid is expelled. Be sure to put your finger back over the hole each time before releasing the piston, and when the bleeding procedure is complete for that outlet, replace the plug and snug it before going on to the other port.

Installation

23   Install the master cylinder over the studs on the power brake booster and tighten the attaching nuts only finger tight at this time.
24   Thread the brake line fittings into the master cylinder. Since the master cylinder is still a bit loose, it can be moved slightly for the fittings to thread in easily. Do not strip the threads as the fittings are tightened.
25   Tighten the mounting nuts to the torque listed in this Chapter's Specifications, then tighten the fittings securely.
26   Fill the master cylinder reservoir with fluid, then bleed the master cylinder (only if the cylinder has not been bench bled) and the brake system as described in Section 11. To bleed the cylinder on the vehicle, have an assistant pump the brake pedal several times and then hold the pedal to the floor. Loosen the fitting nut to allow air and fluid to escape. Repeat this procedure on both fittings until the fluid is clear of air bubbles. Test the operation of the brake system carefully before placing the vehicle into normal service.

9   Load Sensing Proportioning Valve (LSPV) – removal and installation (Sidekick/Tracker only)

Refer to illustration 9.4
Note: *Special tools, test equipment and skills are required to diagnose problems with the LSPV. The home mechanic should not attempt such diagnosis; take the vehicle to a dealer service department or other properly equipped shop. If the LSPV is defective, the home mechanic can replace it using the procedure below. The LSPV must be replaced as a unit; do not disassemble it.*

1   Remove as much brake fluid as you can from the master cylinder reservoir with a syringe.
2   Raise the rear of the vehicle and support it securely on jackstands. Block the front wheels to keep the vehicle from rolling.
3   Remove the brake lines from the LSPV.
4   Remove the LSPV assembly, along with the load sensing spring and stay, as a unit **(see illustration)**.

5   Before installing the new LSPV, apply multi-purpose grease to the upper and lower joint of the load sensing spring.
6   Installation is the reverse of removal.
7   Fill the master cylinder reservoir with brake fluid and bleed the air from the brake system (see Section 11).

10   Brake hoses and lines – inspection and replacement

Inspection

1   About every six months, with the vehicle raised and supported securely on jackstands, the rubber hoses which connect the steel brake lines with the front and rear brake assemblies should be inspected for cracks, chafing of the outer cover, leaks, blisters and other damage. These are important and vulnerable parts of the brake system and inspection should be complete. A light and mirror will be helpful for a thorough check. If a hose exhibits any of the above conditions, replace it with a new one.

Replacement

Front and rear brake hoses

Refer to illustrations 10.2a, 10.2b and 10.3
2   Disconnect the brake line from the hose fitting on the frame bracket, being careful not to bend the frame bracket or brake line **(see illustrations)**.

10.2a   On Samurai models, use a flare-nut wrench to prevent rounding off the corners of the nut

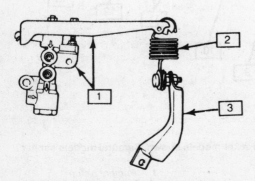

9.4   Typical LSPV assembly

1	LSPV	3	LSPV stay
2	Load sensing spring		

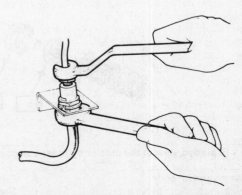

10.2b   On Sidekick and Tracker models, hold the hose fitting with a wrench to prevent twisting the line, then loosen the tube nut with a flare-nut wrench

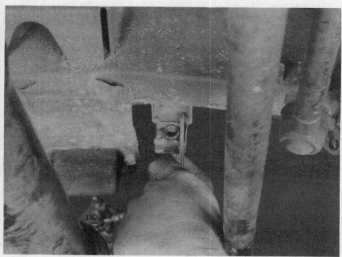

10.3   Using a pair of pliers or a screwdriver, pry the U-clip off the hose

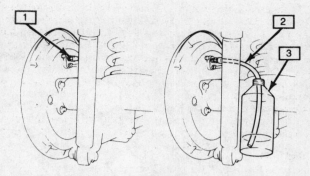

11.8   When bleeding the brakes, a hose is connected to the bleeder screw at the caliper or wheel cylinder and then submerged in brake fluid – air will be seen as bubbles in the tube and container (all air must be expelled before moving to the next wheel)

1	Bleeder screw	3	Container partially filled
2	Hose		with brake fluid

3   Use a pair of pliers or a screwdriver to remove the U-clip from the female fitting at the frame bracket, then detach the hose from the bracket **(see illustration)**.

4   If you are replacing a front brake hose, remove the union bolt from the fitting at the caliper end of the hose, then separate the hose from the caliper. Note that there are two copper sealing washers on either side of the fitting – they should be replaced with new ones upon installation.

5   If you are replacing the rear brake hose, disconnect it at the axle end the same way you disconnected it at the frame end.

6   If you are installing a front hose, pass the caliper fitting end through the bracket, then connect the fitting to the caliper with the union bolt and copper washers. Make sure that the locating lug on the fitting is engaged with the hole in the caliper, then tighten the fitting to the specified torque.

7   To attach a front hose to the frame bracket, or to attach either end of the rear hose, install the female fitting of the hose in the bracket. It will fit the bracket in only one position. Be careful not to twist the hose.

8   Install the U-clip retaining the female fitting to the bracket.

9   Attach the brake line to the hose fitting.

10   When the brake hose installation is complete, there should be no kinks in the hose. Make sure the hose doesn't contact any part of the suspension. Check this by turning the wheels to the extreme left and right positions. If the hose makes contact, remove it and correct the installation as necessary. Bleed the system (Section 11).

Metal brake lines

11   When replacing brake lines be sure to use the correct parts. Don't use copper tubing for any brake system components. Purchase steel brake lines from a dealer or auto parts store.

12   Prefabricated brake line, with the tube ends already flared and fittings installed, is available at auto parts stores and dealers. These lines are also bent to the proper shapes.

13   When installing the new line make sure it's securely supported in the brackets and has plenty of clearance between moving or hot components.

14   After installation, check the master cylinder fluid level and add fluid as necessary. Bleed the brake system as outlined in the next Section and test the brakes carefully before driving the vehicle in traffic.

11   Brake system bleeding

Refer to illustration 11.8

Warning: *Wear eye protection when bleeding the brake system. If the fluid comes in contact with your eyes, immediately rinse them with water and seek medical attention.*

Note: *Bleeding the hydraulic system is necessary to remove any air that*

manages to find its way into the system when it's been opened during removal and installation of a hose, line, caliper or master cylinder.

1   It will probably be necessary to bleed the system at all four brakes if air has entered the system due to low fluid level, or if the brake lines have been disconnected at the master cylinder.

2   If a brake line was disconnected only at a wheel, then only that caliper or wheel cylinder must be bled.

3   If a brake line is disconnected at a fitting located between the master cylinder and any of the brakes, that part of the system served by the disconnected line must be bled.

4   Remove any residual vacuum from the brake power booster by applying the brake several times with the engine off.

5   Remove the master cylinder reservoir cover and fill the reservoir with brake fluid. Reinstall the cover. **Note:** *Check the fluid level often during the bleeding operation and add fluid as necessary to prevent the fluid level from falling low enough to allow air bubbles into the master cylinder.*

6   Have an assistant on hand, as well as a supply of new brake fluid, a clear container partially filled with clean brake fluid, a length of 3/16-inch plastic, rubber or vinyl tubing to fit over the bleeder screw and a wrench to open and close the bleeder screw.

7   Beginning at the left rear wheel, loosen the bleeder screw slightly, then tighten it to a point where it is snug but can still be loosened quickly and easily.

8   Place one end of the tubing over the bleeder screw and submerge the other end in brake fluid in the container **(see illustration)**.

9   Have the assistant pump the brakes slowly a few times to get pressure in the system, then hold the pedal firmly depressed.

10   While the pedal is held depressed, open the bleeder screw just enough to allow a flow of fluid to leave the valve. Watch for air bubbles to exit the submerged end of the tube. When the fluid flow slows after a couple of seconds, tighten the screw and have your assistant release the pedal.

11   Repeat Steps 9 and 10 until no more air is seen leaving the tube, then tighten the bleeder screw and proceed to the right rear wheel on Samurai models or the load sensing proportioning valve on Sidekick and Tracker models (see Section 9). Perform the same procedure, then repeat the procedure at the right front wheel and the left front wheel, in that order. Be sure to check the fluid in the master cylinder reservoir frequently.

12   Never use old brake fluid. It contains moisture which will deteriorate the brake system components.

13   Refill the master cylinder with fluid at the end of the operation.

14   Check the operation of the brakes. The pedal should feel solid when depressed, with no sponginess. If necessary, repeat the entire process.

Warning: *Do not operate the vehicle if you are in doubt about the effectiveness of the brake system.*

9

12.7   Remove the cotter pin and slide out the clevis pin – the booster is fastened to the firewall by four nuts, three of which are visible in this photo (arrows)

12   Power brake booster – check, removal and installation

Refer to illustrations 12.7, 12.12 and 12.13

Operating check

1   Depress the brake pedal several times with the engine off and make sure that there is no change in the pedal reserve distance.
2   Depress the pedal and start the engine. If the pedal goes down slightly, operation is normal.

Air tightness check

3   Start the engine and turn it off after one or two minutes. Depress the brake pedal several times slowly. If the pedal goes down farther the first time but gradually rises after the second or third depression, the booster is air tight.
4   Depress the brake pedal while the engine is running, then stop the engine with the pedal depressed. If there is no change in the pedal reserve travel after holding the pedal for 30 seconds, the booster is air tight.

Removal

5   Power brake booster units should not be disassembled. They require special tools not normally found in most service stations or shops. They are fairly complex and because of their critical relationship to brake performance it is best to replace a defective booster unit with a new or rebuilt one.
6   To remove the booster, first remove the brake master cylinder as described in Section 8.
7   Locate the pushrod clevis connecting the booster to the brake pedal (see illustration). This is accessible from the interior in front of the driver's seat.
8   Remove the cotter pin from the clevis pin with pliers and pull out the pin.
9   Disconnect the hose leading from the engine to the booster. Be careful not to damage the hose when removing it from the booster fitting.
10   Remove the four nuts and washers holding the brake booster to the firewall. You may need a light to see them – they are up under the dash area (see illustration 12.7).
11   Slide the booster straight out from the firewall until the studs clear the holes and pull the booster, brackets and gaskets from the engine compartment area.

Installation

12   Installation procedures are basically the reverse of those for removal. Check the length of the booster pushrod before installing the booster (see

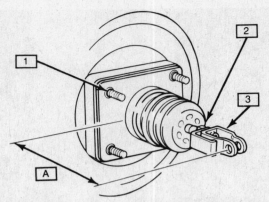

12.12   To adjust the length of the booster pushrod, loosen the locknut and turn the pushrod in or out, as necessary, to achieve the specified setting

A	Pushrod length (see this Chapter's Specifications)	1	Gasket
		2	Pushrod locknut
		3	Pushrod clevis

illustration). Compare the length with this Chapter's Specifications. Tighten the pushrod locknut securely. Tighten the booster mounting nuts to the torque listed in this Chapter's Specifications.
13   If the power booster unit is being replaced, the clearance between the master cylinder piston and the pushrod in the vacuum booster must be measured. Using a depth micrometer or vernier calipers, measure the distance from the seat (recessed area) in the master cylinder to the master cylinder mounting flange. Next, apply a vacuum of 20 in-Hg to the booster (using a hand vacuum pump) and measure the distance from the end of the vacuum booster pushrod to the mounting face of the booster (including gasket) where the master cylinder mounting flange seats. Subtract the two measurements to get the clearance (see illustration). If the clearance is more or less than specified, turn the adjusting screw on the end of the power booster pushrod until the clearance is within the specified range.

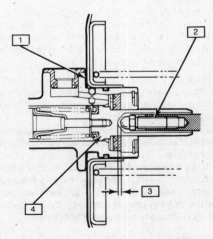

12.13   The booster pushrod-to-master cylinder clearance must be as specified – if there is interference between the two, the brakes may drag; if there is too much clearance, there will be excessive brake pedal travel

| 1 | Gasket | 3 | Clearance |
| 2 | Booster pushrod | 4 | Master cylinder |

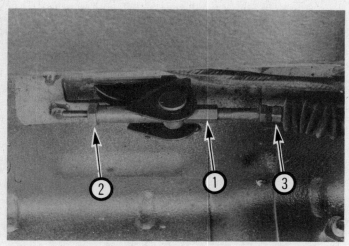

13.4   On Samurai models, loosen the stopper nut (1) and turn the adjusting nut (2) while holding the hold nut (3) with a wrench to prevent the inner cable from twisting – tighten or loosen until the parking brake lever travel is as specified

14   After the final installation of the master cylinder and brake hoses and lines, the brake pedal height and free play must be adjusted and the system must be bled. See the appropriate Sections of this Chapter for the procedures.

---

13   Parking brake – adjustment

Refer to illustrations 13.4 and 13.5

1   The adjustment of the parking brake, often overlooked or put off by many motorists, is actually a fairly critical adjustment. If the parking brake cables are too slack, the brake won't hold the vehicle on an incline – if they're too tight, the brakes may drag, causing them to wear prematurely. Another detrimental side effect of a tightly adjusted parking brake cable is the restriction of the automatic adjuster assembly on the rear drum brakes, which will not allow them to function properly.

2   The first step in adjusting slack parking brake cables is to ensure the correct adjustment of the rear drum brakes. This can be accomplished by making a series of forward and reverse stops (approximately 10 of them), which will bring the brake shoes into proper relationship with the brake drums.

3   Raise the rear of the vehicle and support it securely on jackstands.

4   On Samurai models, loosen the stopper nut and turn the adjusting nut while holding the hold nut **(see illustration)**.

5   On Sidekick and Tracker models, loosen or tighten the self-locking nut **(see illustration)**.

6   Release the parking brake and apply it, making sure it travels within specifications. If it travels too far, tighten the equalizer locknut a little more. If the travel is less than the Specifications, the locknut will have to be loosened.

7   After the parking brake has been properly adjusted, place the handle in the released position and rotate the rear wheels, making sure the brakes don't drag.

8   Lower the vehicle and test the operation of the parking brake on an incline.

---

14   Parking brake cables – replacement

1   Release the parking brake. On Sidekick and Tracker models loosen the rear wheel lug nuts. Raise the rear of the vehicle and support it securely on jackstands.

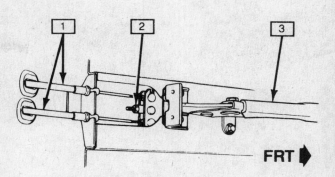

13.5   On Sidekick and Tracker models, loosen or tighten the self-locking nut until the parking brake lever travel is as specified

| 1 | Parking brake cable | 3 | Parking brake lever |
| 2 | Self-locking nut | | |

Sidekick/Tracker

Refer to illustration 14.4

2   Remove the rear wheel and brake drum. Loosen the self-locking nut **(see illustration 13.5)**.

3   Following the procedure in Section 6, remove the brake shoes, then disconnect the parking brake cable end from the parking brake lever.

4   Compress the cable housing retainer tangs at the brake backing plate **(see illustration)** and push the cable and housing through the backing plate.

5   Remove the self-locking nut and disconnect the cable at the lever, then pry cable out of the slot in the frame bracket.

Samurai

Refer to illustrations 14.6a and 14.6b

6   With a pair of pliers, remove the parking brake lever return spring, then remove the clip and pin **(see illustrations)**.

7   Loosen the stopper nut and remove the adjusting nut while holding the hold nut **(see illustration 13.4)**.

All models

8   Installation is the reverse of the removal procedure. Be sure to adjust the parking brake as described in Section 13.

9

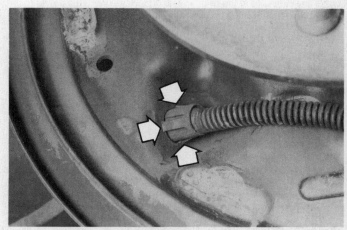

14.4   Compress the retainer tangs (arrows) to free the cable and housing from the backing plate

14.6a   Using a pair of pliers, remove the parking brake lever return spring, . . .

14.6b . . . then remove the parking brake cable clip and pin

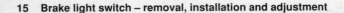

15   Brake light switch – removal, installation and adjustment

Refer to illustration 15.4

1   Remove the lower dash panel trim under the steering column (Chapter 11).
2   Locate the brake light switch, which is mounted at the top of the brake pedal support and unplug it.
3   Unscrew the locknut on the switch and unscrew the switch from its bracket.
4   Installation is the reverse of removal. To adjust the switch, loosen the locknut and turn the switch in or out until the plunger clearance is within the range listed in this Chapter's Specifications **(see illustration)**. Tighten the locknut when the correct adjustment is obtained.

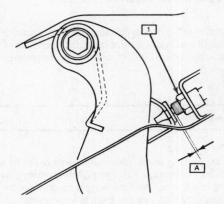

15.14 To adjust the brake light switch, loosen the locknut (1) and turn switch in or out until the clearance (A) is as specified

16   Rear Wheel Anti-lock (RWAL) brake system – general information

The Rear Wheel Anti-lock (RWAL) brake system is designed to maintain vehicle maneuverability, directional stability and optimum deceleration under severe braking conditions on most road surfaces. It does so by monitoring the rotational speed of the rear wheels and controlling the brake line pressure to the rear wheels during braking. This prevents the rear wheels from locking up prematurely during hard braking.

Actuator assembly

The actuator assembly includes the master cylinder and a control valve which consists of a dump valve and an isolation valve. The valve operates by changing the rear brake fluid pressure in response to signals from the control module.

Control module

The RWAL control is mounted behind the left side of the instrument panel adjacent to the fuse block and is the "brain" for the system. The function of the control module is to accept and process information received from the speed sensor and brake light switch to control the hydraulic line pressure, avoiding wheel lock up. The control module also constantly monitors the system, even under normal driving conditions, to find faults with the system.

If a problem develops within the system, the BRAKE warning light will glow on the dashboard. A diagnostic code will also be stored, which, when retrieved by a service technician, will indicate the problem area or component.

Speed sensor

A speed sensor is mounted in the rear differential carrier. The speed sensor sends a signal to the control module indicating rear wheel rotational speed.

Brake light switch

The brake light switch (see Section 15) signals the control module when the driver steps on the brake pedal. Without this signal the anti-lock system won't work.

Diagnosis and repair

If the BRAKE warning light on the dashboard comes on and stays on, make sure the parking brake is not applied and there's no problem with the brake hydraulic system. If neither of these is the cause the RWAL system is probably malfunctioning. Although a special electronic tester is necessary to properly diagnose the system, the home mechanic can perform a few preliminary checks before taking the vehicle to a dealer service department which is equipped with this tester.

a   Make sure the brakes, calipers and wheel cylinders are in good condition.
b   Check the electrical connectors at the control module assembly.
c   Check the fuses.
d   Follow the wiring harness to the speed sensor and brake light switch and make sure all connections are secure and the wiring isn't damaged.

If the above preliminary checks don't rectify the problem, the vehicle should be diagnosed by a dealer service department.

Chapter 10 Suspension and steering systems

Contents

10

Specifications

Torque specifications

	Ft-lbs
Front suspension	
Samurai	
Leaf spring U-bolt nuts	44 to 58
Leaf spring shackle pin nut	22 to 40
Leaf spring eye-to-frame bolt	33 to 50
Sidekick and Tracker	
Front strut/shock absorber upper mounting nuts	14 to 22
Front strut/shock absorber-to-steering knuckle nuts	58 to 75
Lower control arm	
Front nut	50 to 75
Rear nut	65 to 100
Balljoint stud nut	32 to 50
Balljoint-to-lower arm nuts	50 to 75
Spindle-to-steering knuckle bolts	29 to 43
Rear suspension	
Samurai	See Front suspension
Sidekick and Tracker	
Rear balljoint boss bolts	29 to 43
Upper arm bolts	58 to 72
Proportioning stay bolts	17
Trailing rod nuts	58 to 72
Steering	
Steering wheel nut	18 to 28
Steering gear mounting bolts	51 to 65
Intermediate shaft pinch bolt	14 to 22
Pitman arm-to-steering gear nut	101 to 129
Tie-rod end ballstud nut	22 to 40
Steering shaft rubber joint bolts	11 to 18
Pitman arm nut	101 to 129
Samurai	
Drag rod nut	22 to 50
Sidekick and Tracker	
Center link nut	22 to 50
Idler arm nut	50 to 72
Wheel lug nuts	See Chapter 1

1   General information

Refer to illustrations 1.1 and 1.2

Samurai models covered by this manual utilize a solid front axle, suspended by two leaf springs. A dual-action shock absorber is mounted on each side. The steering knuckles pivot on kingpins and a stabilizer bar controls body roll **(see illustration)**.

The rear axle on Samurai models is also suspended by two leaf springs and two dual-action telescopic shock absorbers **(see illustration)**. A stabilizer bar is installed on most models.

Tracker and sidekick models employ a strut/shock absorber design front suspension. Coil springs are mounted between the lower arm and the frame. The rear suspension uses coil springs and a solid axle, located by trailing rods and a control arm.

Steering is either manual or power assisted. A recirculating ball type steering gearbox transmits the turning force through the steering linkage to the steering knuckle. A steering damper is mounted between the frame and the Pitman arm to reduce unwanted bump steer. An intermediate shaft connects the steering gear to the steering column.

Frequently, when working on the suspension or steering system components, you may come across fasteners which seem impossible to loosen. These fasteners on the underside of the vehicle are continually subjected to water, road grime, mud, etc., and can become rusted or "frozen", making them extremely difficult to remove. In order to unscrew these stubborn fasteners without damaging them (or other components), be sure to use lots of penetrating oil and allow it to soak in for a while. Using a wire brush to clean exposed threads will also ease removal of the nut or bolt and prevent damage to the threads. Sometimes a sharp blow with a hammer and punch is effective in breaking the bond between a nut and bolt threads, but care must be taken to prevent the punch from slipping off the fastener and ruining the threads. Heating the stuck fastener and surrounding area with a torch sometimes helps too, but isn't recommended because of the obvious dangers associated with fire. Long breaker bars and extension, or "cheater," pipes will increase leverage, but never use an extension pipe on a ratchet – the ratcheting mechanism could be damaged. Sometimes, turning the nut or bolt in the tightening (clockwise) direction first will help to break it loose. Fasteners that require drastic measures to unscrew should always be replaced with new ones.

Since most of the procedures that are dealt with in this chapter involve jacking up the vehicle and working underneath it, a good pair of jackstands will be needed. A hydraulic floor jack is the preferred type of jack to lift the vehicle, and it can also be used to support certain components during various operation. **Warning:** *Never, under any circumstances, rely on a jack to support the vehicle while working on it. Whenever any of the suspension or steering fasteners are loosened or removed they must be inspected and, if necessary, be replaced with new ones of the same part number or of original equipment quality and design. Torque specifications must be followed for proper reassembly and component retention. Never attempt to heat or straighten any suspension or steering component. Instead, replace any bent or damaged part with a new one.*

1.1 Underside view of the front suspension and steering components (Samurai)

1   Tie-rod end
2   Pitman arm
3   Steering damper

4   Stabilizer bar
5   Drag rod
6   Spring shackle

7   Leaf spring
8   Steering knuckle
9   Shock absorber

10

1.2 Underside view of rear suspension (Samurai)

1   Leaf spring
2   Spring shackle
3   Shock absorber
4   Differential housing

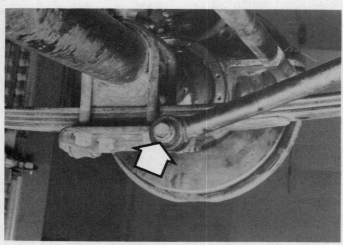

2.2   Remove the stabilizer bar-to-leaf spring plate bolt (arrow) to detach the bar

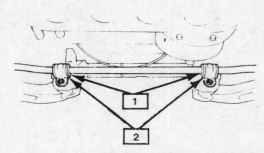

2.5   Before removing the stabilizer bar, be sure there are alignment marks where indicated

1   Alignment paint   2   Bar mount bushing

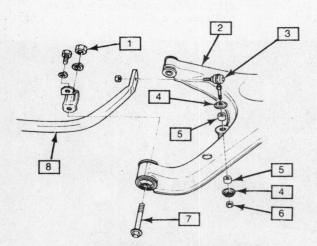

2.6   Stabilizer bar mounting details (Sidekick and Tracker models)

1	Nut	5	Bushing
2	Suspension arm	6	Nut
3	Stabilizer ball joint	7	Bolt
4	Washer	8	Stabilizer bar

2.3   The stabilizer bar is attached to the frame with two brackets like this – remove the bolts (arrows) to detach the bar – the rubber bushings should be replaced if they are hard, cracked or otherwise deformed

2   Front stabilizer bar – removal and installation

Removal

1   Apply the parking brake. Raise the front of the vehicle and support it securely on jackstands.

Samurai
Refer to illustrations 2.2 and 2.3

2   Remove the stabilizer bar-to-leaf spring plate bolts, **(see illustration)**.

3   Remove the stabilizer bar bracket bolts and detach the bar from the vehicle **(see illustration)**.

4   Pull the brackets off the stabilizer bar and inspect the bushings for cracks, hardness and other signs of deterioration. If the bushings are damaged, replace them.

Sidekick and Tracker
Refer to illustrations 2.5 and 2.6

5   Before removing the stabilizer bar, check to see if alignment marks are present where the bushings support the bar **(see illustration)**. If none are visible, apply them (this will help center the bar when installing it).

6   Remove the stabilizer ball joint from the front suspension lower arms noting how the spacers, washers and bushings are positioned **(see illustration)**.

7   Remove the stabilizer bar bracket bolts and detach the bar from the vehicle **(see illustration 2.6)**.

Installation

Samurai

8   Position the stabilizer bar bushings on the bar with the slits facing the top of the vehicle.

9   Push the brackets over the bushings and raise the bar up to the frame. Install the bracket bolts but don't tighten them completely at this time.

10   Install the stabilizer bar-to-lower control arm bolts, washers, spacers and rubber bushings and tighten the nuts securely.

11   Tighten the bracket bolts.

Sidekick and Tracker

12   Position the stabilizer bar bushings on the bar with the slits facing the front of the vehicle. **Note:** *Align the bushings with the alignment marks on the bar* **(see illustration 2.5)**.

13   Push the brackets over the bushings and raise the bar up to the frame. Install the bracket bolts but do not tighten them completely at this time.

14   Install the stabilizer ball joint.

15   Tighten all the fasteners securely.

10

**3.2   When removing the front shock absorber, remove the lock-
nut first then the stem nut – it may be necessary to hold the stem
with an open end wrench or locking pliers to prevent it
from turning**

**3.3   The lower end of the shock absorber is connected to the
front axle housing by a nut and washer**

**3   Front shock absorber (Samurai models) – removal
     and installation**

Refer to illustrations 3.2 and 3.3

Removal

1   Loosen the wheel lug nuts, raise the vehicle and support it securely on
jackstands. Apply the parking brake. Remove the wheel.
2   Remove the upper shock absorber locknut, then remove the upper
shock absorber stem nut **(see illustration)**. Use an open end wrench to
keep the stem from turning. If the nut won't loosen because of rust, squirt
some penetrating oil on the stem threads and allow it to soak in for awhile.
It may be necessary to keep the stem from turning with a pair of locking
pliers, since the flats provided for a wrench are quite small.
3   Remove the lower shock mount nut **(see illustration)** and remove the
shock absorber. Remove the washers and the rubber grommets from the
top of the shock absorber.

Installation

4   Extend the new shock absorber as far as possible. Position a new
washer and rubber grommet on the stem and guide the shock up and into
the upper mount.
5   Install the upper rubber grommet and washer and wiggle the stem
back-and-forth to ensure that the grommets are centered in the mount.
Tighten the stem nut securely, then install the locknut.
6   Install the lower mounting nut and tighten it securely.

---

4   Front leaf spring (Samurai models) – removal and installation

Refer to illustrations 4.4 and 4.6
Warning: *Whenever any of the suspension or steering fasteners are loosened or removed they must be inspected and, if necessary, replaced with
new ones of the same part number or of original equipment quality and design. Torque specifications must be followed for proper reassembly and
component retention.*

Removal

1   Loosen the front wheel lug nuts, raise the front of the vehicle and support it securely on jackstands. Remove the wheel.
2   Support the axle assembly with a floor jack positioned underneath the
differential. Raise the axle just enough to take the spring pressure off the
shock absorbers.

**4.4   The front axle must be supported before removing the
stabilizer bolt (1), front shock absorber nut (2) and
the four U-bolt nuts (3)**

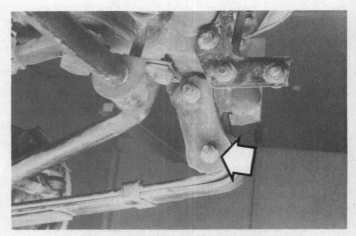

4.6   Remove the shackle pin bolt and nut (arrow)

3   Disconnect the shock absorber from the axle bracket (see Section 3).
4   Support the axle, then unscrew the U-bolt nuts **(see illustration)**. Remove the spring plate.
5   Remove the spring eye-to-frame bracket bolt.
6   Remove the spring-to-shackle bolt and remove the spring from the
vehicle **(see illustration)**.

Installation

7   Installation is the reverse of the removal procedure. Be sure to tighten the spring mounting bolts and the spring plate U-bolt nuts to the specified torque. **Note:** *The vehicle must be standing at normal ride height before tightening the front and rear mounting bolts.*

---

5   Front strut/shock absorber assembly (Sidekick and Tracker models) – removal and installation

---

Refer to illustrations 5.3, 5.4 and 5.5
Note: *The shock absorbers are not serviceable and must be replaced as complete assemblies.*

Removal

1   Loosen the front wheel lug nuts, raise the vehicle and support it securely on jackstands. Remove the wheel.

2   Place a floor jack under the lower control arm and raise it slightly. The jack must remain in this position throughout the entire procedure.
3   Remove the clip securing the brake hose to the strut/shock absorber **(see illustration)**.
4   Unscrew the three upper mount-to-strut tower retaining nuts **(see illustration)**.
5   Remove the strut-to-spindle nuts and bolts **(see illustration)**.
6   Separate the strut/shock absorber assembly from the spindle and remove it from the vehicle. Be careful not to overextend the driveaxle.

Installation

7   Guide the assembly into position in the wheel well, pushing the upper mount studs through the holes in the strut tower. Install the three nuts and tighten them to the specified torque.
8   Insert the spindle into the lower mounting flange of the strut/shock assembly and install the two bolts from the front side. Install the nuts and tighten them to the specified torque.
9   Remove the jack from under the lower control arm and install the brake hose clip without twisting the brake hose.

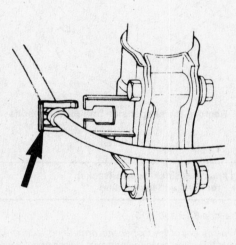

5.3   Using a pair of pliers, remove the clip – when reattaching the clip, don't twist the brake hose

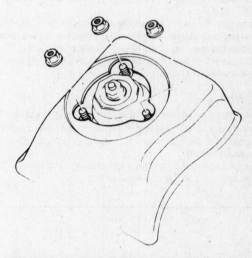

5.4   The upper end of the front strut/shock absorber assembly is fastened to the shock tower with three nuts

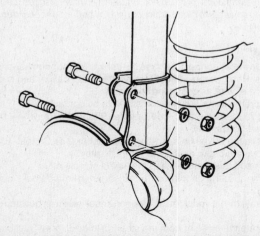

5.5   Remove the strut-to-spindle bolts – it may be necessary to drive out the bolts with a hammer and punch

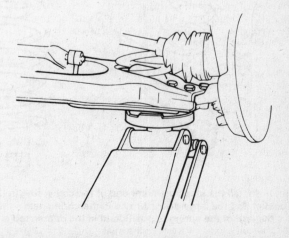

6.8   Use a floor jack to support the suspension arm and slowly release the spring pressure

10

10   Install the wheel, lower the vehicle and tighten the lug nuts to the torque specified in Chapter 1.

6   Front coil spring (Sidekick and Tracker models) – removal and installation

Refer to illustrations 6.8 and 6.11

Warning: *The following procedure is potentially dangerous – be very careful when lowering the jack to release the spring pressure.*

Removal

1   Loosen the wheel lug nuts on the side to be dismantled. Raise the vehicle, support it securely on jackstands and remove the wheel.
2   Remove the locking hub (see Chapter 8).
3   Remove the front driveaxle snap-ring and washer (see Chapter 8).
4   Remove the brake caliper and hang it out of the way with a piece of wire (see Chapter 9).
5   Remove the brake disc (see Chapter 9).
6   Disconnect the stabilizer bar joint from the lower control arm (see Section 2).
7   Remove the tie-rod end from the steering knuckle (see Section 18).
8   Use a jack to support the lower suspension arm **(see illustration)**.
9   Remove the steering knuckle (see Section 8).
10   Slowly lower the jack until the coil spring is completely extended, then remove the coil spring.

Installation

Note: *The upper and lower diameters of the coil spring are different.*

11   Guide the small diameter end of the coil spring up into the upper pocket and place the larger diameter end in the spring seat area of the control arm **(see illustration)**.
12   The remainder of the installation procedure is the reverse of removal. Tighten all fasteners to the specified torque.

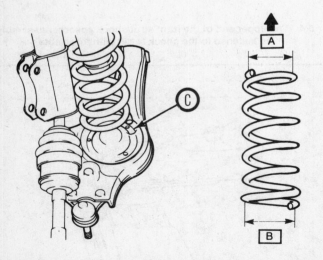

6.11   Install the small diameter end of the coil spring in the upper pocket and the large diameter end in the spring seat – make sure the end of the spring is positioned in the depressed area of the seat

A   Small diameter
B   Large diameter
C   Spring seat

7   Front suspension lower arm (Sidekick and Tracker models) – removal and installation

Refer to illustration 7.3

1   Loosen the wheel lug nuts, raise the vehicle and support it securely on jackstands. Remove the wheel.
2   Remove the coil spring (see Section 6).
3   Remove the suspension arm-to-frame bolts **(see illustration)**.
4   Installation is the reverse of removal. The vehicle should be sitting at normal ride height before tightening the arm-to-frame bolts to the torque listed in this Chapter's Specifications.

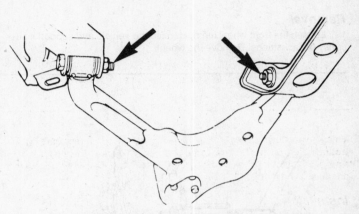

7.3   Remove the suspension arm-to-frame bolts

8   Steering knuckle (Sidekick and Tracker models) – removal and installation

Refer to illustrations 8.10 and 8.15

Warning: *Whenever any of the suspension or steering fasteners are loosened or removed they must be inspected and, if necessary, replaced with new ones of the same part number or of original equipment quality and design. Torque specifications must be followed for proper reassembly and component retention. Dust created by the brake system may contain asbestos, which is harmful to your health. Never blow it out with compressed air and don't inhale any of it. Do not, under any circumstances, use petroleum-based solvents to clean brake parts. Use brake cleaner or denatured alcohol only.*

Removal

1   Loosen the wheel lug nuts, raise the vehicle and support it securely on jackstands. Remove the wheel. Remove the brake caliper and support it with a piece of wire as described in Chapter 9.
2   Support the lower suspension arm with a floor jack.
3   Remove the brake disc (see Chapter 9) and the freewheel hub assembly (see Chapter 8).
4   Remove the driveaxle snap-ring and washer (see Chapter 8).
5   Remove the brake dust cover (see Chapter 9).
6   With a soft face hammer, tap the wheel spindle off.
7   Remove the strut/shock absorber-to-steering knuckle bolts/nuts (see Section 5).
8   Separate the tie-rod from the steering knuckle arm as outlined in Section 18.
9   Separate the balljoint from the steering knuckle (see Section 9).
10   Remove the steering knuckle assembly from the strut/shock, balljoint and driveaxle. If the steering knuckle will not break loose from the balljoint,

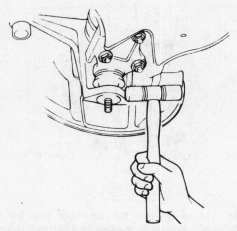

8.10   It may be necessary to tap the steering knuckle with a hammer to break the balljoint loose

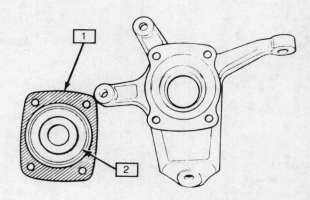

8.15   When attaching the wheel spindle to the steering knuckle, be sure to use the sealant and lubricant in the areas shown

1   *GM silicone sealer #1052751 (or equivalent)*
2   *GM lubricant #1052196 (or equivalent)*

it may be necessary to hit the steering knuckle with a hammer **(see illustration)**. If the driveaxle sticks in the hub splines, push it from the hub with a puller tool. Support the end of the driveaxle with a piece of wire to prevent damage to the inner CV joint.

Installation

11   Guide the knuckle assembly into position, inserting the driveaxle into the hub.
12   Push the knuckle into the shock flange and install the bolts, but don't tighten them yet.
13   Insert the balljoint stud into the steering knuckle hole and install the nut, but don't tighten it yet.
14   Attach the tie-rod to the steering knuckle arm as described in Section 18. Tighten the strut bolt nuts, the balljoint nut and the tie-rod nut to the specified torque values.
15   Attach the wheel spindle to the steering knuckle using GM sealant 1052751 and GM lubricant 1052196 **(see illustration)** or equivalent.
16   Install the brake dust cover, tightening the fasteners to the torque listed in the Chapter 9 Specifications.
17   Install the freewheel hub assembly and brake disc.
18   Install the driveaxle snap-ring and washer.
19   Install the caliper as outlined in Chapter 9.
20   Remove the floor jack supporting the suspension arm.
21   Install the wheel and lug nuts.
22   Lower the vehicle and tighten the lug nuts to the torque listed in the Chapter 1 Specifications.

9   Balljoints (Sidekick and Tracker models) – check and replacement

Refer to illustration 9.8
Warning: *Whenever any of the suspension or steering fasteners are loosened or removed, they must be inspected and, if necessary, replaced with new ones of the same part number or of original equipment quality and design. Torque specifications must be followed for proper reassembly and component retention.*

Check

1   Raise the vehicle and support it securely on jackstands.
2   Visually inspect the rubber boot for cuts, tears or leaking grease. If any of these conditions are noticed, the balljoint should be replaced.

3   Place a large pry bar under the balljoint and attempt to push the balljoint up. Next, position the pry bar between the steering knuckle and the lower arm and apply downward pressure. If any movement is seen or felt during either of these checks, a worn out balljoint is indicated.
4   Have an assistant grasp the tire at the top and bottom and shake the top of the tire in an in-and-out motion. Touch the balljoint stud nut. If any looseness is felt, suspect a worn out balljoint stud or a widened hole in the steering knuckle boss. If the latter problem exists, the steering knuckle should be replaced as well as the balljoint.

Replacement

5   Loosen the wheel lug nuts, raise the vehicle and support it securely on jackstands. Remove the wheel.
6   Support the lower suspension arm with a floor jack.
7   Remove the steering knuckle (see Section 8).
8   Unscrew the three balljoint-to-lower arm bolts and remove the balljoint **(see illustration)**.
9   To install the balljoint, position it on the lower arm and install the three bolts to the specified torque.
10   Install the steering knuckle (see Section 8) and remove the floor jack.
11   The remainder of the installation procedure is the reverse of removal.
12   Install the wheel and lug nuts. Lower the vehicle and tighten the lug nuts to the specified torque.

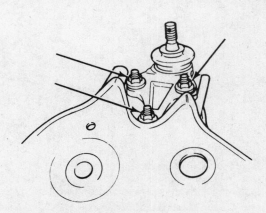

9.8   Location of the three balljoint stud nuts on the lower suspension arm

10

10.2a   The lower end of the rear shock absorber on Samurai models mounts to a stud on the leaf spring plate and is retained by a nut and washer

---

10   Rear shock absorber – removal and installation

Refer to illustrations 10.2a, 10.2b, 10.3a and 10.3b

Warning: *Whenever any of the suspension or steering fasteners are loosened or removed, they must be inspected and, if necessary, replaced with new ones of the same part number or of original equipment quality and design.*

Removal

1   Loosen the rear wheel lug nuts, raise the rear of the vehicle and support it securely on jackstands. Block the front wheels and remove the rear wheel(s).
2   Position a floor jack under the rear axle housing and raise it just enough to take some of the spring pressure off the shock absorber. On Samurai models, remove the lower nut and washer. On Sidekick and Tracker models, remove the shock absorber lower mounting bolt **(see illustrations)**.
3   On Samurai models, remove the upper mounting nut and washer **(see illustration)** and detach the shock absorber. On Sidekick and Track-

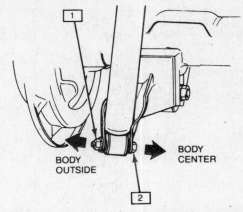

10.2b   The lower end of the rear shock absorber on Sidekick/Tracker models is retained by a bolt and nut – when installing the shock, be sure to install the bolt and nut as shown

1 Lower nut	2 Bolt

er models, remove the shock absorber lock nut, then remove the shock absorber nut and detach the shock absorber **(see illustration)**.

Installation

4   Installation is the reverse of the removal procedure. Be sure to tighten the fasteners securely.

---

11   Rear leaf spring (Samurai models) – removal and installation

Warning: *Whenever any of the suspension or steering fasteners are loosened or removed they must be inspected and, if necessary, replaced with new ones of the same part number or of original equipment quality and design. Torque specifications must be followed for proper reassembly and component retention.*

Removal

1   Loosen the rear wheel lug nuts, raise the rear of the vehicle and support it securely on jackstands. Remove the wheel.

10.3a   The upper end of the rear shock absorber on Samurai models mounts to a stud on the frame by a nut and washer

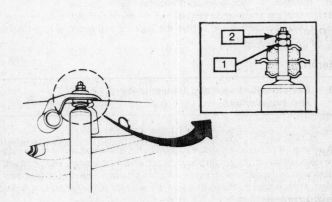

10.3b   The upper end of the rear shock absorber on Sidekick/Tracker models mounts on the frame and is retained by two nuts

1 Shock absorber nut	2 Locknut

2   Support the rear axle assembly with a floor jack positioned underneath the differential. Raise the axle just enough to take the spring pressure off of the shock absorbers.
3   Disconnect the shock absorber from the axle bracket (see Section 10).
4   Support the axle, then unscrew the U-bolt nuts **(see illustration 4.5)**. Remove the spring plate.
5   Remove the spring eye-to-frame bracket bolt.
6   Remove the spring-to-shackle bolt and remove the spring from the vehicle.

Installation

7   Installation is the reverse of the removal procedure. Be sure to tighten the spring mounting bolts and the spring plate U-bolt nuts to the specified torque. **Note:** *The vehicle must be standing at normal ride height before tightening the front and rear mounting bolts.*

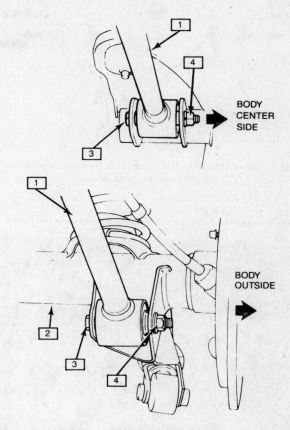

---

12   Rear suspension trailing rod (Sidekick and Tracker models) – removal and installation

Refer to illustration 12.2

Removal

1   Loosen the wheel lug nuts, raise the vehicle and support it securely on jackstands. Remove the wheel and place a floor jack under the rear axle to support it when the trailing rod is removed.
2   Remove the trailing rod rear attaching nut and bolt from the axle bracket **(see illustration)**, then unbolt the parking brake cable guide.
3   Remove the front attaching bolt and nut and remove the trailing rod from the vehicle.

Installation

4   Place the trailing rod in the front mounting bracket and install the bolt and nut (don't tighten it yet).
5   Position the trailing rod in the axle bracket and install the nut and bolt (don't tighten it yet).
6   Install the parking brake cable guide on the trailing rod.
7   Remove the floor jack supporting the rear axle.
8   Install the wheel and lug nuts and lower the vehicle. Tighten the lug nuts to the torque listed in the Chapter 1 Specifications.
9   With the vehicle off the jackstands and in a non-loaded condition, tighten the trailing rod front and rear bolts and nuts to the specified torque.

12.2   Trailing rod mounting details – when installing the trailing rod, make sure the nuts and bolts are installed as shown

1	Trailing rod	3	Bolt
2	Rear axle housing	4	Nut

---

13   Rear suspension upper arm (Sidekick and Tracker models) – removal and installation

Upper arm

Refer to illustrations 13.4 and 13.6

Removal

1   Raise the rear of the vehicle and support it securely on jackstands placed beneath the frame rails. Block the front wheels.
2   Remove the proportioning valve stay from the rear suspension upper arm (see Chapter 9).
3   Position a jack under the differential and raise it slightly.
4   Remove the balljoint boss from the differential carrier **(see illustration)**.
5   Remove the upper arm-to-frame pivot bolts and nuts and remove the arm from the vehicle.

Installation

6   Position the leading end of the suspension arm in the frame bracket. Install the pivot bolts and nuts with the bolts installed from the inside, but don't fully tighten the nuts at this time **(see illustration)**.
7   Place the other end of the arm over the differential carrier. It may be necessary to jack up the rear axle to align the holes. Install the balljoint

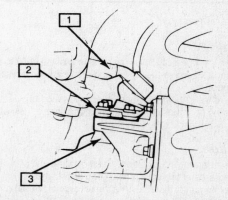

13.4   The upper suspension arm balljoint boss mounting bolts

1	Rear suspension upper arm	2	Balljoint boss
		3	Differential carrier

---

boss bolts and tighten them to the specified torque.
8   Install the proportioning valve stay.
9   Remove the floor jack supporting the differential housing.
10   Lower the vehicle and tighten the upper arm-to-frame pivot bolts to the specified torque.

10

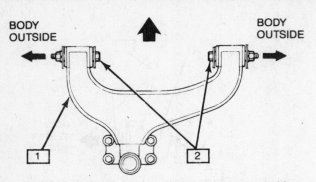

13.6   When installing the upper arm, be sure to position the nuts and bolts as shown

1   *Rear suspension*   2   *Bolts*
    upper arm

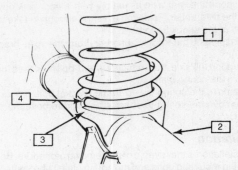

14.4   When installing the coil spring, make sure the end of the spring sits in the stepped area

1   *Rear coil spring*   3   *Spring seat*
2   *Rear axle housing*   4   *Stepped area*

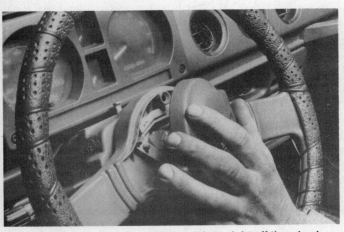

15.2   To remove the horn pad, pull it straight off the wheel

15.3   Before removing the steering wheel, check to see if any alignment marks exist (arrows) – if not, use a sharp scribe or white paint to make your own marks

14   Rear coil spring (Sidekick and Tracker models) – removal and installation

Refer to illustration 14.4

Removal

1   Loosen the wheel lug nuts, raise the rear of the vehicle and support it on jackstands. Remove the wheel and place a floor jack under the rear axle to support it.
2   Remove the shock absorber lower mounting bolt.
3   Lower the floor jack slowly until the coil spring is fully extended, then remove the spring from the vehicle.

Installation

4   Guide the spring into position. Make sure the end of the spring rests in the stepped area of the spring seat **(see illustration)**.
5   The remainder of installation is the reverse of the removal procedure.

15   Steering wheel – removal and installation

Refer to illustrations 15.2, 15.3 and 15.4

1   Disconnect the cable from the negative terminal of the battery.
2   Detach the horn pad from the steering wheel **(see illustration)**.
3   Remove the steering wheel retaining nut then mark the relationship of the steering shaft to the hub (if marks don't already exist or don't line up) to

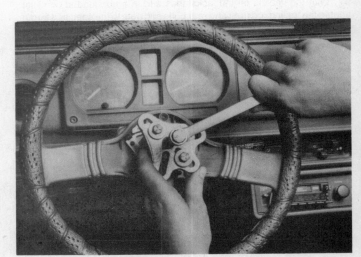

15.4   Remove the wheel from the shaft with a puller – DO NOT HAMMER ON THE SHAFT!

simplify installation and ensure steering wheel alignment **(see illustration)**.
4   Use a puller to detach the steering wheel from the shaft **(see illustration)**. Don't hammer on the shaft to dislodge the steering wheel.

16.2a   Mark the upper end of the intermediate shaft and universal joint, then mark the universal joint to steering shaft relationship (Samurai)

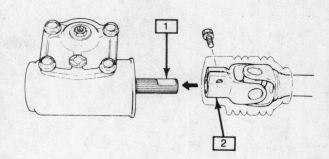

16.2b   On Sidekick and Tracker models, slide the protective boot back to gain access to the lower joint pinch bolt – be sure to mark the lower end of the intermediate shaft and the steering gear input shaft

1   *Steering gear box shaft*   2   *Lower joint*

5   To install the wheel, align the mark on the steering wheel hub with the mark on the shaft and slip the wheel onto the shaft. Install the nut and tighten it to the specified torque.
6   Install the horn pad.
7   Connect the negative battery cable.

16   Intermediate shaft – removal and installation

Refer to illustrations 16.2a and 16.2b
Warning: *Whenever any of the suspension or steering fasteners are loosened or removed they must be inspected and if necessary, replaced with new ones of the same part number or of original equipment quality and design. Torque specifications must be followed for proper reassembly and component retention. Never attempt to heat, straighten or weld any suspension or steering component. Instead, replace any bent or damaged part with a new one.*
1   Turn the front wheels to the straight ahead position.
2   Using white paint, place alignment marks on the upper universal joint, the steering shaft, the lower universal joint or lower flexible coupling and the steering gear input shaft **(see illustrations)**.
3   Remove the upper and lower universal joint pinch bolts.
4   Pry the intermediate shaft out of the steering shaft universal joint with a large screwdriver, then pull the shaft from the steering gearbox.
5   Installation is the reverse of the removal procedure. Be sure to align the marks and tighten the pinch bolts to the specified torque.

17   Steering gear – removal and installation

Refer to illustrations 17.5 and 17.6
Warning: *Whenever any of the suspension or steering fasteners are loosened or removed they must be inspected and if necessary, replaced with new ones of the same part number or of original equipment quality and design. Torque specifications must be followed for proper reassembly and component retention. Never attempt to heat, straighten or weld any suspension or steering component. Instead, replace any bent or damaged part with a new one.*

Removal

1   Raise the front of the vehicle and support it securely on jackstands. Apply the parking brake.

2   Place a drain pan under the steering gear (power steering only). Remove the hoses/lines and cap the ends to prevent excessive fluid loss and contamination.
3   Mark the relationship of the lower intermediate shaft universal joint to the steering gear input shaft. Remove the lower intermediate shaft pinch bolt.
4   On Samurai models, mark the relationship of the Pitman arm to the shaft so it can be installed in the same position. Remove the nut and washer. On Sidekick and Tracker models, disconnect the center link from the Pitman arm (see Section 18).
5   Remove the Pitman arm from the shaft with a two-jaw puller **(see illustration)**.

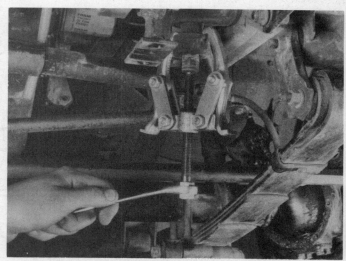

17.5   Use a two-jaw puller to separate the pitman arm from the steering gear shaft

6   Support the steering gear and remove the mounting bolts **(see illustration)**. Lower the unit, separate the intermediate shaft from the steering gear input shaft and remove the steering gear from the vehicle.

Installation

7   Raise the steering gear into position and connect the intermediate shaft, aligning the marks.
8   Install the mounting bolts and washers and tighten them to the specified torque.

10

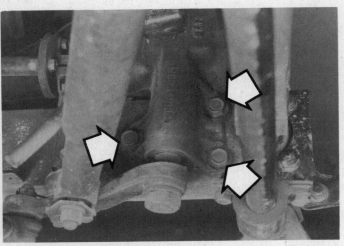

17.6   The steering gear is mounted to the frame rail with three bolts (arrows)

9   On Samurai models, slide the Pitman arm onto the shaft. Make sure the marks are aligned. Install the washer and nut and tighten the nut to the specified torque. On Sidekick and Tracker models, attach the center link to the Pitman arm and tighten the nut to the specified torque.
10   Install the lower intermediate shaft pinch bolt and tighten it to the specified torque.
11   Connect the power steering hoses/lines to the steering gear and fill the power steering pump reservoir with the recommended fluid (see Chapter 1).

12   Lower the vehicle and bleed the steering system as outlined in Section 20.

18   Steering linkage – inspection, removal and installation

Warning: *Whenever any of the suspension or steering fasteners are loosened or removed they must be inspected and if necessary, replaced with new ones of the same part number or of original equipment quality and design. Torque specifications must be followed for proper reassembly and component retention. Never attempt to heat, straighten or weld any suspension or steering component. Instead, replace any bent or damaged part with a new one.*

Caution: *DO NOT use a "pickle fork" type balljoint separator – it may damage the balljoint seals.*

Inspection
Refer to illustrations 18.1a and 18.1b
1   The steering linkage connects the steering gear to the front wheels and keeps the wheels in proper relation to each other **(see illustrations)**. The linkage consists of the Pitman arm which is fastened to the steering gear shaft. On Samurai models, the Pitman arm moves the drag rod back-and-forth. The back-and-forth motion of the drag rod is transmitted to the steering knuckles through a tie-rod assembly. On Sidekick and Tracker models, the Pitman arm moves the center link back-and-forth. The center link is supported on the other end by an idler arm. The back-and-forth motion of the center link is transmitted to the steering knuckles through a pair of tie-rod assemblies.

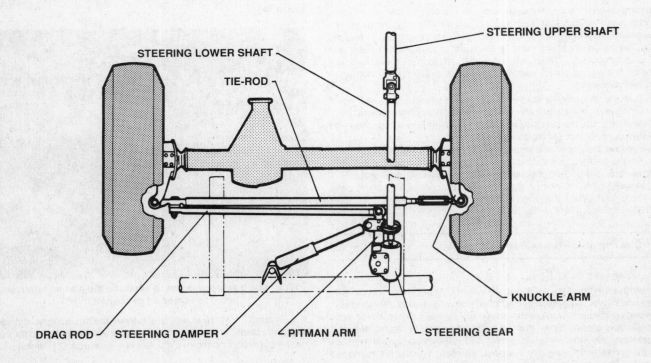

0142H

18.1a   Samurai steering linkage components

18.1b   Sidekick and Tracker steering linkage components

1   Knuckle
2   Center link
3   Steering wheel
4   Steering intermediate shaft
6   Tie-rod
7   Steering gear
8   Pitman arm
9   Idler arm

2   Set the wheels in the straight ahead position and lock the steering wheel.

3   Raise one side of the vehicle until the tire is approximately 1-inch off the ground.

4   Mount a dial indicator with the needle resting on the outside edge of the wheel. Grasp the front and rear of the tire and using light pressure, wiggle the wheel back-and-forth and note the dial indicator reading. If the play in the steering system is excessive, inspect each steering linkage pivot point and ball stud for looseness and replace parts if necessary.

5   On Sidekick and Tracker models, raise the vehicle and support it on jackstands. Push up, then pull down on the center link of the idler arm, exerting a force of approximately 25 pounds each way. Measure the total distance the end of the arm travels. If the play is excessive, replace the idler arm.

6   Check for torn ball stud boots, frozen joints and bent or damaged linkage components.

Removal and installation

Refer to illustrations 18.9, 18.10 and 18.33

Tie-rod

7   Loosen the wheel lug nuts, raise the vehicle and support it securely on jackstands. Apply the parking brake. Remove the wheel.

8   Remove the cotter pin and loosen, but do not remove, the castellated nut from the ball stud.

9   Using a two jaw puller, separate the tie-rod end from the steering knuckle **(see illustration)**. Remove the castellated nut and pull the tie-rod end from the knuckle.

10   If the tie-rod or tie-rod end must be replaced, measure the distance from the end of the rod end connector to the center of the ball stud and record it. Loosen the locknut and unscrew the tie-rod end **(see illustration)**.

11   Lubricate the threaded portion of the tie-rod end with chassis grease. Screw the new tie-rod end into the adjuster tube and adjust the distance from the tube to the ball stud to the previously measured dimension. The

number of threads showing on the tie-rod and tie-rod end should be equal within three threads. Don't tighten the locknut yet.

12   To install the tie-rod, insert the tie-rod end ball stud into the center link or drag rod until it's seated. Install the nut and tighten it to the specified torque. If the ball stud spins when attempting to tighten the nut, force it into the tapered hole with a large pair of pliers.

13   Connect the tie-rod end to the steering knuckle and install the castellated nut. Tighten the nut to the specified torque and install a new cotter pin. If necessary, tighten the nut slightly to align a slot in the nut with the hole in the ball stud.

18.9   Use a two-jaw puller to detach the tie-rod end from the steering knuckle

10

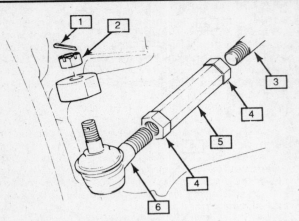

18.10   Exploded view of the tie-rod end

1	Cotter pin	4	Nut
2	Nut	5	Tie-rod end connector
3	Tie rod	6	Tie-rod end

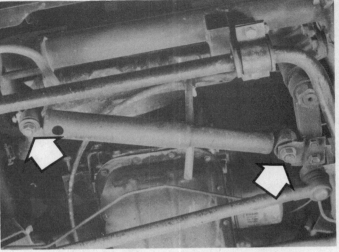

18.33 Remove the nuts and bolts (arrows) to remove the steering damper

14   Tighten the locknuts on the tie-rod connector.
15   Install the wheel and lug nuts, lower the vehicle and tighten the lug nuts to the specified torque. Drive the vehicle to an alignment shop to have the front end alignment checked and, if necessary, adjusted.

Idler arm (Sidekick and Tracker)

16   Raise the vehicle and support it securely on jackstands. Apply the parking brake.
17   Loosen but do not remove the idler arm-to-center link nut.
18   Separate the idler arm from the center link with a two jaw puller. Remove the nut.
19   Remove the idler arm-to-frame bolts.
20   To install the idler arm, position it on the frame and install the bolts, tightening them to the specified torque.
21   Insert the idler arm ball stud into the center link and install the nut. Tighten the nut to the specified torque. If the ball stud spins when attempting to tighten the nut, force it into the tapered hole with a large pair of pliers.

Drag rod (Samurai)

22   Raise the vehicle and support it securely on jackstands. Apply the parking brake.
23   Separate the tie-rod end from the drag rod.
24   Separate the drag rod from the Pitman arm.
25   Installation is the reverse of the removal procedure. If the ball studs spin when attempting to tighten the nuts, force them into the tapered holes with a large pair of pliers. Be sure to tighten all of the nuts to the specified torque.

Center link (Sidekick and Tracker)

26   Raise the front of the vehicle and support it securely on jackstands. Apply the parking brake.
27   Loosen, but do not remove, the nut securing the center link to the tie-rod. Separate the joint with a two jaw puller then remove the nut.
28   Separate the center link from the Pitman arm.
29   Separate the center link from the idler arm.
30   Installation is the reverse of the removal procedure. If the ball studs spin when attempting to tighten the nuts, force them into the tapered holes with a large pair of pliers. Be sure to tighten all of the nuts to the specified torque.

Pitman arm

31   Refer to Section 17 of this Chapter for the Pitman arm removal procedure.

Steering damper (Samurai)

32   Raise the front of the vehicle and support it securely on jackstands.
33   Unbolt the damper from the damper stay **(see illustration)**.

34   Remove the damper to frame nut and remove the damper from the vehicle.
35   Installation is the reverse of the removal procedure.

19   Power steering pump (Sidekick and Tracker models) – removal and installation

Refer to illustration 19.7

Removal

1   Disconnect the cable from the negative terminal of the battery.
2   Place a drain pan under the power steering pump. Remove the drivebelt (see Chapter 1).
3   Loosen the power steering pressure hose union bolt and let the fluid drain out, then remove the hose.
4   Disconnect the power steering suction hose from the power steering fluid reservoir.
5   Disconnect the power steering pressure switch electrical connector from the pump.
6   Remove the engine oil filter (see Chapter 2).
7   Remove the power steering pump mounting and adjusting bolts **(see illustration)**.
8   Remove the pump from the vehicle, taking care not to spill fluid on the painted surfaces.

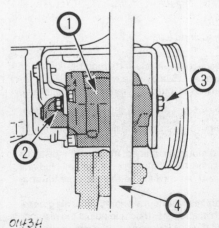

19.7   Power steering pump mounting details – (Sidekick and Tracker models)

1   Power steering pump
2   Power steering pump mounting bolt
3   Power steering pump adjusting bolt
4   Center link

0143H

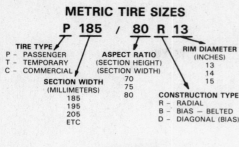

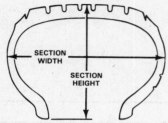

21.1   Metric tire size code

Installation

9   Installation is the reverse of removal.
10   Fill the power steering reservoir with the recommended fluid and bleed the system following the procedure described in the next Section.

20   Power steering system – bleeding

1   Following any operation in which the power steering fluid lines have been disconnected, the power steering system must be bled to remove all air and obtain proper steering performance.
2   With the front wheels in the straight ahead position, check the power steering fluid level and, if low, add fluid until it reaches the Cold mark on the dipstick.
3   Start the engine and allow it to run at fast idle. Recheck the fluid level and add more if necessary to reach the Cold mark on the dipstick.
4   Bleed the system by turning the wheels from side-to-side, without hitting the stops. This will work the air out of the system. Keep the reservoir full of fluid as this is done.
5   When the air is worked out of the system, return the wheels to the straight ahead position and leave the vehicle running for several more minutes before shutting it off.
6   Road test the vehicle to be sure the steering system is functioning normally and noise free.
7   Recheck the fluid level to be sure it is up to the Hot mark on the dipstick while the engine is at normal operating temperature. Add fluid if necessary (see Chapter 1).

21   Wheels and tires – general information

Refer to illustration 21.1

    All vehicles covered by this manual are equipped with metric-sized fiberglass or steel belted radial tires **(see illustration)**. Use of other size or type of tires may affect the ride and handling of the vehicle. Don't mix different types of tires, such as radials and bias belted, on the same vehicle as handling may be seriously affected. It's recommended that tires be replaced in pairs on the same axle, but if only one tire is being replaced, be sure it's the same size, structure and tread design as the other.
    Because tire pressure has a substantial effect on handling and wear, the pressure on all tires should be checked at least once a month or before any extended trips (see Chapter 1).
    Wheels must be replaced if they are bent, dented, leak air, have elongated bolt holes, are heavily rusted, out of vertical symmetry or if the lug nuts won't stay tight. Wheel repairs that use welding or peening are not recommended.
    Tire and wheel balance is important to the overall handling, braking and performance of the vehicle. Unbalanced wheels can adversely affect handling and ride characteristics as well as tire life. Whenever a tire is installed on a wheel, the tire and wheel should be balanced by a shop with the proper equipment.

22   Front end alignment – general information

Refer to illustration 22.1

    A front end alignment refers to the adjustments made to the front wheels so they are in proper angular relationship to the suspension and the ground. Front wheels that are out of proper alignment not only affect steering control, but also increase tire wear. The only front end adjustment possible on these vehicles is toe-in **(see illustration)**.
    Getting the proper front wheel alignment is a very exacting process, one in which complicated and expensive machines are necessary to perform the job properly. Because of this, you should have a technician with the proper equipment perform these tasks. We will, however, use this space to give you a basic idea of what is involved with front end alignment so you can better understand the process and deal intelligently with the shop that does the work.
    Toe-in is the turning in of the front wheels. The purpose of a toe specification is to ensure parallel rolling of the front wheels. In a vehicle with zero toe-in, the distance between the front edges of the wheels will be the same as the distance between the rear edges of the wheels. The actual amount of toe-in is normally only a fraction of an inch. Toe-in adjustment is controlled by the tie-rod end position on the inner tie-rod. Incorrect toe-in will cause the tires to wear improperly by making them scrub against the road surface.

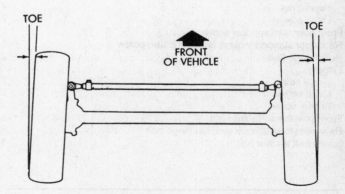

22.1   Toe-in is the only alignment setting that is adjustable

10

Chapter 11   Body

Contents

Specifications

Torque specifications

	Ft-lb
Door	
Glass stud nut	4
Hinge bolt	26
Handle nut	4
Latch screw	7
Front door vent window screw	1
Rear door stationary glass channel frame screw	1
Hood hinge bolt	23
Liftgate	
Hinge bolt	7
Latch screw	7
Striker screw	22
Front seat frame-to-floor nut	18
Rear seat-to-seat back cushion hinge bolt	33
Safety belt anchor bolt	36

1   General information

The vehicles covered in this manual have a separate frame and body. Certain components are particularly vulnerable to accident damage and can be unbolted and repaired or replaced. Among these parts are the body moldings, bumpers, hood, doors and all glass.

Only general body maintenance practices and body panel repair procedures within the scope of the do-it-yourselfer are included in this Chapter.

2   Body – maintenance

1 The condition of your vehicle's body is very important, because the resale value depends a great deal on it. It's much more difficult to repair a neglected or damaged body than it is to repair mechanical components. The hidden areas of the body, such as the wheel wells, the frame and the engine compartment, are equally important, although they don't require as frequent attention as the rest of the body.

2 Once a year, or every 12,000 miles, it's a good idea to have the underside of the body steam cleaned. All traces of dirt and oil will be removed and the area can then be inspected carefully for rust, damaged brake

lines, frayed electrical wires, damaged cables and other problems. The front suspension components should be greased after completion of this job.

3 At the same time, clean the engine and the engine compartment with a steam cleaner or water soluble degreaser.

4 The wheel wells should be given close attention, since undercoating can peel away and stones and dirt thrown up by the tires can cause the paint to chip and flake, allowing rust to set in. If rust is found, clean down to the bare metal and apply an anti-rust paint.

5 The body should be washed about once a week. Wet the vehicle thoroughly to soften the dirt, then wash it down with a soft sponge and plenty of clean soapy water. If the surplus dirt is not washed off very carefully, it can wear down the paint.

6 Spots of tar or asphalt thrown up from the road should be removed with a cloth soaked in solvent.

7 Once every six months, wax the body and chrome trim. If a chrome cleaner is used to remove rust from any of the vehicle's plated parts, remember that the cleaner also removes part of the chrome, so use it sparingly.

3 Upholstery and carpets – maintenance

1 Every three months remove the carpets or mats and clean the interior of the vehicle (more frequently if necessary). Vacuum the upholstery and carpets to remove loose dirt and dust.

2 Leather upholstery requires special care. Stains should be removed with warm water and a very mild soap solution. Use a clean, damp cloth to remove the soap, then wipe again with a dry cloth. Never use alcohol, gasoline, nail polish remover or thinner to clean leather upholstery.

3 After cleaning, regularly treat leather upholstery with a leather wax. Never use car wax on leather upholstery.

4 In areas where the interior of the vehicle is subject to bright sunlight, cover leather seats with a sheet if the vehicle is to be left out for any length of time.

4 Body repair – minor damage

See photo sequence

Repair of minor scratches

1 If the scratch is superficial and does not penetrate to the metal of the body, repair is very simple. Lightly rub the scratched area with a fine rubbing compound to remove loose paint and built up wax. Rinse the area with clean water.

2 Apply touch-up paint to the scratch, using a small brush. Continue to apply thin layers of paint until the surface of the paint in the scratch is level with the surrounding paint. Allow the new paint at least two weeks to harden, then blend it into the surrounding paint by rubbing with a very fine rubbing compound. Finally, apply a coat of wax to the scratch area.

3 If the scratch has penetrated the paint and exposed the metal of the body, causing the metal to rust, a different repair technique is required. Remove all loose rust from the bottom of the scratch with a pocket knife, then apply rust inhibiting paint to prevent the formation of rust in the future. Using a rubber or nylon applicator, coat the scratched area with glaze-type filler. If required, the filler can be mixed with thinner to provide a very thin paste, which is ideal for filling narrow scratches. Before the glaze filler in the scratch hardens, wrap a piece of smooth cotton cloth around the tip of a finger. Dip the cloth in thinner and then quickly wipe it along the surface of the scratch. This will ensure that the surface of the filler is slightly hollow. The scratch can now be painted over as described earlier in this section.

Repair of dents

4 When repairing dents, the first job is to pull the dent out until the affected area is as close as possible to its original shape. There is no point in trying to restore the original shape completely as the metal in the damaged area will have stretched on impact and cannot be restored to its original contours. It is better to bring the level of the dent up to a point which is

about 1/8-inch below the level of the surrounding metal. In cases where the dent is very shallow, it is not worth trying to pull it out at all.

5 If the back side of the dent is accessible, it can be hammered out gently from behind using a soft-face hammer. While doing this, hold a block of wood firmly against the opposite side of the metal to absorb the hammer blows and prevent the metal from being stretched.

6 If the dent is in a section of the body which has double layers, or some other factor makes it inaccessible from behind, a different technique is required. Drill several small holes through the metal inside the damaged area, particularly in the deeper sections. Screw long, self tapping screws into the holes just enough for them to get a good grip in the metal. Now the dent can be pulled out by pulling on the protruding heads of the screws with locking pliers.

7 The next stage of repair is the removal of paint from the damaged area and from an inch or so of the surrounding metal. This is easily done with a wire brush or sanding disk in a drill motor, although it can be done just as effectively by hand with sandpaper. To complete the preparation for filling, score the surface of the bare metal with a screwdriver or the tang of a file or drill small holes in the affected area. This will provide a good grip for the filler material. To complete the repair, see the Section on filling and painting.

Repair of rust holes or gashes

8 Remove all paint from the affected area and from an inch or so of the surrounding metal using a sanding disk or wire brush mounted in a drill motor. If these are not available, a few sheets of sandpaper will do the job just as effectively.

9 With the paint removed, you will be able to determine the severity of the corrosion and decide whether to replace the whole panel, if possible, or repair the affected area. New body panels are not as expensive as most people think and it is often quicker to install a new panel than to repair large areas of rust.

10 Remove all trim pieces from the affected area except those which will act as a guide to the original shape of the damaged body, such as headlight shells, etc. Using metal snips or a hacksaw blade, remove all loose metal and any other metal that is badly affected by rust. Hammer the edges of the hole inward to create a slight depression for the filler material.

11 Wire brush the affected area to remove the powdery rust from the surface of the metal. If the back of the rusted area is accessible, treat it with rust inhibiting paint.

12 Before filling is done, block the hole in some way. This can be done with sheet metal riveted or screwed into place, or by stuffing the hole with wire mesh.

13 Once the hole is blocked off, the affected area can be filled and painted. See the following subsection on filling and painting.

Filling and painting

14 Many types of body fillers are available, but generally speaking, body repair kits which contain filler paste and a tube of resin hardener are best for this type of repair work. A wide, flexible plastic or nylon applicator will be necessary for imparting a smooth and contoured finish to the surface of the filler material. Mix up a small amount of filler on a clean piece of wood or cardboard (use the hardener sparingly). Follow the manufacturer's instructions on the package, otherwise the filler will set incorrectly.

15 Using the applicator, apply the filler paste to the prepared area. Draw the applicator across the surface of the filler to achieve the desired contour and to level the filler surface. As soon as a contour that approximates the original one is achieved, stop working the paste. If you continue, the paste will begin to stick to the applicator. Continue to add thin layers of paste at 20-minute intervals until the level of the filler is just above the surrounding metal.

16 Once the filler has hardened, the excess can be removed with a body file. From then on, progressively finer grades of sandpaper should be used, starting with a 180-grit paper and finishing with 600-grit wet-or-dry paper. Always wrap the sandpaper around a flat rubber or wooden block, otherwise the surface of the filler will not be completely flat. During the sanding of the filler surface, the wet-or-dry paper should be periodically rinsed in water. This will ensure that a very smooth finish is produced in the final stage.

11

17   At this point, the repair area should be surrounded by a ring of bare metal, which in turn should be encircled by the finely feathered edge of good paint. Rinse the repair area with clean water until all of the dust produced by the sanding operation is gone.

18   Spray the entire area with a light coat of primer. This will reveal any imperfections in the surface of the filler. Repair the imperfections with fresh filler paste or glaze filler and once more smooth the surface with sandpaper. Repeat this spray-and-repair procedure until you are satisfied that the surface of the filler and the feathered edge of the paint are perfect. Rinse the area with clean water and allow it to dry completely.

19   The repair area is now ready for painting. Spray painting must be carried out in a warm, dry, windless and dust free atmosphere. These conditions can be created if you have access to a large indoor work area, but if you are forced to work in the open, you will have to pick the day very carefully. If you are working indoors, dousing the floor in the work area with water will help settle the dust which would otherwise be in the air. If the repair area is confined to one body panel, mask off the surrounding panels. This will help minimize the effects of a slight mismatch in paint color. Trim pieces such as chrome strips, door handles, etc., will also need to be masked off or removed. Use masking tape and several thicknesses of newspaper for the masking operations.

20   Before spraying, shake the paint can thoroughly, then spray a test area until the spray painting technique is mastered. Cover the repair area with a thick coat of primer. The thickness should be built up using several thin layers of primer rather than one thick one. Using 600-grit wet-or-dry sandpaper, rub down the surface of the primer until it is very smooth. While doing this, the work area should be thoroughly rinsed with water and the wet-or-dry sandpaper periodically rinsed as well. Allow the primer to dry before spraying additional coats.

21   Spray on the top coat, again building up the thickness by using several thin layers of paint. Begin spraying in the center of the repair area and then, using a circular motion, work out until the whole repair area and about two inches of the surrounding original paint is covered. Remove all masking material 10 to 15 minutes after spraying on the final coat of paint. Allow the new paint at least two weeks to harden, then use a very fine rubbing compound to blend the edges of the new paint into the existing paint. Finally, apply a coat of wax.

5   Body repair – major damage

1   Major damage must be repaired by an auto body shop specifically equipped to repair major damage. These shops have the specialized equipment required to do the job properly.

2   If the damage is extensive, the body must be checked for proper alignment or the vehicle's handling characteristics may be adversely affected and other components may wear at an accelerated rate.

3   Due to the fact that all of the major body components (hood, fenders, etc.) are separate and replaceable units, any seriously damaged components should be replaced rather than repaired. Sometimes the components can be found in a wrecking yard that specializes in used vehicle components, often at considerable savings over the cost of new parts.

6   Hinges and locks – maintenance

Once every 3000 miles, or every three months, the hinges and latch assemblies on the doors, hood and tailgate should be given a few drops of light oil or lock lubricant. The door latch strikers should also be lubricated with a thin coat of grease to reduce wear and ensure free movement. Lubricate the door and tailgate locks with spray-on graphite lubricant.

7   Fixed glass – replacement

Replacement of the windshield and fixed glass requires the use of special fast-setting adhesive/caulk materials and some specialized tools and techniques. These operations should be left to a dealer service department or a shop specializing in glass work.

8   Radiator grille – removal and installation

Refer to illustration 8.1, 8.2, 8.4a, 8.4b and 8.5
Note: The radiator grille on some Tracker and Sidekick models is not removable.

1   If the vehicle is equipped with optional headlight guards, remove the screws and pull off the guards (see illustration). Note: The screws have backing plates located inside the fender. Reach inside the fender to hold them so they won't fall when you remove the screws.

2   If the vehicle is equipped with an optional grille guard, remove the bolts under the bumper and remove the guard (see illustration).

3   Remove the screws that attach the grille to the body. Note that many later models have no screws.

8.1 Remove the mounting screws and pull off the headlight guards

8.2 Unscrew the lower mounting bolts and remove the grille guard (if equipped)

8.4a   Carefully pry the grille away from the fender to free the locating pins (arrows) – be careful not to break the grille!

8.5   Remove the mesh insert from the body

4   Pry the grille away from the fender to free the locating pins (**see illustrations**).
5   If equipped, remove the mesh insert from the body (**see illustration**).

9   Hood – removal and installation

Refer to illustrations 9.2
Note: *The hood is heavy and somewhat awkward to remove and install – at least two people should perform this procedure. There is no provision for adjustment of the hood latch, so the hood alignment cannot be adjusted*

1   Use blankets or pads to cover the cowl area of the body and the fenders. This will protect the body and paint as the hood is lifted off.
2   Scribe or paint alignment marks around the hinges to insure proper alignment during installation (**see illustration**).
3   Disconnect any cables or wire harnesses which will interfere with removal.
4   Have an assistant support the weight of the hood. Remove the hinge-to-hood bolts.
5   Lift off the hood.
6   Installation is the reverse of removal.

10   Bumpers – removal and installation

Refer to illustrations 10.3 and 10.4
1   Detach the bumper cover (if equipped).
2   Disconnect the turn signal electrical connectors located under the hood, near each headlight assembly.
3   Support the bumper with a jack or jackstand. Alternatively, have an assistant support the bumper as the bolts are removed (**see illustration**).
4   Remove the retaining bolts located under the wheelwells (**see illustration**) and detach the bumper.

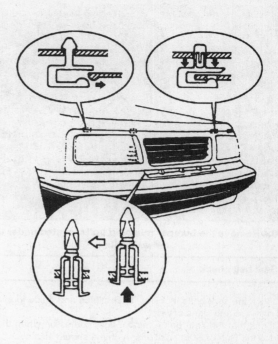

8.4b On many later models, the grille is attached with clips only

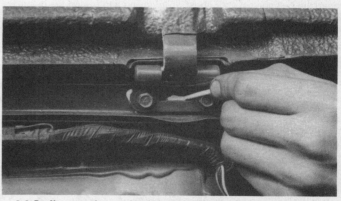

9.2 Scribe or paint marks around the hinges to insure proper alignment on installation

10.3 Support the bumper with a jack – place a wood block between the jack head and bumper

5   Installation is the reverse of removal.
6   Tighten the retaining bolts securely.
7   Install the bumper cover and any other components that were removed.

11

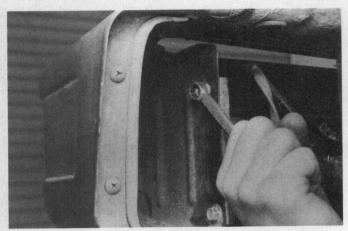

10.4 Remove the bumper retaining bolts located under the wheel wells

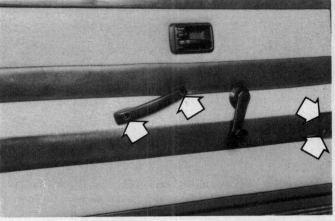

12.2a Remove all door trim panel retaining screws and the armrest (Samurai shown)

11   Seat belt check

1   Check the seat belts, buckles, latch plates and guide loops for obvious damage and signs of wear.
2   Check that the seat belt reminder light comes on when the key is turned to the Run or Start positions. A chime should also sound.
3   The seat belts are designed to lock up during a sudden stop or impact, yet allow free movement during normal driving. Check that the retractors return the belt against your chest while driving and rewind the belt fully when the buckle is unlatched.

4   If any of the above checks reveal problems with the seat belt system, replace parts as necessary.

12   Door trim panel – removal and installation

Refer to illustrations 12.2a, 12.2b, 12.3 and 12.6
1   Disconnect the negative cable from the battery.
2   Remove all door trim panel retaining screws and door pull/armrest assemblies **(see illustrations)**.

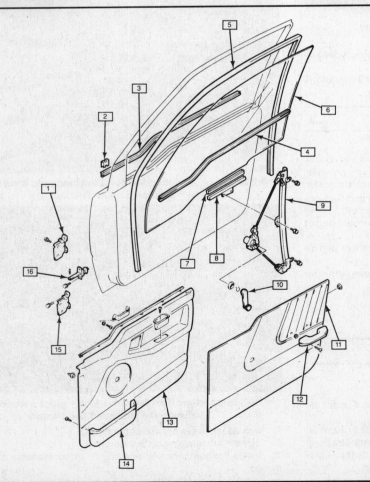

12.2b Door assembly – exploded view (Sidekick/Tracker)

1   *Door hinge*
2   *Clip*
3   *Weatherstrip (outside)*
4   *Weatherstrip (inside)*
5   *Door glass run*
6   *Door glass*
7   *Glass bottom channel rubber*
8   *Glass bottom channel*
9   *Window regulator assembly*
10   *Window crank handle*
11   *Trim panel (standard interior)*
12   *Armrest*
13   *Trim panel (deluxe interior)*
14   *Door trim pocket*
15   *Door hinge*
16   *Door open stop*

12.3   Remove the snap-ring by working a cloth back-and-forth under the crank handle

3   Remove the window crank handle. Pop out the snap-ring using a cloth **(see illustration)**.
4   Insert a putty knife between the trim panel and the door and disengage the retaining clips. Work around the outer edge until the panel is free.
5   Once all of the clips are disengaged, detach the trim panel, unplug any wire harness connectors and remove the trim panel from the vehicle.
6   For access to the inner door, carefully peel back the plastic watershield **(see illustration)**.
7   Prior to installation of the door panel, be sure to reinstall any clips in the panel which may have come out during the removal procedure and remain in the door itself.
8   Plug in the wire harness connectors and place the panel in position in the door. Press the door panel into place until the clips are seated and install the armrest/door pulls. Install the window crank handle.

13   Door – removal, installation and adjustment

Refer to illustration 13.6

1   Remove the door trim panel (see Section 12). Disconnect any wire harness connectors and push them through the door opening so they won't interfere with door removal.
2   Place a jack or jackstand under the door or have an assistant on hand to support it when the hinge bolts are removed. **Note:** *If a jack or jackstand is used, place a rag between it and the door to protect the door's painted surfaces.*
3   Scribe around the door hinges **(see illustration 12.2b)**.
4   Remove the hinge-to-door bolts and carefully lift off the door.
5   Installation is the reverse of removal.
6   Following installation of the door, check the alignment and adjust it if

12.6   Remove the plastic watershield, being careful not to tear it

necessary as follows:
   a) Up-and-down and forward-and-backward adjustments are made by loosening the hinge-to-body bolts and moving the door as necessary.
   b) The door lock striker can also be adjusted both up-and-down and side-to-side to provide positive engagement with the lock mechanism. This is done by loosening the mounting screws and moving the striker as necessary **(see illustration)**.
   c) If the striker is too far to the front or rear to properly engage the door latch, the striker may be adjusted by adding or removing shims from beneath it.

14   Tailgate – removal, installation and adjustment (hardtop models only)

Removal

1   Remove the spare tire assembly.
2   Remove the trim panel by pushing the plastic stud retainers in the center to release them.
3   Remove the plastic watershield. Be careful not to tear it.
4   Disconnect the electrical connectors for the rear window defogger and wiper and also disconnect the license plate lamp.
5   To ensure proper adjustment when the tailgate is reinstalled, use a scribe or a marker to mark around the tailgate hinge plates.

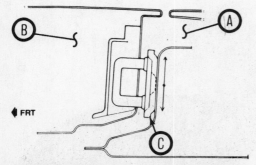

13.6   To adjust the door latch striker, loosen the mounting screws and move it, as necessary

   A   Body   C   Door latch striker
   B   Door

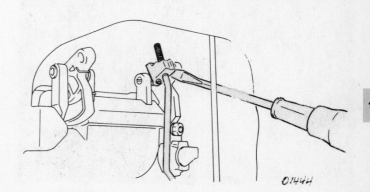

16.3   Pry the door opening control rod from the outside door handle

11

These photos illustrate a method of repairing simple dents. They are intended to supplement *Body repair - minor damage* in this Chapter and should not be used as the sole instructions for body repair on these vehicles.

1   If you can't access the backside of the body panel to hammer out the dent, pull it out with a slide-hammer-type dent puller. In the deepest portion of the dent or along the crease line, drill or punch hole(s) at least one inch apart . . .

2   . . . then screw the slide-hammer into the hole and operate it. Tap with a hammer near the edge of the dent to help 'pop' the metal back to its original shape. When you're finished, the dent area should be close to its original contour and about 1/8-inch below the surface of the surrounding metal

3   Using coarse-grit sandpaper, remove the paint down to the bare metal. Hand sanding works fine, but the disc sander shown here makes the job faster. Use finer (about 320-grit) sandpaper to feather-edge the paint at least one inch around the dent area

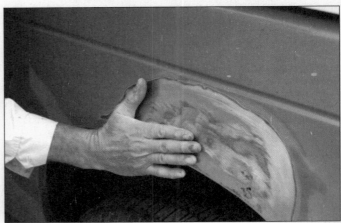

4   When the paint is removed, touch will probably be more helpful than sight for telling if the metal is straight. Hammer down the high spots or raise the low spots as necessary. Clean the repair area with wax/silicone remover

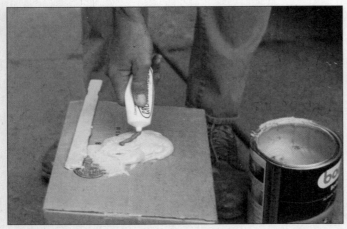

5   Following label instructions, mix up a batch of plastic filler and hardener. The ratio of filler to hardener is critical, and, if you mix it incorrectly, it will either not cure properly or cure too quickly (you won't have time to file and sand it into shape)

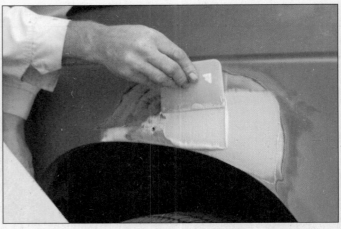

6   Working quickly so the filler doesn't harden, use a plastic applicator to press the body filler firmly into the metal, assuring it bonds completely. Work the filler until it matches the original contour and is slightly above the surrounding metal

7   Let the filler harden until you can just dent it with your fingernail. Use a body file or Surform tool (shown here) to rough-shape the filler

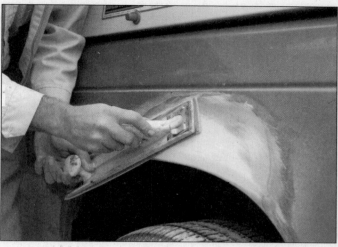

8   Use coarse-grit sandpaper and a sanding board or block to work the filler down until it's smooth and even. Work down to finer grits of sandpaper - always using a board or block - ending up with 360 or 400 grit

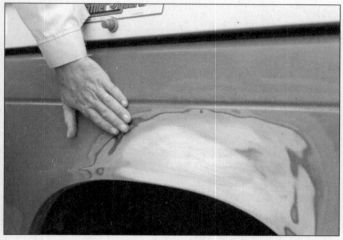

9   You shouldn't be able to feel any ridge at the transition from the filler to the bare metal or from the bare metal to the old paint. As soon as the repair is flat and uniform, remove the dust and mask off the adjacent panels or trim pieces

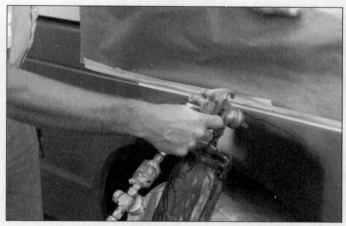

10   Apply several layers of primer to the area. Don't spray the primer on too heavy, so it sags or runs, and make sure each coat is dry before you spray on the next one. A professional-type spray gun is being used here, but aerosol spray primer is available inexpensively from auto parts stores

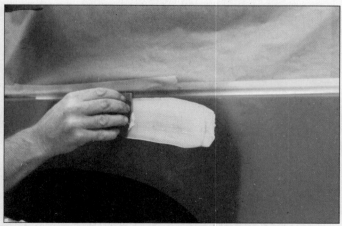

11   The primer will help reveal imperfections or scratches. Fill these with glazing compound. Follow the label instructions and sand it with 360 or 400-grit sandpaper until it's smooth. Repeat the glazing, sanding and respraying until the primer reveals a perfectly smooth surface

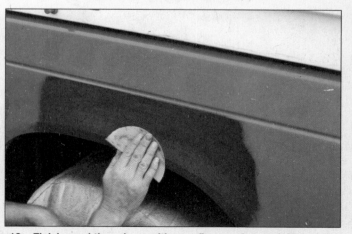

12   Finish sand the primer with very fine sandpaper (400 or 600-grit) to remove the primer overspray. Clean the area with water and allow it to dry. Use a tack rag to remove any dust, then apply the finish coat. Don't attempt to rub out or wax the repair area until the paint has dried completely (at least two weeks)

6   Disconnect the support strut from the tailgate.
7   Have an assistant support the tailgate. Alternatively, support the tailgate using a wood block and a floor jack. Place a towel or cloth between
the wood and the tailgate.
8   Remove the upper and lower hinge bolts from the tailgate.
9   Remove the tailgate.

Installation

10   Have an assistant help you lift the tailgate into position. Alternatively,
lift it with a floor jack and a wood block.
11   Install the tailgate following the reverse order of the above procedure.
To ensure proper adjustment, be sure to align the marks you made during
removal.

Adjustment

12   After installation, close the tailgate and check that it is in proper alignment with the surrounding body panels. Adjustments to the tailgate are
made by moving the position of the hinge bolts in their slots. To adjust,
loosen the hinge bolts, reposition the tailgate the desired amount and retighten the bolts.
13   The engagement of the tailgate can be adjusted by loosening the lock
striker screws, repositioning the striker on the body and retightening the
screws. If the striker is too far to the left or right to properly engage the the
latch on the tailgate, add or remove shims from beneath the striker. **Note:**
Do not adjust the latch.

15   Center console – removal and installation (Sidekick/Tracker only)

1   Remove the two Phillips screws on the side of the console, then remove the two clips at the rear and pull off the rear console cover. To remove the clips, push in the center pins first.
2   Use a 3 mm hex drive to remove the two screws at the rear of the console. Lift off the console.
3   Installation is the reverse of removal.

16   Door latch, lock cylinder and handles – removal and installation

Refer to illustrations 16.3, 16.4 and 16.5
1   Remove the door trim panel as described in Section 12.
2   Remove the plastic watershield, taking care not to tear it **(see illustration 12.6)**.
3   Disengage the door opening control rod from the connection at the
door outside handle. Pry gently with a screwdriver **(see illustration)**.
4   Remove the screw(s) that retain the interior handle assembly and lift it
out **(see illustration)**.

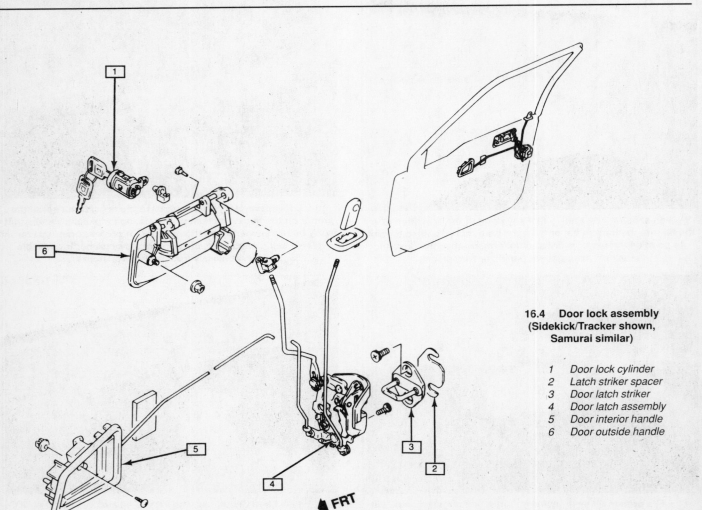

**16.4   Door lock assembly
(Sidekick/Tracker shown,
Samurai similar)**

1   *Door lock cylinder*
2   *Latch striker spacer*
3   *Door latch striker*
4   *Door latch assembly*
5   *Door interior handle*
6   *Door outside handle*

◀ **FRT**

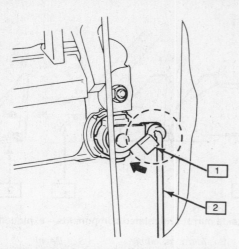

16.5   Unclip the retainer (1) and remove the door lock control rod (2)

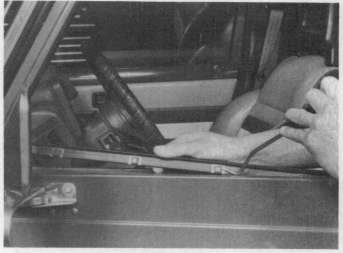

17.2   Locate the molding clips and pry them up to remove the molding pieces

17.3a   With the window rolled down, remove the two mounting screws (Samurai shown, Sidekick/Tracker similar)

17.3b   Remove the glass by carefully pulling it up – tilt it so it clears the channel

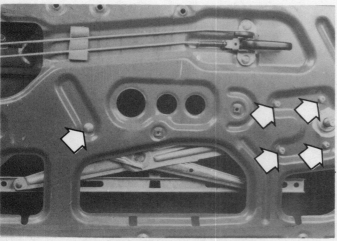

17.4a   Locations of the regulator mounting screws (Samurai)

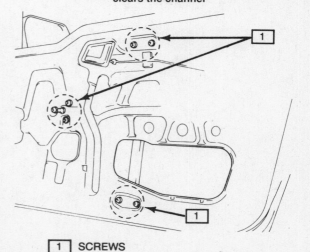

1   SCREWS

17.4b   Locations of the regulator mounting screws (Sidekick/Tracker)

11

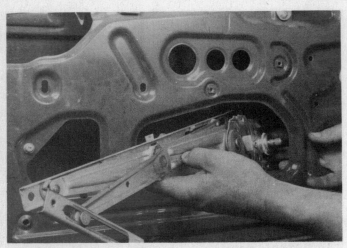

17.4c   The regulator can be removed through the large access hole in the door

5   Disengage the door lock rod from the door lock assembly **(see illustration)**.
6   Remove the retaining clip from the door lock cylinder and remove the cylinder.
7   Remove the door latch assembly mounting screws, located on the outside rear of the door, and lift out the latch assembly.
8   If necessary, remove the two nuts retaining the exterior handle and lift it out.
9   Installation is the reverse of removal. **Note:** *During installation, apply grease to the sliding surface of all levers and springs.*

17   Door window glass and regulator – removal and installation

Refer to illustrations 17.2, 17.3a, 17.3b, 17.4a, 17.4b and 17.4c
1   Remove the door trim panel and watershield (see Section 12).
2   Using a curved tool, remove the two molding pieces located on the top of the door **(see illustration)**.
3   Remove the glass mounting screws and pull the glass out the top of the door **(see illustrations)**.
4   If necessary, remove the regulator mounting screws and remove the regulator through the large access hole **(see illustrations)**.

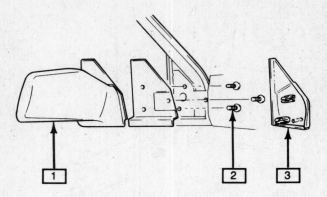

18.1   Outside mirror and related components – exploded view

    1   Mirror assembly   3   Bezel
    2   Screws

5   Prior to installing the regulator and guide channel, apply a light coat of lithium-based grease to all their sliding surfaces.
6   Installation is the reverse of the removal procedure. Following installation of the window, roll it up completely and use the following procedure to bring it into correct alignment.
  a) The tilt of the window can be adjusted by loosening the regulator retaining screws and moving the glass so that its upper edge is parallel with the upper edge of the door. Following adjustment, retighten the screws.
  b) To adjust the window in the fore-and-aft position, loosen the regulator retaining screws, then adjust the glass so that its rear edge and upper rear corner are seated firmly in the rubber of the door frame. Following adjustment, retighten the retaining screws.

18   Outside mirror – removal and installation

Refer to illustration 18.1
1   Remove the mirror bezel **(see illustration)**.
2   Remove mirror attaching screws.
3   Remove mirror assembly.
4   Installation is the reverse of the above procedure.

Chapter 12   Chassis electrical system

Contents

---

1   General information

The electrical system is a 12-volt, negative ground type. Power for the lights and all electrical accessories is supplied by a lead/acid-type battery which is charged by the alternator.

This Chapter covers repair and service procedures for the various electrical components not associated with the engine. Information on the battery, alternator, distributor and starter motor can be found in Chapter 5.

It should be noted that when portions of the electrical system are serviced, the negative battery cable should be disconnected from the battery to prevent electrical shorts and/or fires.

---

2   Electrical troubleshooting – general information

A typical electrical circuit consists of an electrical component, any switches, relays, motors, fuses, fusible links or circuit breakers related to that component and the wiring and connectors that link the component to both the battery and the chassis. To help you pinpoint an electrical circuit problem, wiring diagrams are included at the end of this book.

Before tackling any troublesome electrical circuit, first study the appropriate wiring diagrams to get a complete understanding of what makes up that individual circuit. Trouble spots, for instance, can often be narrowed down by noting if other components related to the circuit are operating properly. If several components or circuits fail at one time, chances are the

12

problem is in a fuse or ground connection, because several circuits are often routed through the same fuse and ground connections.

Electrical problems usually stem from simple causes, such as loose or corroded connections, a blown fuse, a melted fusible link or a bad relay. Visually inspect the condition of all fuses, wires and connections in a problem circuit before troubleshooting it.

If testing instruments are going to be utilized, use the diagrams to plan ahead of time where you will make the necessary connections in order to accurately pinpoint the trouble spot.

The basic tools needed for electrical troubleshooting include a circuit tester or voltmeter (a 12-volt bulb with a set of test leads can also be used), a continuity tester, which includes a bulb, battery and set of test leads, and a jumper wire, preferably with a circuit breaker incorporated, which can be used to bypass electrical components. Before attempting to locate a problem with test instruments, use the wiring diagram(s) to decide where to make the connections.

Voltage checks

Voltage checks should be performed if a circuit is not functioning properly. Connect one lead of a circuit tester to either the negative battery terminal or a known good ground. Connect the other lead to a connector in the circuit being tested, preferably nearest to the battery or fuse. If the bulb of the tester lights, voltage is present, which means that the part of the circuit between the connector and the battery is problem free. Continue checking the rest of the circuit in the same fashion. When you reach a point at which no voltage is present, the problem lies between that point and the last test point with voltage. Most of the time the problem can be traced to a loose connection. **Note:** *Keep in mind that some circuits receive voltage only when the ignition key is in the Accessory or Run position.*

Finding a short

One method of finding shorts in a circuit is to remove the fuse and connect a test light or voltmeter in its place to the fuse terminals. There should be no voltage present in the circuit. Move the wiring harness from side-to-side while watching the test light.

If the bulb goes on, there is a short to ground somewhere in that area, probably where the insulation has rubbed through. The same test can be performed on each component in the circuit, even a switch.

Ground check

Perform a ground test to check whether a component is properly grounded. Disconnect the battery and connect one lead of a selfpowered test light, known as a continuity tester, to a known good ground. Connect the other lead to the wire or ground connection being tested. If the bulb goes on, the ground is good. If the bulb does not go on, the ground is not good.

Continuity check

A continuity check is done to determine if there are any breaks in a circuit – if it is passing electricity properly. With the circuit off (no power in the circuit), a self-powered continuity tester can be used to check the circuit.

Connect the test leads to both ends of the circuit (or to the "power" end and a good ground), and if the test light comes on the circuit is passing current properly. If the light doesn't come on, there is a break somewhere in the circuit. The same procedure can be used to test a switch, by connecting the continuity tester to the switch terminals. With the switch turned On, the test light should come on.

Finding an open circuit

When diagnosing for possible open circuits, it is often difficult to locate them by sight because oxidation or terminal misalignment are hidden by the connectors. Merely wiggling a connector on a sensor or in the wiring harness may correct the open circuit condition. Remember this when an open circuit is indicated when troubleshooting a circuit. Intermittent problems may also be caused by oxidized or loose connections.

Electrical troubleshooting is simple if you keep in mind that all electrical circuits are basically electricity running from the battery, through the wires, switches, relays, fuses and fusible links to each electrical component (light bulb, motor, etc.) and to ground, from which it is passed back to the battery. Any electrical problem is an interruption in the flow of electricity to and from the battery.

---

3   Fuses – general information

Refer to illustrations 3.1a, 3.1b and 3.3

The electrical circuits of the vehicle are protected by a combination of fuses, circuit breakers and fusible links. The fuse block is located under the instrument panel on the left side of the dashboard **(see illustrations)**.

3.1a   The fuse box is located under the left side of the dash, on the firewall (Samurai)

FUSE BOX DESIGNATION

1	2	3	4	5	6	7
10A HEAD R	10A HEAD L	15A TAIL	15A STOP HORN	15A HAZARD	20A CIGAR	
8	9	10	11	12	13	14
15A IG. COIL METER	10A TURN BACK	15A WIPER WASHER	15A REAR DEFG.	20A HEATER		DIAG.

3.1b   Sidekick/Tracker fuse block details

1   *Right headlight*
2   *Left headlight, high beam indicator*
3   *Marker light, taillight, interior light*
4   *Brake light, horn*
5   *Hazard*
6   *Cigar lighter, radio*
8   *Ignition coil, distributor, meter*
9   *Turn signal light, back-up light*
10   *Rear defogger*
11   *Wiper, washer*
12   *Heater*
14   *Diagnosis*

OK   Burned out

3.3   The type of fuse used on these models can be easily checked visually

Each of the fuses is designed to protect a specific circuit, and the various circuits are identified on the fuse panel itself.

Miniaturized fuses are employed in the fuse block. These compact fuses, with blade terminal design, allow fingertip removal and replacement. If an electrical component fails, always check the fuse first. A blown fuse is easily identified through the clear plastic body. Visually inspect the element for evidence of damage **(see illustration)**. If a continuity check is called for, the blade terminal tips are exposed in the fuse body.

Be sure to replace blown fuses with the correct type. Fuses of different ratings are physically interchangeable, but only fuses of the proper rating should be used. Replacing a fuse with one of a higher or lower value than specified is not recommended. Each electrical circuit needs a specific amount of protection. The amperage value of each fuse is molded into the fuse body.

If the replacement fuse immediately fails, don't replace it again until the cause of the problem is isolated and corrected. In most cases, the cause will be a short circuit in the wiring caused by a broken or deteriorated wire.

4.2   A fusible link protects the wire harness from overload and possible damage (Samurai)

4   Fusible links – general information

Refer to illustration 4.2

Some circuits are protected by fusible links. The links are used in circuits which are not ordinarily fused, such as the ignition circuit.

Although the fusible links appear to be a heavier gauge than the wire they are protecting, the appearance is due to the thick insulation. All fusible links are four wire gauges smaller than the wire they are designed to protect **(see illustration)**.

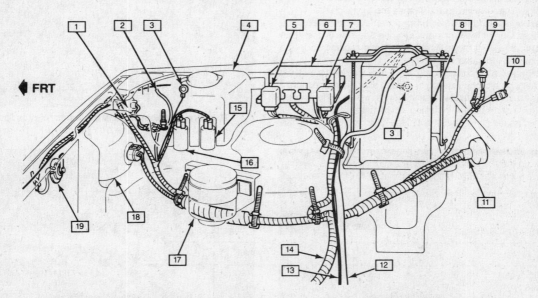

5.2   Engine compartment relays, wiring and related components (Sidekick/Tracker models)

1	Turn signal and small light	8	Battery	13	Battery ground cable
2	Right turn signal/parking light	9	To pressure sensor	14	Main wiring harness no. 1
3	Ground	10	To recirculated exhaust gas	15	Front washer pump
4	Washer tank		temperature sensor (California only)	16	Rear washer pump (optional)
5	P.T.C. relay (A/T only)	11	To instrument panel	17	Canister
6	Main fuse box	12	To alternator and starter	18	Headlight
7	Lock up relay			19	Horn

12

Fusible links cannot be repaired, but a new link of the same size wire can be put in its place. The procedure is as follows:
a) Disconnect the negative cable from the battery.
b) Disconnect the fusible link from the wiring harness.
c) Cut the damaged fusible link out of the wiring just behind the connector.
d) Strip the insulation back approximately 1/2-inch.
e) Position the connector on the new fusible link and crimp it into place.
f) Use rosin core solder at each end of the new link to obtain a good solder joint.
g) Use plenty of electrical tape around the soldered joint. No wires should be exposed.
h) Connect the battery ground cable. Test the circuit for proper operation.

5   Relays – general information

Refer to illustration 5.2

Several electrical accessories in the vehicle use relays to transmit the electrical signal to the component. If the relay is defective, that component will not operate properly.

The various relays are grouped together in several locations **(see illustrations)**.

If a faulty relay is suspected, it can be removed and tested by a dealer service department or a repair shop. Defective relays must be replaced as a unit.

6   Turn signal and hazard flashers – check and replacement

Refer to illustration 6.1

Turn signal flasher

1   The turn signal flasher, a small canister or box-shaped unit located above the fuse block **(see illustration)**, flashes the turn signals.
2   When the flasher unit is functioning properly, an audible click can be heard during its operation. If the turn signals fail on one side or the other and the flasher unit does not make its characteristic clicking sound, a faulty turn signal bulb is indicated.
3   If both turn signals fail to blink, the problem may be due to a blown fuse, a faulty flasher unit, a broken switch or a loose or open connection. If a quick check of the fuse box indicates that the turn signal fuse has blown, check the wiring for a short before installing a new fuse.
4   To replace the flasher, simply pull it out of the fuse block or wiring harness.

5   Make sure that the replacement unit is identical to the original. Compare the old one to the new one before installing it.
6   Installation is the reverse of removal.

Hazard flasher

7   The hazard flasher, which is integral with the turn signal flasher, flashes all four turn signals simultaneously when activated.
8   The hazard flasher is checked in a fashion similar to the turn signal flasher (see Steps 2 and 3).
9   To replace the hazard flasher, pull it from the back of fuse block.
10   Make sure the replacement unit is identical to the one it replaces. Compare the old one to the new one before installing it.
11   Installation is the reverse of removal.

7   Ignition switch – removal and installation

Refer to illustrations 7.2, 7.3a, 7.3b and 7.4

Removal

1   Disconnect the negative cable at the battery.
2   Remove the steering column covers. Locate the set screws on the bottom cowl directly below the ignition switch and remove the bottom cowl first **(see illustration)**.
3   Locate the shear bolts that attach the ignition lock onto the steering column **(see illustration)** and remove the shear bolts. **Note:** *There are*

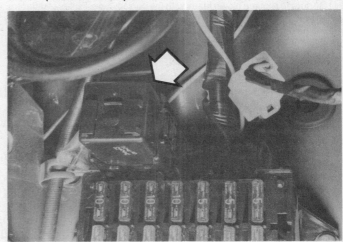
6.1   The turn signal and hazard flasher relay is located above the fuse box (Samurai)

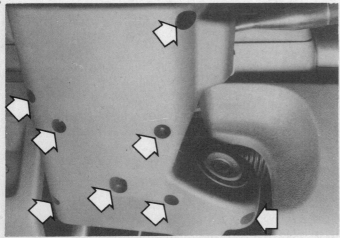
7.2   Remove the screws securing the bottom cowl and detach the cowl from the steering column (Samurai model shown).

7.3a   The ignition switch/lock is fastened to the steering column with two shear bolts (arrows)

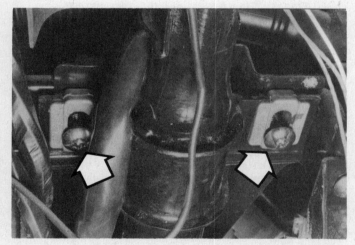

7.3b   Use a sharp chisel to turn the bolts counterclockwise

| 1 | Chisel | 2 | Shear bolts |

7.4   Unplug the electrical connector and remove the lock from the steering column

several methods used to remove these specialized locking bolts. The most common method is to use a sharp chisel to notch the head and turn the bolt counterclockwise while tapping the chisel with a hammer **(see illustration)**. If that method does not work, use a medium size drill bit and an easy-out.

4   Disconnect the electrical connectors from the switch **(see illustration)**.

Installation

5   Installation is the reverse of the removal procedure. **Note:** *Use new shear bolts and tighten them until the heads break off, as an anti-theft measure.*

8   Turn signal switch – removal and installation

Refer to illustrations 8.4, 8.5 and 8.6

1   Disconnect the negative cable at the battery.
2   Remove the bottom cowl below the steering column **(see illustration 7.2)**.
3   Remove the steering wheel (see Chapter 10).
4   Lower the steering column by removing the two Torx-head bolts located under the dash **(see illustration)**.
5   Remove the two upper and the two lower screws that hold the turn signal switch to the column **(see illustration)**.
6   Disconnect the turn signal harness connectors under the dash and remove the switch assembly **(see illustration)**. **Note:** *On Samurai models the switch is a combination turn signal, dimmer and wiper/washer switch.*
7   Installation is the reverse of the removal procedure.

8.4   Use a Torx-drive socket to remove the steering column bolts

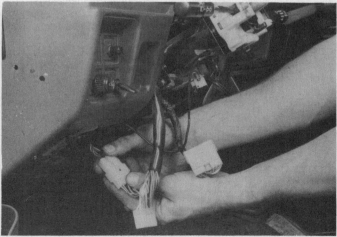

8.5   Remove the two upper and two lower mounting screws

8.6   Disconnect the turn signal switch electrical connectors

12

9.3   Remove only the screws that retain the bulb (arrows) – do not disturb the adjustment screws

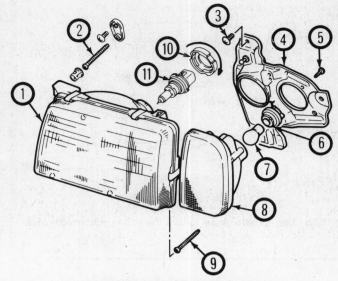

9.9   Headlight details (Sidekick/Tracker)

1	Headlight unit	7	Bulb
2	Adjusting upper screw	8	Turn signal light unit
3	Headlight screw	9	Adjusting lower screw
4	Bracket	10	Retaining ring
5	Turn signal light screw	11	Halogen bulb
6	Turn signal light socket		

9   Headlights – removal and installation

1   Disconnect the negative cable from the battery.

Sealed-beam type

Refer to illustration 9.3

2   Remove the front grille assembly (see Chapter 11).
3   Remove the headlight retainer screws, taking care not to disturb the adjustment screws **(see illustration)**.
4   Remove the retainer and pull the headlight out sufficiently to allow the connector to be unplugged.
5   Remove the headlight.
6   To install, plug the connector securely into the headlight, place the headlight in position and install the retainer and screws. Tighten the screws securely.
7   Install the front grille assembly.

Bulb type

Refer to illustration 9.9

Warning: *The halogen gas filled bulbs used on these models are under pressure and may shatter if the surface is scratched or the bulb is dropped. Wear eye protection and handle the bulbs carefully, grasping only the base whenever possible. Do not touch the surface of the bulb with your fingers because the oil from your skin could cause it to overheat and fail prematurely. If you do touch the bulb surface, clean it with rubbing alcohol.*

8   Open the hood. Unplug the electrical connector.
9   Reach behind the headlight assembly, grasp the bulb retaining ring and turn it counterclockwise to remove it **(see illustration)**. Lift the holder assembly out for access to the bulb.
10   Push in and rotate the bulb counterclockwise to remove it.
11   Insert the new bulb into the holder and turn it clockwise to seat it in the holder.
12   Install the bulb holder in the headlight assembly.

10   Headlights – adjustment

Note: *The headlights must be aimed correctly. If adjusted incorrectly they could blind the driver of an oncoming vehicle and cause a serious accident or seriously reduce your ability to see the road. The headlights should be checked for proper aim every 12 months and any time a new headlight is*

installed or front end body work is performed. It should be emphasized that the following procedure is only an interim step which will provide temporary adjustment until the headlights can be adjusted by a properly equipped shop.

1   Headlights have two spring loaded adjusting screws, one on the top controlling up-and-down movement and one on the side controlling left-and-right movement **(see illustrations 9.3 and 9.9)**.
2   There are several methods of adjusting the headlights. The simplest method requires a blank wall 25 feet in front of the vehicle and a level floor.
3   Position masking tape vertically on the wall in reference to the vehicle centerline and the centerlines of both headlights.
4   Position a horizontal tape line in reference to the centerline of all the headlights. **Note:** I*t may be easier to position the tape on the wall with the vehicle parked only a few inches away.*
5   Adjustment should be made with the vehicle sitting level, the gas tank half-full and no unusually heavy load in the vehicle.
6   Starting with the low beam adjustment, position the high intensity zone so it is two inches below the horizontal line and two inches to the right of the headlight vertical line. Adjustment is made by turning the top adjusting screw clockwise to raise the beam and counterclockwise to lower the beam. The adjusting screw on the side should be used in the same manner to move the beam left or right.
7   With the high beams on, the high intensity zone should be vertically centered with the exact center just below the horizontal line. **Note:** *It may not be possible to position the headlight aim exactly for both high and low beams. If a compromise must be made, keep in mind that the low beams are the most used and have the greatest effect on driver safety.*
8   Have the headlights adjusted by a dealer service department or service station at the earliest opportunity.

11   Radio and speakers – removal and installation

1   Disconnect the cable from the negative terminal of the battery.

11.2   Remove the retaining plate nuts with a deep socket

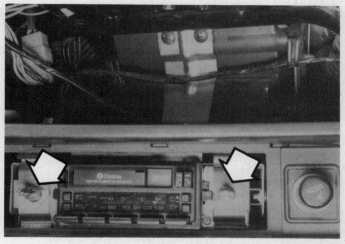

11.4   Unscrew the nuts on the front brace (arrows) and remove the radio from the back

Radio
Samurai
Refer to illustrations 11.2 and 11.4

2   Pull off the radio knobs and remove the retaining plate nuts with a deep socket **(see illustration)**.

3   Remove the bottom retaining screws and allow the radio/console unit to drop slightly.

4   Unscrew the nuts on the front brace and remove the radio from the back **(see illustration)**.

5   Installation is the reverse of the removal.

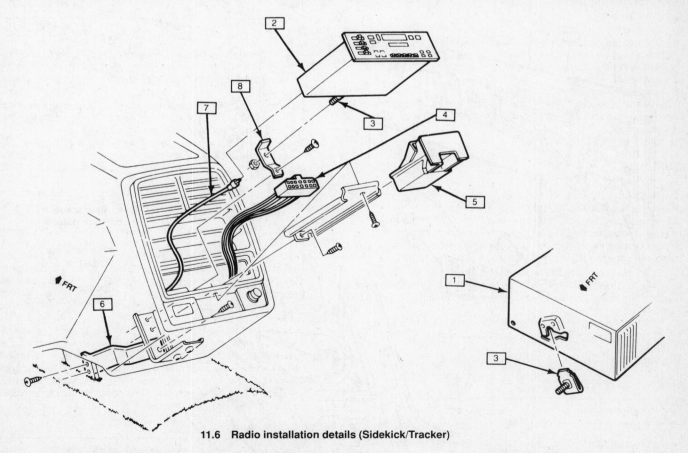

11.6   Radio installation details (Sidekick/Tracker)

1	Radio (rear view)	4	Electrical connector	6	Support bracket
2	Radio	5	Ashtray	7	Antenna lead
3	Stud			8	Rear retaining bracket

12

Sidekick/Tracker

Refer to illustration 11.6

6   Remove the rear retaining bracket screw **(see illustration)**.
7   Remove the four pins from the four corners of the radio front.
8   Disconnect the electrical connectors and antenna lead from the radio.
9   Installation is the reverse of removal

Front speaker

Refer to illustration 11.10

10   Remove the speaker grilles from the instrument panel by removing the two screws **(see illustration)**.
11   Remove the screws from the speaker.
12   Disconnect the electrical connector from the speaker.
13   Installation is the reverse of removal.

Rear speaker

Refer to illustration 11.14

14   Remove the interior trim side panel **(see illustration)**.
15   Remove the speaker securing screws.
16   Disconnect the electrical connector from the speaker.
17   Installation is the reverse of removal.

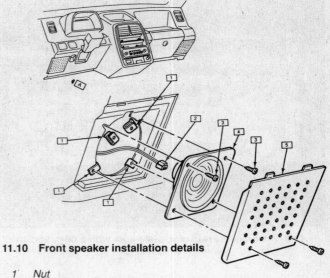

11.10   Front speaker installation details

1   *Nut*
2   *Electrical connector*
3   *Screw*
4   *Speaker assembly*
5   *Grille*

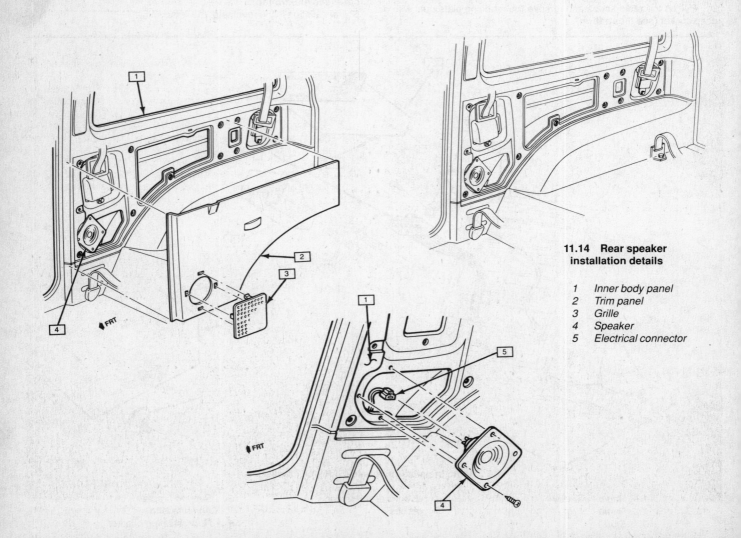

11.14   Rear speaker installation details

1   *Inner body panel*
2   *Trim panel*
3   *Grille*
4   *Speaker*
5   *Electrical connector*

12.3   Push the bulb in and twist it counterclockwise to remove it – when installing the bulb, make sure the pins on the bulb line up with the proper slots in the socket

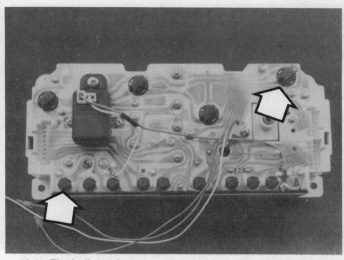

12.4   The bulb retainers are removed from the printed circuit board for access to the bulbs

13.2   Remove the upper mounting screws and pull the dashboard away from the firewall

12   Bulb replacement

Refer to illustrations 12.3 and 12.4

1   The lenses of many lights are held in place by screws, which makes it a simple procedure to gain access to the bulbs.

2   On some lights the lenses are held in place by clips. The lenses can be removed either by unsnapping them or by using a small screwdriver to pry them off.

3   Several types of bulbs are used. Some are removed by pushing in and turning them counterclockwise **(see illustration)**. Others can simply be unclipped from the terminals or pulled straight out of the socket.

4   To gain access to the instrument panel lights, the instrument cluster will have to be removed first (see Chapter 11). The bulb retainers twist off the rear of the printed circuit board for easy access **(see illustration)**.

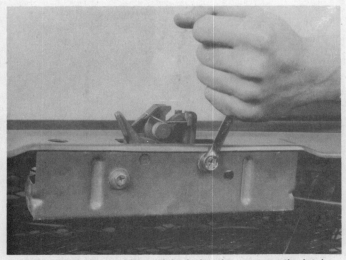

13.5a   Mark the positions of the bolts, then remove the latch

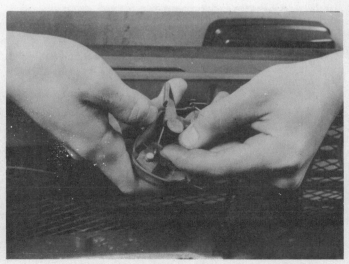

13.5b   To disconnect the cable, pull it up and slide it through the slot in the latch

12

13.6   Remove the glove box with the hood latch cable

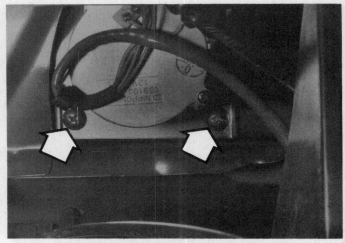

13.7   Remove the two lower windshield wiper motor mounting
screws from inside the glove box compartment (arrows)

13   Windshield wiper motor – removal and installation

Samurai

Refer to illustrations 13.2, 13.5a, 13.5b, 13.6, 13.7 and 13.9

1   Disconnect the negative cable at the battery.
2   Remove the plastic molding covers (**see illustration**) on the top of the dashboard to expose the dashboard mounting screws.
3   Remove the upper mounting screws and pull the dashboard out slightly.
4   Open the glove box and remove the glove box mounting screws.
5   Mark the hood latch bolts with a scribe or paint. Remove the hood latch and disconnect the cable from it (**see illustrations**).
6   Pull the glove box with the hood latch cable out of the dashboard (**see illustration**).
7   The windshield wiper motor is located under the dash on the passenger side, in the corner near the windshield. Remove the two lower mounting screws through the glove box compartment (**see illustration**).
8   Remove the two upper mounting bolts from above the dashboard.
9   Carefully pull the windshield wiper motor out from the firewall and remove the nut that attaches the wiper motor arm to the linkage (**see illus-

tration**). Disconnect the electrical connectors and remove the motor through the glove box compartment.
10   Installation is the reverse of the removal.

Sidekick/Tracker

Refer to illustration 13.11

11   The windshield wiper motor is located on the driver's side of the engine compartment, on the firewall (**see illustration**). Disconnect the electrical connector, remove the mounting screws and pull the motor out partially.
12   Remove the linkage nut and remove the windshield wiper motor.
13   Installation is the reverse of the removal.

14   Instrument cluster – removal and installation

Refer to illustration 14.7

1   Disconnect the negative cable at the battery.
2   Remove the steering wheel (see Chapter 10).
3   Remove the steering column covers (see Section 8).
4   Remove the torx drive bolts that support the steering column and lower the steering column (see Section 8).

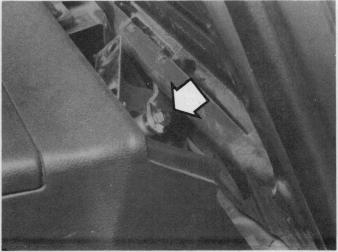

13.9   Remove the windshield wiper motor-to-linkage nut

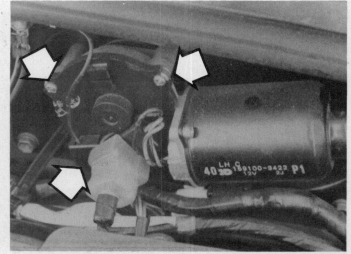

13.11   Remove the mounting screws and pull the motor out to
partially expose the linkage nut

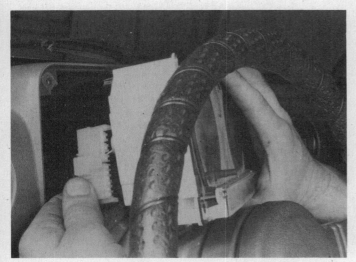

14.7   Press the locking tab on the electrical connector then unplug the connector from the instrument cluster

15.2   Remove the retaining bolt and pull the speedometer cable out of the transfer case

5   Remove the instrument cluster cover screws and remove the cover.
6   Disconnect the speedometer cable from the rear of the cluster.
7   Disconnect the wire harness connector **(see illustration)**.
8   Remove the combination meter.
9   Check the printed circuit board for any flaws or breaks before replacing any of the combination meter's components.
10   Installation is the reverse of removal.

4   Remove the instrument cluster screws, pull the cluster out and disconnect the speedometer cable from the back of the cluster.
5   Remove the cable from the vehicle.
6   Prior to installation, lubricate the speedometer end of the cable with spray-on speedometer cable lubricant (available at auto parts stores).
7   Installation is the reverse of removal.

16   Wiring diagrams – general information

Since it isn't possible to include all wiring diagrams for every model and year covered by this manual, the following diagrams are those that are typical and most commonly needed.

Prior to troubleshooting any circuit, check the fuse and circuit breakers (if equipped) to make sure they're in good condition. Make sure the battery is properly charged and check the cable connections (see Chapter 1).

When checking a circuit, make sure that all connectors are clean, with no broken or loose terminals. When unplugging a connector, do not pull on the wires. Pull only on the connector housings themselves.

15   Speedometer cable – replacement

Refer to illustration 15.2

1   Disconnect the negative cable from the battery.
2   Disconnect the speedometer cable from the transfer case **(see illustration)** by removing the retaining bolt.
3   Detach the cable from the routing clips in the engine compartment and pull it up to provide enough slack to allow disconnection from the speedometer.

WIRING DIAGRAM COLOR CODES

BLU/BLK : BLUE/BLACK
RED : RED
BLK/WHT : BLACK/WHITE
PNK : PINK
YEL : YELLOW
LT GRN : LIGHT GREEN
BLK : BLACK
YEL/BLU : YELLOW/BLUE
BLU/RED : BLUE/RED
BLK/YEL : BLACK/YELLOW
PNK/BLK : PINK/BLACK
BLU : BLUE
YEL/GRN : YELLOW/GREEN
WHT/BLU : WHITE/BLUE

WIRE COLOR

B	: Black	Gr/G	: Gray with Green tracer
Bl	: Blue	Gr/R	: Gray with Red tracer
Br	: Brown	Gr/Y	: Gray with Yellow tracer
G	: Green	Lg/B	: Light green with Black tracer
Gr	: Gray	Lg/R	: Light green with Red tracer
Lbl	: Light blue	Lg/W	: Light green with White tracer
Lg	: Light green	Lg/Y	: Light green with Yellow tracer
O	: Orange	O/B	: Orange with Black tracer
R	: Red	O/Bl	: Orange with Brown tracer
W	: White	O/G	: Orange with Green tracer
Y	: Yellow	O/R	: Orange with Red tracer
P	: Pink	O/W	: Orange with White tracer
V	: Violet	O/Y	: Orange with Yellow tracer
B/Bl	: Black with Blue tracer	P/B	: Pink with Black tracer
B/G	: Black with Green tracer	P/Bl	: Pink with Blue tracer
B/R	: Black with Red tracer	P/G	: Pink with Green tracer
B/W	: Black with White tracer	P/W	: Pink with White tracer
B/Y	: Black with Yellow tracer	V/R	: Violet with Red tracer
Bl/B	: Blue with Black tracer	V/Y	: Violet with Yellow tracer
Bl/G	: Blue with Green tracer	R/B	: Red with Black tracer
Bl/R	: Blue with Red tracer	R/Bl	: Red with Blue tracer
Bl/W	: Blue with White tracer	R/G	: Red with Green tracer
Bl/Y	: Blue with Yellow tracer	R/W	: Red with White tracer
Br/B	: Brown with Black tracer	R/Y	: Red with Yellow tracer
Br/R	: Brown with Red tracer	W/B	: White with Black tracer
Br/W	: Brown with White tracer	W/Bl	: White with Blue tracer
Br/Y	: Brown with Yellow tracer	W/G	: White with Green tracer
G/B	: Green with Black tracer	W/R	: White with Red tracer
G/Bl	: Green with Blue tracer	W/Y	: White with Yellow tracer
G/R	: Green with Red tracer	Y/B	: Yellow with Black tracer
G/W	: Green with White tracer	Y/Bl	: Yellow with Blue tracer
G/Y	: Green with Yellow tracer	Y/G	: Yellow with Green tracer
Gr/B	: Gray with Black tracer	Y/R	: Yellow with Red tracer
		Y/W	: Yellow with White tracer

12

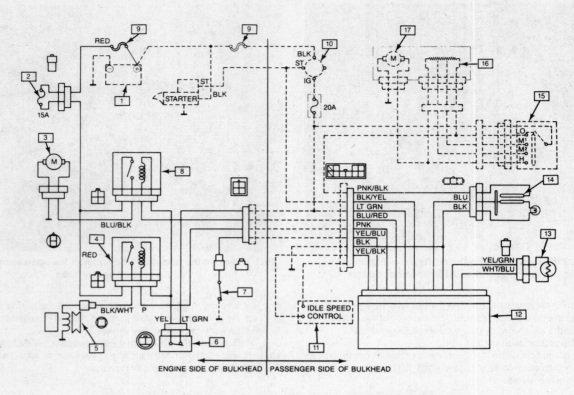

Air conditioning/cooling fan motor wiring diagram (Sidekick/Tracker models)

1	Battery	5	Compressor	9
2	Fuse	6	Dual switch	10
3	Condenser fan motor	7	Water temperature switch	11
4	Compressor magnetic clutch relay	8	Condenser fan motor relay	12

1 Battery
2 Fuse
3 Condenser fan motor
4 Compressor magnetic
   clutch relay

5 Compressor
6 Dual switch
7 Water temperature switch
8 Condenser fan motor relay

9   Slow blow fuse
10 Ignition switch
11 Engine control module
12 Air conditioner amplifier

13 Evaporator thermister
14 A/C switch
15 Blower fan switch
16 Blower resistor assembly
17 Blower fan motor

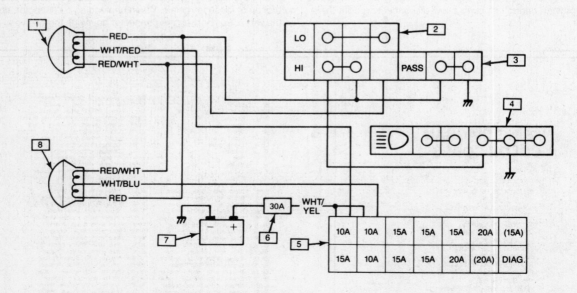

Headlight circuit (Sidekick/Tracker models)

1 Right headlight
2 Dimmer switch

3 Passing switch
4 Light switch

5 Fuse box
6 Main fuse

7 Battery
8 Left headlight

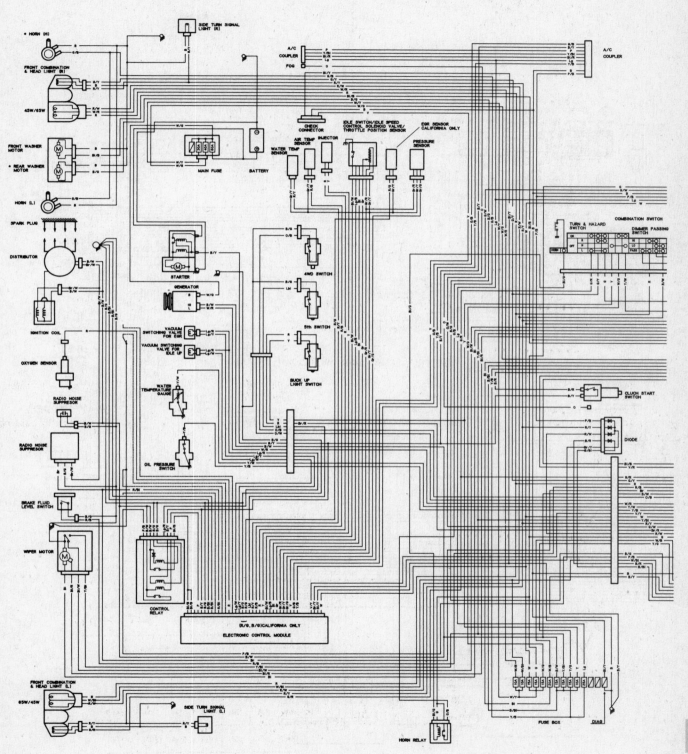

Sidekick/Tracker wiring diagram – typical manual transmission equipped models (1 of 2)

Chapter 12   Chassis electrical system

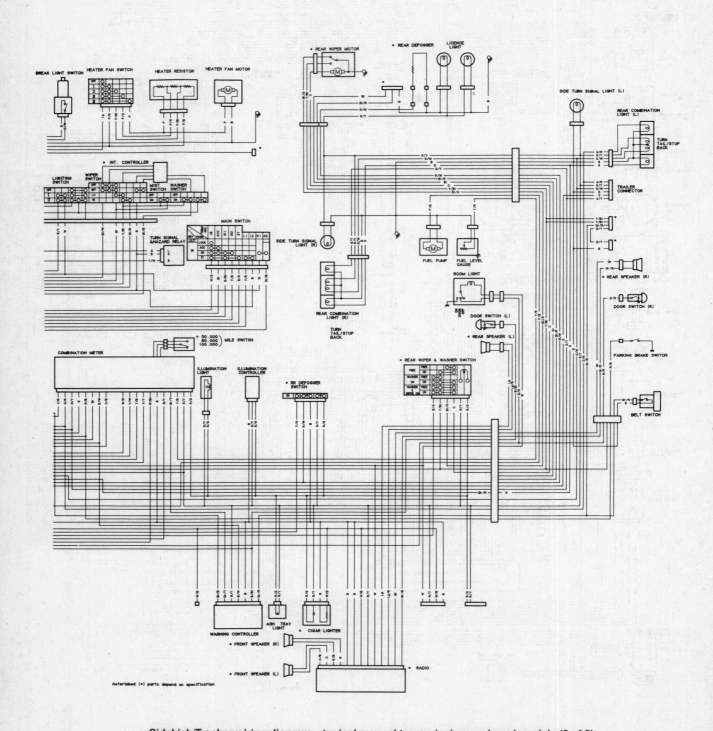

Sidekick/Tracker wiring diagram – typical manual transmission equipped models (2 of 2)

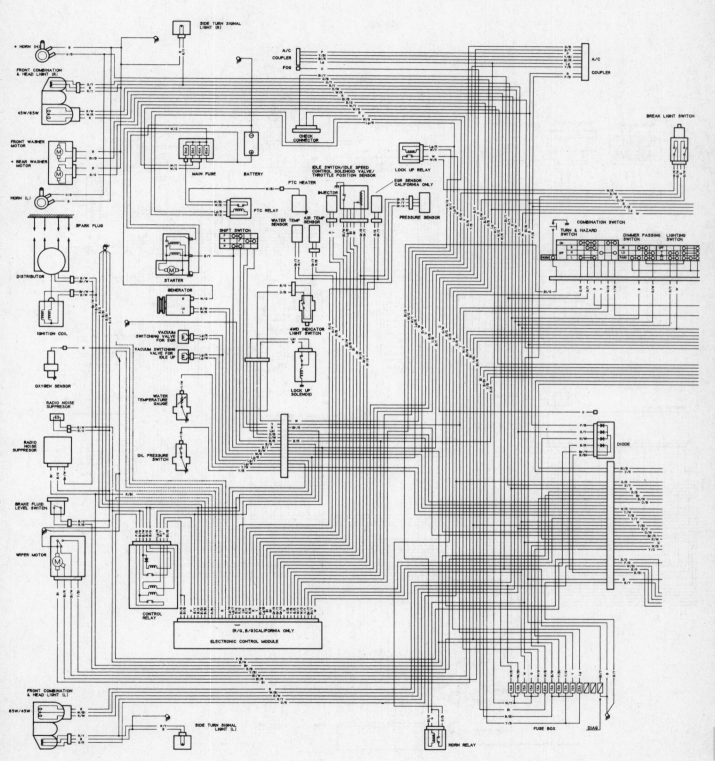

Sidekick/Tracker wiring diagram – typical automatic transmission equipped models (1 of 2)

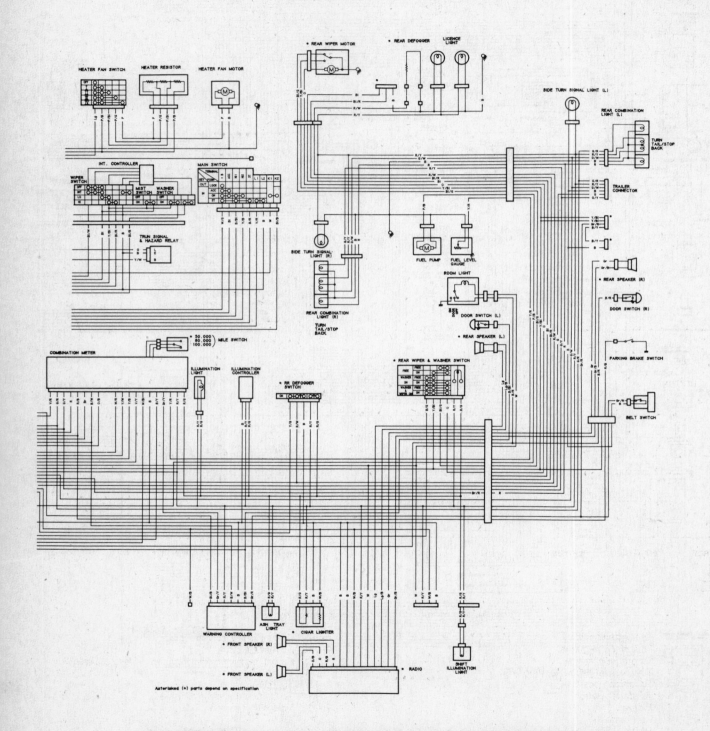

Sidekick/Tracker wiring diagram – typical automatic transmission equipped models (2 of 2)

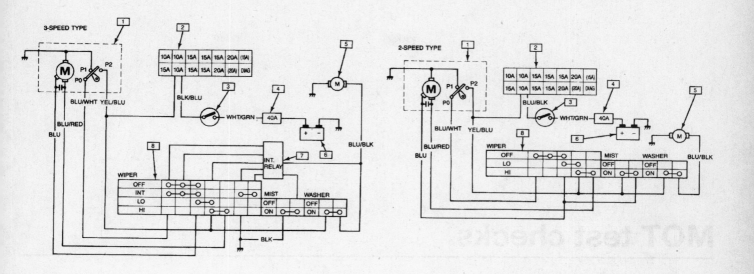

Windshield wiper circuit (Sidekick/Tracker models)

1   Wiper motor
2   Fuse box
3   Main switch
4   Main fuse

5   Washer motor
6   Battery
7   Intermittent wiper relay
8   Wiper, mist and washer switch

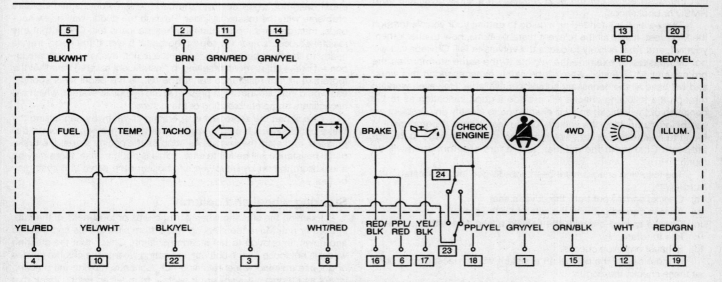

Combination meter wiring (Sidekick/Tracker models)

1   To seat belt switch
2   To ignition negative
3   To ground
4   To fuel level gauge sending unit
5   To ignition positive
6   To starter switch
7   Blank
8   To alternator
9   Blank
10 To coolant temperature gauge sending unit
11 To turn signal switch (left)
12 To battery (fuse box) positive
13 To dimmer and passing switch

14 To turn signal switch (right)
15 To 4WD switch
16 To brake fluid level switch and parking brake switch
17 To oil pressure switch
18 To ECM
19 To illumination controller
20 To lighting switch
21 Blank
22 To ground (Fuel pump)
23 Cancel switch (other than Calif. spec.)
24 Mileage sensor switch (other than Calif.
    Spec. 50,000/80,000/100,000)

MOT test checks

Introduction

Motor vehicle testing has been compulsory in Great Britain since 1960, when the Motor Vehicle (Tests) Regulations were first introduced. At that time, testing was only applicable to vehicles ten years old or older, and the test itself only covered lighting equipment, braking systems and steering gear. Current vehicle testing is far more extensive and, in the case of private vehicles, is now an annual inspection commencing three years after the date of first registration. Test standards are becoming increasingly stringent; for details of changes, consult the latest edition of the MOT Inspection Manual (available from HMSO or bookshops).

This section is intended as a guide to getting your vehicle through the MOT test. It lists all the relevant testable items, how to check them yourself, and what is likely to cause the vehicle to fail. Obviously, it will not be possible to examine the vehicle to the same standard as the professional MOT tester, who will be highly experienced in this work, and will have all the necessary equipment available. However, working through the following checks will provide a good indication as to the condition of the vehicle, and will enable you to identify any problem areas before submitting the vehicle for the test. Where a component is found to need repair or renewal, reference should be made to the appropriate Chapter in the manual, where further information will be found.

The following checks have been sub-divided into four categories, as follows:

(a) Checks carried out from the driver's seat.
(b) Checks carried out with the vehicle on the ground.
(c) Checks carried out with the vehicle raised and with the wheels free to rotate.
(d) Exhaust emission checks.

In most cases, the help of an assistant will be necessary to carry out these checks thoroughly.

Checks carried out from the driver's seat

Handbrake (parking brake)

Test the operation of the handbrake by pulling on the lever until the handbrake is in the normal fully-applied position. Ensure that the travel of the lever (the number of clicks of the ratchet) is not excessive before full resistance of the braking mechanism is felt. If so, this would indicate a fault in the rear brakes and/or handbrake mechanism.

With the handbrake fully applied, tap the lever sideways and make sure that it does not release, which would indicate wear in the ratchet and pawl. Release the handbrake, and move the lever from side to side to check for excessive wear in the pivot bearing. Check the security of the lever mountings, and make sure that there is no corrosion of any part of the body structure within 30 cm of the lever mount-ing. If the lever mountings cannot be readily seen from inside the vehicle, carry out this check later when working underneath.

Footbrake

Check that the brake pedal is sound, without visible defects such as excessive wear of the pivot bushes, or broken or damaged pedal pad. Check also for signs of fluid leaks on the pedal, floor or carpets, which would indicate failed seals in the brake master cylinder.

Depress the brake pedal slowly at first, then rapidly until sustained pressure can be held. Maintain this pressure, and check that the pedal does not creep down to the floor, which would again indicate problems with the master cylinder. Release the pedal, wait a few seconds, then depress it once until firm resistance is felt. Check that this resistance occurs near the top of the pedal travel. If the pedal travels nearly to the floor before firm resistance is felt, this would indicate incorrect brake adjustment, resulting in "insufficient reserve travel" of the footbrake. If firm resistance cannot be felt, ie the pedal feels spongy, this would indicate that air is present in the hydraulic system, which will necessitate complete bleeding of the system.

Check that the servo unit is operating correctly by depressing the brake pedal several times to exhaust the vacuum. Keep the pedal depressed, and start the engine. As soon as the engine starts, the brake pedal resistance will be felt to alter. If this is not the case, there may be a leak from the brake servo vacuum hose, or the servo unit itself may be faulty.

Steering wheel and column

Examine the steering wheel for fractures or looseness of the hub, spokes or rim. Move the steering wheel from side to side and then up and down, in relation to the steering column. Check that the steering wheel is not loose on the column, indicating wear in the column splines or a loose steering wheel retaining nut. Continue moving the steering wheel as before, but also turn it slightly from left to right. Check that there is no abnormal movement of the steering wheel, indicating excessive wear in the column upper support bearing, universal joint(s) or flexible coupling.

Windscreen and mirrors

The windscreen must be free of cracks or other damage which will seriously interfere with the driver's field of view, or which will prevent the windscreen wipers from operating properly. Small stone chips are acceptable. Any stickers, dangling toys or similar items must also be clear of the field of view.

Rear view mirrors must be secure, intact and capable of being adjusted. The nearside (passenger side) door mirror is not included in the test unless the interior mirror cannot be used - for instance, in the case of a van with blacked-out rear windows.

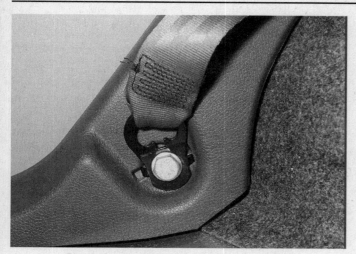

Check the security of all seat belt mountings

Seat belts and seats

Note: *The following checks are applicable to all seat belts, front and rear. Front seat belts must be of a type that will restrain the upper part of the body; lap belts are not acceptable. Various combinations of seat belt types are acceptable at the rear.*

Carefully examine the seat belt webbing for cuts, or any signs of serious fraying or deterioration. If the seat belt is of the retractable type, pull the belt all the way out, and examine the full extent of the webbing.

Fasten and unfasten the belt, ensuring that the locking mechanism holds securely, and releases properly when intended. If the belt is of the retractable type, check also that the retracting mechanism operates correctly when the belt is released.

Check the security of all seat belt mountings and attachments which are accessible, without removing any trim or other components, from inside the vehicle **(see illustration)**. Any serious corrosion, fracture or distortion of the body structure within 30 cm of any mounting point will cause the vehicle to fail. Certain anchorages will not be accessible or even visible from inside the vehicle; in this instance, further checks should be carried out later, when working underneath. If any part of the seat belt mechanism is attached to the front seat, then the seat mountings are treated as anchorages, and must also comply as above.

The front seats themselves must be securely attached so that they cannot move unexpectedly, and the backrests must lock in the upright position.

Doors

Both front doors must be able to be opened and closed from outside and inside, and must latch securely when closed. In the case of a pick-up, the tailgate must be securely attached, and capable of being securely fastened.

Electrical equipment

Switch on the ignition, and operate the horn. The horn must operate, and produce a clear sound audible to other road users. Note that a gong, siren or two-tone horn fitted as an alternative to the manufacturer's original equipment is not acceptable.

Check the operation of the windscreen washers and wipers. The washers must operate with adequate flow and pressure, and with the jets adjusted so that the liquid strikes the windscreen near the top of the glass.

Operate the windscreen wipers in conjunction with the washers, and check that the blades cover their designed sweep of the windscreen without smearing. The blades must effectively clean the glass so that the driver has an adequate view of the road ahead, and to the front nearside and offside of the vehicle. If the screen smears or does not clean adequately, it is advisable to renew the wiper blades before the MOT test.

Depress the footbrake with the ignition switched on, and have your assistant check that both rear stop-lights operate, and are extinguished when the footbrake is released. If one stop-light fails to operate, it is likely that a bulb has blown or there is a poor electrical contact at, or near, the bulbholder. If both stop-lights fail to operate, check for a blown fuse, faulty stop-light switch, or possibly two blown bulbs. If the lights stay on when the brake pedal is released, it is possible that the switch is at fault.

Checks carried out with the vehicle on the ground

Vehicle identification

Front and rear number plates must be in good condition, securely fitted and easily read. Letters and numbers must be correctly spaced, with the gap between the group of numbers and the group of letters at least double the gap between adjacent numbers and letters.

The vehicle identification number (see "Buying spare parts and vehicle identification numbers") must be legible. It will be checked during the test, as part of the measures taken to prevent the fraudulent acquisition of certificates.

Electrical equipment

Switch on the sidelights, and check that both front and rear sidelights and the number plate lights are illuminated, and that the lenses and reflectors are secure and undamaged. This is particularly important at the rear, where a cracked or damaged lens would allow a white light to show to the rear, which is unacceptable. Note in addition that any lens that is excessively dirty, either inside or out, such that the light intensity is reduced, could also constitute a fail.

Switch on the headlights, and check that both dipped beam and main beam units are operating correctly and at the same light intensity. If either headlight shows signs of dimness, this is usually attributable to a poor earth connection or severely-corroded internal reflector. Inspect the headlight lenses for cracks or stone damage. Any damage to the headlight lens will normally constitute a fail, but this is very much down to the tester's discretion. Bear in mind that with all light units, they must operate correctly when first switched on. It is not acceptable to tap a light unit to make it operate.

The headlights must not only be aligned so as not to dazzle other road users when switched to dipped beam, but also so as to provide adequate illumination of the road. This can only be accurately checked using optical beam-setting equipment, so if you have any doubts about the headlight alignment, it is advisable to have this professionally checked and if necessary reset, before the MOT test.

With the ignition switched on, operate the direction indicators, and check that they show amber lights to the front and to the rear, that they flash at the rate of between one and two flashes per second, and that the "tell-tale" on the instrument panel also functions. Operation of the sidelights and stop-lights must not affect the indicators - if it does, the cause is usually a bad earth at the rear light cluster. Similarly check the operation of the hazard warning lights, which must work with the ignition on and off. Examine the lenses for cracks or damage as described previously.

Check the operation of the rear foglight(s). The test only concerns itself with the statutorily-required foglight, which is the one on the offside (driver's side). The light must be secure, and emit a steady red light. The warning light on the instrument panel (or in the switch) must also work.

Footbrake

From within the engine compartment, examine the brake pipes for signs of leaks, corrosion, insecurity, chafing or other damage. Check the master cylinder and servo unit for leaks, security of their mountings, or excessive corrosion in the vicinity of the mountings. The master cylinder reservoir must be secure; if it is of the translucent type, the fluid level must be between the upper and lower level markings.

Turn the steering as necessary so that the right-hand front brake

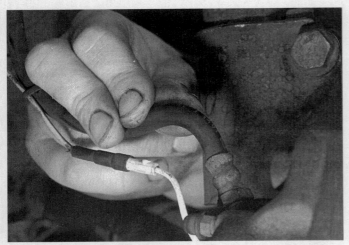

Check the braking system pipes and hoses for signs of damage
or deterioration

Shake the roadwheel vigorously to check for excess play in the
wheel bearing and suspension components

flexible hose can be examined. Inspect the hose carefully for any sign of cracks or deterioration of the rubber. This will be most noticeable if the hose is bent in half, and is particularly common where the rubber portion enters the metal end fitting **(see illustration)**. Turn the steering onto full-left then full-right lock, and ensure that the hose does not contact the wheel, tyre, or any part of the steering or suspension mechanism. While your assistant depresses the brake pedal firmly, check the hose for any bulges or fluid leaks under pressure. Now repeat these checks on the left-hand front hose. Should any damage or deterioration be noticed, renew the hose.

Steering mechanism and suspension

Have your assistant turn the steering wheel from side to side slightly, up to the point where the steering gear just begins to transmit this movement to the roadwheels. Check for excessive free play between the steering wheel and the steering gear, which would indicate wear in the steering column joints, wear or insecurity of the steering column-to-steering gear coupling, or insecurity, incorrect adjustment, or wear in the steering gear itself. Generally speaking, free play greater than 1.3 cm for vehicles with rack-and-pinion type steering (or 7.6 cm for vehicles with steering box mechanisms) should be considered excessive.

Have your assistant turn the steering wheel more vigorously in each direction, up to the point where the roadwheels just begin to turn. As this is done, carry out a complete examination of all the steering joints, linkages, fittings and attachments. Any component that shows signs of wear, damage, distortion, or insecurity should be renewed or attended to accordingly. On vehicles equipped with power steering, also check that the power steering pump is secure, that the pump drivebelt is in satisfactory condition and correctly adjusted, that there are no fluid leaks or damaged hoses, and that the system operates correctly. Additional checks can be carried out later with the vehicle raised, when there will be greater working clearance underneath.

Check that the vehicle is standing level and at approximately the correct ride height. Ensure that there is sufficient clearance between the suspension components and the bump stops to allow full suspension travel over bumps.

Shock absorbers

Depress each corner of the vehicle in turn, and then release it. If the shock absorbers are in good condition, the corner of the vehicle will rise and then settle in its normal position. If there is no noticeable damping effect from the shock absorber, and the vehicle continues to rise and fall, then the shock absorber is defective and the vehicle will fail. A shock absorber which has seized will also cause the vehicle to fail.

Exhaust system

Start the engine, and with your assistant holding a rag over the tailpipe, check the entire system for leaks, which will appear as a rhythmic fluffing or hissing sound at the source of the leak. Check the effectiveness of the silencer by ensuring that the noise produced is of a level to be expected from a vehicle of similar type. Providing that the system is structurally sound, it is acceptable to cure a leak using a proprietary exhaust system repair kit or similar method.

Checks carried out with the vehicle raised and with the wheels free to rotate

Jack up the front and rear of the vehicle, and securely support it on axle stands positioned at suitable load-bearing points under the vehicle structure. Position the stands clear of the suspension assemblies, ensure that the wheels are clear of the ground, and that the steering can be turned onto full-right and full-left lock.

Steering mechanism

Examine the steering rack rubber gaiters for signs of splits, lubricant leakage or insecurity of the retaining clips. If power steering is fitted, check for signs of deterioration, damage, chafing, or leakage of the fluid hoses, pipes or connections. Also check for excessive stiffness or binding of the steering, a missing split pin or locking device, or any severe corrosion of the body structure within 30 cm of any steering component attachment point.

Have your assistant turn the steering onto full-left then full-right lock. Check that the steering turns smoothly, without undue tightness or roughness, and that no part of the steering mechanism, including a wheel or tyre, fouls any brake flexible or rigid hose or pipe, or any part of the body structure.

On vehicles with four-wheel steering, similar considerations apply to the rear wheel steering linkages. However, it is permissible for a rear wheel steering system to be inoperative, provided that the rear wheels are secured in the straight-ahead position, and that the front wheel steering system is operating effectively.

Front and rear suspension and wheel bearings

Starting at the front right-hand side of the vehicle, grasp the roadwheel at the 3 o'clock and 9 o'clock positions, and shake it vigorously. Check for any free play at the wheel bearings, suspension balljoints, or suspension mountings, pivots and attachments. Check also for any serious deterioration of the rubber or metal casing of any mounting bushes, or any distortion, deformation or severe corrosion of any components. Look for missing split pins, tab washers or other locking devices on any mounting or attachment, or any severe corrosion of the vehicle structure within 30 cm of any suspension component attachment point.

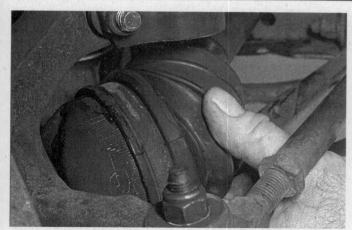

Inspect the constant velocity joint gaiters (where applicable) for splits or damage

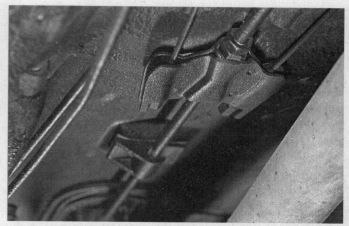

Check the handbrake mechanism - typical example shown - for signs of frayed or broken cables, or insecurity of the linkage

If any excess free play is suspected at a component pivot point, this can be confirmed by using a large screwdriver or similar tool, and levering between the mounting and the component attachment. This will confirm whether the wear is in the pivot bush, its retaining bolt or in the mounting itself (the bolt holes can often become elongated).

Now grasp the wheel at the 12 o'clock and 6 o'clock positions, shake it vigorously and repeat the previous inspection (see illustration). Rotate the wheel, and check for roughness or tightness of the front wheel bearing such that imminent failure of the bearing is indicated.

Carry out all the above checks at the other front wheel, and then at both rear wheels.

Roadsprings and shock absorbers

On vehicles with strut type suspension units, examine the strut assembly for signs of serious fluid leakage, corrosion or severe pitting of the piston rod, or damage to the casing. Check also for security of the mounting points.

If coil springs are fitted, check that the spring ends locate correctly in their spring seats, that there is no severe corrosion of the spring, and that it is not cracked, broken, or in any way damaged.

If the vehicle is fitted with leaf springs, check that all leaves are intact, that the axle is securely attached to each spring, and that there is no wear or deterioration of the spring eye mountings, bushes, and shackles.

The same general checks apply to vehicles fitted with other suspension types, such as torsion bars, hydraulic displacer units, etc. In all cases, ensure that all mountings and attachments are secure, that there are no signs of excessive wear, corrosion, cracking, deformation or damage to any component or bush, and that there are no fluid leaks, or damaged hoses or pipes (hydraulic types).

Inspect the shock absorbers for signs of serious fluid leakage. (Slight seepage of fluid is normal for some types of shock absorber, and is not a reason for failing.) Check for excessive wear of the mounting bushes or attachments, or damage to the body of the unit.

Driveshafts (referred to as driveaxles in US)

With the steering turned onto full-lock, rotate each front wheel in turn, and inspect the constant velocity joint gaiters (where applicable) for splits or damage (see illustration). Also check the gaiter is securely attached to its respective housings by clips or other methods of retention.

Continue turning the wheel, and check that each driveshaft is straight, with no sign of damage.

Braking system

If possible, without dismantling, check the brake pads and the condition of the discs. Ensure that the friction lining material has not worn excessively, and that the discs are not fractured, pitted, scored, or worn excessively.

Carefully examine all the rigid brake pipes underneath the vehicle, and the flexible hoses at the rear. Look for signs of excessive corrosion, chafing or insecurity of the pipes, and for signs of bulging under pressure, chafing, splits, or deterioration of the flexible hoses.

Look for signs of hydraulic fluid leaks at the brake calipers or on the brake backplates, indicating failed hydraulic seals in the components concerned.

Slowly spin each wheel, while your assistant depresses the footbrake then releases it. Ensure that each brake is operating, and that the wheel is free to rotate when the pedal is released. It is not possible to test brake efficiency without special equipment, but (traffic and local conditions permitting) a road test can be carried out to check that the vehicle pulls up in a straight line.

Examine the handbrake mechanism, and check for signs of frayed or broken cables, excessive corrosion, or wear or insecurity of the linkage (see illustration). Have your assistant operate the handbrake, while you check that the mechanism works on each relevant wheel, and releases fully without binding.

Fuel and exhaust systems

Inspect the fuel tank, fuel pipes, hoses and unions (including the unions at the pump, filter and carburetor). All components must be secure, and free from leaks. The fuel filler cap must also be secure, and of an appropriate type.

Examine the exhaust system over its entire length, checking for any damaged, broken or missing mountings, security of the pipe retaining clamps, and condition of the system with regard to rust and corrosion (see illustration).

Check the condition of the exhaust system - typical example shown - paying particular attention to the mountings

Wheels and tyres

Carefully examine each tyre in turn, on both the inner and outer walls, and over the whole of the tread area. Check for signs of cuts, tears, lumps, bulges, separation of the tread, and exposure of the ply or cord due to wear or other damage. Check also that the tyre bead is correctly seated on the wheel rim, and that the tyre valve is sound and properly seated. Spin the wheel, and check that it is not excessively distorted or damaged, particularly at the bead rim.

Check that the tyres are of the correct size for the vehicle, and that they are of the same size and type on each axle. (Having a "space saver" spare tyre in use is not acceptable.) The tyres should also be inflated to the specified pressures (see Chapter 10 Specifications).

Using a suitable gauge, check the tyre tread depth. The current legal requirement states that the tread pattern must be visible over the whole tread area, and must be of a minimum depth of 1.6 mm over at least three-quarters of the tread width. It is acceptable for some wear of the inside or outside edges of the tyre to be apparent, but this wear must be in one even circumferential band, and the tread must be visible. Any excessive wear of this nature may indicate incorrect front wheel alignment, which should be checked before the tyre becomes excessively worn. See the appropriate Chapters for further information on tyre wear patterns and front wheel alignment.

Body corrosion

Check the condition of the entire vehicle structure for signs of corrosion in any load-bearing areas. For the purpose of the MOT test, all chassis box sections, side sills, crossmembers, pillars, suspension, steering, braking system and seat belt mountings and anchorages, should all be considered as load-bearing areas. As a general guide, any corrosion which has seriously reduced the metal thickness of a load-bearing area to weaken it, is likely to cause the vehicle to fail. Should corrosion of this nature be encountered, professional repairs are likely to be needed.

Body damage or corrosion which causes sharp or otherwise dangerous edges to be exposed will also cause the vehicle to fail.

Exhaust emission checks

Have the engine at normal operating temperature, and make sure that the preliminary conditions for checking idle speed and mixture (ignition system in good order, air cleaner element in good condition, etc) have been met.

Before any measurements are carried out, raise the engine speed to around 2500 rpm, and hold it at this speed for 20 seconds. Allow the engine speed to return to idle, and watch for smoke emissions from the exhaust tailpipe. If the idle speed is obviously much too high, or if dense blue or clearly-visible black smoke comes from the tailpipe for more than 5 seconds, the vehicle will fail. As a rule of thumb, blue smoke signifies oil being burnt (worn valve stem oil seals, valve guides, piston rings or bores) while black smoke signifies unburnt fuel (dirty air cleaner element, mixture extremely rich, or other carburetor or fuel injection system fault).

If idle speed and smoke emission are satisfactory, an exhaust gas analyser capable of measuring carbon monoxide (CO) and hydrocarbons (HC) is now needed. The following paragraphs assume that such an instrument can be hired or borrowed - it is unlikely to be economic for the home mechanic to buy one. Alternatively, a local garage may agree to perform the check for a small fee.

CO emissions (mixture)

Current MOT regulations specify a maximum CO level at idle of 4.5% for vehicles first used after August 1983. The CO level specified by the vehicle maker is well inside this limit.

If the CO level cannot be reduced far enough to pass the test (and assuming that the fuel and ignition systems are otherwise in good condition) it is probable that the carburetor is badly worn, or that there is some problem in the fuel injection system. On carburetors with an automatic choke, it may be that the choke is not releasing as it should.

It is possible for the CO level to be within the specified maximum for MOT purposes, but well above the maximum specified by the manufacturer. The tester is entitled to draw attention to this, but it is not in itself a reason for failing the vehicle.

HC emissions

With the CO emissions within limits, HC emissions must be no more than 1200 ppm (parts per million). If the vehicle fails this test at idle, it can be re-tested at around 2000 rpm; if the HC level is then 1200 ppm or less, this counts as a pass.

Excessive HC emissions can be caused by oil being burnt, but they are more likely to be due to unburnt fuel. Possible reasons include:

(a) Spark plugs in poor condition or incorrectly-gapped.
(b) Ignition timing incorrect.
(c) Valve clearances incorrect.
(d) Engine compression low.

Note that excessive HC levels in the exhaust gas can cause premature failure of the catalytic converter (when fitted).

Chapter 13 UK Supplement

Note: *The following Sections contain information applicable to UK models only.*

Contents

1 Introduction

This Supplement contains information applicable to models manufactured for the UK market only.

The Sections in the Supplement follow the same order as the Chapters to which they relate in the main part of the manual. The Specifications are all grouped together for convenience, but they too follow Chapter order.

It is recommended that before any particular operation is undertaken, reference be made to the appropriate Section(s) of this Supplement before reference is made to the main Chapters of the manual. In this way, any procedures which apply to UK models only can be noted first.

2   Specifications

Note: *The following specifications are for UK models only.*

Capacities

Engine oil capacity (970 cc)	3.2 litres (5.7 pints)
Cooling system (970 cc)	3.8 litres (6.7 pints)
Fuel tank (SJ410)	40 litres (8.8 pints)
Manual transmission (SJ410)	1.0 litre (1.8 pints)
Differential	1.3 litres (2.3 pints)
Transfer box	0.7 litre (1.2 pints)

Engine (general)

Capacity:

SJ410/Santana (1983 to 1991)	970 cc
SJ413/Samurai/Santana (1986 to 1992)	1324 cc
Samurai (1992 to 1994)	1298 cc
Vitara JLX (1988 to 1994)	1590 cc
Vitara EFI CAT (1991 to 1994)	1590 cc

Compression ratio/pressure:

SJ410 and Santana (1983 to 1991)	8.8 : 1/11.7 bars
SJ413 and Samurai/Santana (1986 to 1992)	8.9 : 1/11.7 bars
Samurai (1992 to 1994)	9.5 : 1/13.7 bars
Vitara JLX (1988 to 1994)	8.9 : 1/11.7 bars
Vitara EFI CAT (1991 to 1994)	9.5 : 1/12.0 bars
Firing order	1 - 3 - 4 - 2 (No 1 at front of engine)
Camshaft endfloat (970 cc engine)	0.3 mm (maximum)

Valve clearances (cold):

	Inlet	Exhaust
SJ410 and Santana (1983 to 1991)	0.13 to 0.18 mm (0.005 to 0.007 in)	0.13 to 0.18 mm (0.005 to 0.007 in)
SJ413 and Samurai/Santana (1986 to 1992)	0.13 to 0.18 mm (0.005 to 0.007 in)	0.16 to 0.20 mm (0.006 to 0.008 in)
Samurai (1992 to 1994)	0.13 to 0.18 mm (0.005 to 0.007 in)	0.16 to 0.20 mm (0.006 to 0.008 in)
Vitara JLX (1988 to 1994)	0.13 to 0.18 mm (0.005 to 0.007 in)	0.16 to 0.20 mm (0.006 to 0.008 in)
Vitara EFI CAT (1991 to 1994)	0.08 mm (0.003 in)	0.12 mm (0.005 in)

Oil pressure:

SJ410, SJ413 and Samurai/Santana	3.0 to 4.1 bars
Vitara	3.6 to 4.4 bars

Engine (970 cc)

Oil pump

Inner gear-to-crescent clearance	0.60 to 0.80 mm
Outer gear-to-crescent clearance	0.25 to 0.40 mm
Outer gear-to-housing	0.3 mm
Gear endfloat	0.17 mm

Rocker arms and shafts

Rocker arm inner diameter	14.985 to 15.005 mm
Shaft outer diameter	14.965 to 14,980 mm

Shaft-to-arm clearance:

Standard	0.005 to 0.040 mm
Limit	0.07 mm

Camshaft

Endfloat (limit)	0.30 mm

Journal diameter (front-to-rear):

1	43.425 to 43.450 mm
2	43.625 to 43.650 mm
3	43.825 to 43.850 mm
4	44.025 to 44.050 mm
5	44.225 to 44.250 mm

Journal bore (inside) diameter:

1	43.500 to 43.516 mm
2	43.700 to 43.716 mm
3	43.900 to 43.916 mm
4	44.100 to 44.116 mm
5	44.300 to 44.316 mm

Valves

Valve stem diameter:
- Inlet .... 6.965 to 6.980 mm
- Exhaust .... 6.955 to 6.970 mm

Valve stem-to-guide clearance:
- Inlet:
  - Standard .... 0.020 to 0.050 mm
  - Limit .... 0.07 mm
- Exhaust:
  - Standard .... 0.030 to 0.060 mm
  - Limit .... 0.09 mm

Valve springs:
- Free length:
  - Standard .... 48.9 mm
  - Limit .... 47.6 mm
- Preload:
  - Standard .... 23.6 to 27.6 kg at 40 mm
  - Limit .... 22 kg at 40 mm

Crankshaft and connecting rods

Crankshaft endfloat:
- Standard .... 0.130 to 0.280 mm
- Service limit .... 0.350 mm

Crankshaft runout limit (at middle) .... 0.060 mm

Connecting rod journal:
- Diameter .... 37.985 to 38.000 mm
- Bearing oil clearance:
  - Standard .... 0.020 to 0.040 mm
  - Service limit .... 0.080 mm

Connecting rod endfloat (side clearance):
- Standard .... 0.10 to 0.20 mm
- Service limit .... 0.30 mm

Main bearing journal:
- Diameter .... 49.985 to 50.000 mm
- Bearing oil clearance:
  - Standard .... 0.020 to 0.040 mm
  - Service limit .... 0.080 mm

Cylinder bore

Diameter .... 65.505 to 65.520 mm

Pistons and rings

Piston diameter:
- Standard .... 65.460 to 65.475 mm
- Oversizes .... 0.25 and 0.50 mm

Piston-to-bore clearance .... 0.040 to 0.050 mm

Piston ring end gap:
- Compression rings:
  - Standard .... 0.15 to 0.35 mm
  - Limit .... 0.7 mm
- Oil ring:
  - Standard .... 0.30 to 0.90 mm
  - Limit .... 1.8 mm

Piston ring side clearance:
- No 1 (top) compression ring:
  - Standard .... 0.03 to 0.07 mm
  - Limit .... 0.12 mm
- No 2 compression ring:
  - Standard .... 0.02 to 0.06 mm
  - Limit .... 0.10 mm

Torque wrench settings	Nm	lbf ft
Cylinder head bolts	55 to 60	41 to 44
Camshaft pulley bolt	50 to 60	37 to 44
Valve clearance adjusting nut	15 to 20	11 to 15
Timing belt cover	3 to 4	2 to 3
Timing belt tensioner nut/bolts	15 to 23	11 to 17
Crankshaft pulley bolt	50 to 60	37 to 44
Connecting rod cap nut	28 to 32	21 to 24
Main bearing cap bolt	43 to 48	32 to 35
Flywheel bolt	40 to 45	30 to 33
Oil pump	12 to 15	9 to 11
Oil pump relief valve	15 to 20	11 to 15
Oil drain plug	20 to 25	15 to 19

13

Torque wrench settings	Nm	lbf ft
Sump	4 to 5	3 to 4
Front mounting nut	23 to 28	17 to 21
Camshaft cover	4 to 5	3 to 4
Rear engine mounting bolt	11 to 14	8 to 10

Cooling system
Thermostat opening temperature (all engines) ... 82° C or 88° C
Radiator cap pressure (all engines) ... 0.90 bars (13.1 lbf/in2)

Fuel system
SJ410 and Santana (1983 to 1991)
Idle speed ... 850 ± 50 rpm
CO% at idle speed ... 1.5 ± 0.5
Carburettor:
  Type ... Aisan side draught
  Venturi diameter ... 25 mm
  Main jet ... 1.08 mm
  Main air jet ... 0.55 mm
  Slow jet ... 0.46 mm
  Slow air jet No 1 ... 1.10 mm
  Slow air jet No 2 ... 1.35 mm
  Enrichment jet ... 0.65 mm
  Float level ... 44.5 to 46.5 mm
SJ413 and Samurai (1986 to 1994)
Idle speed ... 850 ± 50 rpm
CO% at idle speed ... 1.5 ± 0.5
Fast idle speed (engine cold) ... 1500 to 2500 rpm
Fast idle speed (engine hot) ... 4000 to 4500 rpm
Carburettor:
  Type ... Aisan 2V downdraught
  Throttle cable play ... 10 to 15 mm
  Float level (viewed through glass) ... 20.5 to 23.5 mm
  Float height ... 7.0 mm
  Accelerator pump stroke ... 3.8 to 4.2 mm
Vitara JLX (1988 to 1994)
Idle speed ... 790 to 810 rpm
CO% at idle speed ... 1.0 to 2.0
Fast idle speed (engine cold) ... 1500 to 2500 rpm
Fast idle speed (engine hot) ... 3500 to 4500 rpm
Carburettor:
  Type ... Aisan 2V downdraught
  Float height ... 17.1 to 18.2 mm
  Choke valve opening ... 5.7 to 7.3 mm
  Accelerator pump lever stroke ... 7.7 to 11.7 mm
Vitara EFI CAT (1991 to 1994)
Idle speed ... 850 ± 50 rpm
CO% at idle speed ... 0.5 to 1.2
Fuel injection:
  Type ... Suzuki MPI

Torque wrench setting	Nm	lbf ft
Inlet and exhaust manifold	18 to 23	13 to 17

Ignition system
SJ410/Santana (1983 to 1991)
Type ... Contact breaker
Ignition coil primary resistance ... 3.0 ohms
Points gap ... 0.40 to 0.50 mm (0.016 to 0.020 in)
Dwell angle ... 52° ± 3°
Distributor rotation ... Clockwise
Ignition timing ... 10° BTDC @ 850 ± 50 rpm
Spark plug type ... NGK BPR5ES or Champion RN9YC
Spark plug electrode gap ... 0.7 to 0.8 mm (0.028 to 0.032 in)
SJ413/Samurai (1986 to 1994)
Type ... Electronic
Ignition coil primary resistance ... 1.35 to 1.65 ohms
Distributor rotation ... Clockwise
Air gap ... 0.2 to 0.4 mm (0.008 to 0.016 in)
Ignition timing ... 10° BTDC @ 850 ± 50 rpm
Spark plug type ... NGK BPR5ES or Champion RN9YC
Spark plug electrode gap ... 0.7 to 0.8 mm (0.028 to 0.032 in)

Vitara JLX (1988 to 1994)

Type..	Electronic
Ignition coil primary resistance....................................	1.35 to 1.65 ohms
Distributor rotation..	Clockwise
Ignition timing (with vacuum).......................................	8° BTDC @ 800 ± 50 rpm
Spark plug type	NGK BP6ES, NGK BPR6ES or Champion N9YC
Spark plug electrode gap	0.7 to 0.8 mm (0.028 to 0.032 in)

Vitara EFI CAT (1991 to 1994)

Type..	Electronic
Ignition coil primary resistance....................................	0.9 to 1.1 ohms
Air gap	0.2 to 0.4 mm (0.008 to 0.016 in)
Ignition timing (with vacuum).......................................	8° BTDC @ 800 ± 50 rpm
Spark plug type	NGK BKR6E
Spark plug electrode gap	0.7 to 0.8 mm (0.028 to 0.032 in)

Torque wrench setting	**Nm**	**lbf ft**
Spark plugs..	20 to 30	15 to 22

Braking system

Minimum friction material thickness:	
SJ410, SJ413:	
Front (disc)	6.0 mm
Front (drum)	3.0 mm
Rear	3.0 mm
Vitara:	
Front..	3.0 mm
Rear	1.0 mm
Handbrake/transmission brake shoes (SJ410 and early SJ413 models)...	3.0 mm

Torque wrench settings	**Nm**	**lbf ft**
Propeller shaft-to-centre handbrake drum nuts (SJ410 and early SJ413 models)..	23 to 30	17 to 22
Transfer box shaft centre nut (centre handbrake models)	110 to 130	80 to 94

Tyres

Size:	
SJ410/Santana (1983 to 1991)................................	600 x 16 or 195 x 15
SJ413/Samurai (1986 to 1994)................................	195 x 15 or 205/70 x 15
Vitara	195 x 15
Pressure:	
SJ410/SJ413/Santana/Samurai	1.4 bars (20 lbf/in2)
Vitara	1.6 bars (23 lbf/in2)

13

Engine compartment components (SJ410)

1	Battery	12	Wheel changing jack
2	Brake vacuum servo unit	13	Washer fluid reservoir
3	Brake hydraulic fluid reservoir	14	Coolant reservoir
4	Clutch cable	15	Radiator filler cap
5	Throttle cable	16	Thermostat housing
6	Engine oil level dipstick	17	Radiator top hose
7	Distributor	18	Air cleaner warm-air hose
8	Fuel pump	19	Air cleaner inlet hose
9	Engine oil filler cap	20	Air cleaner body
10	Ignition coil	21	Carburettor
11	Bonnet opening cable		

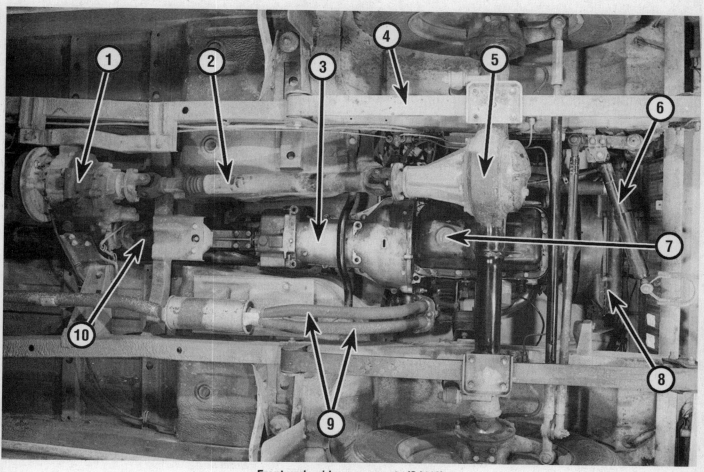

Front underside components (SJ410)

1   Transfer box
2   Front propeller shaft
3   Manual transmission
4   Front leaf spring
5   Front axle assembly

6   Steering damper
7   Engine oil drain plug
8   Radiator
9   Exhaust downpipe
10 Propeller shaft (transmission to transfer box)

Rear underside components (SJ410)

1	Rear silencer and exhaust pipe	6	Rear propeller shaft
2	Rear leaf spring	7	Rear brake proportioning valve
3	Rear shock absorber	8	Handbrake assembly (transmission brake)
4	Fuel tank	9	Transfer box
5	Rear axle assembly		

3   Routine maintenance

UK maintenance schedule

Every 250 miles or weekly, whichever comes first

Check the engine oil level (Chapter 1, Section 4)
Check the engine coolant level (Chapter 1, Section 4)
Check the windscreen washer fluid level (Chapter 1, Section 4)
Check the brake and clutch fluid levels (Chapter 1, Section 4)
Check the tyres and tyre pressures (Chapter 1, Section 5)

Every 6000 miles or 6 months, whichever comes first

Carry out all the weekly checks above, plus the following:
Change the engine oil and oil filter (Chapter 1, Section 12)
Renew the spark plugs (Chapter 1, Section 28)
On the 970 cc engine, renew the contact breaker points (later in this Section)
Check and adjust the ignition timing (later in this Section and in Chapter 1, Section 46)
Clean the air filter element (Chapter 1, Section 31)
Check and lubricate the accelerator cable, choke cable and levers, as applicable
Check the clutch adjustment (not on Vitara models) (Chapter 1, Section 15)
Check the brake pedal, handbrake lever and cable (not on Vitara models) (Chapter 1, Section 17)
Check the brake discs and pads, and/or brake drums and shoes as applicable (not on Vitara models) (later in this Section and also in Chapter 1, Section 18)
Check all brake hoses and pipes (not on Vitara models) (Chapter 1, Section 18)
Check the tyres for wear (Chapter 1, Sections 5 and 14)
Check the tightness of all wheel and hub nuts
Check the shock absorbers (Chapter 1, Section 22)
Check the transmission, transfer box and differential oil levels (on Vitara models, change the oil at the first 6000-mile service) (Chapter 1, Sections 19 and 37)
Check the steering (including the power steering system, where applicable) (Chapter 1, Section 22)
Lubricate locks and door hinges
Road-test the vehicle, and check for correct functioning of all components

Every 12 000 miles or 12 months, whichever comes first

Carry out all the operations listed previously, plus the following:
Check the fanbelt for wear, condition and tension (Chapter 1, Section 13)
Check the timing belt for wear and condition (later in this Section)

Check and if necessary adjust the valve clearances (later in this Section and also in Chapter 1, Section 16)
On SJ410 models, tighten the cylinder head bolts and all inlet and exhaust manifold nuts and bolts
Check all cooling system hoses and connections (Chapter 1, Section 9)
Check the complete exhaust system for leaks and condition (Chapter 1, Section 35)
Check the ignition wiring, including all HT leads
Check the condition of the distributor cap and rotor
Check that the distributor centrifugal advance mechanism is functioning correctly
Check and adjust the idle speed and mixture (later in this Section and also in Chapter 1, Section 33)
Check and if necessary clean the crankcase ventilation hoses and connections
Check the fuel evaporative control system hoses and connections (Chapter 1, Section 45)
Check the headlights operation
Check all wiring connections
Check the clutch adjustment (Vitara models only) (Chapter 1, Section 15)
Check the brake pedal, handbrake lever and cable (Vitara models only) (Chapter 1, Section 17)
Check all brake hoses and pipes (Vitara models only)
Check the brake discs and pads, and brake drums and shoes (Vitara models only) (Chapter 1, Section 18)
Check the wheel bearings (Vitara models only)
Check and grease all propeller shaft universal joints (Chapter 1, Section 24)
Tighten all nuts and bolts as necessary, in particular on the suspension

Every 24 000 miles or 24 months, whichever comes first

Carry out all the operations listed previously, plus the following:
Renew the fanbelt (Chapter 1, Section 13)
On SJ413 and Vitara models, tighten the cylinder head bolts and all inlet and exhaust manifold nuts and bolts
Renew the coolant (Chapter 1, Section 34)
Check all fuel lines and connections for security and condition. Also check the fuel tank for damage and condition
Renew the air filter element (Chapter 1, Section 31)
Renew the fuel filter (Chapter 1, Section 40)
Where fitted on SJ413 and Vitara models, check the PCV valve (Chapter 1, Section 42)
Change the brake fluid (Chapter 1, Section 44)
Change the transmission, transfer box and differential oil

Every 60 000 miles

Carry out all the operations listed previously, plus the following:
Renew the timing belt (if not renewed during the previous routine maintenance intervals)

13

3.5 Adjusting the valve clearances on the 970 cc engine

3.7 Unscrew the wing nut and remove the cap from the air cleaner

Timing belt (970 cc engine) - inspection

1   Unbolt and remove the radiator shroud panel.
2   On some early models, the timing belt may be viewed through a hole in the outer timing cover. On other models, it will be necessary to remove the outer timing cover as described in Section 4.
3   Turn the engine slowly using a spanner on the crankshaft pulley bolt, and inspect the belt for signs of excessive wear or damage. If there is any doubt about the condition of the belt on early models, re-move the outer timing cover for a complete inspection. The manufac-turers do not specify that the belt should be renewed at any particular mileage (although it must be checked every 12 000 miles); it is strongly recommended that it be renewed at least every 60 000 miles, as a pre-caution. If the belt should fail in service, the engine will suffer serious damage.
4   Refit the cover and radiator shroud panel after making the inspec-tion.

Valve clearances (970 cc engine) - check and adjustment

Refer to illustration 3.5

5   The procedure is similar to that described in Chapter 1, Section 16. However, the actual valve clearance is different (refer to the Speci-fications at the beginning of this Supplement). The adjustment should be carried out with the engine cold (see illustration).
6   There are several ways to set the engine position in order to ad-just the valve clearances. One way is to follow the instructions given in Chapter 2, Section 3. Another way is to remove the timing belt outer cover, and set the engine according to the position of the camshaft sprocket key. When the key is facing directly downwards, at the 6 o'clock position (ie pointing towards the crankshaft), No 1 piston is at TDC compression; when the key is at the 9 o'clock position, No 3 pis-ton is at TDC compression; at the 12 o'clock position, No 4 piston is at TDC compression, and at the 3 o'clock position, No 2 piston is at TDC compression. A further way is to first remove the No 1 or No 4 spark plug (as applicable); turn the engine clockwise with your finger over the plug hole until compression is felt. Continue turning the engine until the "T" mark on the flywheel is aligned with the mark on the transmission timing hole.

Air filter renewal (970 cc engine)

Refer to illustrations 3.7 and 3.8

7   Unscrew the wing nut or release the clips, then remove the cap from the front of the air cleaner (see illustration).
8   Extract the air cleaner element from the air cleaner body (see il-lustration).
9   If the air cleaner element is to be cleaned, first shake all loose dust from it, then blow through it from the inside using compressed air. Warning: Wear eye protection when using compressed air.

3.8 Removing the air cleaner element

10   If the element is to be renewed, discard it and obtain a new one.
11   Wipe clean the inside of the air cleaner body and cap.
12   Locate the element in the air cleaner body, and refit the cap. Make sure that all the clips are correctly engaged, or the wing nut tightened, as applicable.
13   The air cleaner incorporates a manual adjustment for the inlet air temperature. Check that this is set correctly for the prevailing tempera-ture conditions. An incorrect setting could cause the engine to over-heat in Summer, or the carburettor to "ice-up" in Winter. The air cleaner should be set to the Winter setting (ie adjusted away from the engine) when the outside air temperature is 15° C or below; at temper-atures above this, it should be set to the Summer position (ie adjusted towards the engine).

Contact breaker points and condenser (970 cc engine) - check, adjustment and renewal

Refer to illustrations 3.17a, 3.17b, 3.18a to 3.18e, 3.19a, 3.19b, 3.25, and 3.28

14   Release the two spring clips, and lift off the distributor cap. Note that the cap will only locate on the distributor in the one position, where the cast lug engages the cut-out in the cap. Pull the rotor arm off the shaft, and remove the dust cover.
15   With the ignition switched off, use a screwdriver to open the con-tact breaker points, then visually check their surfaces for pitting, roughness and discoloration. If the points have been arcing, there will be a build-up of metal on the moving contact, and a corresponding pit in the fixed contact; if this is the case, they should be renewed. On models where the contact points are located beneath the baseplate, a

3.17a Unscrew the screw . . .

3.17b . . . and remove the fixed contact from the baseplate

3.18a Unscrew the baseplate securing screws . . .

3.18b . . . then unscrew the terminal nut and disconnect the condenser lead

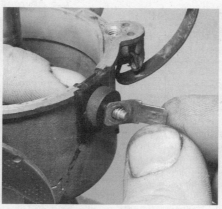

3.18c Remove the terminal blade . . .

3.18d . . . and spacer . . .

3.18e . . . then remove the screw from inside the distributor

3.19a Extract the C-clip . . .

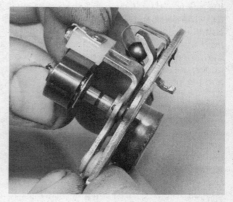

3.19b . . . and remove the moving contact from the baseplate

torch will be helpful, as it is not easy to view the points.

16 Another method of checking the contact breaker points is by using a test meter (available from most car accessory shops). Follow the instructions provided with the test meter, if they differ from the following. Rotate the engine using a spanner on the crankshaft pulley bolt until the points are fully shut. Connect the meter between the distributor LT terminal and earth, and read off the condition of the points. Note that the ignition must be switched off before carrying out this test.

17 **Note:** *The following paragraphs describe removal and refitting of the contact points on distributors with the contact points mounted beneath the baseplate. The procedure is similar on distributors with the contact points mounted on top of the baseplate. The distributor has been removed from the engine for photographic purposes.* To remove the points, first unscrew the screw retaining the fixed contact to the baseplate, and lift out the fixed contact **(see illustrations)**.

18 Unscrew the screws securing the baseplate to the distributor body, then unscrew the terminal nut and disconnect the condenser lead. Lift off the baseplate, then remove the terminal blade and spacer. Remove the terminal screw from inside the distributor, and remove the baseplate assembly **(see illustrations)**. Note that the moving contact lead is secured by the terminal screw.

19 With the baseplate removed, extract the C-clip, and slide the moving contact from the pin while releasing the spring and plastic holder from the post **(see illustrations)**.

13

20   The condenser is located externally, on the side of the distributor body. Its purpose is to ensure that when the contact breaker points open, there is no sparking across them, which would cause wear of their faces and prevent the rapid collapse of the magnetic field in the coil. Failure of the condenser would cause a reduction in coil HT voltage, and ultimately lead to engine misfire.

21   If the engine becomes very difficult to start, or begins to miss after several miles of running, and the contact breaker points show signs of excessive burning, the condition of the condenser must be suspect. A further test can be made by separating the points with a screwdriver with the ignition switched on. If this is accompanied by a strong bright flash, it is indicative that the condenser has failed.

22   Without special test equipment, the only sure way to diagnose condenser trouble is to substitute a suspect unit with a new one, and note if there is any improvement.

23   To remove the condenser, first unscrew the terminal nut on the side of the distributor, and disconnect the condenser lead. Unscrew the mounting screw, and remove the condenser. If the baseplate is still in position, take care not to push the terminal screw into the distributor.

24   Refitting of the condenser is a reversal of the removal procedure.

25   When fitting the new contact breaker points, first check if there is any greasy deposit on them, and if necessary clean them using methylated spirit. If a genuine Suzuki contact breaker set has been obtained, a sachet of grease will be supplied. Apply this grease to the cam on the distributor shaft **(see illustration)**.

26   Fit the points using a reversal of the removal procedure, then adjust them as follows. Using a socket or spanner on the crankshaft pulley bolt, turn the engine over until the heel of the contact breaker arm is on the peak of one of the four cam lobes.

27   With the points fully open, a feeler blade equal to the contact breaker points gap (given in the Specifications) should now just fit between the contact faces. The feeler blade should be a firm sliding fit.

28   If the gap is too large or too small, loosen the points retaining screw, and adjust the position of the fixed contact until the specified gap is obtained **(see illustration)**.

29   With the points correctly adjusted, refit the dust cover, rotor arm and distributor cap.

30   If a dwell meter is available, a far more accurate method of setting the points is by adjusting the distributor dwell angle.

31   The dwell angle is the number of degrees of distributor shaft rotation during which the contact breaker points are closed (ie the period from when the points close after being opened by one cam lobe until they are opened again by the next cam lobe). Using this method, any uneven wear of the distributor shaft or cam lobes is taken into account, and the inherent inaccuracies of using a feeler gauge are eliminated.

32   To check the dwell angle, connect the dwell meter in accordance with the meter manufacturer's instructions.

33   Start the engine, allow it to idle, and observe the reading on the dwell meter scale. If the dwell angle is too large, increase the contact points gap. If the angle is too small, reduce the points gap. Only very slight adjustments should be made to the gap before re-checking. **Note:** *Owing to machining tolerances, or wear in the distributor shaft or bushes, it is not uncommon for a points gap correctly set with feeler gauges, to give a dwell angle outside the specified tolerances. If this is the case, the dwell angle should be regarded as the preferred setting.*

34   After completing the adjustment, switch off the engine and disconnect the dwell meter. The ignition timing should be checked, and if necessary adjusted, after fitting a new set of points.

Ignition timing (970 cc engine) - check and adjustment

35   In order that the engine can run efficiently, it is necessary for a spark to occur at the spark plug and ignite the fuel/air mixture at the instant just before the piston on the compression stroke reaches the top of its travel (top dead centre). The precise instant at which the spark occurs is determined by the ignition timing, and this is quoted in degrees before top dead centre (BTDC).

36   The timing may be checked and adjusted in one of two ways, either by using a test bulb to obtain a static setting with the engine sta-

3.25 Applying grease to the cam on the distributor shaft

tionary, or by using a stroboscopic timing light to obtain a dynamic setting with the engine running.

37   Before checking or adjusting the ignition timing, make sure that the contact breaker points are in good condition and correctly adjusted, as described previously.

Static setting

38   Refer to the Specifications at the start of this Supplement, and note the specified setting for the ignition timing.

39   Pull off the HT lead and remove No 1 spark plug (nearest the front of the engine).

40   Place a finger (or suitable long length of wooden dowel) over the plug hole, and turn the engine in the normal direction of rotation (clockwise from the crankshaft pulley end) until pressure is felt in No 1 cylinder. This indicates that the piston is commencing its compression stroke. The engine can be turned using a socket or spanner on the crankshaft pulley bolt.

41   Prise out the rubber plug from the timing hole on the left-hand side of the transmission bellhousing, just behind the cylinder block.

42   Continue turning the engine until the relevant timing mark on the flywheel is aligned with the pointer on the bellhousing. Note that the "T" mark indicates top dead centre, and the "10" indicates 10° BTDC.

43   Remove the distributor cap, and check that the rotor arm is pointing towards the No 1 spark plug HT lead segment in the cap. The HT lead positions are marked with the corresponding cylinder number on the top of the distributor cap.

44   Connect a 12-volt test light and leads between a good earth point and the LT terminal nut on the side of the distributor body.

45   Slacken the distributor clamp retaining bolt, and then switch on the ignition.

46   If the test light is on, turn the distributor slightly clockwise until the light goes out.

47   Now turn the distributor anti-clockwise until the test light just comes on. Hold the distributor in this position, and tighten the clamp retaining bolt.

48   Test the setting by turning the engine two complete revolutions and observing when the light comes on in relation to the timing marks.

49   Switch off the ignition and remove the test light. Refit No 1 spark plug, the distributor cap and HT lead. Also refit the plug to the transmission bellhousing.

Dynamic setting

Refer to illustration 3.54

50   Refer to the Specifications at the start of this Supplement, and note the specified setting for the ignition timing.

51   Run the engine to bring it to normal operating temperature, then

3.28 Adjusting the contact breaker points gap

3.54 Timing access hole (highlighted) on the left-hand side of the transmission bellhousing

3.73 Idle speed adjusting screw location (arrowed)

switch it off.

52   Connect the timing light in accordance with the equipment manu-facturer's instructions (the connection is usually made between the end of No 1 spark plug HT lead and No 1 spark plug terminal).

53   Prise out the rubber plug from the timing hole on the left-hand side of the transmission bellhousing, just behind the cylinder block. Start the engine and leave it idling at the specified idle speed (refer to the Specifications).

54   Point the timing light at the timing marks (see illustration). They should appear to be stationary, with the mark on the flywheel aligned with the pointer on the transmission bellhousing.

55   If adjustment is necessary, slacken the distributor clamp retaining bolt. Turn the distributor body either anti-clockwise to advance the timing, or clockwise to retard it. Tighten the clamp bolt when the setting is correct.

56   Gradually increase the engine speed while still pointing the timing light at the marks. The mark on the flywheel should appear to advance further, indicating that the distributor centrifugal advance mechanism is functioning. If the mark remains stationary, or moves in a jerky, er-ratic fashion, the advance mechanism must be suspect.

57   After completing the checks and adjustments, switch off the en-gine and disconnect the timing light.

HT leads, distributor cap and rotor arm (970 cc engine) - check and renewal

58   The spark plug HT leads should be checked whenever new spark plugs are fitted.

59   Ensure that the leads are numbered before removing them, to avoid confusion when refitting. Pull one HT lead from its plug by grip-ping the end fitting, not the lead, otherwise the lead connection may be fractured.

60   Check inside the end fitting for signs of corrosion, in the form of a white crusty powder. Push the end fitting back onto the spark plug, en-suring that it is a tight fit on the plug. If it is not, remove the lead again, and use pliers to carefully crimp the metal connector inside the end fit-ting until it fits securely on the end of the spark plug.

61   Using a clean rag, wipe the entire length of the lead, to remove any built-up dirt and grease. Once the lead is clean, check for burns, cracks and other damage. Do not bend the lead excessively, or pull the lead lengthwise - the conductor inside might break.

62   Disconnect the other end of the lead from the distributor cap. Again, pull only on the end fitting. Check for corrosion and for a tight fit in the same manner as the spark plug end. If an ohmmeter is available, check the continuity of the HT lead by connecting the meter between the spark plug end of the lead and the segment inside the distributor

cap. Refit the lead securely on completion.

63   Check the remaining HT leads one at a time, in the same way.

64   If new HT leads are required, purchase a complete set.

65   Remove the distributor cap, and carefully inspect it inside and out for signs of cracks, carbon tracks (tracking) and worn, burned or loose contacts. Similarly inspect the rotor arm. Renew these components if any defects are found. Wipe the cap clean inside and out. If a new cap is being fitted, remove the HT leads from the old cap one at a time, and fit them to the new cap in the same location - do not simultaneously re-move all the leads from the old cap, or firing-order confusion may oc-cur.

66   Even with the ignition system in first-class condition, some en-gines may still occasionally experience poor starting attributable to damp ignition components. To disperse moisture, use a proprietary water-dispersant obtainable from any car accessory shop.

Idle speed (970 cc engine) - check and adjustment

Refer to illustrations 3.73, 3.74a and 3.74b

Note: *A special tool with a curved section is required to adjust the idle mixture screw. It should be possible to obtain one of these from a car accessory shop, or failing this from a Suzuki dealer.*

67   Before attempting to make an adjustment, make sure that the ig-nition system is in good order, that the air filter element is clean, and that the engine itself is in good condition.

68   Some adjustment screws may be protected by "tamperproof" plugs, caps or seals. The purpose of these is to discourage and to de-tect adjustment by unqualified operators. In some countries, it is an of-fence to drive a vehicle without the necessary tamperproof devices fit-ted. Satisfy yourself that current legislation permits the removal of tamperproof devices before making adjustments, and fit new devices on completion if required. Note that removal of these tamperproof de-vices may also invalidate the vehicle warranty, when applicable.

69   As these adjustments are made with the engine running, particu-lar care is needed to avoid personal injury. Keep away from moving drivebelts, the cooling fan blades and the HT leads.

70   Note that an exhaust gas analyser (CO meter) will be required in order to obtain the necessary levels of accuracy when setting the idle mixture.

71   The adjustments should be made with the engine at normal oper-ating temperature, with the air filter fitted and the choke completely off.

72   Connect an exhaust gas analyser and tachometer (rev counter) in accordance with the equipment manufacturer's instructions.

73   Start the engine, and turn the idle adjusting screw to obtain an en-gine speed of 880 rpm (see illustration).

13

3.74a Showing the special end of the tool (arrowed) for adjusting the idle mixture setting

3.74b Turning the idle mixture screw with the special tool

3.83a Unscrew the nuts . . .

3.83b . . . and disconnect the front of the driveshaft from the rear of the handbrake drum

3.85a Removing the handbrake drum centre nut . . .

3.85b . . . and washer

3.86 Removing the handbrake drum from the transfer box output shaft

3.88 Staking the centre nut rim into the groove in the transfer box output shaft

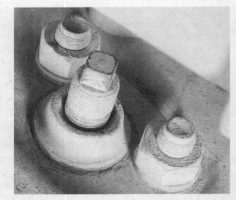

3.90 Adjustment screw on the handbrake drum backplate

74   Turn the idle mixture adjusting screw clockwise or anti-clockwise as necessary to obtain the highest engine speed **(see illustrations)**.

75   Repeat the procedure in the previous two paragraphs, and then if necessary adjust the idle adjusting screw to maintain the idle speed at 880 rpm.

76   Finally turn the idle mixture adjusting screw slowly clockwise until the idle speed drops into the idle speed tolerance given in the Specifications at the beginning of this Supplement. The CO% should also come into the specified range at the same time.

77   Check that the CO% is as given in the Specifications, and if necessary make any final adjustments necessary.

78   Fit a new tamperproof cap if applicable, and disconnect the test equipment from the engine.

Front drum brakes (early SJ410 models) - check and adjustment

79   Remove the brake drum, and check the brake shoes using the procedure described for the rear brakes in Chapter 1, Section 18. Note, however, that the front brakes have two wheel cylinders, located at the 3 o'clock and 9 o'clock positions.

80   The renewal procedure is similar to that for the rear shoes.

81   When adjusting the front drum brakes, first turn the wheel until the adjuster serrations can be seen through the access hole. Turn the adjuster nut until the drum is held tight, then back it off approximately 3 to 6 notches so that the drum is free. Now turn the wheel until the remaining adjuster is visible through the access hole, and adjust it using the same procedure.

4.7 Removing the rubber plug from the timing access hole in the transmission bellhousing

4.14 Removing the drivebelt from the alternator pulley

4.15a Unbolt the cooling fan . . .

Centre handbrake (SJ410 and early SJ413 models) - check and shoe renewal

Refer to illustrations 3.83a, 3.83b, 3.85a, 3.85b, 3.86, 3.88 and 3.90

82 Jack up the front and rear of the vehicle, and support on axle stands. Select Neutral.

83 Unscrew the four nuts, and disconnect the front of the driveshaft (propeller shaft) from the rear of the handbrake drum **(see illustrations)**. If necessary, use a lever to prise the shaft off the studs on the drum. Tie the shaft to one side.

84 Using a pin punch, bend out the staking on the centre nut from the groove in the transfer box output shaft.

85 Fully apply the handbrake, then unscrew the centre nut retaining the handbrake drum on the transfer box shaft. Remove the washer **(see illustrations)**.

86 Release the handbrake, then slide the drum off the splined transfer box output shaft **(see illustration)**. If it is tight due to the shoes binding on the drum inner surface, release the handbrake adjustment first. On some models, the adjustment screw is on the backplate; on other models, it is necessary to position the access hole in the drum over the anchor assembly, and use a screwdriver to rotate the serrated adjustment nut.

87 Check the shoe linings and the drum for wear, and if necessary renew the shoes with reference to Section 10 of this Supplement.

88 Refit the drum using a reversal of the removal procedure. After tightening the centre nut to the specified torque, stake its rim into the groove in the shaft using a pin punch **(see illustration)**.

89 Refit the driveshaft (propeller shaft) using a reversal of the removal procedure then adjust the shoes as follows.

90 Turn the shoe adjustment screw until the drum is held tight, then back it off until the drum can be rotated freely **(see illustration)**.

91 Apply the handbrake by 6 notches, and check that the drum is held firm. Release the handbrake, and check again that the drum is free to rotate. If the drum is not held firm with the lever applied by 6 notches, adjust as required and check it again.

92 Apply the handbrake, then lower the vehicle to the ground.

---

4 Engine (970 cc)

General information

1 This Section describes procedures for the 970 cc engine which are different from the procedures described in Chapter 2, Parts A and B.

Top Dead Centre (TDC) - locating

Refer to illustration 4.7

2 Refer to the information given in Chapter 2A, Section 3, para-graphs 1 to 4 inclusive, but note that if the TDC position is being found in order to install the distributor, No 4 piston should be at TDC instead (see also information given in Section 7 later in this Supplement).

3 Note the position of the terminal for the No 1 spark plug on the distributor cap. Each terminal has the corresponding cylinder number moulded in the distributor cap.

4 Use a felt-tip pen or chalk to make a mark on the distributor body directly under the terminal. Alternatively, scribe a mark on the body.

5 Unclip and remove the distributor cap, and move it to one side.

6 Turn the crankshaft clockwise (using a socket on the crankshaft pulley bolt) until the distributor rotor arm is approaching the mark made on the distributor body.

7 Prise the rubber plug from the timing access hole in the left-hand side of the transmission bellhousing **(see illustration)**.

8 Continue turning the crankshaft in a clockwise direction until the "T" mark on the flywheel is aligned exactly with the edge of the pointer on the bellhousing. Note that there are no timing marks on the crankshaft pulley and outer timing cover.

9 Check that the rotor arm is now aligned with the mark made on the distributor body.

10 After the TDC position has been established for No 1 piston, TDC for any of the remaining pistons can be located by turning the crankshaft and following the firing order.

Timing belt and sprockets - removal, inspection and refitting

Caution 1: *Do not try to turn the crankshaft using the camshaft sprocket bolt, and do not rotate the crankshaft anti-clockwise.*

Caution 2: Do not bend, twist or turn the timing belt inside-out if it is to be re-used. Do not allow it to come in contact with oil, coolant or fuel. Do not utilise timing belt tension to keep the camshaft or crankshaft from turning when installing the pulley bolt(s). Do not turn the crankshaft or camshaft more than a few degrees (as necessary for tooth alignment) while the timing belt is removed.

Removal

Refer to illustrations 4.14, 4.15a, 4.15b, 4.15c, 4.17a, 4.17b, 4.18a, 4.18b, 4.24a, 4.24b, 4.25a, 4.25b, 4.26a, and 4.26b

11 Position No 4 piston (**not** No 1) at TDC, as described earlier in this Section.

12 Disconnect the negative cable from the battery.

13 For ease of access, it is recommended that the radiator be removed.

14 Loosen the pivot and adjustment bolts on the alternator. Swivel the alternator towards the engine, and remove the drivebelt from the pulleys on the alternator, water pump and crankshaft **(see illustration)**.

15 Unbolt the cooling fan, spacer and pulley from the front of the water pump **(see illustrations)**.

13

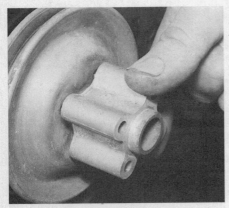

4.15b . . . spacer . . .

4.15c . . . and pulley from the front of the water pump

4.17a Remove the crankshaft pulley bolt . . .

4.17b . . . and slide off the pulley

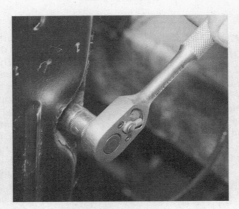

4.18a Unscrew the bolts . . .

4.18b . . . and remove the outer timing cover

16   The crankshaft pulley bolt must now be loosened. To do this, first select 4th gear and apply the handbrake firmly. If the handbrake does not keep the engine stationary, it will be necessary to remove the starter motor and have an assistant hold the flywheel stationary using a wide-bladed screwdriver engaged with one of the starter ring gear teeth. Alternatively, the method described in Chapter 2A, Section 7 may be used, but take care not to damage the pulley.

17   With the bolt removed, withdraw the pulley from the front of the crankshaft (see illustrations). With the pulley removed, mark the outer face of the crankshaft sprocket to ensure correct refitting.

18   Unscrew the bolts and remove the outer timing cover (see illustrations).

19   If you plan to re-use the timing belt, and it doesn't already have arrows marked on it, mark it to indicate the direction of rotation (clockwise).

20   Where applicable, release the end of the timing belt tensioner spring on the tensioner. On later models, this is not possible.

21   Unscrew the nut and bolt, or two bolts (as applicable), and remove the tensioner from the front of the engine.

22   Slip the timing belt from the camshaft and crankshaft sprockets.

23   To remove the camshaft sprocket, first note its fitted position. On early models, it has two keyways, and it is important that it is refitted correctly. As a precaution, the sprocket should be marked in relation to the camshaft with a dab of paint. Because the retaining washer covers the end of the camshaft, the sprocket position must be marked *after* removing the bolt as described in the following paragraph.

24   Hold the sprocket stationary using a suitable tool, then unscrew the bolt, and slide the sprocket off the front of the camshaft (see illustrations). If necessary, remove the Woodruff key from the camshaft. **Do not** turn the camshaft with the timing belt removed, as there is the possibility of the tops of the pistons touching the valves.

25   To remove the crankshaft sprocket, carefully lever it off with a screwdriver. With the sprocket removed, remove the timing belt guide, then if necessary prise out the Woodruff key (see illustrations).

26   If necessary, unscrew the nuts and bolts, and remove the timing belt inner cover. Note the position of the spacers and bushes which locate over the studs on the front of the cylinder head (see illustrations).

Inspection

27   Rotate the tensioner by hand, and move it from side-to-side to detect roughness and excess play. Inspect the sprockets for any signs of damage and wear. Renew if necessary.

28   Inspect the timing belt for cracks, separation, wear, missing teeth and oil contamination. Renew the belt if it's worn or damaged. **Note:** *Unless the engine has a very low mileage, it's common practice to renew the timing belt every time it's removed. Don't refit the existing belt unless it's in like-new condition, and never refit a belt which is in questionable condition.*

Installation

Refer to illustrations 4.35, 4.36a, 4.36b, 4.37, 4.39, 4.42, 4.44, 4.46, and 4.48

29   Check that the spacers for the studs on the front of the cylinder head are correctly located in the bushes in the inner timing cover, then refit the cover and tighten the nuts and bolts. If the spacer studs have been disturbed, their threads should be coated with a suitable sealant before tightening into the cylinder head.

30   Press the Woodruff key fully into its slot on the front of the crankshaft, and make sure that its upper edge is parallel to the crankshaft surface. Use a light hammer to carefully tap it into the slot.

31   Locate the timing belt guide over the key on the front of the

4.24a Unscrew the bolt . . .

4.24b . . . and slide the camshaft sprocket off the front of the camshaft

4.25a Removing the crankshaft sprocket . . .

4.25b . . . and timing belt guide

4.26a Unscrew the nuts and bolts . . .

4.26b . . . and remove the timing belt inner cover

4.35 Tightening the camshaft sprocket retaining bolt

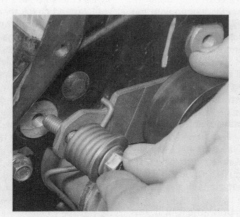

4.36a Inserting the timing belt tensioner outer retaining bolt . . .

4.36b . . . and inner retaining bolt

crankshaft, making sure that it is the correct way round. The convex side should be facing outwards (ie towards the sprocket position).

32   Align the keyway with the key, then slide the sprocket onto the front of the crankshaft. Make sure that it is the correct way round, as previously noted.

33   Check that the key on the front of the camshaft is facing upwards - if the camshaft has not been moved since removing the timing belt, it should still be in this position.

34   On early engines, the camshaft sprocket has two keyways at 90° to each other, one with a single punch mark, and the other with two

punch marks. The sprocket must be located on the camshaft with the single punch mark keyway facing upwards and located on the camshaft key. Sprockets with only one keyway can only be fitted one way round.

35   Insert the sprocket bolt and tighten while holding the sprocket stationary (see illustration). Do not rotate the camshaft, otherwise the valves may touch the tops of the pistons.

36   Refit the tensioner to its location on the front of the engine, and fit the retaining nut and bolt, or bolts (as applicable) loosely (see illustrations).

13

4.37 TDC timing marks (arrowed) on the camshaft sprocket and inner timing cover (No 4 piston and TDC)

4.39 Locating the timing belt on the camshaft sprocket

4.42 Tightening the timing belt tensioner bolts (later model shown)

4.44 Method of checking the timing belt tension without the special Suzuki tool

4.46 Tightening the crankshaft pulley bolt

4.48 Adjusting the drivebelt tension

37   Check that the punch mark on the perimeter of the camshaft sprocket (the one in line with the keyway) is exactly aligned with the TDC timing mark on the top of the inner timing cover **(see illustration)**.

38   Check that the keyway on the front of the crankshaft is facing upwards and exactly aligned with the TDC timing mark on the rear cover (just above the timing belt guide).

39   Locate the timing belt on the camshaft and crankshaft sprockets and around the tensioner roller, so that the straight portion of belt between the sprockets is free of any slack **(see illustration)**. Do not move the sprockets during this operation. If the original belt is being refitted, make sure that the previously-made rotation arrows point the correct way.

40   On early engines, engage the end of the timing belt tensioner spring on the tensioner so that the tensioner applies tension to the belt. On later engines, the tension will already be applied. Check that the sprockets are still in their TDC positions, and that the belt is engaged with the sprocket teeth correctly.

41   Temporarily refit the crankshaft pulley bolt, then turn the crankshaft two full turns clockwise to tension the belt correctly.

42   Remove the tensioner retaining bolts in turn on later engines, or the single bolt on early engines, and apply thread-locking fluid to the threads. Tighten the nut and bolt, or bolts, to the specified torque **(see illustration)**.

43   Turn the crankshaft two full turns clockwise, then check again that all of the TDC timing marks align correctly.

44   Check that the timing belt is correctly tensioned as follows. Suzuki technicians use a special push-gauge, which applies a force of 3 kg (6.6 lb) midway between the camshaft and crankshaft sprockets. The gauge checks that the deflection of the timing belt is between 5.5 mm and 6.5 mm. A home-made alternative to this gauge can be set up using a steel rule, spring balance and stout wire bent to engage the timing belt. Hook the spring balance and wire on the belt midway be-

tween the sprockets: Hold the steel rule in place, then apply the force of 3 kg and check that the belt has deflected by the specified amount **(see illustration)**. If not, re-position the tensioner as required and check the tension again. Some trial-and-error will be necessary. Make sure that the tensioner nut and bolt, or bolts, are tightened to the specified torque on completion.

45   Refit the outer timing cover, and tighten the bolts.

46   Locate the pulley on the front of the crankshaft, making sure that the keyway engages onto the key. Insert the bolt and tighten it to the specified torque while holding the crankshaft stationary using one of the methods described previously **(see illustration)**.

47   Refit the pulley and cooling fan to the front of the water pump, and tighten the bolts.

48   Refit and adjust the alternator drivebelt with reference to Chapter 1 **(see illustration)**.

49   Refit the radiator, and fill the cooling system.

50   Reconnect the battery negative cable.

Crankshaft front oil seal - renewal

51   Remove the timing belt, tensioner, crankshaft sprocket, camshaft sprocket and timing belt inner cover as described earlier. It is also recommended that the Woodruff key is removed from the front of the crankshaft, to prevent any damage to the oil seal in the oil pump.

52   Note the fitted position of the oil seal in the oil pump to ensure correct fitting of the new seal.

53   Prise the oil seal from the oil pump casing using a suitable hooked instrument, taking care not to damage the surface of the crankshaft (wrap the tip of the instrument with tape if necessary). An alternative method of removing the oil seal is to drill two small holes diagonally opposite each other in the end face of the oil seal. Insert two small self-tapping screws, and use grips to pull the oil seal from the casing. Clean away all traces of swarf, and wipe clean the casing and

4.61 Note the shouldered end (A) on the front of the intake rocker shaft, and the plain end (B) on the front of the exhaust rocker shaft

4.65 Removing the spark plugs

4.69a Note the position of the engine lifting eye when removing the exhaust manifold

4.69b Removing the exhaust manifold gasket

4.69c Engine lifting eye position on the intake manifold

4.69d Removing the intake manifold

crankshaft.

54   Smear a little clean engine oil on the lip of the new oil seal, then locate it on the front of the oil pump. Using a suitable metal tube or socket, press the seal squarely into the casing until it is located in the previously-noted position.

55   The remaining procedure is a reversal of removal.

Camshaft oil seal - renewal

56   Remove the timing belt, tensioner, crankshaft sprocket, camshaft sprocket and timing belt inner cover as described earlier.

57   Note the fitted position of the oil seal in the cylinder head to ensure correct fitting of the new seal.

58   Prise the oil seal from the cylinder head using a suitable hooked instrument, taking care not to damage the surface of the camshaft (wrap the tip of the instrument with tape if necessary). An alternative method of removing the oil seal is to drill two small holes diagonally opposite each other in the end face of the oil seal. Insert two small self-tapping screws, and use grips to pull the oil seal from the cylinder head.

59   Smear a little clean engine oil on the lip of the new oil seal, then locate it carefully over the end of the camshaft and into the front of the cylinder head. Using a suitable metal tube or socket, press the seal squarely into the casing until it is located in the previously-noted position.

60   The remaining procedure is a reversal of removal.

Rocker arms and shafts - removal, inspection and refitting

Refer to illustration 4.61

61   The procedure is similar to that described in Chapter 2A, Section 10, except that the tensioner, crankshaft sprocket and timing belt

inner cover must be removed in addition to the timing belt and camshaft sprocket. Make sure that the shafts are refitted the correct way round as shown in illustration 10.23 (page 2A-11). On the 970 cc engine (ie the engine covered by this Section) the dimensions of the shoulders on the shaft ends are different to that shown. On this engine, both shafts are identical, but must be fitted as shown with the shoulders at opposite ends **(see illustration)**. If they are fitted with the shoulders at the same end, the oil supply holes in one of the shafts will not line up correctly, and oil pressure will be lost. Also note that the threaded end of the screw location holes must be uppermost.

Cylinder head - removal and refitting

Caution: Allow the engine to cool completely before following this procedure.

Removal

Refer to illustrations 4.65, 4.69a, 4.69b, 4.69c, 4.69d, 4.69e, 4.70a, 4.70b, 4.71, 4.72 and 4.73

62   Position No 4 piston (**not** No 1) at TDC as described earlier in this Section.

63   Disconnect the battery negative cable.

64   Drain the cooling system and remove the radiator.

65   Remove the spark plugs (see Chapter 1) **(see illustration)**.

66   Remove the distributor (including the HT leads and cap) as described in Section 7.

67   Remove the fuel pump as described in Section 6.

68   Remove the timing belt and rear cover as described earlier in this Section.

69   Unbolt the intake and exhaust manifolds - these may remain in the engine compartment if wished. Leave the exhaust manifold attached to the downpipe, and leave the carburettor attached to the in-

13

4.69e Removing the intake manifold gaskets

4.70a Note the position of the sealing washers when removing the camshaft cover

4.70b Removing the camshaft cover

4.71 Removing the cylinder head bolts

4.72 Lifting the cylinder head from the cylinder block

4.73 Removing the cylinder head gasket from the block

4.74 Check that the locating dowels are fitted to the block

take manifold. Move the manifolds away from the cylinder head, and if necessary tie them to the inner wings to keep them clear of the cylinder head. Note the position of the engine lifting eyes (see illustrations). On the intake manifold, the front mounting nut retains the lifting eye, the second nut retains the dipstick bracket, and the third nut retains a hose clip.

70   Remove the camshaft cover, noting the position of the sealing washers (see illustrations).

71   Loosen the cylinder head bolts a quarter-turn at a time, in the reverse of the sequence shown in illustration 4.77, until they can be re-

moved by hand (see illustration). Keep the washers together with the bolts.

72   Carefully lift the cylinder head straight up, and place the head on wooden blocks to prevent damage to the sealing surfaces (see illustration). If the head sticks to the block, dislodge it by levering against a protrusion on the head casting. Do not lever between the mating faces.

73   Lift off the gasket, then remove all traces of gasket from the cylinder block and head (see illustration). Do not allow anything to fall into the engine. Clean and inspect all nuts and bolts, and be sure the threaded holes in the block are clean and dry.

4.77a Cylinder head bolt TIGHTENING sequence (970 cc engine) -
to loosen the bolts, reverse this sequence

4.77b Tightening the cylinder head bolts with a torque wrench

4.80a Renewing the camshaft
cover gasket

4.80b Renewing the ventilation baffle
gasket located inside the camshaft cover

4.87a Remove the transmission
bellhousing cover . . .

Refitting

Refer to illustrations 4.74, 4.77a, 4.77b, 4.80a and 4.80b

74   Check that the locating dowels are fitted to the block **(see illustration)**.

75   Locate a new gasket on the block, making sure that it engages with the dowels. The "TOP" mark should be uppermost and at the front of the engine. Where applicable, the "IN" and "EX" marks on the gasket refer to the intake (right) and exhaust (left) sides of the engine.

76   Carefully lower the cylinder head onto the gasket, then insert the bolts in their locations.

77   Tighten the cylinder head bolts in several stages following the proper sequence **(see illustrations)** to the torque listed in the Specifications at the beginning of this Supplement.

78   Refit the rear cover and timing belt as described earlier in this Section.

79   If necessary, check and adjust the valve clearances with reference to Section 3.

80   Check the camshaft cover gasket, and renew it if necessary. Also if necessary renew the ventilation baffle gasket located inside the cover **(see illustrations)**. Refit the camshaft cover and tighten the bolts.

81   Refit the exhaust and intake manifolds.

82   Refit the fuel pump, distributor, HT leads and spark plugs.

83   Refit the radiator and refill the cooling system.

84   Reconnect the battery negative cable.

85   Start the engine, and run it until normal operating temperature is reached. Check for leaks and proper operation, and set the ignition timing. Switch off the engine, remove the camshaft cover, and re-torque the cylinder head bolts. Recheck the valve clearances.

4.87b . . . and sump . . .

Oil pump - removal, inspection and refitting
Removal

Refer to illustrations 4.87a, 4.87b, 4.87c, 4.87d, 4.87e, 4.88a, 4.88b, 4.89a and 4.89b

86   Remove the timing belt, tensioner, crankshaft sprocket, camshaft sprocket and rear cover as described earlier. Also make sure that the Woodruff key is removed from the front of the crankshaft, to prevent any damage to the oil seal in the oil pump.

87   Remove the transmission bellhousing cover and sump, then unbolt the oil pickup tube from the main bearing cap and oil pump **(see il-**

13

4.87c ... then unscrew the mounting bolts for the oil pickup tube from the main bearing cap ...

4.87d ... and oil pump ...

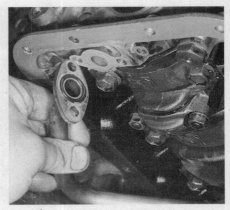

4.87e ... and remove the pickup tube (note the location of the O-ring in the flange)

4.88a Removing the alternator

4.88b Removing the alternator lower pivot support bracket

4.89a Unscrew the mounting bolts ...

4.89b ... and remove the oil pump over the front of the crankshaft

4.90 Removing the crankshaft front oil seal from the oil pump casing

4.91a Remove the screws ...

lustrations). If it is difficult to remove the pan over the bottom of the oil pickup tube, raise the front of the vehicle so that the gap between the front axle and engine is increased. An alternative method is to unbolt the sump, then unbolt the pickup tube before actually removing the sump. Remove the rubber O-ring from the flange on the oil pickup tube.

88   Remove the alternator, and unbolt the lower pivot support bracket **(see illustrations)**.

89   Unscrew the mounting bolts, then remove the oil pump over the

front of the crankshaft and from the front of the cylinder block. Remove the gasket **(see illustrations)**.

Inspection

Refer to illustrations 4.90, 4.91a, 4.91b, 4.92a, 4.92b, 4.92c, 4.94a to 4.94d, and 4.96

90   Remove the crankshaft front oil seal from the oil pump casing, using a screwdriver to lever it out **(see illustration)**.

91   Using a cross-head screwdriver, remove the screws, then lift the

4.91b . . . and lift the cover from the rear of the oil pump

4.92a Removing the oil pump inner gear . . .

4.92b . . . and outer gear

4.92c Relief valve and spring removed from the oil pump

4.94a Checking the clearance between the oil pump inner gear and crescent . . .

4.94b . . . outer gear and crescent . . .

4.94c . . . outer gear and body . . .

4.94d . . . and gear endfloat

cover from the rear of the oil pump **(see illustrations)**.

92   Note the fitted positions of the oil pump gears, then withdraw them from the casing. The outer gear has a punch mark on its outer face. Unscrew the plug bolt, and remove the relief valve and spring **(see illustrations)**.

93   Clean all parts thoroughly, and remove all traces of old gasket material from the sealing surfaces. Inspect all parts for wear, cracks

and other damage.

94   Install the oil pump outer and inner gears, and measure the clearances with a feeler gauge **(see illustrations)**. Make sure the gears are the correct way round. Compare the clearances to those given in the Specifications at the beginning of this Supplement. If they are not within the specified tolerances, the oil pump should be renewed.

95   Fill the oil pump with fresh engine oil, then refit the cover to the

13

4.96 Installing a new crankshaft front oil seal in the oil pump casing

4.97 Oil pump gasket located on the front of the cylinder block

4.99 Trimming off the excess oil pump gasket

4.100 Locating a new sump gasket on the bottom of the crankcase

4.102a Removing the rocker shaft retaining screws

4.102b Removing the rocker arms . . .

rear of the oil pump and tighten the screws. Insert the relief valve and spring, and tighten the plug bolt.

96   Press the new crankshaft front oil seal into the oil pump casing using a socket or suitable-size metal tube **(see illustration)**. Smear a little engine oil onto the lips of the oil seal.

Refitting

Refer to illustrations 4.97, 4.99, and 4.100

97   Locate a new gasket on the front of the cylinder block **(see illustration)**.

98   Position the oil pump over the crankshaft and onto the gasket on the front of the cylinder block. Insert the mounting bolts and tighten them progressively to the specified torque.

99   Using a sharp knife, cut off any excess gasket protruding onto the sump mounting face **(see illustration)**. Apply a little suitable sealant to the cut ends of the gasket joint to ensure an oil-tight seal when the sump is fitted.

100 Refit the remaining parts in the reverse order to removal. Locate a new rubber O-ring in the oil pickup tube flange where it contacts the bottom of the oil pump, and fit a new sump gasket **(see illustration)**.

101 Fill the engine with the correct quantity of oil, then start it and check for leaks.

Cylinder head - dismantling

Refer to illustrations 4.102a to 4.102c, 4.103a to 4.103c, 4.104, 4.105a, 4.105b, and 4.106a to 4.106e

Note: New and rebuilt cylinder heads are commonly available for most engines at dealerships and engine overhaul specialists. Due to the fact that some specialised tools are necessary for the dismantling and in-

4.102c . . . and springs

spection procedures, and parts may not be readily available, it may be more practical and economical for the home mechanic to purchase a rebuilt head rather than taking the time to dismantle, inspect and re-condition the original.

102 Cylinder head dismantling involves removal of the camshaft, intake and exhaust valves and related components. If they're still in place, remove the rocker arms and shafts from the cylinder head (see

4.103a Unscrew the bolts . . .

4.103b . . . remove the distributor drive housing . . .

4.103c . . . and remove the gasket

4.104 Checking the camshaft endfloat with a feeler gauge

4.105a Remove the thrust plate . . .

4.105b . . . then carefully guide the camshaft out of the cylinder head

4.106a Use a spring compressor to compress the valve springs and remove the keepers

4.106b Remove the retainer . . .

4.106c . . . and valve spring, followed by the valve itself . . .

Chapter 2A, Section 10) (see illustrations). Label the parts, or store them separately, so they can be refitted in their original locations.
103 Unscrew the bolts and remove the distributor drive housing from the end of the cylinder head. Recover the gasket (see illustrations).
104 Before removing the camshaft, check its endfloat as follows. Using a feeler gauge, check the clearance between the thrust plate on the rear of the cylinder head and the shoulder of the camshaft (see illustration). Compare this with the maximum amount given in the Specifications at the beginning of this Supplement.
105 Unscrew the cross-head screws and remove the thrust plate. Carefully guide the camshaft out of the cylinder head (see illustration).
106 Remove the valves with reference to Chapter 2B, Section 8 (see illustrations).

4.106d . . . the valve stem oil seal . . .

13

4.106e . . . and the spring seat

4.108 Lubricating a valve as it is being inserted into the cylinder head

5.4a Unbolting the alternator upper adjustment link

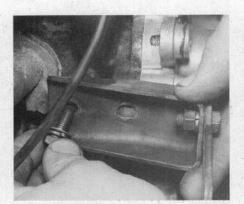

5.4b Unbolting the alternator upper adjustment bracket from the cylinder block

5.5a Unscrew the mounting bolts and nuts . . .

Cylinder head and camshaft - cleaning and inspection

107 The procedure is as described in Chapter 2B, Section 9. However, it will be necessary to check the camshaft thrust plate and the relevant contact surfaces on the camshaft for signs of excessive wear. If the endfloat checked previously was in excess of the specified amount, it will be necessary to decide what components have been worn in order to renew them. If the thrust plate is worn excessively, it may be sufficient to renew it to restore the correct endfloat.

Cylinder head - reassembly

Refer to illustration 4.108

108 Follow the procedure given in Chapter 2B, Section 11. However, after locating the camshaft in the cylinder head, locate the thrust plate in the groove, then insert and tighten the cross-head screws **(see illustration)**. Turn the camshaft to ensure it rotates freely.

5　Cooling system (970 cc engine)

Water pump - renewal

Refer to illustrations 5.4a, 5.4b, 5.5a, 5.5b and 5.5c

Warning: *Wait until the engine is completely cold before beginning this procedure.*

1　Disconnect the battery negative cable.
2　Drain the cooling system (see Chapter 1). If the coolant is relatively new or in good condition, save it and re-use it.

5.5b . . . and remove the water pump from the front of the cylinder block

3　Remove the timing belt, tensioner, crankshaft sprocket, camshaft sprocket and timing belt inner cover as described in Section 4.
4　Unbolt the alternator upper adjustment link from the alternator, then unbolt the bracket from the cylinder block **(see illustrations)**.
5　Unscrew the mounting bolts and nuts, and remove the water pump from the front of the cylinder block. Remove the gasket **(see illustrations)**.

5.5c Removing the water pump gasket from the cylinder block

6.2a Disconnecting the warm-air hose from the exhaust manifold shroud

6   Clean the sealing surface on the block, and also the sealing surface on the water pump if it is to be refitted.
7   Locate a new gasket on the cylinder block.
8   Locate the water pump on the block, then insert the bolts and tighten progressively to the specified torque.
9   Refit the alternator and support bracket.
10   Refit the timing belt with reference to Section 4.
11   Refill the cooling system.
12   Reconnect the battery negative cable.
13   Start the engine and run it to normal operating temperature. Check for leaks.

Cylinder block coolant inlet elbow - removal and refitting

Removal

14   Disconnect the battery negative cable.
15   Drain the cooling system (see Chapter 1). If the coolant is relatively new or in good condition, save it and re-use it.
16   Remove the alternator and support bracket.
17   Loosen the clips and disconnect the bottom hose, heater hose and intake manifold hose from the cylinder block inlet elbow.
18   Unscrew the bolts and remove the elbow from the cylinder block. Remove the gasket.
19   Clean the sealing surfaces of the cylinder block and elbow.

Refitting

20   Refitting is a reversal of removal, but always use a new gasket, and tighten the mounting bolts and hose clips securely.

---

6   Fuel and exhaust systems (970 cc engine)

Warning: *Petrol is extremely flammable, so take extra precautions when you work on any part of the fuel system. Don't smoke, or allow open flames or bare light bulbs, near the work area. Don't work in a garage where a natural gas-type appliance (such as a water heater or clothes dryer) with a pilot light is present. If you spill any fuel on your skin, rinse it off immediately with soap and water. When you perform any kind of work on the fuel system, wear safety glasses.*

Air cleaner assembly - removal and refitting
Refer to illustrations 6.2a, 6.2b, 6.3a, 6.3b and 6.4

Removal

1   Remove the air cleaner element as described in Section 3.
2   Disconnect the warm-air hose from the air cleaner and exhaust manifold shroud, and the air inlet hose from the air cleaner **(see illustrations)**.
3   Loosen the clip and disconnect the carburettor air inlet hose from the air cleaner. Also disconnect the crankcase ventilation hoses from the camshaft cover, intake manifold and air cleaner **(see illustrations)**.

6.2b Disconnecting the air inlet hose from the air cleaner

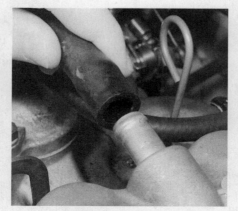

6.3a Disconnecting the crankcase ventilation hoses from the camshaft cover . . .

6.3b . . . and intake manifold

6.4 Removing the air cleaner assembly from the engine compartment mounting

6.6 Disconnecting the fuel inlet hose from the float chamber cover inlet tube

6.7a Removing the central cover from the carburettor

6.7b Removing the float chamber cover

6.8a Removing the float . . .

6.8b . . . and gasket

6.10 Checking the float level dimension (note that the gasket is removed)

4   Unscrew the mounting nuts and withdraw the air cleaner assembly from the engine compartment **(see illustration)**.

Refitting

5   Refitting is a reversal of removal.

Carburettor - check and adjustment

Float level adjustment

Refer to illustrations 6.6, 6.7a, 6.7b, 6.8a, 6.8b and 6.10

6   Loosen the clip and disconnect the fuel inlet hose from the float chamber cover inlet tube **(see illustration)**. Plug the end of the hose to prevent leakage of fuel.

7   Remove the screws, then lift off the carburettor central cover and the float chamber cover **(see illustrations)**.

8   Invert the float chamber cover, then extract the pin and remove the float. Remove the gasket, then refit the float and pin **(see illustrations)**. Take care not to let the needle valve drop out while the float is removed.

9   Cut a 10 mm square piece of lightweight paper, and stick it on the side of the float as shown in illustration 6.10. The type of paper used for self-adhesive (yellow) note pads is ideal for this, as the gummed edge is normally about 10 mm wide.

10   With the weight of the float only on the needle valve, measure the distance between the cover joint surface and the point 10 mm inwards

6.14 Disconnecting the wiring from the stop solenoid

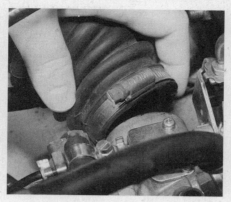

6.15 Disconnecting the air cleaner inlet hose from the carburettor

6.16a Disconnecting the throttle cable from the bracket . . .

6.16b . . . and lever

6.16c Disconnecting the choke cable from the bracket

6.18a Unscrewing the carburettor mounting nuts

6.18b Removing the carburettor from the intake manifold

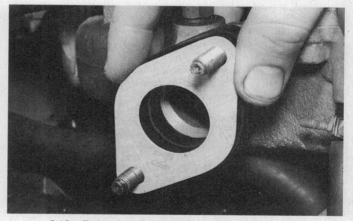

6.18c Removing the gaskets and insulation block

from the top edge of the float (see illustration). If the resulting dimension is not the same as that given in the Specifications at the beginning of this Supplement, bend the tongue on the float arm as necessary and check the dimension again.

11 Refit the float chamber cover and central cover, together with new gaskets, and tighten the screws.

12 Reconnect the fuel inlet hose.

Carburettor - removal and refitting

Removal

Refer to illustrations 6.14, 6.15, 6.16a, 6.16b, 6.16c, 6.18a, 6.18b and 6.18c

13 Disconnect the battery negative cable.

14 Disconnect the wiring from the stop solenoid on the carburettor (see illustration).

15 Loosen the clip and disconnect the air cleaner inlet hose from the carburettor (see illustration).

16 Loosen the choke and throttle cable adjustment nuts, and release the cables from the brackets on the carburettor. Disconnect the cables from the levers (see illustrations).

17 Loosen the clip and disconnect the fuel inlet hose from the inlet tube on the float chamber cover on top of the carburettor. Plug the end of the hose to prevent leakage of fuel.

18 Unscrew the mounting nuts and remove the carburettor from the studs on the intake manifold. Recover the gaskets and insulation block if necessary (see illustrations).

13

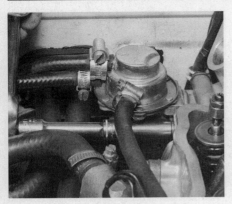
6.30a Unscrew the fuel pump bolts . . .

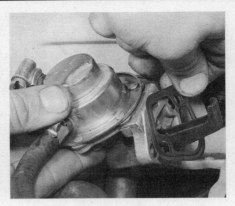
6.30b . . . and remove the fuel pump and gasket

7.23 Rotor arm pointing to the No 4 spark plug segment position

Refitting

19   Remove all traces of gasket from the mating surfaces of the car-burettor and intake manifold.

20   Place the insulation block, together with new gaskets, over the studs.

21   Position the carburettor on the studs and refit the mounting nuts.

22   Tighten the mounting nuts progressively to the specified torque (see Chapter 4). **Note:** *If the nuts are not tightened progressively, the carburettor flange may be distorted.*

23   Reconnect the fuel inlet hose to the inlet tube on the float cham-ber cover, and tighten the clip.

24   Reconnect the throttle cable to the throttle lever, and adjust it with reference to Chapter 4, Section 9.

25   Reconnect the air cleaner inlet hose to the carburettor, and tighten the clip.

26   Reconnect the wiring to the stop solenoid on the carburettor.

27   Reconnect the battery negative cable.

28   Start the engine and check carefully for fuel leaks.

29   Check and adjust the idle speed and mixture settings with refer-ence to Section 3.

Fuel pump - removal and refitting

Refer to illustrations 6.30a and 6.30b

30   The procedure is similar to that described in Chapter 4, Section 5. However, the fuel pump is located on a separate housing instead of on the cylinder head **(see illustrations)**.

---

7   Engine electrical systems (970 cc engine)

Ignition system - general information

Contact breaker ignition is fitted to the 970 cc engine, with a con-ventional low-tension (LT) circuit and high-tension (HT) circuit.

The low-tension circuit (sometimes also known as the primary cir-cuit) consists of the battery, the lead to the ignition switch, the lead to the low-tension or primary coil windings, and the lead from the low-tension coil windings to the contact breaker points and condenser in the distributor.

The high-tension circuit (sometimes also known as the secondary circuit) consists of the high-tension or secondary coil winding, the heavily-insulated lead from the centre of the coil to the centre of the distributor cap, the rotor arm, the spark plug leads and the spark plugs.

The ignition system operation is as follows. Low-tension voltage from the battery is changed within the ignition coil to high-tension volt-age by the opening and closing of the contact breaker points in the low-tension circuit. High-tension voltage is then fed, via a contact in the centre of the distributor cap, to the rotor arm of the distributor. The rotor arm revolves inside the distributor cap, and each time it passes one of the four metal segments in the cap, the opening and closing of the contact breaker points causes the high-tension voltage to build up, jump the gap from the rotor arm to the appropriate metal segment and so, via the spark plug lead, to the spark plug where it finally jumps the gap between the two spark plug electrodes, one being earthed.

The ignition timing is advanced and retarded automatically to en-sure the spark occurs at just the right instant for the prevailing engine speed.

The ignition advance is controlled mechanically on the 970 cc en-gine. The mechanical governor mechanism consists of two weights which move out under centrifugal force from the central distributor shaft as the engine speed rises. As they move outwards, they rotate the cam relative to the distributor shaft, and so advance the spark. The weights are held in position by two light springs, and it is the tension of these springs which is largely responsible for correct spark advance-ment.

Ignition system - testing

1   There are two main symptoms indicating faults in the ignition sys-tem. Either the engine will not start or fire, or the engine is difficult to start and misfires. If it is a regular misfire (ie the engine is running on only two or three cylinders), the fault is almost sure to be in the sec-ondary (high-tension) circuit. If the misfiring is intermittent, the fault could be in either the high- or low-tension circuits. If the engine stops suddenly, or will not start at all, it is likely that the fault is in the low-ten-sion circuit. Loss of power and overheating, apart from faulty carbura-tion settings, are normally due to faults in the distributor, or to incorrect ignition timing.

Engine fails to start

2   If the engine fails to start, yet was running normally when it was last used, first check that there is fuel in the fuel tank. If the engine turns over normally on the starter motor and the battery is fully charged, then the fault may be in either the high- or low-tension cir-cuits. First check the high-tension circuit. If the battery is known to be fully charged, the ignition lights come on, but the starter motor fails to turn the engine, check the tightness of the leads on the battery termi-nals, and also the security of the earth lead to its connection on the body. It is quite common for the leads to have worked loose, even if they look and feel secure. If one of the battery terminal posts gets very hot when trying to work the starter motor, this is a sure indication of a faulty connection to that terminal.

3   One of the most common reasons for bad starting is wet or damp spark plug leads and distributor. Remove the distributor cap. If con-densation is visible internally, dry the cap with a rag, and also wipe over the leads. Refit the cap. Alternatively, using a moisture-dispersant aerosol (obtainable at any car accessory shop) can be very effective in starting the engine.

4   If the engine still fails to start, check that the current is reaching the plugs. Disconnect each plug lead in turn at the spark plug end, and hold the end of the cable (with rubber-insulated pliers, to avoid electric shocks) about 5 mm away from the cylinder block. Spin the engine on the starter motor.

7.24 Disconnecting the low-tension lead from the distributor

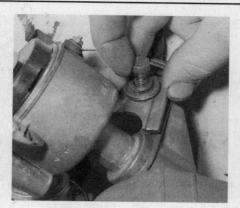

7.26a Remove the clamp bolt and clamp . . .

7.26b . . . and withdraw the distributor from the cylinder head

5   Sparking between the end of the cable and the block should be fairly strong with a good, regular blue spark. If current is reaching the plugs then remove, clean and regap them. The engine should now start.

6   If there is no spark at the plug leads, take off the HT lead from the centre of the distributor cap and hold it to the block as before. Spin the engine on the starter once more. A rapid succession of blue sparks between the end of the lead and the block indicates that the coil is in order, and that either the distributor cap is cracked, the rotor arm is faulty, or the carbon brush in the distributor cap is not making good contact with the rotor arm.

7   If there are no sparks from the end of the lead from the coil, check the connections at the coil end of the lead. If it is in order, start checking the low-tension circuit.

8   With the ignition switched on and the points open, test between the low-tension wire to the coil positive (+) terminal and earth. Use a 12-volt voltmeter or a 12-volt bulb and two lengths of wire. No reading indicates a break in the supply from the ignition switch. Check the connections at the switch to see if any are loose. Refit them and the engine should run. If a reading is indicated, this shows a faulty coil or condenser, or broken lead between the coil and the distributor.

9   Disconnect the condenser wire from the points, and with the points open, test between the moving point and earth. If there is now a reading, then the fault is in the condenser. Fit a new one and the fault should clear.

10   With no reading from the moving point to earth, take a reading between earth and the coil negative (-) terminal. A reading here shows a broken wire between the coil and distributor. No reading confirms that the coil has failed and must be renewed, after which the engine should run (check the coil first). Remember to refit the condenser wire to the points assembly. For these tests it is sufficient to separate the points with a piece of paper while testing with the points open.

Engine misfires

11   If the engine misfires regularly, run it at a fast idle speed. Pull off each of the plug caps in turn and listen to the note of the engine. Hold the plug cap in a dry cloth or with a rubber glove, as additional protection against a shock from the HT supply.

12   No difference in engine running will be noticed when the lead from the defective circuit is removed. Removing the lead from one of the good cylinders will accentuate the misfire.

13   Remove the plug lead from the end of the defective plug, and hold it about 5 mm away from the block. Restart the engine. If the sparking is fairly strong and regular, the fault must lie in the spark plug.

14   The plug may be loose, the insulation may be cracked, or the electrodes may have burnt away, giving too wide a gap for the spark to jump. Worse still, one of the electrodes may have broken off. Renew the spark plugs as a set if necessary.

15   If there is no spark at the end of the plug lead, or if it is too weak and intermittent, check the ignition lead from the distributor to the plug. If the insulation is cracked or perished, renew the lead. Check the

connections at the distributor cap.

16   If there is still no spark, examine the distributor cap carefully for tracking. This can be recognised by a very thin black line running between two or more electrodes, or between an electrode and some other part of the distributor. These lines are paths which will conduct electricity across the cap, thus letting it run to earth. The only answer is to fit a new distributor cap.

17   Apart from the ignition timing being incorrect, other causes of misfiring have already been dealt with under the Section dealing with the failure of the engine to start. To recap, these are as follows.
(a)   The coil may be faulty, giving an intermittent misfire.
(b)   There may be a damaged wire or loose connection in the low-tension circuit.
(c)   The condenser may be short-circuiting.
(d)   There may be a mechanical fault in the distributor (broken driving spindle or contact breaker spring).

18   If the ignition is too far retarded, it should be noted that the engine will tend to overheat, and there will be quite a noticeable drop in power. If the engine is overheating and the power is down, and the ignition timing is correct, then the carburettor should be checked, as it is likely that this is where the fault lies.

Distributor - removal, overhaul and refitting
Removal
Refer to illustrations 7.23, 7.24, 7.26a and 7.26b

19   If necessary, mark the spark plug HT leads to aid refitting, and then disconnect them from the spark plugs. Note that if the original Suzuki distributor cap is fitted, the cylinder numbers are marked on the top of the cap. Pull the end connectors, not the actual leads, otherwise the leads may be damaged.

20   Release the clips, then withdraw the cap from the distributor. Place the cap to one side.

21   Remove the spark plug from No 4 cylinder, and then turn the crankshaft using a spanner on the crankshaft pulley bolt. Place a finger (or long wooden dowel rod) over the plug hole, and feel for the compression being generated as the piston rises up the cylinder bore. If the camshaft cover is removed, note that the valves of No 4 cylinder will both be closed.

22   Continue turning the crankshaft until the ignition timing marks on the flywheel and transmission bellhousing are in alignment. If necessary, clean the marks and apply a dab of white paint or chalk to highlight them. No 4 piston is now in the firing position.

23   Check that the rotor arm is pointing to the relative position of the No 4 spark plug segment in the distributor cap (see illustration).

24   Disconnect the low-tension lead from the terminal on the side of the distributor (see illustration).

25   Mark the distributor body in relation to the housing on the rear of the cylinder head. Also mark the position of the rotor arm in relation to the rim of the distributor body, with a felt-tip pen or scriber.

26   Unbolt the clamp bolt, remove the clamp and withdraw the distributor straight up from the cylinder head (see illustrations). With the

13

distributor removed, mark the body in line with the new position of the rotor arm, as an aid to refitting.

Overhaul

27   Renewal of the contact breaker assembly, condenser, rotor arm and distributor cap should be regarded as the limit of overhaul, as few other spares are available separately. Refer to Section 3 of this Supplement for these procedures.
28   When the distributor has seen extended service, and the shaft, bushes and centrifugal mechanism become worn excessively, it is advisable to purchase a new distributor.

Refitting

29   To refit the distributor, first check that the ignition timing marks are still aligned with No 4 cylinder on compression. If the engine has been turned while the distributor was removed, return it to the correct position as previously described.
30   Align the rotor arm with the mark made in paragraph 26, then hold the distributor directly over its mounting hole with the marks aligned on the cylinder head and distributor body.
31   Lower the distributor into position. As the distributor gear engages the gear on the end of the camshaft, the rotor arm will turn anti-clockwise until it is aligned with the first mark made on the body.
32   Turn the distributor as necessary to align the marks previously made on the body and cylinder head. If a new distributor is being fitted, temporary alignment marks should be made in the same positions made on the old distributor. This should be sufficient to start the engine and check the ignition timing.
33   Refit the clamp and bolt and tighten. Check that the alignment marks and timing marks are still aligned.
34   Reconnect the low-tension lead, then refit the distributor cap. Refit the spark plug.
35   Check and adjust the ignition timing as described in Section 3.

Ignition coil - testing, removal and refitting

Testing

36   The coil is mounted on the left-hand side of the bulkhead in the engine compartment. The coil windings can be tested as follows. First ensure that the ignition is switched off, then disconnect the low-tension and high-tension leads from the coil, having first noted their positions.
37   To test the primary winding, connect an ohmmeter between the two low-tension terminals and compare the values obtained with the values given in the Specifications at the beginning of this Supplement. Similarly, check the secondary windings by connecting the ohmmeter between the low-tension negative terminal and the high-tension terminal. No values were available at the time of writing, but a typical value would be approximately 10 000 ohms. Renew the coil if the values are incorrect.

Removal

38   To remove the coil, disconnect the low-tension and high-tension leads as previously described, then unscrew the mounting screws and remove the coil from the engine compartment.

Refitting

39   Refitting is a reversal of removal, but if necessary wipe clean the top of the coil to prevent any tracking of the HT current. Make sure that the low-tension leads are connected correctly.

---

8   Manual transmission (4-speed) and transfer case

Manual transmission (4-speed) - general information

1   SJ410 models manufactured before November 1988 were fitted with a 4-speed transmission.
2   Access to the front oil seal entails the complete dismantling of the

10.4 View of the handbrake shoes with the drum removed

transmission, and is therefore outside the scope of this manual.
3   Renewal of the rear oil seal is identical to the procedure described in Chapter 7A, Section 2.

Transfer case - overhaul

4   The exploded diagram (illustration 4.4) shown in Chapter 7C, Section 4 depicts the chain-driven type fitted to Vitara models. The type fitted to SJ410 and SJ413 models is of a different design, incorporating an intermediate shaft and gears instead of the chain. It is recommended that any repairs to the transfer case be entrusted to a qualified specialist.

---

9   Clutch and drivetrain

Pilot bearing - general information

1   The needle roller pilot bearing (spigot bearing) described in Chapter 8, Section 5 is only fitted to early SJ410 models. Later models (including SJ413 and Vitara models) are fitted with a ball-bearing type pilot bearing. A suitable tool (such as a slide hammer and adapter) should be used to remove the bearing, as it is unlikely that the heavy grease method described in Chapter 8 will be successful. When installing the new bearing, make sure that only the outer track is in contact with the refitting tool, otherwise damage may occur to the bearing inner track and balls.

Free-wheeling hubs - general information

2   Note that some early UK models do not have free-wheeling (or automatic-locking) hubs. When 4-wheel drive is selected on these models, drive is direct to the front wheels.

---

10   Brakes

Front drum brakes (SJ410 models) - general information

1   On UK SJ410 models manufactured prior to July 1983, the front brakes are of drum type instead of the disc type described in Chapter 9. The front drum brakes are of twin-leading shoe type, incorporating two wheel cylinders. The shoe adjustment nuts are serrated, so that they can be turned with a screwdriver inserted through a hole in the brake drum.
2   Checking and renewal procedures are similar to those described for rear drum brakes.

Centre handbrake shoes (SJ410 and early SJ413 models) - renewal

Refer to illustration 10.4

3   All SJ410 models are equipped with a "centre" handbrake (or "transmission" handbrake), which operates on a drum located behind the transfer box.

4   To renew the brake shoes, first remove the handbrake drum as described in Section 3 of this Supplement **(see illustration)**.

5   The procedure for renewal of the shoes is similar to that described for the rear brake shoes in Chapter 9, Section 6.

6   After fitting the new shoes, adjust them as described in Section 3 of this Supplement.

11   Chassis electrical system

Wiring diagrams - general information

The wiring diagrams shown at the end of this manual are of US origin. At the time or writing, no UK-specific wiring diagrams were available, but in most cases the US diagrams can be used for guidance on UK models.

13

Index